The Swiss Alps: the castle and church of Spiez, on Lake Thun   EDWARD HOLMES

LAROUSSE

encyclopedia of

GEOGRAPHY

Europe

GENERAL EDITOR **PIERRE DEFFONTAINES**

Director of the French Institute, Barcelona

ASSISTED BY **MARIEL JEAN-BRUNHES DELAMARRE**

ADVISER (ENGLISH EDITION) **W. G. MOORE**, B.SC., F.R.G.S.

FOREWORD BY **L. DUDLEY STAMP**, C.B.E.,

Emeritus Professor of Social Geography in the University of London

PROMETHEUS PRESS NEW YORK

1961

Uniform with this edition

LAROUSSE ENCYCLOPEDIA OF MYTHOLOGY

LAROUSSE ENCYCLOPEDIA OF ASTRONOMY

LAROUSSE ENCYCLOPEDIA OF THE EARTH

LAROUSSE ENCYCLOPEDIA OF GEOGRAPHY: EUROPE

Translated by P. J. Spink, A. H. Brodrick and M. Heron

from GEOGRAPHIE UNIVERSELLE LAROUSSE

first published in France by Augé, Gillon, Hollier-Larousse, Moreau & Cie.

LIBRAIRIE LAROUSSE, PARIS

PRINTED IN HOLLAND BY KONINKLIJKE DRUKKERIJEN LANKHOUT-IMMIG N.V., THE HAGUE

CONTRIBUTORS

Paul Akamatsu

Edgar Aubert de la Rüe

Georges Azambre

Édouard Berlan

Jean-Jacques Berreby

Jacques Besançon

Pierre Birot

André Blanc

Antoine Bon

Jean Borde

André Cailleux

Jean Canu

Robert Capot-Rey

Auguste Cauneille

Jean Chardonnet

Jean Chesneaux

François Chevalier

André Chouraqui

Claude Collin-Delavaud

Jean Delvert

Jean Demangeot

Jean Dollfus

Claude Dubois

Jean-Pierre Dufourg

Frans Dussart

Vadime Elisseeff

Simon Farzami

Maurice Fevret

Alfred Fichelle

Robert Ficheux

Pierre Flatrès

Jean-François Gravier

Joseph Grelier

Francisco Hernández-Pacheco

Alain Huetz de Lemps

Hildebert Isnard

Louis C. D. Joos

Georges Jorré

Guy Lasserre

Jean Malaurie

Pierre Meile

André Meynier

Jean Michéa

Juliette Monbeig

Pierre Monbeig

Robert Nollet

Gabriel Ollivier

Henri Onde

André Pauly

Eugène Pépin

Marie-Magdeleine del Perugia

Paul Poumaillou

Pierre Rondot

Gabriel Rougerie

Gilles Sautter

Jean Sermet

Jean Sirol

Joseph Earl Spencer

L. Dudley Stamp

François Tabuteau

Michel Tabuteau

François Taillefer

Jules Vidal

Mariano Zamorano

*The relief maps of Northern Europe, the North Sea,
Central Europe and Mediterranean Europe were
prepared by Geographical Projects Ltd., London.*

CONTENTS

8   List of colour maps and colour plates

9   Foreword

13   Introduction: The Earth

NORTHERN EUROPE

21   **Scandinavia** by André Cailleux

31   **Denmark** by André Cailleux

41   **Norway** by André Cailleux

47   **Sweden** by André Cailleux

55   **Finland** by François Taillefer

63   **Iceland** by Marie-Magdeleine del Perugia

OCEANIC EUROPE

69   **The British Isles** by André Meynier

73   **Great Britain** by André Meynier

      **England – Scotland – Wales –
Isle of Man – Scilly Isles**

109   **Ireland** by Pierre Flatrès

      Northern Ireland – Republic of Ireland

117   **The Netherlands, Belgium and Luxembourg**
by Frans Dussart

143   **France** by Pierre Deffontaines
and Jean-François Gravier

179   **Portugal** by Pierre Birot

186   **The Portuguese Islands of the Atlantic**
by Pierre Birot

      **The Azores – Madeira –
Cape Verde Islands**

CENTRAL EUROPE

189   **The Alps** by Henri Onde

195   **Switzerland** by Henri Onde

205   **Liechtenstein** by Henri Onde

206   **Austria** by Henri Onde

217   **Germany** by Jean Dollfus

253   **Czechoslovakia** by Alfred Fichelle

263   **Hungary** by André Blanc

271   **Poland** by Jean Chardonnet

283   **Rumania** by Robert Ficheux

295   **Bulgaria** by Alfred Fichelle

MEDITERRANEAN EUROPE

301   **Yugoslavia** by André Blanc

319   **Albania** by André Blanc

323   **Greece** by Antoine Bon

335   **Cyprus** by Antoine Bon

336   **Malta** by André Pauly

339   **Italy** by Jean Demangeot

377   **The Vatican City** by Jean Demangeot

378   **San Marino** by Jean Demangeot

379   **The Principality of Monaco** by Gabriel Ollivier

381   **Andorra** by Jean Sermet

383   **Spain** by Jean Sermet

425   Bibliography

429   General statistics

446   Index

      Atlas Section

COLOUR MAPS

38—39 Northern Europe

100—101 The North Sea

British Isles, Belgium, Netherlands, Luxembourg

172—173 The World (physical relief)

228—229 Central Europe

374—375 Mediterranean Europe

Atlas Section

1 Europe (political)

2 Europe (climate)

3 Europe (physical)

4 Europe (population)

5 Spain and Portugal

6—7 Scandinavia

8—9 British Isles

10—11 France

12—13 Germany and the Alps

14—15 Italy and the Balkans

16 World vegetation

COLOUR PLATES

Frontispiece: The Swiss Alps: the castle and church of Spiez, on Lake Thun

27 Floating logs down a Finnish river

81 Big Ben and the Houses of Parliament, London, by night

119 Bruges, Belgium

The cheese market at Alkmaar, Holland

A tulip field in the Netherlands

153 Aerial view of the Château-Gaillard, near Les Andelys, France

The Old Port of Marseilles

191 The old quarter of Salzburg, Austria

209 The Rhine at St Goar

209 Hamburg harbour

247 Niedzica Castle, in the Beskids of Poland

313 The old harbour and ramparts of Dubrovnik

Albanian national dress

The market outside a mosque at Sarajevo

347 A view from the Temple of the Oracle at Delphi

401 St Mark's Cathedral and the Palace of the Doges, Venice

A Sicilian cart at Taormina

419 General view of Avila, Spain

Holy week at Seville

A bullfight: the kill

Andalusian dancer

FOREWORD

L. DUDLEY STAMP, C.B.E., D.SC., D.LIT., LL.D., EKON.D.

Emeritus Professor of Social Geography in the University of London

The name of Larousse has long been associated with all that is best in French geographical literature. Perhaps through the entirely erroneous idea that French is known and used in educational institutions throughout Britain so that translation of French works into English is unnecessary, many publications of the Librairie Larousse have remained little known in the English-speaking world. It will be surprising if a warm welcome is not waiting for this English translation of GEOGRAPHIE UNIVERSELLE LAROUSSE. In the first place 'magnificent' is a mild word to apply to the whole production. Even with the high standard of colour reproduction to which we have become accustomed, the plates reach quite a remarkable excellence and some — Popper's Houses of Parliament at dusk for example — are works of art in their own right. Further, all the pictorial illustrations have a freshness and originality as well as a balance which places one of the latest *autostrade* opposite the Ponte Vecchio of Florence and includes both the châteaux from the past and the atomic power stations looking to the future.

In the second place the work is authoritative. The list of the sixty-three contributors to the whole work includes the names of most geographers of eminence in France and of many leaders of French culture throughout the world, together with specialists of other nationalities on the remoter parts of the world.

But the work is far from being a mere compilation of regional articles by specialists. Editorial care has produced a consistent style in text, well documented and well illustrated, with maps and adequate references. Above all there is clearly the inspired direction of a unique figure — Pierre Deffontaines: poet and patriot as well as geographer and historian, who has for long headed the French Institute in Barcelona and is as much at home in Spanish as in French. His broad human viewpoint, his artistic appreciation of the telling illustration, stand out clearly and he has been ably assisted by Mariel Jean-Brunhes Delamarre.

Those already familiar with the French text will appreciate that this is no mere translation. The opportunity has been taken of adding a 16-page atlas section especially printed, and numerous black and white maps which are an essential feature of British geographical works. There is a considerable addition of new illustrations and statistics, whilst the bibliography now includes sources more natural to readers in English. To the original editorship has been added the overall supervision of W. G. Moore with the needs of an English-speaking audience always in mind.

In this first volume which covers the continent of Europe excluding the U.S.S.R. there is abundant evidence of the balanced, logical presentation which has long characterized French geographical writing. Pierre Deffontaines in his introductory remarks is quick to remind us that the earth is the home of man, but a home in which the physical factors are ever present and operative, and that the proper study of geography is one particularly appropriate for all who look to the future of the human race, so charged with hopes and fears.

The balance between the broad regional approach and the natural interest in national groupings is well preserved by taking in sequence Northern Europe — the five Scandinavian or countries of Norden — then 'Oceanic Europe' of the north-west, Central Europe and Mediterranean Europe. In both the French and English editions the same space is given to the British Isles as to France, and this is an excellent example of the sense of proportion maintained throughout. At the same time the Vatican City, San Marino, Malta and Andorra are each given their separate treatment, so that national prestige is maintained.

There can be no doubt that here is a book which, whilst fascinating the general reader, and finely presented, makes no sacrifice of scholarly accuracy, and so is equally valuable in classroom and home.

L.D.S. 1961.

Peat cutting in Eire. Even in the nuclear age this most primitive form of fuel extracted from the earth is important.   J. ALLAN CASH

THE EARTH

WHAT is the Earth? The planet inhabited by mankind? We are not even sure if that is an accurate
definition. Let us begin by taking stock of what we do know.

Our knowledge of the Earth is comparatively recent. Human history and pre-history have
lasted for millions of years, but we have known that the Earth is round and mapped its regions only during
the last few centuries.

Space projects apart, we human beings cling to the tiny pinhead of our planet which remains our
terrestrial prison somewhere in the midst of an enormous universe. There are a number of special features about the Earth which fundamentally affect our behaviour and our way of living.

The most important feature is the tilting of the Earth's axis. The Earth both rotates on its own axis
daily and revolves in its orbit around the sun annually, tilted at an angle of 66½° to the plane of the path
it traces during its revolution. Without this marked tilting the Earth would be infinitely more regular,
with the sun rising and setting at the same time throughout the year; climates, too, would not vary.

The tilting of the Earth's axis is responsible for the seasons, in particular those periods of bad weather
which regularly affect all forms of life. These periods, which we call *winters*, differ regionally in duration and severity, but they endow the whole of life with a cyclic aspect which has enabled us to measure
and define time more accurately. The season of growth and abundance after winter which we call *summer*
once served to measure age, and the longest day of the year was celebrated accordingly. The return of
winter brings great hardship in its train. In the vegetable world many plants disappear from the surface
of the Earth to escape the cold — annual plants contrasting with perennial plants. There is a vital distinction between two types of tree: the deciduous species, which are bare in winter, and the non-deciduous (conifers and evergreens).

Aerial view of Manhattan, United States. This island, surrounded by two branches of the Hudson River, forms the City of New York. It is famous for its skyscrapers, the highest of which is the Empire State Building (1,250 feet). New York had 2,500 inhabitants in 1664, 16,000 in 1789, nearly 600,000 in 1858, and today its population is 8,074,000 (more than 12,000,000 including the suburbs). AEROFILM LIBRARY

Animals' behaviour in winter is largely determined by their mobility. Many of them undertake periodic migrations to escape, others have lives as ephemeral as those of certain plants, while still others undergo physical changes enabling them to withstand the rigours of the winter. A distinction as fundamental as that between deciduous and non-deciduous trees divides the animal world into cold- and warm-blooded species.

Man, on the other hand, is not particularly well-equipped to face inclement weather with his relatively high body temperature. His skin is a poor insulator and he has no protective fur. The regular recurrence of cold weather set him one of his most difficult problems. In many regions he has concentrated all his forces on combatting the weather. He has been driven to invent a series of devices: first clothing, then increasingly elaborate houses. He is the only living being who has had to make clothes, just as he is the sole genus to have used fire — a mysterious discovery whose use is taken by archaeologists as a defining characteristic of man.

But man has not been daunted by the winter; with the help of better clothing, housing, heating and food, he has done his utmost to overcome the cold and has become one of the most ubiquitous of living beings, despite the severe handicaps imposed on him by his constitution.

In spite of multiple protective devices, marked variations in temperature constitute a severe test for man. Isotherm maps marking off the zones with the severest winters also define the regions where he finds it hardest to survive. The Earth undergoes only relatively minor changes in temperature, yet these differences are enough to have a marked effect on mankind's distribution on the Earth. As far as possible men have avoided regions with lengthy winters. Since these regions are situated in the interior of continental land masses where the modifying influence of the oceans cannot affect the seasons, humanity was driven towards the edges of the continents. This phenomenon is particularly striking in Eurasia, where there are two zones of high density separated by a desert zone: the Far East, extending from Japan to the Indies, with the shores of the China Sea and the Indian Ocean alone containing more than half the world's population (one milliard three hundred millions), and the West, linked with the North Atlantic and

Mediterranean littorals, which has a population of more than half a milliard. This is one more fundamental consequence of the tilting of the Earth's axis.

But the distribution of the population still presents many anomalies; nearly three-quarters of the continents have less than one inhabitant to the square mile, whereas certain regions have densities of more than 1,000 inhabitants for the same area. There is still much room for rationalisation of population distribution.

However, it is possible that man's settlement on the Earth is as yet in its early stages. The rapid growth of world population is a comparatively recent phenomenon. In 1800 it was estimated at about seven hundred million; it exceeded one milliard around 1850, two milliards towards 1900, and today the Earth supports more than two-and-a-half milliards. In one hundred and fifty years the number of men has more than tripled. This is a sensational event in world history, with consequences which are only beginning to make themselves felt. It challenges mankind to take new measures and perhaps to adopt a more systematic demographic policy.

Moreover we must take into account not only the men who live, work and consume today, but also the men of the past who have contributed to the progressively better living conditions which we now enjoy. Geographers find it useful to establish the value of the past which blends so intimately with the present and weighs so heavily on it, and their work is thus linked with that of historians and archaeologists. Countries which have supported an ancient human civilisation look very different from those with a short human history.

There are certain zones of the Earth which have had the privilege of being cradles of civilisation. These pioneer regions are mainly found grouped around those semi-closed seas which we call 'mediterranean'. Physically they are relatively unstable, with marine deeps cheek by jowl with high reliefs, and they exhibit considerable evidence of the effects of vulcanism and earthquakes. In addition, their relief is broken and peninsulas are numerous.

A desolate landscape in Patagonia, South America. This vast territory extends over the south of Chile and the Argentine, from the Colorado River to the Straits of Magellan. In this region of semi-desert, man still contrives to make a living. One of the main occupations is sheep-farming.
GISELLE FREUND

Left: *A family of Pygmies in the Congo (Equatorial Africa). The Pygmies are negroes of small stature (average height less than 5 feet), whose origins are lost in antiquity. They live exclusively by hunting.* PH. LENNART NILSSON, RAPHO. Right: *A family of Ainu in Japan. The Ainu are a strange people of Eastern Asia; they are short, but very strong and hairy. The women simulate beards with tattooing round their mouths. The Ainu are mainly hunters and fishermen.* PAUL POPPER, ATLAS PHOTO

The most ancient human peoples did not live in these zones — they are, in fact, poor in prehistoric remains — but history began in them. Here for the first time civilisation emerged from primitive anonymity; every product of the human mind appeared in these regions astonishingly early. The Mediterranean saw the beginnings of philosophy, religion, political systems, art, law and science. If a map could be made showing where the greatest works of mankind were concentrated, the Mediterranean zone would easily be the richest, during antiquity at least. The names of the cities built around it make an impressive list: Thebes, Memphis, Carthage, Rome, Syracuse, Alexandria and Constantinople.

This tiny Mediterranean region was the point of departure for man's first reconnaissance of the Earth, as if the rest of the globe (forty-nine fiftieths) was but an appendage. Around it the continents of Europe, Asia and Africa were born; in their infancy they existed only as the hinterland of this sea.

So perhaps it is not surprising that another roughly similar advance post existed in the New World in and around the other 'mediterranean' formed by the Caribbean Sea. Here, too, appeared the most ancient political systems of the American continents, the oldest towns and monuments. The most prosperous European colonies were maintained around the Carribbean until the beginning of the nineteenth century. In 1789, New York had only 16,000 inhabitants, whereas Mexico contained more than 100,000. In both 'mediterraneans' the violence of the physical features went hand in hand with an equally dynamic human outburst.

If we find it hard to understand the reasons why this intensive human activity was concentrated as it was, it is just as difficult for us to find a logical way of differentiating between the various groups comprising the human species.

The concept of race is very deceptive; what criterion are we to adopt to classify the different types of men? The most obvious distinction, the colour of the skin, must be discarded. We do not even know whether it is a racial characteristic or an acquired quality. In addition, the distribution of men according to their colour is singularly complicated. To allot the white races to Europe, black races to Africa and yellow races to Asia is a common but greatly oversimplified distinction. Asia has its whites: the Iranians, a number of Indians and undoubtedly the ancient Ainus of Japan. Africa, too, has hers: the peoples of North Africa and the Tuaregs in the Sahara. It is the same in Oceania, where the Polynesians and perhaps the Malays should be classified among the whites. As for the yellow races, they have descendants in Europe: the Turks and the Tartars. The great majority of American Indians are also of yellow origin. The blacks have many representatives in Asia or Oceania: the Dravidians in the Indies and the Melanesians in the Pacific archipelagos. And what are we to make of the even more primitive races still existing: the Pygmies, Hottentots and Australian aborigines? What colour are they to be assigned? And what was the colour of the skin of the most ancient Palaeolithic men whose remains have recently been discovered?

Left: *A village in the Upper Volta (French West Africa). In the foreground are round dwelling huts, in the background, granaries for millet.* Centre: *A floating market on Lake Iule in Burma (Southern Asia). The vendors sell their wares to the pilgrims coming by boat to visit the sacred temples on the lake.* MICHEL HUET, EDITIONS HOA-QUI, AND ROSS MADEN. Right: *Restoration of one of the outer walls of the pillared hall of the great Temple of Amen Ra at Karnak, Upper Egypt. Karnak is one of the villages built on the site of Thebes, capital of Egypt, with a population of more than 100,000 throughout the second millenium B.C.* R. VIOLLET

The classification of men by their language does not give any better results, for languages do not correspond to races but jump from continent to continent in a remarkable way. The distribution of languages today is frankly disconcerting. Fortunately, in the midst of this tangled forest, certain major tongues stand out, some because they are the mother tongues of a vast number of people, such as Russian or Chinese (although there are many varieties of Chinese), others because they serve as the vehicles for certain needs of expression and are spoken in addition to their mother tongues by the inhabitants of widely varied regions. English, for example, is the language of trade, Latin the language of the Catholic liturgy and French the language of diplomacy and culture.

Nor can religions well be used for classification, both on account of their dispersion and their astonishing variety, though religious edifices are so notable a feature of the landscape that they have geographical significance. They are far more characteristic of mankind than dwellings and paths, which other animal species make as well.

How then are we to conduct this study of mankind and the present-day world? We propose here to abandon the classical division into continents, which appears increasingly arbitrary and inapt.

Europe was never able to define its eastern frontier precisely in the past. It is still less able to do so today when the vast Eurasian plains are farmed on a fairly uniform collective system from the Oder and the Vistula to the shores of the Seas of Japan and China. We have felt it indispensable to treat these vast flat expanses as a single unit, since they have no natural barriers, overlap into Europe and Asia and have been the scene of large-scale migrations of peoples for so long. Moreover why separate the European peninsula from the Asiatic land mass any more than the Indian or Indo-Chinese peninsulas? It would undoubtedly be easier to define an Indian continent than a European continent from both the physical and human geographical points of view.

In addition, the traditional division into continents has the serious drawback of destroying the unity of the Mediterranean basin which is so obvious, to the physical geographer at least. For the human geographer too, the types of farming and ways of life in the basin have more in common with each other than they have with the continental regions which stretch out behind them.

No doubt the Mediterranean basin varies considerably within itself, but the elements which separate its regions do not correspond to the continental divisions; the Muslim world straddles Africa and Asia and even overlaps a little into Europe; the Latin world overflowed into North Africa and at one time into the Middle East; the ancient Greek world, in common with the most ancient Phoenician and Aegean civilisations, occupied the Asian as well as the African and European shores.

As for the Americas, for so long centred on the other mediterranean, the Carribbean Sea, it was also the meeting-place for the Latin and Anglo-Saxon worlds. Here again we, shall not restrict ourselves to continental divisions. South America is not south in the way that North America is north; rather, it is central, more so than Central America, since it is crossed at its widest point by the equator.

We have, then, attempted to establish groupings in relation to the human problems they pose. Our geographical picture of the present-day world must be a realistic, positive picture, alive to the modern situation, and we must discard outmoded divisions.

Some may object that there has never been so much talk of continents as now. A United States of Europe is planned. Successful slogans are coined: Asia for the Asiatics, Africa for the Africans. But this should not be considered as a reassertion of traditional continental divisions so much as the symptom of new aspirations which have not yet found their real name.

Human geography inevitably faces the question of the destiny of the human race. No doubt *homo sapiens* has reached a high level today, but the process of evolution is not finished. Perhaps we are entering on a phase when the individual human being will be transcended by society. Already men are moving towards a gregarious way of life. In contradistinction to other species which live exclusively together (bees, ants, etc.) or as individuals, mankind has always had the choice. It seems that in the past dispersion won the day, but today a gregarious impulse of unknown force is driving men into larger and larger agglomerations, some becoming so monstrous that they have more than ten million inhabitants. Is humanity going to opt for the life of the hive? Could not current tendencies also lead to a new 'charitable' order which might finally integrate humanity into a single community? No doubt we are still a long way from that!

Will the population of the Earth increase indefinitely? It has been said that in Asia, with its destructive monsoons, the vast swarms of men are necessary to keep pace with the forces of nature. Is there then a struggle between man and nature? The new sources of power which are increasing in number so rapidly may change the whole nature of the world population problem. The growing of food may be revolutionised at short notice; already there is talk of irradiated seeds, of hydroponic crops grown in ionised solutions of water and needing no earth. Should we not also envisage a far more extensive agricultural use of the seas? For how much longer will human geography remain confined to the planet Earth?

We hear a great deal about the difficulties facing the future of the human race, but despite present demographic and political trends, there is some hope that technological discoveries may be applied for the benefit of mankind rather than for its destruction.

A Lapp driving a sledge drawn by two reindeer in Swedish Lapland. Their simple warm clothing (a long jacket of reindeer skin and narrow trousers tucked into boots or shoes of the same material) and their remarkable powers of endurance enable the Lapps to withstand the rigours of an extremely harsh climate. JEAN MARQUIS, MAGNUM PHOTO

A landscape in Finnish Lapland.
WERNER BISCHOF, MAGNUM PHOTO

A sawmill in Angermanland, a province in the north of Sweden. Timber is an extremely important element of Swedish industry. K. W. GULLERS, RAPHO

The Little Mermaid in Copenhagen harbour, Denmark.

SCANDINAVIA

SCANDINAVIA, the land of the Northern Lights and deep fiords, of trim, smiling farms and bright spotless towns, combines the charms and virtues of Holland and Switzerland, of sea and mountain, with the distinctive qualities conferred on it by its climate and history.

Today it consists of Denmark, Sweden and Norway, and has rarely formed a single state in the whole course of history. Yet the three countries composing modern Scandinavia are so closely allied by ties of soil, language, customs and common interest, as well as by general outlook, that they call each other the 'three brothers', an expression of the strong solidarity which unites them now as it has united them in the past. The Scandinavian family also includes two more distant members: Iceland, whose isolated situation has preserved the oldest archives, the sagas, and the language closest to old Scandinavian, and Finland who, though linguistically different, was long united with Sweden and still feels a close affinity with her.

ON THE EDGE OF EUROPE. On a map or, better still, a globe, Scandinavia proper emerges as the north-west flank of Europe, or rather of Eurasia, with only about 900 miles separating Lapland from the Urals. On the other side is the Skandik, the Scandinavian (Norwegian) sea, an extension of the North Atlantic opening into the Arctic Ocean. Beyond it, less than 900 miles to the north-west, Greenland's icy wastes

mark the beginning of the American continent. The distance by sea to Spitsbergen, to the north, is barely 400 miles, to Iceland 650 miles, and to Scotland 300 miles. Thus the Scandinavians' vocation as a seafaring people was encouraged from earliest times, and was further emphasised by the deep penetration of the Baltic Sea, which is connected with the North Sea by the Great and Little Belts and by the Sound, the Kattegat and the Skagerrak. These waters separate two very different peninsulas: to the north, the Scandinavian peninsula proper, composed of Norway and Sweden, larger in area than France, measuring 1,185 miles from Scania (Skåne) to the North Cape in latitude 71°, and connected with Finland and Russia by a frozen and virtually uninhabited isthmus; to the south of the straits, the Jutland peninsula which, together with the neighbouring archipelago, makes up Denmark and is separated from Germany rather than connected with it by the narrow marshy isthmus of Schleswig-Holstein. Thus Scandinavia is bounded by the sea on nearly all sides; including the indentations of its fiords and archipelagos, its total coastline length is nearly 22,000 miles. So it is by no means surprising that the Scandinavians have always been attracted by the sea. Nor is it surprising, in view of their tenuous physical connections with Europe and their comparative remoteness, that they have preserved as marked an individuality as their British cousins.

The land surface of Scandinavia is extremely varied, with

rugged mountains in Norway, low hills in Denmark, and undulating broken plains in Sweden. This variety is paralleled along its coastline. The sea itself, so essential in the lives of the Scandinavians, reaches their shores in many different guises: the giant breakers and heavy tides of the Atlantic and the North Sea in the west; the limpid mirrors of the Norwegian fiords; the calm grey waters of the homely Baltic, which are tideless and only slightly saline. From 35 grams per litre in the Atlantic, salinity falls to 24 in the Kattegat, 14 in the Danish archipelago, and a mere 4 in the Gulf of Bothnia. Marine flora and fauna are obviously affected by this; oceanic species disappear one by one, the further one penetrates the straits and the Baltic, until most of the fish caught in the depths of the Gulf of Bothnia are freshwater species.

In complete contrast to the Atlantic, the Baltic is shallow, generally less than 300 feet deep, although there is one deep of 1,540 feet north of the island of Gotland, and another of 970 feet in the Gulf of Bothnia. The two Belts are less than 164 feet deep, and in the Sound there is a shelf less than 26 feet below sea level that is a hazard to ships of heavy tonnage. The Baltic Sea and the straits as a whole are classified as epicontinental seas and, in fact, geophysical samples taken in their southern waters reveal the same strata as those found in neighbouring Sweden and Denmark.

A REGION OF EARLY GLACIATION. The geological structure of Scandinavia is simple: an ancient rock shield on which other strata have since been deposited and which was subjected to Quaternary glaciation several times in the not so distant past.

The ancient shield is composed of barren siliceous rocks, gneiss, mica schists and granite; it also includes some strata of metalliferous deposits, notably iron, which is a source of wealth. Like other ancient shields in the world, it is of great antiquity, and is between 500 and 3,500 million years old. The whole of its surface underwent several vigorous foldings with the result that its rocks are very steeply inclined. Subsequently they have been worn down into a peneplain which accounts for much of the monotony of central Sweden. Schists, sandstone and limestone were deposited on top of the peneplain, and when a pedestrian walks through the streets of Swedish towns, he is treading on stones full of *Orthoceras*, 350 million-year-old shells.

Some 320 million years ago, the west of Scandinavia underwent one last violent folding, and the rock formations of Norway were moved from west to east. Today, towards Sweden, the glint-line and a number of mountains still mark the limit of the erosion of the ancient *nappes*. From then until the Quaternary era, the heart of the Scandinavian peninsula remained above sea level, while the sea made frequent inroads into the Baltic and Danish coastline. This was the time of the chalk deposits which even now, worn down by sea and ice, can be found in the dazzling white cliffs at Moen in Denmark. Fossil remains of the period bear witness to climates considerably warmer than the present-day 61° to 64° F. in Danish waters.

Then, at the end of the Tertiary and the beginning of the Quaternary era — about a million years ago — the climate gradually grew very much colder, although there were occasional violent fluctuations. In the west, which had risen progressively in the meantime, glaciers formed on the Norwegian mountains. On one side, to the west, they flowed into the Scandinavian sea where they broke up; on the other, towards the east, they spread out over the high Swedish and Finnish plains, meeting in a piedmont glacier which gradually rose higher. The snow lingered on it and was transformed into firn; the glacier bulged, becoming an enormous dome of ice covering the whole of the interior of the country, whence its name *inlandsis* (from *is*, ice, and *inland*, interior of the country).

Soon the *inlandsis* crossed the Baltic and invaded Denmark, Germany, Poland and Russia. Then, as the climate grew warmer, it receded and disappeared or was confined to the highest mountains.

There were several successive glacial periods, separated by interglacial phases, and they have left distinctive marks on the physiognomy of the Scandinavian countries: cirques, glaciated valleys and fiords in Norway; countless lakes in Sweden; lines of moraines marking the ice sheet's final recession from Denmark to Sweden, Norway and Lapland; ancient shore-lines around the Baltic (a lake at periods when the Danish land mass formed a barrier, a sea when it did not) and vast expanses of sand and gravel from the ancient deltas. Other features are the *oses*, deposits from the ancient subglacial watercourses, which dominate the plains with their strange, sinuous, elongated ridges; and, covering the low plains there is boulder clay deposited in the lakes, with thin parallel layers (*varves*) marking the passing years and dating the history of the final recession of the ice sheet. Towards 18,000 B.C. the glacial front cut Jutland in two; towards 11,000 B.C. it freed the south, and towards 6,000 B.C. the north of Sweden.

Glacial and allied deposits cover most of the plains and part of the mountains. Except in the east of Denmark they are mostly siliceous and naturally rather infertile, and the blocks of stone with which they are dotted are a hindrance to cultivation. The natural land use would seem to be primarily afforestation or pasturage, which still predominate to a large extent in the north. The lush, well-cultivated fields of Denmark, southern Sweden and some Norwegian valleys are a signal tribute to the tenacity of the Scandinavian farmer.

As the ice sheet retreated and grew narrower, it exposed the rocky shield which has tended to rise. Thus the north of Sweden is already about 1,200 feet higher than once it was, and the land still continues to rise in relation to the sea. At Stockholm the uplift is 20 inches a century, and 3 feet at the bottom of the Gulf of Bothnia. Harbour installations rapidly become inadequate in such a situation and have to be moved to remain of practical use. This explains the curious siting of the commercial port of Stockholm, which today lies far from the old city. Copenhagen has been luckier: uplift there does not exceed 4 inches a century, and the port has been able to expand normally.

A WET REGION OF MANY RIVERS. Since 6,000 B.C. the climate of Scandinavia has been, apart from a few fluctuations, the same as it is today: of the cool temperate type, verging on cold in the north. The mean annual temperature varies from 46° F. in the south to 28° F. in the north. In actual fact, the high latitudes (from 55° to 71°), which are shared by eastern Siberia, Labrador and Baffin Island, would normally impose a genuinely cold climate, but Scandinavia has a western façade, most of which is open to maritime influences, and Norway is washed by the warm waters of the Gulf Stream. This has a modifying influence on the temperature and causes heavy rainfall, particularly in the west. The east and north are drier and colder than the west in winter and hotter in summer; in short, they are less maritime. It is nevertheless true that of all countries in these latitudes Scandinavia is the most habitable and, in fact, the most densely populated.

Everywhere it is well watered. Its rivers and countless lakes together occupy six per cent of its surface, an excessively high proportion that is exceeded only in Finland and certain districts of Canada. The lakes are a legacy of recent glaciations; they have formed an obstacle to opening up the country and to communications and land development generally. This inconvenience is slightly compensated for by the fishing they offer; they have also fostered the Scandinavians' love of sailing, even in the interior of the country.

The Rjukanfossen waterfall (315 feet) in Telemark. This fall has been harnessed in enormous conduits which supply the great hydro-electric station at Rjukan.

KOBBINS, RAPHO

The rivers are extremely numerous, but their basins are very small: the largest and most navigable, that of the Klar-Väner-Göta, does not exceed 19,300 sq. miles. None is big enough to be accepted as a natural frontier, though there are exceptions; on the Lapland plateaus watercourses are the only natural landmarks, and the River Torne separates Sweden from Finland for 250 miles. The river systems of the peninsula are usually regular, most courses flowing down from the mountains to the sea in parallel lines. In the plains, the systems have varied according to the vicissitudes of the glacial retreat.

In the north and in the mountains most of the precipitation consists of snow, which covers the whole of the country during the winter, accumulating and melting little, if at all. Skiing was invented here and although it now offers both pleasure and sport, it was first — and still is to a large extent — a means of everyday communication. The thaw takes place in the spring, bringing belated floods in its train.

In the plains of Denmark and the south of Sweden, rainfall plays a more important part in feeding the rivers; evaporation is stronger owing to the summer heat; the waters are low in summer, and the main floods take place in winter and at the beginning of spring. The proportion of water carried away in relation to the total precipitation is 40 to 50 per cent even in the southern plains. In the mountains and the north it reaches 80 to 85 per cent. This proportion accounts for the great volume of the rivers; in conjunction with heavy precipitation it assures Norway and Sweden of. the world's largest resources of hydro-electric power, both exploitable

and already exploited. In Norway an annual average of 7,700 kWh per head is produced, in Sweden 2,850, and in Denmark a mere 550.

FINE FORESTS. To judge by those forests which have been preserved in more or less their original state, the country's woodland scenery must have been magnificent when the first men penetrated into Scandinavia. There are fine forests of beech trees with smooth majestic trunks to be found in Denmark and the south-west of Sweden. Farther north, more and more conifers are mixed with the deciduous trees. Still farther north, the conifers' sombre foliage reigns alone — pines in the past, with spruces on the increase. In the far north, near the North Cape, the desolate treeless stretches of the tundra predominate, with their grey lichens, willows and dwarf birches scarcely rising above ground level.

Similar gradations may be observed on the mountains. The upper limit of forest, marked here by a zone of pale-coloured birches, begins at 3,600 feet in the south of Norway and falls to 1,200 feet in Lapland. In the south of Sweden it takes 90 years for a tree to reach a height of 60 feet and a diameter of 1 foot; in the north it takes 150 to 180 years. Throughout the whole country excessively humid areas are covered with peat-bogs, some of which are wooded.

Wild animals include the reindeer (the basis of the traditional Lapp economy) in the north, and the elk in south-east Norway. In other parts of Scandinavia wolves, foxes, lynxes, otters and beavers can be found, although they are

	DEGREE OF LATITUDE	MEAN ANNUAL TEMPERATURE (in degrees Fahrenheit)	VASCULAR PLANTS	PERMANENT SEAWEED	LICHENS	LAND MOLLUSCS	FRESHWATER MOLLUSCS	INSHORE MOLLUSCS	BATRACHIA	REPTILES	NEST-BUILDING BIRDS
Spitsbergen	78	18	130	50	180			70		0	30
Lapland	70	32	340	150	400	10	10	200	1	1	
Norway	60	43		290		33	43		5	3	100
Central Sweden	59	43	900		600	40	64			3	
Denmark	56	46	1,100			60		110 (a)	11	6	
Western France	48	52	1,300	400	600	80	64	310	14	13	160

(a) Low figure because of the unbroken sandy coasts.

becoming rarer. Prominent among the birds is the caper-cailzie, a game-bird with magnificent plumage. The lemming, a kind of miniature guinea-pig, is extremely common in the mountains.

The landscape changes as physical conditions become more severe from south to north, and this is paralleled by a decrease in the number and variety of species. Scandinavia is one of the best regions for the study of the phenomenon of variation in the abundance of flora and fauna in relation to latitude. Some examples are given in the table above.

THE ARRIVAL OF MAN. We know that man appeared some hundreds of millenia ago, but we are not certain that he reached Scandinavia in those far distant epochs. If he did, subsequent glaciations which scoured the surface of the country destroyed any deposits which may have offered evidence of his presence. In about 18,000 B.C. the ice sheet still covered the whole of the peninsula, and its front extended into Jutland. It is known that towards 13,000 B.C. Magdalenian reindeer hunters were pitching their tents near Hamburg, which was then as cold as present-day Lapland. Tillage, the raising of

Dolmen at Knebel in Djursland, Denmark. There are thousands of megaliths in Denmark, bearing witness to a very ancient civilisation.
PAUL POPPER, ATLAS PHOTO

livestock, iron (Sweden's mainstay today) and even pottery were unknown to them; their only tools were made of chipped stone or bone. Later, as the climate grew milder, the ice-cap receded from the Danish islands and then from the south of Sweden. Towards 7000 B.C. Stockholm was freed, and during the same epoch men entered Denmark. Between 7000 and 6000 B.C., while the ice-cap was finally breaking up in the north and on the mountain peaks, men lived by hunting and picking nuts in the forests of Denmark and southern Sweden, or by gathering shellfish if they inhabited the coast. The mounds or piles of shells known as *kjökk-enmöddings* are their culinary remains — no more than refuse heaps admittedly, but valuable as evidence of early man's way of life.

Between 5000 and 4000 B.C. some progress was made. The dog, the first domestic animal, was introduced — probably for hunting — and man learned to polish stone and make pots. Then, towards 3500 B.C., came primitive cultivation of wheat and barley with the hoe, not the plough; the rearing of cows, pigs and sheep; and soon, between 2400 and 2000 B.C., the megalithic monuments, the tumuli, dolmens, covered alleys and lines of menhirs. Next came the domestic horse, and towards 1800 B.C. copper, bronze, oats, millet and the first swingploughs. Yet all these had already appeared in other parts of the world. Their late arrival in Scandinavia was the penalty for isolation.

The types of skeletons and the evolution of the burial-places in Denmark around 2200 B.C. have been taken as evidence of an important invasion; the theory is that at that time Indo-European invaders speaking a Germanic tongue mingled with the ancient farming people, while further south their cousins, the Celts, invaded Gaul and the British Isles and mixed with the aboriginal peoples there.

Technical and artistic progress continued in Scandinavia: in 700 B.C. there were rock engravings; in 500 B.C. iron was being extracted from ore taken from the marshes; the first ploughs and the first ships were in use. Towards the beginning of the Christian era came the introduction of rye, and the first attempts at manuring land and at marling, a technique which originated in Gaul. About 300 B.C. windmills with revolving millstones were used on the land. At about the same period the runic alphabet appeared. Writing had already been known for 4,000 years in Asia Minor, but there was a considerable time-lag before Scandinavia, being on the borders of Eurasia, acquired the necessary technical and intellectual knowledge for its early development.

WHO ARE THE SCANDINAVIANS? The Scandinavians belong to the white Nordic race, of which they are the

A Lapp and his wife lassooing a reindeer near Kiruna, in Swedish Lapland. Twice a year (in May and October), the herds are collected in a special park so that the animals can be counted and stamped with owners' brands. ROGER PERRIN

An example of modern Scandinavian architecture. This is a new block in Aalborg, Denmark. DANISH EMBASSY

purest members. They are tall (average height 5 ft. 8 in.), slim and broad-shouldered, with pinkish-white skins that freckle easily in the sun. Their hair is fair, their eyes blue, their faces and skulls long. They have thin, prominent noses, thin-set lips and prominent chins. By nature they are serious, even taciturn. The type is purest in central Sweden. Here physical characteristics are so homogeneous that the newly arrived visitor who has just left his first Swedish friend is sure that he is running into him again at every street corner.

There are exceptions of course — notably the Lapps, who display totally different features. A minority resident in the north, they are short (a little over 5 feet) and dark-complexioned, with small heads and round skulls.

Like many other peoples, the Scandinavians have known many changes in sovereignty in the course of history. At first they were ruled by minor chieftains; after 872 first Norway became a kingdom, then followed Denmark and Sweden. From 1375 Denmark was the dominant nation, and even effected a union of the three countries under its government from 1389 to 1523. In 1520 Sweden revolted, won back its independence, and itself became a great European power during the reigns of Gustavus Adolphus and Charles XII. After 1720 it began to decline again, losing its conquests one after another; at the same time the fall in Danish power continued. Norway, under the Danish monarchy from 1375 to 1814 and afterwards ceded to Sweden, finally regained its independen in 1905 and, helped by the development of its navy, established sovereignty over bases in the Arctic and Antarctic.

Like all civilised peoples, the Scandinavians have developed economically over the centuries. At first they were essentially a rural people growing crops or raising livestock; later they became increasingly townsmen and industrialists. In 1954 the proportion of the urban population amounted to 37 per cent in Denmark, where one-fifth of the population (nearly one million) lives in the city of Copenhagen alone.

The Scandinavians are distinguished by several particular traits. The sea, never far away and easily navigable, has fostered their remarkable unity, strengthening it with frequent exchanges and visits between the various countries. Indeed, the sea is and has been down the centuries a tremendously powerful force in the lives of the people, inspiring the daring expeditions of the Vikings from the eighth to the tenth centuries, the conquests of Normandy in 911 and of England in 1013, the discovery of Iceland in 874, and of Greenland and North America towards 1000. Even before the Christian era the Goths and the Suevi crossed the Baltic, while in the thirteenth century the Danes gained a foothold in Estonia. The Swedes established themselves in Finland from the ninth to the fourteenth century and, pushing on from there, founded Novgorod. They played an important part, perhaps even a dominant part, among the peoples who were to become the Russians and they even gave them their name: Rus. One of their number, Rurik, was the founder of the Tsarist dynasty.

In the seventeenth century the Swedes settled in Pomerania. In the eighteenth century the Danes colonised Greenland again. Even before this date, emigration to America had begun; under the pressure of overpopulation it speeded up in the nineteenth century. The upper limit was reached towards 1882 in Sweden; from 1846 to 1924, some two million people left Sweden and Norway to settle in other lands. It is a very curious fact that wherever the Scandinavians have encountered other peoples in their overseas settlements — except in the West Indies — they have ultimately adopted their language. Perhaps this is because the numbers of their own settlers in any one place were never very large.

The persistence of maritime enterprises in the course of Scandinavian history explains the importance of shipping in the region's life today. If tonnage is related to the number of inhabitants, there are 0.28 tons to every Dane; 0.33 to every

Swede, and 1.9 to every Norwegian, a figure which no other power in the world can equal. External trade also reaches record heights per head of population. Commerce on such a large scale, made possible by the large merchant fleet, is necessary because of the lack of natural resources. A long list of foodstuffs has to be imported. Copenhagen, which means 'port of the merchants', richly deserves its name.

The only important activity connected with the soil common to all the Scandinavian countries is the raising of livestock. There are approximately 340 cattle per 1,000 inhabitants in Sweden, 310 in Norway, and 720 in Denmark.

The average Scandinavian is fond of meat and drinks milk as a Frenchman drinks wine. One of his favourite meals consists of *smörrebröd*, small open, buttered sandwiches with a wide variety of fillings. He is astonished and almost scandalised at the idea of anyone eating unbuttered bread. He drinks a lot of coffee. He has simple tastes; he prefers rye bread to wheaten bread and eats more potatoes than any other vegetable.

Isolation accounts for other features peculiar to Scandinavian life. Roman influence was slight and indirect. Christianity was a late arrival, penetrating slowly from the ninth to the twelfth century. On the other hand, no other country accepted the Reformation so easily or so unanimously; according to

Top left: *An old Swedish peasant couple.*
T. ULMERUDH, SWEDISH INTERNATIONAL PRESS BUREAU

Bottom left: *A farmer's wife selling produce at a fruit and vegetable market on the island of Amager in Denmark.*
NATIONAL TRAVEL ASSOCIATION OF DENMARK

Bottom right: *A Norwegian Lapp family in their gay clothes.*
J. ALLAN CASH

Floating wood down a Finnish river. MOLINARD, RAPHO

official statistics Lutherans form 92 per cent of the population in Sweden, 97 per cent in Norway, and 99 per cent in Denmark, though there are very few practising members in any of the three countries. Some vague hints of past religiosity, perhaps the vestiges of ancient pagan rites, do seem to linger on. There is, for example, the complicated ceremonial of 'skåling' when drinking a guest's health, and there is the strange meal of crayfish (*kraftormiddag*) eaten in semi-darkness on tables lit by subdued lamps and in a silence broken only by whispers.

A REGION WITH A HIGH STANDARD OF LIVING.
In the country areas the tendency is towards dispersed communities, the principal exception being the oldest Danish villages, established under early influences. Elsewhere farms are isolated, as is usual in stock-farming countries; water is ubiquitous and presents no problem. In this land of forests the rural house is generally built of wood, except sometimes in Denmark. A typical feature is a garden surrounded by trees adjoining the farm.

Small towns all offer the same delightful prospect. The most careful observer will see at first only one or two houses tucked unobtrusively behind a clump of trees. But behind that clump another house is hidden, and behind it more trees. The little town is one big garden.

In the middle of the forest, in a clearing overlooking a lake, stands a lovely spacious villa, freshly painted, with intricately carved woodwork. The home of a rich landowner? No: the village school. The Scandinavians build well, because they know that in sound construction they have an equally sound investment for the future.

Social and political development is curious in that it has never kept in step with the rest of Europe; sometimes it has lagged behind, sometimes it has set the pace. Europe's oldest democracy was established in Iceland in 874, yet today Sweden, Norway and Denmark are still monarchies with respected and well-loved ruling houses. Sweden has had a Parliament since 1435, and neither she nor Norway experienced the oppression of the feudal system, but it was not until 1907—09 that universal suffrage was introduced. Norway extended it to women in 1919 and Sweden in 1918. Such reforms as the Scandinavian countries made after the French Revolution were at their own gentle pace. But from 1920 onwards they were caught up in a wave of enthusiasm for socialism that produced a programme of economic and social legislation which was unanimously accepted and can be quoted as a model of such reforms: it included a strict campaign against alcoholism; social insurance; three weeks' holidays with pay; encouragement of co-operatives, which expanded enormously; co-operative restaurants; a ban on radio advertising; aid for schools and adult education.

The tree is judged by its fruits. Scandinavia has one of the highest standards of living in Europe, and, indeed, in the world. Heavy imports ensure a diet that is extremely varied. Per head of population average consumption is 3,100 calories a day, against 2,750 in France; of this total the percentage of animal products is high.

The amount of power used annually per head of population provides interesting evidence of the national wealth. Expressed in weight of coal per head and per annum, total power, including electricity and paraffin but excluding wood, amounts to more than 2 tons per annum in Denmark, 4 in Sweden and 5 in Norway. This is considerably in excess of the global average of 1.5, and means that the Scandinavians are well provided with mechanical appliances. They owe this less to the unevenly distributed natural resources of their country than to the way in which they have developed them, to their neutrality since 1815, to their bold social and economic policy, to their acute and far-seeing social sense, and to their national discipline.

Hand in hand with social and economic prowess went wide-scale intellectual development. Large sums were devoted

Swedish children.   LENNART NILSSON, RAPHO

Norwegian boys.   J. ALLAN CASH

A young Norwegian lumber-jack.   K. W. GULLERS, RAPHO

to education, at least before the Second World War in 1940. The whole population attaches the utmost importance to the teaching profession, and this creates an atmosphere favourable to education and work in the schools. The biggest Danish industrialist, Carlsberg, a brewer, has devoted all his income to scientific research. Denmark publishes 3,100 books a year, Sweden 3,000 and Norway 2,700. The dissemination of news is more widespread here than elsewhere; one newspaper is sold for every two inhabitants in Sweden, and almost as many in Denmark and Norway. The telephone, which strengthens social contacts, is very widely installed; there is one to every seven Norwegians, one to every six Danes and one to every four Swedes.

A THRIVING POPULATION. Scandinavians' expectation of life is high. Neutrality, a high standard of living, a balanced but strict campaign against alcoholism, a high level of medical care and organisation, excellent hospitals and sanatoriums, and constant regard for the public health, all contribute to general longevity. The mortality rate is the lowest in the world: 0.9 per cent annually. For every 1,000 healthy children born, only 20 to 29 die before the age of one — another world record.

Towards the beginning of this century, the birth-rate had fallen. The new generations were decreasing in number and were insufficient to replace the older ones and ensure their maintenance in old age. But warned of the danger by the example of France, which had preceded them in this fatal trend, the Scandinavians set about combatting the menace. Family allowances and loans to young couples were introduced. Today the birth-rate level has been restored. The new generations are numerous enough to take over from their elders. Between 15 and 19 Scandinavians are born annually per 1,000 inhabitants; the death rate is almost half that figure. The population is increasing by almost 1 per cent per annum: to be more exact, 0.8 in Sweden and Norway, and 0.9 in Denmark. As resources are growing even more rapidly, the standard of living should go on rising, and the Scandinavians can face the future with confidence.

'L'ETAT, C'EST NOUS'. All in all, development has made enormous strides, especially in the last half-century. The reason lies not so much in individual initiative as in the way in which it is co-ordinated in the common effort, in the nation's wisdom and in its conception of the State. Everything in their behaviour bears witness to the fact that the Scandinavians live and act with a feeling of conscious solidarity with their brothers; their personal interest is the public interest. 'L'Etat, c'est moi!' claimed Louis XIV. The Scandinavians could more justifiably say: 'L'Etat, c'est nous!'.

Interior of a Scandinavian home. The rooms are almost entirely built of wood and are furnished with rustic chairs and a table of varnished deal, and brightly coloured rugs. The indispensable fireplace has an open grate. This décor, which combines the traditional with the modern, gives a feeling of warmth and comfort. ROGER PERRIN

A landscape in the rich cereal-growing district of North Zealand, Denmark. The houses in the hollow are sheltered from the wind.

DENMARK

THE kingdom of Denmark, the smallest of the Scandinavian states and only a little larger than Belgium, is a flat country made up of fragments of land. Including the irregular peninsula of Jylland (Jutland), it comprises about 500 islands, of which about 100 are habitable. The largest are grouped in the straits: Zealand, Funen, Lolland and Falster. Bornholm, which is appreciably further away, is the sunniest island, and the only one where there is good building stone. Elsewhere houses are made of brick or wood; roofs are tiled.

The population is about 4,500,000; its density, at 274 to the square mile, is by far the highest of the Scandinavian states. While the Lutheran church (the State religion) claims 99 per cent of the population, there is freedom of worship. Roman Catholicism, with 23,000, is increasing its numbers; there are 6,000 Jews.

The government is a constitutional monarchy, supported by two Houses. The socialist party is the most powerful. Denmark, neutral and virtually without an army until 1940, became a member of the North Atlantic Pact, and since then has introduced a period of compulsory military service lasting about eighteen months. The budget for national education is generally equal to two-thirds of the defence budget. Defence taxes are paid only by the very rich.

SIMPLE LIVING BUT A WIDE-AWAKE ECONOMY.

The Danes are simple people. In a country where agricultural production is industrialised and more standardised than any-

where else, the women still make it a point of honour to bake their own cakes and cure their own hams and sausages, and in many country districts they still bake their own bread as their grandmothers did before them. Every Dane has a bicycle, a machine well-suited to the flat country; even in Copenhagen, when the offices and factories cease work, the streets are jammed with hordes of cyclists.

For all their apparent calm and simplicity the Danes have always exhibited great economic activity. For a long time their vocation was agricultural and maritime. In the eighteenth century landed property was in the hands of the nobility: the peasants were subject to residential restrictions, cultivation was on a clumsy communal system, the division of each farm into a number of widely spaced lots entailed pointless journeys, and yields were very low. After 1788 the State recognised the dangers of such a system and prescribed the re-allocation of land, freed the peasants, and encouraged the development of small properties as opposed to large ones. Following the age-old Scandinavian pattern, the farms then became more widely scattered. The compact village centre was still not abandoned; it continued to exist but tended to play a new rôle, as an administration unit and a handicrafts centre. Since 1899 the State has bought up properties and distributed them to deserving small farmers, who became the owners of the farm buildings, though the land itself has remained the property of the State since 1919.

Agricultural production, as well as the distribution of land, has been developed by intelligent adaptation to changing circumstances. Until 1860, cereals had predominated. Towards 1870, the competition of the United States, with their large-scale production and low prices, was felt. Rather than introduce protective tariffs and risk stagnation, the Danes, who were firm supporters of free trade, preferred to make a radical change and concentrate on stock-farming. From 1880 onwards they developed grassland and crops of mangelwurzels. Over certain periods livestock rearing progressed so rapidly that fodder had to be imported.

It was realised at a very early stage that products would have to be standardised to achieve good sales. Co-operatives have contributed largely to this end. They centralise nine-tenths of the milk produced and slaughter 85 per cent of the pigs. The enormous slaughter-houses are an impressive sight with their endless rows of identical carcasses, all the pigs being carefully selected and killed according to a planned schedule. There are even slaughter-houses for poultry. Eggs are graded in screening-machines, and by the time they reach the grocer, they are graded to less than a millimetre. Butter bought anywhere in the country at any time can be relied on to be of standard quality. This uniformity is the only shortcoming of a system which otherwise has many advantages and which is being increasingly developed by the Danes.

Co-operatives aiming at quality rather than profit encourage and subsidise scientific and technical research. If the land in West Jutland is in poor condition, they appoint a team of scientists to study it. Farmers benefit from all the advances made in agronomic research. On the whole their soil is less fertile than that of, say, France, but the Danes obtain yields which are greater by 30 per cent from beetroot, 50 per cent from rye and potatoes, and 100 per cent from wheat, oats and barley. The only country in the world which surpasses Denmark is Holland, and then only by a small margin.

In the past bovine tuberculosis caused heavy losses. In 1952 at the request of the dairy industry the Danish Government undertook a vigorous campaign with the help of an army of veterinary surgeons. All herds are periodically examined, and if a single beast is diseased the co-operatives are legally bound to refuse the milk. These Draconian but wise methods have proved highly successful; Denmark is the first and, so far, the only country in the world in which bovine tuberculosis has been completely stamped out.

Apart from agriculture and stock-farming, fishing has always been one of Scandinavia's resources, but its growth has been particularly rapid in Denmark in the last twenty years.

Mineral resources are negligible. There is a little lignite. Prospecting for petroleum goes on apace, but so far unsuccessfully. There are no metalliferous deposits. On the other hand, large reserves of limestone and marl support a flourishing cement industry. An abundance of clay in the glacial deposits provides the raw material for Denmark's famous pottery. Copenhagen porcelain is noted for its elegance and the sobriety of its decoration.

The deficiencies of the soil are compensated for by the proximity of the sea, which has encouraged commerce and processing industries. Iron, coal and other imported raw materials are transported by sea and processed in the factories. Shipbuilding is the most important industry. (The first diesel-engined ship was launched in Denmark in 1912.) The production of the shipyards increased by 43 per cent in one short period of four years (from 1947 to 1951), and by 1958 had reached an annual total of 250,000 tons.

Lying between Sweden, the islands and Jutland, the Danish straits, with their shores devoted to commerce, are the key to the Baltic. The Danes were quick to realise this and trade has always played an important rôle at home and in overseas undertakings. Today exports consist primarily of farm produce: cattle and meat, eggs, cheese and butter. In addition, there are some manufactured products and, quite recently,

fresh fish. Great Britain is the principal customer, followed by Western Germany, Sweden and France. Export to England has encouraged the recent development of the port of Esbjerg, a drab town on the flat, dreary North Sea coast, but a vital trading centre.

Quite recently another trading channel has acquired importance: the Schleswig-Holstein isthmus. Long and barren, with marshes and gulfs hindering communications, it had long separated Germany and Denmark. Today the two countries are connected by two rail routes and two main roads. There is very heavy traffic through the small frontier town of Krusaa. Through it pass the refrigerated lorries exporting fresh fish to the rest of the continent.

From time to time there are acute crises in Denmark's export trade: with competition for agricultural produce severe in today's international markets a keen eye on the general economy will be needed to ensure continued prosperity.

Copenhagen

The recognised hub of all Danish activities and trade is the capital, Copenhagen. Today it houses about one-fifth of the population of Denmark, and is the biggest city in Scandinavia. Bishop Absalon, who founded it in the twelfth century, chose an admirable site on the Sound; a tiny, easily fortified islet between the large islands of Zealand and Amager became the heart of the city. It rapidly earned the name of København (*havn*, harbour, and *køben*, merchants) and was chosen as the capital in 1443, when it lay in the geographical centre of the country, which then included what is now southern Sweden. Since that time its predominance in all spheres has been emphasised. The university was founded in 1478. A library was built in the sixteenth century, and several academic establishments founded in the eighteenth century. Theatres and museums play their part in making Copenhagen the intellectual capital not only of Denmark but of Scandinavia as a whole. Also at Copenhagen are the Royal Palace, rich in historical souvenirs, and the headquarters of civil service departments and important

Preparing bacon at a modern Danish bacon factory. DANISH EMBASSY

An egg packing station in Denmark. The eggs are so carefully sorted that eggs in the same grade vary no more than a fraction of an inch in size. DANISH EMBASSY

At the Government research institute for dairy farming at Hillerod in north Zealand. DANISH EMBASSY

A cement factory near Aalborg in East Jutland. One of Denmark's most important industries is the manufacture of Portland Cement.
INGA AISTRUP, RAPHO

Below: A characteristic bicycle park near the main station in Copenhagen. Most Danes own a bicycle, a means of transport well suited to the flat country. There are more than 2,000,000 bicycles in Denmark. PHOTO AND FEATURE

Above left: *The Faeroe Islands. These islands, which are a Danish dependency, are situated in the North Atlantic halfway between Scotland and Iceland. They are volcanic in origin. In an austere setting, their 30,000 inhabitants live by sheep-farming and fishing.* Right: *Kronborg Castle at Elsinore, built in Renaissance style and situated at the entrance to the Sund. It was the setting for Shakespeare's* Hamlet.

ALAIN CARLE AND ANDRÉ GAMET, RAPHO

Below: *The old town of Aarhus in Jutland. A notable feature is its unusual museum of folk art. It is also the seat of an important university.*

INGA AISTRUP, RAPHO

Above left: *The fishing port at Esbjerg. The town has been growing rapidly in importance with the great increase in the export trade to Britain.*
DANISH EMBASSY.   Right: *the Radhuspladsen (Town Hall Square), Copenhagen. The busiest square in the capital, it is dominated by the Radhuset (Town Hall) on the right of the photograph. This brick building in Renaissance style was erected by Martin Wyrap from 1892 to 1905.*
INGA AISTRUP, RAPHO

Below: *Old houses along the Nyhavn, one of the canals which stretch into the centre of old Copenhagen.*   J. ALLAN CASH

commercial associations. The town is criss-crossed with canals, and the port is by far the busiest in Denmark. Raw materials unloaded here supply the most important industries in the country.

The population, industries and other activities are concentrated in Copenhagen to an extent rarely paralleled elsewhere. But there is no hypertrophy in the strict sense of the term, because the various administrative, intellectual, industrial and commercial activities are well balanced. The population total has followed an ascending curve: 130,000 inhabitants in 1850, 380,000 in 1900, 942,000 in 1958.

Copenhagen today is a charming, hospitable city of handsome monuments and well-kept streets, tasteful window displays, peaceful parks and cheerful church bells. In the calm waters of the Baltic Hans Andersen's Little Mermaid, her eyes turned landwards, still dreams of immortality.

No other town in Denmark is more than one-eighth the size of the capital. Aarhus, in Jutland, is the seat of a university founded in 1933. It also boasts a remarkable folklore museum where old Danish houses, full of period articles, furniture and costumes, can be visited in their natural setting. There are many small Danish towns of historic interest, dating from the Middle Ages to the eighteenth century. The castle of Elsinore, the setting of Shakespeare's 'Hamlet', still guards the entrance to the Sound.

The Danish countryside is a medley of gentle hills, fields and meadows dotted with smiling farms and copses, through which countless meandering country roads twist and turn. Far from the main towns, there are places where the traveller follows tracks dating from neolithic times, and where the peaceful silhouettes of ancient tumuli stand out against the sky.

The Faeroe Islands

A dependency of Denmark, like Greenland, the Faeroe Islands are situated in the North Atlantic, halfway between Scotland and Iceland. They are entirely volcanic, and are covered with black rocks and green grass. Trees on the islands are now rare. The 32,000 inhabitants, who live mainly by fishing and sheepfarming, settled there in the ninth century. Their language is similar to Icelandic, and they cling to local traditions and costume. Some foster dreams of an independence which could never be anything but illusory; the more practical islanders are satisfied with the autonomy which Denmark granted them of its own accord in 1948. Since then, the Faeroes have had their own parliament and their own flag. The capital is Thorshavn, a small, peaceful town of single-storeyed houses, where the roads are little more than lanes running between blossoming gardens.

AN IMAGINATIVE SOCIAL AND CULTURAL POLICY. Denmark's social development is as distinguished as its economic development. All the Scandinavian countries have taken bold measures in this field, but Denmark has done so in its own special way: parks with bricks and cement for children, to satisfy their desire to build and to develop their manual dexterity; waste land leased to citizens for cultivation as temporary gardens until the plots are required for future urban development; free school canteens and hospitals for everyone; maternity benefits; free medicine for all but the very rich; and a vastly expanded programme of adult education.

Both the arts and science are actively and widely cultivated, and scholarship is appreciated and respected by the masses. Notable contributions have been made to linguistics and oceanography and, in the artistic field, to sculpture. Denmark is the home of many eminent men: Absalon (1128—1201) who became an archbishop; Tycho Brahe, the astronomer (1546—1601); Steno (1638—1686), one of the founders of the study of fossils; Roemer (1644—1710), who measured the speed of light; Bering, the navigator employed by the Russians, who discovered the strait named after him; Hans Andersen, the sensitive author of the traditional tales; the physicist Niels Bohr, one of the pioneers of atomic theory.

Though small in size, Denmark has made its mark as a source of ingenuity and wisdom.

A beach on the west coast of North Jutland. The coast is low and consists of sand dunes and enormous beaches. The waves break on the broad and shallow shelf which surrounds the Jutland coast. NATIONAL TRAVEL ASSOCIATION OF DENMARK

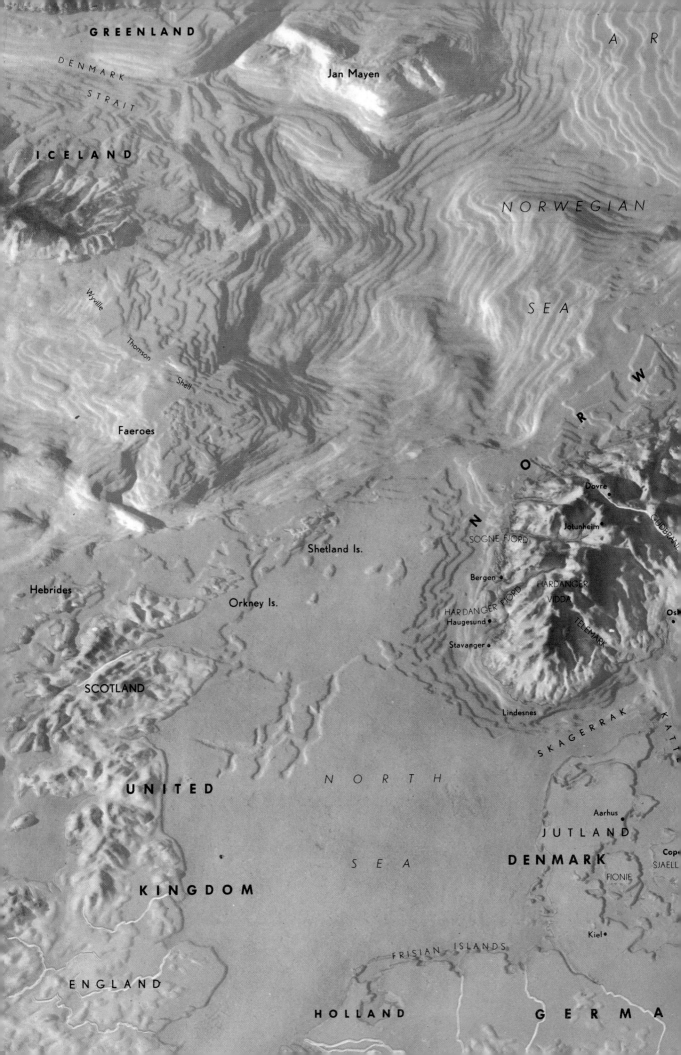

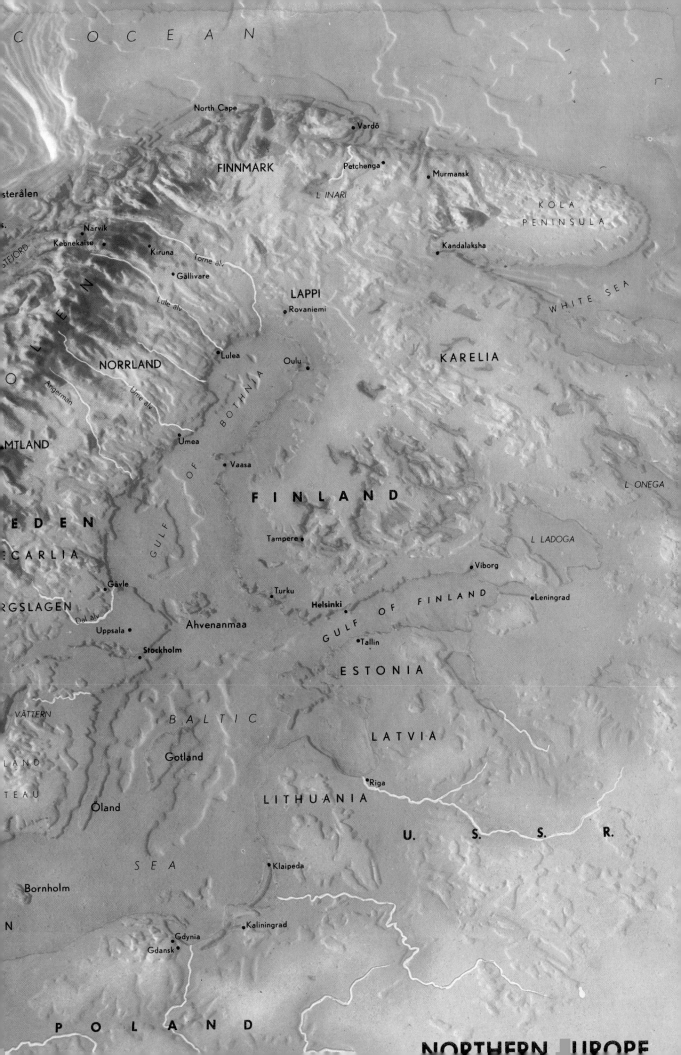

C OCEAN

North Cape
FINNMARK
Vardö
Petchenga
Murmansk
L INARI

KOLA
PENINSULA

sterålen
Narvik
Kebnekaise
Kiruna
Torne älv
Kandalaksha
TEFJORD
Gällivare
WHITE SEA
Lule älv
LAPPI
Rovaniemi
KARELIA
Lulea
Oulu
NORRLAND
Angerman
Ume älv
BOTHNIA
MTLAND
Umea
Vaasa
FINLAND
EDEN
L ONEGA
CARLIA
GULF
Tampere
L LADOGA
Viborg
RGSLAGEN
Gävle
OF
Turku
GULF OF FINLAND
Leningrad
Dal älv
Helsinki
Uppsala
Ahvenanmaa
Stockholm
Tallin
ESTONIA
VÄTTERN
BALTIC
LATVIA
LAND
Gotland
TEAU
Riga
Öland
LITHUANIA
U. S. S. R.
SEA
Klaipeda
Bornholm
N
Kaliningrad
Gdynia
Gdansk

POLAND

NORTHERN EUROPE

The fishing port of Stamsund on the island of Vestvågóy. A modern port, whose main activity is cod fishing, Stamsund is the largest town (7,800 inhabitants) in the Lofoten Islands, an archipelago off the north-west coast of Norway and inside the Arctic Circle. K. W. GULLERS, RAPHO

NORWAY

NORWAY'S is the loveliest and the most varied of the Scandinavian landscapes, the rockiest and the most precipitous. This supremacy it owes to its regal mountains divided by lush green valleys and intersected by majestic, sheer-sided fiords, some as deep as 4,000 feet. The length of the country from north to south is 1,100 miles; width varies considerably, from about 270 miles in the central part of the South Country to a mere 4-mile strip separating fiord from Swedish frontier at a point near Narvik. Its area is 124,556 square miles, less than that of France and rather more than that of the United Kingdom.

Norway is surrounded by the sea on all sides except the east, where it is bounded by Sweden for 1,027 miles, by Finland for 460 miles, and by the U.S.S.R. for 116 miles. Its fiords and mountains make it a land of separate valleys. · Seven per cent of the country's area is occupied by 150,000 islands, the largest of which is Hinnöy (about 850 sq. miles), one of the Lofoten Islands lying north of the Arctic Circle. The small coastal islands, often eroded until they barely rise above sea-level, form the *skjaergard*, or 'skerry guard'. The 200,000 lakes are all very small; the largest, Lake Mjösa, is only about 140 sq. miles in area. The rivers are impetuous torrents rushing down from the mountains and, with the exception of the 365-mile-long Glomma, are all very short. Their courses are frequently interrupted by magnificent waterfalls; Vettisfoss,

the highest, has a fall of 853 feet. Altogether, lakes and rivers cover about 4 per cent of the country's surface, and glaciers 1 per cent.

The mountain ranges, last folded in Caledonian times, about 320 million years ago, have since had plenty of time in which to be worn down by erosion. An upthrust assumed to be of comparatively recent origin made possible the embanking of river valleys which were then attacked by Quaternary glaciation and finally swept clear by the glaciers as if by a bulldozer. The upper slopes are somewhat flattened and monotonous, and even today they bear *fjell* (mountain) glaciers which cap them with white. This is the firn zone where the tongues of the glaciers flow down through the valleys. Some, among them Frostisen, descend right to sea-level.

The population of Norway is about 3,500,000, including 200,000 Lapps — more than in any other country. Density is in the region of 28 inhabitants per square mile, a relatively high figure for a country both mountainous and sub-arctic. Nearly three-quarters of the population live in villages or on isolated farms, for Norway is the most rural of the Scandinavian countries, just as Denmark is the most urban. The houses are built of wood, even in the towns, with the exception of Oslo. Until 1940 the country had not been invaded since the Middle Ages, and the farms are casually situated on any habitable site, their buildings often widely scattered. Scrupulous

Cod hanging up to dry on 'kjell' (raised wooden poles). JEAN MARQUIS, MAGNUM-PHOTO

honesty is the rule and no one worries about thieves. If a visitor seeks to leave a suitcase in the left-luggage office of a country station, the staff are surprised at the departure from normal custom, which is to leave luggage in a corner of the waiting room until it is collected again next day with perfect safety.

The ancient language was Old Norse. From the fourteenth to the nineteenth century, under the Danish monarchy, it was supplanted by Danish. In the mid-nineteenth century there was a reaction which successfully revived the Norwegian language under the name of *nynorsk*. At the same time Norwegian Danish was modified until it grew more and more like native Norwegian. Today the two languages tend to merge into a single common tongue, *samnorsk*.

Lutheran Protestantism has been the State religion since 1536 and embraces 97 per cent of the population. The Norwegians are very proud of their independence, recovered peacefully in 1905, when they chose as king a Danish prince who assumed the name of Haakon VII (the reign of Haakon VI had ended 525 years earlier). On 9 April, 1940, Norway was invaded by Germany without warning. For two months she put up a valiant defence before being forced to submit to occupation. In 1949 she signed the North Atlantic Pact. Her national defence budget is the largest of all the Scandinavian countries.

THE THIRD LARGEST MERCHANT NAVY. Heirs of the Viking tradition, the Norwegians have a merchant navy that ranks third in the world in tonnage, and an easy first in relation to the number of inhabitants, with 2 tons per head. Expansion dates from 1870. Today eight or nine out of every ten Norwegian ships navigate in foreign waters and never put into Norwegian ports.

Fishing has always played an important rôle; until the fourteenth century it paid for all imports. Today Norway's catch is 1 million tons per annum, or 660 lb. per head. The areas fished are mainly along the coasts of Norway and Iceland, but some are in the North Sea, others off Greenland and Bear Island. The fishing grounds change according to the season, with catches of cod off the Lofoten Islands from December to April and in the Norwegian Sea from April to November. Mackerel is sought along the southern coasts from May to October, and still further south, in the North Sea, from July to October. Sprats are caught from May to February in the fiords and gulfs of southern Norway. Herring fishing begins south of Bergen in February; later it shifts northwards. From May to September it takes place in the open sea off Bergen, and from July to September along the north coast of Iceland. When autumn comes, the herring fleets move towards central Norway, near Namsos, and may stay there from November to February, when the whole cycle begins all over again.

In the course of time changes have taken place, and some of today's richest fishing grounds were comparatively empty at the beginning of the century.

Fish is an important item in the national diet, and a popular combination is bread and butter and *sill* (anchovies).

Whaling is another of Norway's traditional occupations. The harpoon gun was invented by the Norwegian Sven Foyn in 1872, and Norwegian crews man more than half the world's whaling fleet. The catch is about 16,000 whales a year, from which 200,000 tons of oil are extracted in the factory ships.

Almost one-half of the imports are covered by the earnings of the merchant navy, 30 per cent by the export of fishery products, 23 per cent by paper, and 19 per cent by mineral ores. Norway's main customers are Great Britain, Germany and the U.S.A.

FOUR PER CENT AGRICULTURAL LAND. Two-thirds of the country is occupied by rocks, dunes and marshland; only 4 per cent is crop-bearing. Nine farms out of ten have less than 25 acres of arable land, and Norway has to import large quantities of cereals, as well as some fruit and vegetables. Stock-farming, on the other hand, is widespread, with sheep to the fore (550 head per 1,000 inhabitants). Fur-farming also flourishes (300,000 foxes).

Forests cover a quarter of the country, less than in Sweden

but a good deal more than in Denmark. They supply ten million cubic metres of wood, mostly from conifers. Timber is floated down some rivers, such as the Glomma.

POWER TO SPARE. Nature provides Norway with an abundance of power in the shape of numerous waterfalls, heavy falls of rain and snow, high mountains and abrupt slopes. These are optimum conditions for hydro-electric power, and each year 20,000 million kilowatt-hours are consumed out of a potential 100,000 million. The power per inhabitant is 5,700 kWh, an extremely high figure, and twice as high as in Sweden. Coal, on the other hand, is in short supply. Cooking is usually done by electricity. Only a quarter of the urban houses are piped for gas.

Industry has long existed on a small scale, being limited to mining and quarrying. In this country of ancient rocks, slate is abundant; pyrites, iron and copper are also mined. The nitrates industry has flourished since the early work of Birkeland opened the way for the technique of utilising atmospheric nitrogen. Paper is manufactured from wood. Metallurgical and timber works and naval shipyards have been set up, and all are in full production. Industrial production as a whole is increasing at the rate of about 3 per cent per annum.

A MAJOR ROLE OF THE SEA. The sea has always been the most popular means of communication, because it is the most practical in a country scored with mountains and fiords. Buoyage and pilotage are highly organised. Roads, on the other hand, are poor, narrow, interrupted by fiords, and snow-bound in winter. The railway system covers 2,800 miles, including 125 miles of tunnels, but again mountains and fiords are obstacles, making a continuous line linking north to south impossible. Snow ploughs are kept busy clearing the routes in the winter.

While the fiords make excellent landing-grounds for sea-planes, there are only three or four sites suitable as aerodromes for the major world airlines: Oslo, Stavanger and Kristiansand. Everywhere else the precipitous mountain slope is king.

TOWNS, PORTS AND COUNTRYSIDE. The countryside is dotted with trim wooden houses, roofed with slate, tiles, shingles, or even sods of turf. They are healthy to live in and easy to build. The buildings of each valley are distinguished by some special stylistic feature. In some places the old weather-board houses that were used as shelters in bad weather still exist. They date back to the Middle Ages, as does the custom of storing reserve stocks of food or hay in a special isolated building, the *stabbur*, decorated with beautifully carved woodwork.

The Östland, the south-eastern district, is relatively low and open on its east side. It stretches across the border into Sweden, for the frontier is a historical not a natural one. The climate is more or less continental, and agriculture is better developed here than in any other part of Norway. Oslo is situated at the head of the area's most sheltered fiord. Founded towards the ninth century, it was rapidly raised to a bishopric, burnt down in 1618, and reconstructed immediately afterwards by the Danes under the name of Kristiania. It has been Norway's capital ever since. In 1815 it had only 14,000 inhabitants, compared with today's figure nearing the half-million mark. Its expansion dates from the introduction of the railways which, from 1854 onwards, connected it with the hinterland, with Sweden, Trondheim and Bergen.

Today Oslo, a modern town, is the administrative capital, the seat of a young university, the main port for imports and an industrial centre. The islets in Oslo fiord and the surrounding wooded hills make it particularly attractive. One of the hills, Holmenkollen, is the scene of annual ski-jumping championships which are watched by a hundred thousand spectators.

Above left: *A factory at Rjukan in Telemark. By the electrolysis of water, this factory manufactures the heavy water used to slow down neutrons in atomic reactors.* Right: *Haymaking in the Sedestal. During the very short summer the hay is carefully tossed, dried and stored in barns. It provides valuable fodder for the animals, which are kept indoors throughout the winter.* K. W. GULLERS, RAPHO

Below left: *Coal mines at Longyearbyen, Spitsbergen. Because of the harsh climate, these mines on the precipitous slopes of the mountains are only workable during the summer.* INTERNATIONAL PHOTO SERVICE, ATLAS PHOTO. Right: *The Romsdal valley near Andalsues in Norway. It is a bleak glacial valley, littered with morainic deposits.* J. ALLAN CASH

The port of Oslo, capital of Norway. Oslo, which had only 15,000 inhabitants in 1815, now has nearly 500,000. Situated at the head of the Oslo Fiord, which is 65 miles wide and free from ice throughout the year, it is the administrative capital, has a newly-established university, and is an active port and industrial centre.
PAUL POPPER, ATLAS PHOTO

The port of Bergen, and part of the town with its old houses from the Hanseatic period. Bergen was the largest town in Norway for many years; it is now the second largest (after Oslo) and is constantly developing. The harbour traffic is intense. J. ALLAN CASH

The port of Svolvaer in the Lofoten Islands. In its splendid setting, Svolvaer (4,000 inhabitants) is the administrative centre of the Lofoten fishing fleet, whose main catch is cod and herring.
JEAN MARQUIS, MAGNUM PHOTO

The Östland's population is growing more rapidly than the rest of Norway's. It contained 41 per cent of the population as early as 1891; this had risen to 53 per cent in 1950.

In marked contrast to the Östland, the west is rainy; indeed it has one of the heaviest rainfalls in the world. It is mountainous, except for a narrow strip in the south-west. There, in the relatively flat country of Jaeren, in the vicinity of Sola, violent winds of earlier ages sculpted the rocks. Today a large aerodrome is situated on the same site. Jaeren is a dairy-farming district, but depends, too, on fishing, as does the whole of the west. Bergen, farther north, was founded in 1070. It is an important fishing centre, dominated by the mountain from which it takes its name. In the fourteenth century it attracted the attention of the German Hanseatic merchants, who established themselves there and claimed a monopoly of the commerce. Later, the Hanseatic League declined, and from 1750 onwards Bergen became completely Norwegian. It was for long the largest town in Norway, is still the largest town in the west, and continues to expand. It houses a meteorological institute for the benefit of the fishing fleet, a museum and, since 1948, a university. Imports exceed exports in the port's traffic.

Farther north still, there is an expanse of flat, comparatively agricultural land, a region with Trondheim as its principal town. Founded in 995, and originally called Nidaros, this was the country's capital for many years. Its cathedral shelters the venerable remains of St. Olav, the patron saint of Norway. It possesses a teachers' training college and a technical university.

Northern Norway, whose fishermen were exploited for many years by the southern merchants — first German, then Norwegian — extends between latitudes 65° and 71°. Here temperatures grow progressively lower. Wheat is not found above latitude 65°, nor rye above latitude 70°. At latitude 66° population density is still 16 per square mile; towards latitude 70° it falls to 3—5. Straddling the seventieth degree of latitude, the extreme north (or Finnmark) is a hummocky, violently windswept plateau rising from 900—1500 feet to about 3,300 feet. The mean January temperature is 22° F. and may drop as low as 2° F. The tundra reigns supreme, a dreary expanse of moss, dwarf willows and lichens, food only for the herds of reindeer kept by the Lapps. The only centre in which the Lapps are in the majority is Kautokeino, although it is little more than a large village. The region's only real towns are the ports: Narvik, which handles Swedish iron ore exports from Kiruna in the winter, and Tromsö and Hammerfest. This last, a town of about 4,000 inhabitants, lying below latitude 71°, is the most northerly town in Europe. An iron deposit is worked commercially near Kirkenes, but the area's main resource lies in the fisheries. The waters around the Lofoten Islands are so rich in fish that they attract, in addition to the permanent inhabitants, a seasonal population of fishermen who come from the south to occupy the 25,000 chalets or *rorbodars* from December to April.

Svalbard (Spitsbergen) and other Arctic possessions

Encouraged by the restoration of their independence in 1905, the Norwegians have since established sovereignty over a certain number of territories, most of them uninhabited: in the southern hemisphere, they have Bouvet Island and Peter I Island, and a sector of the Antarctic continent; in the north, Svalbard (Spitsbergen), Bear Island and Jan Mayen. Svalbard, a group of islands north of Norway, was known even in the times of the medieval sagas; in 1596 the Dutch-man Barents rediscovered them and rechristened them Spitsbergen and Bear Island.

Svalbard, about 360 miles north of Norway, extends from latitude 76° to latitude 80°, and has a surface area of 23,641 sq. miles. Warmed by the Gulf Stream, it enjoys an exceptionally mild climate. Since 1935 the south has been free of ice nearly all the year round. Mountainous and rugged, Svalbard comprises five main islands. It has some glaciers, particularly in the north-east. In many parts bare rock or tundra predominate, or curious polygonal areas and circles of stones. Svalbard was once frequented by the whaling fleets and later by Russian trappers. Its geological structure is extremely varied. Coal has been mined there by Norway since 1899. In 1925 Norwegian sovereignty was established after an agreement with the U.S.S.R. About 4,000 miners work there seasonally, and numerous tourists visit it in summer. Some of the mines are leased to Russia.

Bear Island is situated halfway between Norway and Svalbard. Discovered at the same time as Svalbard, it too is treeless, with a border of inaccessible cliffs, and wrapped in mist. Its highest point is 1,752 ft. Coal deposits have recently been reported.

The small islands of Kvitöya and Hopen, near Spitsbergen, also belong to Norway.

Jan Mayen Island, in latitude 71° north, between Greenland and the North Cape, is a hideous black mountain of purely volcanic origin. It has a surface area of 144 square miles, with its highest point in the ice-capped Beerenberg (8,347 feet). It is cold: 41° F. in July, 21° F. in January. In the past the only living creature on the island was the Arctic fox. In 1921 the Norwegians set up a permanent meteorological station, and in 1929 annexed the whole island. The station plays an essential rôle in forecasting weather conditions in the Arctic.

Boldness and Originality

The vigorous initiative and boldness of the Norwegians are borne out by their history, from the times of the Vikings to the present day. These characteristics are combined with an individuality that is accentuated by the isolation of the islands and valleys, each of which has its own dialect and costume. In the social field, the Norwegians have campaigned against alcoholism with a state monopoly of wines and spirits, fines for drunken driving, no alcohol on Saturdays and Sundays. In the medical field, tuberculosis is being attacked on a nationwide scale; B.C.G. vaccination is compulsory. Norway has supplied the world with a wealth of brilliant men: Abel, the mathematician; Amundsen, the discoverer of the South Pole; Nansen, another explorer, but a benefactor of refugees and prisoners-of-war in addition.

In this country of rugged rocks and noble mountains reflected in the fiords, thoughts turn naturally to the sky and the sea. Meteorology has made marked progress here with the work of Bjerknes; Birkeland discovered how to produce nitrates from the nitrogen content of the atmosphere. Oceanography is not surprisingly a respected study.

The arts, too, are encouraged: this is the country of the composer Grieg and the dramatist and poet Ibsen. Here Vigeland sculpted groups of men and children so alive and natural that the blood almost pulses through their veins. In an Oslo park stands his *Obelisk of life*, a writhing heap of muscular bodies climbing on each other's backs and reaching upwards, a symbol of mankind's aspiration.

Norway's vigour, variety and sensitivity are her distinctive contributions to the Scandinavian brotherhood.

A bridge over Lake Mälar, Stockholm. The capital of Sweden is situated at the eastern extremity of the lake. This view was taken during one of Sweden's wonderfully luminous June nights. REFOT, ATLAS PHOTO

SWEDEN

SWEDEN is the largest of the Scandinavian countries and the third largest in Europe. Vast plains covering the south and east gradually give way to mountains in the north-west. The highest, Kebnekaise (6,965 feet), still has small glaciers on its slopes. The country teems with lakes — 96,000 of them; together with the rivers, they occupy almost one-tenth of the country's surface. The largest, Lake Väner, covers 2,141 sq. miles, more than most English counties. The largest island, Gotland, covers 1,225 square miles. There are three main natural divisions: the south or Götaland, the centre or Svealand, and the north or Norrland.

In 1959 Sweden's population was 7,436,000, including about 10,000 Lapps, 34,000 Finns and 90,000 other nationalities. Divorce is common: about one in every seven marriages. Ninety-two per cent of the population are Lutheran and 7 per cent Nonconformist. There are 5,000 Jews and very few Catholics.

Sweden is a constitutional monarchy with a warm affection for its King, and a close regard for its personal comfort and its freedom. The people have always played an important part in the country's affairs, and the Government has frequently intervened on their behalf in matters of distribution of land and wealth. At the end of the Middle Ages, the Church's assets formed 21 per cent of the total landed property, against the Crown's 5 per cent. Gustavus Vasa exercised his sovereignty and confiscated them in 1527. In the thirteenth century noblemen were granted the privilege of tax exemption, and enriched themselves to such an extent that by the seventeenth century they owned 72 per cent of the land against 28 per cent in the hands of the peasants. Christian II was responsible for a redistribution which awarded 36 per cent to the Crown and 31 per cent to the peasants, leaving only 33 per cent for the nobles. Today, the Government owns about 20 per cent of the forests, 4 per cent of the arable land and half the hydro-electric power and mines (on a share basis). During the Second World War the Swedes remained neutral, a position which enabled them to help their Finnish, Norwegian and Danish friends by welcoming their refugees and intervening on their behalf with the aggressors. In peace time, the amount of the national budget earmarked for defence is small (15 per cent). Only in times of crisis is the defence allocation increased (from 1940 to 1945 it was as high as 50 to 60 per cent). This policy enables Sweden to buy ultra-modern arms at the psychological moment.

Sweden's natural resources

WOOD AND PAPER. The life of the Swedish people has altered considerably in the course of history, and the principal national occupations have been particularly prone to change. For a long time agriculture predominated. Then, from 1850 onwards, the timber industry developed apace. Today it is the most important in the country.

Left: *Transporting timber in the Province of Värmland.* Right: *A paper factory at Västerås in Västmanland. Forests cover more than half Sweden (six times the area available for agriculture). Logging is the most important industry in the country; timber products head the list of export goods and supply large numbers of paper mills.* K. W. GULLERS, RAPHO AND H. CARTIER-BRESSON, MAGNUM-PHOTO

Sweden is the most heavily wooded of the Scandinavian countries. The vast forests with their dark foliage cover more than half the land, an area six times greater than the cultivated fields. On average there are 600 pines, 720 fir trees, 270 birches and a few oaks and beeches per inhabitant (these figures are for trees with a minimum diameter of 4 inches). Whole districts are covered with forests, particularly in Norrland and the central area. They are broken only by the winding ribbons of the rivers, the straight lines of the railways, and the roads. The trunks, felled and stripped in autumn and winter, are towed down to the river banks by tractor and piled up on the banks or on the ice. In spring, when the heavy thaw comes, loggers armed with hooked poles manoeuvre the trunks into the water. The current does the rest. They make an impressive sight, these expanses of water covered as far as the eye can see with tightly packed logs making their forceful way down to the sea or the lakes. The total cost of transporting one log is no more than the postage rate on an inland letter. Cheapness apart, an additional advantage of floating the logs is that parasites, fungi and insects are destroyed by contact with the water.

The total length of natural waterways in use is 20,000 miles. In addition, where no natural course is near enough, there are artificial canals with plank-boarded sides. Saw-mills and factories are installed at the termini, frequently on the very edge of the Baltic. In their vast open areas piles of logs and planks dry out of doors; in their well-lit buildings the most up-to-date machinery turns the timber into planks, beams, wood pulp or various other products, depending on the nature of the factory. The timber may also be treated chemically, for the products extracted from it become more varied and abundant every year: plastics, dyes, artificial leather, synthetic rubber and cellulose. The waste products are made into wood alcohol and turpentine.

Sweden supplies about 7 per cent of the world's annual total of wood pulp. So it is not surprising that she uses a great deal herself, mainly for newsprint.

For many years it was a Swedish company that manufactured the best matches in the world. Then it developed subsidiaries abroad, and the Swedish match industry, reduced to cater for home consumption only, now employs only about 1,200 workmen.

The volume of wood felled every year represents one-quarter of world production. This high proportion threatens to decimate the forests of the future, and the State has had to take measures to protect young plantations, and to put in hand a programme of research with a view to introducing and acclimatising species more productive than the present trees.

IRON ORE. Sweden's second largest natural resource is iron. Here, as elsewhere, prehistoric man used the iron ore he found in the marshes. In the Middle Ages, rock deposits were exploited, and the mining districts in Bergslagen developed. They play a large rôle in the country's life.

Bergslagen consists of scattered mines and factories hidden amid luxuriant forests. The other large mining district, Kiruna, in the extreme north of Lapland and on the edge of the forest zone, is highly concentrated. It is a mountain of iron ore worked on the open-cast principle and also, more recently, by the shaft system. Almost all the ore from these districts is exported, in summer via the Baltic, in winter via the Norwegian port of Narvik. The quantity of pure iron extracted annually throughout Sweden is about one-tenth of world production. Reserves are 100 to 150 times this amount.

There are deposits of other metals, particularly in Bergslagen. Sweden's own tungsten, vanadium and zinc production meets her home demands; lead and copper very nearly so. Production represents 1 per cent or more of the world total of zinc, lead, tungsten and silver; 0.6 per cent to 0.3 per cent of copper and gold.

Metallurgy has always been an active industry. In the past smelting was done by charcoal, and this still holds good for one-third of the production; the rest is treated by coal (imported) or by electro-metallurgy. Natural resources of water power are responsible for rapid expansion in electro-metallurgical techniques, particularly in the production of the high-grade steels of which the Swedes are legitimately proud.

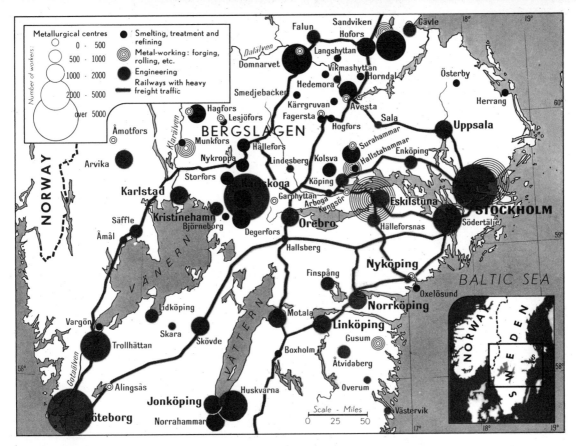

THE METALLURGICAL INDUSTRIES OF CENTRAL SWEDEN. *The concentration of metallurgical industries in the district of central Sweden known as Bergslagen was encouraged by the presence of various high-grade ores and the abundance of forests (charcoal was the only fuel used in blast-furnaces for many years). The factories are concentrated round the mines, close to the sources of power or lines of communication. The railways have played an important part in the industrial development of this sector of Sweden, particularly the Gothenburg railway, known as 'the Bergslagen Line'. A plentiful supply of skilled manpower has contributed to the fame of Swedish iron and steel products and Sweden is justifiably proud of its special steels, in great demand throughout the world.*

The factories are spacious, and their most distinctive feature is their remarkably efficient organisation. Products are varied and designed to make national resources play an important part in everyday life; there are, for example, the all-metal kitchens in which the sink is made of stainless steel. Sweden also manufactures motor-cars, telephonic and electrical apparatus, and ball-bearings.

WATER POWER AND INCREASING PRODUCTIVITY. The main industrial power is water power, which is almost as abundant as in Norway, for the same reasons. The rivers are interrupted by natural waterfalls of singular beauty. Since the fifteenth century an ingenious system of headraces has been developed in the Bergslagen mines to work the hydraulic machinery. During the twentieth century large hydro-electric dams have been built. The Harspranget waterfall centre, very near the Arctic Circle, is particularly powerful, surpassing the Génissiat dam in France. The centre at Stornorrfoss will be even more powerful.

Sweden has no petroleum deposits, and practically no coal. Peat-bogs cover vast expanses, but their exploitation is uneconomical. To compensate for the lack of petroleum, the Swedes began to work the bituminous schists of Kvarntorp in 1942. The schists contain 5 to 6 per cent hydrocarbons. Improved techniques have lowered the initial retail price of this fuel — a further example of the Swedes' skill in industrial organisation.

Today industry plays an increasingly large part in national and private economy. Thirty-eight Swedes out of every 100 live by it, and it supplies 42 per cent of the national income. Productivity per head of population is the highest in Europe. In the twelve years between 1938 and 1950 productivity per inhabitant and per hour increased by 35 per cent in agriculture and 23 per cent in industry. Between 1946 and 1950 it increased by 5 per cent per annum.

The progress made by industry makes a curious contrast with its firm adherence to a policy of decentralisation; factories still avoid concentration in grim industrial areas, and ultra-modern workshops are cleverly and unobtrusively sited in a green landscape. Sweden, in true Scandinavian fashion, still manages to look like a vast park.

AGRICULTURE BASED ON SMALL-SCALE FARMING. Farms are small; 375,000 with less than 25 acres. The majority grow mixed crops and raise different kinds of livestock, which makes for balance. In 1945, 28 per cent of the population still lived on the land. Co-operatives, which are highly developed, handle 97 per cent of the milk and butter, 92 per cent of the cheese, 72 per cent of the meat and 65 per cent of the cereals and eggs. Livestock raising is being improved, and artificial insemination is widely practised.

COMMUNICATIONS AND COMMERCE. As a vast industrialised country, Sweden has an extensive railway network that is particularly luxurious and comfortable. Nine coaches out of ten on the night trains are fitted with couchettes; seven of the ten are third class. Each couchette compartment has its own washbasin. All the main lines are electrified.

A programme of road improvement is under way. Cars are driven on the left, as in England. In winter, sledges and skis are used on the snowbound roads.

The merchant navy is developing rapidly. Sweden's shipyards supply about 8 per cent of world production, which puts them in the sixth place. Total tonnage increased tenfold

*Haymaking in Halland.
As in Norway, the hay is
very carefully harvested
because of the problem of
feeding cattle during the
winter. Only 10 per cent
of the country is suitable
for cultivation and only 14
per cent of Swedish man-
power is engaged in agri-
culture.*
H. CARTIER-BRESSON,
MAGNUM PHOTO

*Floating logs in Swedish Lap-
land. Every year, approximately 180,000,000 tree trunks
are floated down the Swedish
rivers from the forests to the
factories or sawmills. It is
estimated that the transport
of one trunk costs no more
than the inland postage for
a letter.* TAGE ULMERUDH,
SWEDISH INTERNATIONAL
PRESS BUREAU

*Houses at Killingi in Swedish Laple
Two of them are used as a school, the oth
as dwelling houses. The same type of c
struction is found in Russian Laple*
ROGER PER

between 1850 and 1950. From 1938—50 it increased by nearly 50 per cent, in spite of the war.

The main products exported are timber and wood pulp and its derivatives; these represent 55 per cent of all exports. Steel, iron ore and manufactured products account for 35 to 40 per cent. There are many customers, headed by Great Britain taking 20 per cent of the total, followed by West Germany, the Benelux countries and the other Scandinavian countries, each taking about 10 per cent.

The Country and its Scenery

THE SOUTH: GÖTALAND. A country of vast horizons, Sweden has its clearings and its forests, its gardens and its plains. The south or Götaland is one magnificent garden of cornfields, hillocks, plains and woods. In Scania (Skåne), in the extreme south, grapes ripen. This is the country of clear skies, with long sandy beaches where holidaymakers bask in the sun. The beaches in the west are rockier, but offer the additional attraction of fishing.

The mouth of the River Göta is the only point on the west coast that has always been under Swedish sovereignty. The town of Gothenburg (Göteborg) was founded there in the seventeenth century with the help of Dutch settlers. In the nineteenth century the waterway connecting Gothenburg with Lake Väner was made navigable. Thanks to its favourable position, it is today the headquarters of the ocean shipping lines, the largest port in Sweden, and the second largest town, with shipyards and a wide variety of industries.

Further south, in Scania, Malmö, the third largest town in Sweden, is situated on the straits of the Sound, immediately opposite Copenhagen, which is only 11 miles away. It is the port which serves Germany and Western Europe. Scania, which was Danish for many years, boasts some beautiful Renaissance castles. As in Denmark, the density of the population here is comparatively high.

Öland, to the north-east, is the island of sun and windmills, while Gotland is the island of roses and ruins. Thirteenth-century ramparts still stand guard over Visby, its modest capital. Not far away, on the mainland, the Rök stone bears the longest runic inscription so far discovered.

THE CENTRE: SVEALAND. The central region, the country of the Suevi, in contrast to the land of the Goths, is the other great historic region of Sweden. It contains the mining district of Bergslagen. In Dalecarlia the system of *faebods* prospered for many years. The old villages were established, as might be expected, on the best land. In the summer, the farmers used to leave the villages of Dalecarlia, to graze their flocks on inferior marshy or morainal land about five or ten miles away. Here they built wooden chalets, or *faebods*. Some of these (the nearest and the best) later became permanent dwellings and centres of cleared land. Then, from 1850 onwards, the population withdrew, partly the effect of the slump in agriculture. Half the permanent chalets have now been abandoned because half the farmers keep their flocks in the richer pasturage even in summer.

STOCKHOLM. The capital of Svealand ultimately became the capital of Sweden and the second largest town in Scandinavia. It occupies a magnificent site on the strait linking Lake Mälar with the Baltic. In the past, both the Lake and the Baltic were on the same level. Today, because the land has risen, the Lake is eighteen inches higher than the Baltic. Sometimes the difference is even more, and then Stockholm is threatened by floods. At others, after prolonged droughts, the Lake is lower, and then the salt waters of the Baltic infiltrate, as they did in 1930. However, the open sea is 25 to 30 miles away, separated from the town by the Stockholm archipelago. This consists of

SWEDEN. *This map shows how south and central Sweden, the two historic regions of the country, have been influenced by easy communications to the west with Denmark. They contrast with the much more extensive but sparsely settled region of north Sweden with its series of almost parallel rivers flowing east and away from central Europe into the Gulf of Bothnia.*

The Slussen and the Old Town, Stockholm. The Slussen is a lock at the end of Lake Mälar, crossed by a bridge used by heavy traffic. Intersections are avoided by the use of spiral ramps and subways. REFOT, RAPHO

Arctic Sweden. The iron-ore mountains at Kiruna during the winter.
SWEDISH INTERNATIONAL PRESS BUREAU

Höckeberga Castle (now used as a folk-art museum) in Skåne. K. W. GULLERS, RAPHO

The docks at Gothenburg, the most important port and the second town of Sweden. J. ALLAN CASH

Sorting, salting and dispatching fish in a small port in Bohuslan. K. W. GULLERS, RAPHO

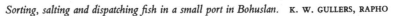

10,000 wooded islands and grassy islets surrounded by calm water and dotted with pretty, brightly painted weekend cottages.

Stockholm is a modern city which still preserves its historic associations in the old quarter. With numerous well-kept parks it is the residence of the King and the headquarters of the Civil Service, as well as being the banking and commercial capital and an important industrial centre. It is surrounded by the small industrial towns of Lake Mälar and the archipelago. Uppsala, a little further away, is the old capital, a cathedral town and the seat of the oldest and most important university in Sweden.

NORRLAND AND SWEDISH LAPLAND. There is a gradual transition from the milder lands of Götaland and Svealand to the Norrland, the country of the north. Larger than the other two regions put together, it is also colder. It was settled very much later than the others, and is still sparsely inhabited — ten inhabitants per square mile, twenty times less than in the extreme south. According to popular saying, it is where 'oaks, crayfish and noblemen cease'. Wheat is cultivated only in the south-east district; rye is planted right up to the Arctic Circle. At low and middle altitudes forest predominates. In addition to this natural resource, which was ruthlessly exploited between 1930 and 1950, it has iron ore deposits and sources of hydro-electric power. Alone, it supplies four-fifths of Sweden's hydro-electric power. Industry is also flourishing there.

Some Norrland farmers still own *faebods*. Along the coast, the Baltic herring is caught. Winter sports are practised in Jämtland from January to March, and in Lapland from March to May — sometimes even in June.

The Lapps, about 10,000 in number, differ widely from the Scandinavians racially, linguistically (they speak Uralo-altaic), and in their way of life. They are nomads, fishermen, and keepers of reindeer, which supply them with meat, leather, skins, milk and dairy produce. The herds are also used to pull sledges. Loaded, a reindeer can carry from 60 to 70 lb. One family can live off a hundred head. The forest Lapps and the mountain Lapps raise different kinds of reindeer. The Lapps' traditional way of life is currently undergoing vast changes as they come into contact with new techniques and as they establish commercial relations.

Part of Lapland lies outside the forest zone. This is the country of long bluish twilights, the land where the midnight sun lasts for 40 days.

Culture and Social Sense

The Swedes have a well-developed sense of social responsibility. They took certain measures in the field of welfare long in advance of many other civilised countries: free milk for school children, free meals for three-quarters of them, interest-free loans to young married couples to help them set up house. (This last is an indirect subsidy to the household appliances industry.) Economic plans have been worked out in advance against a time of possible unemployment. Help for mothers is given at State expense. There are free holiday homes for poor school children, and for their mothers. State loans and allowances encourage the construction of roomy, well-equipped dwelling houses. The sale of alcohol, while not illegal, carries a very high tax as a deterrent to alcoholism.

The Swedish radio is politically independent and is freely used by the various parties. Newspapers and the telephone are more widespread than in any other Scandinavian country.

In the factories, as in the country, the traveller is constantly left with the impression that here is a country which has acquired a certain balance and in which many problems are considered as definitely solved.

If there is another, less ideal, side of the coin, it is the aspect of uniformity throughout the country. From north to south, the farms are painted the same maroon colour, with the same white door frames and the same white window frames. Nor is there any relief in the large towns, where all the buildings are faced with the same sort of stucco.

The Swedes make excellent business men, engineers and town planners. They are noted for their attention to detail and their organising ability. These characteristics emerge in the genius or talent of their national celebrities: the chemists Scheele and Berzelius, the explorers Andree and Nordenskjöld, the industrialist Nobel, who founded the dynamite industry and then devoted his fortune to monetary awards for science, literature and peace. The botanist, Linnaeus, in the eighteenth century, substituted the order of his own classification method for the chaos of the existing systems. His nomenclature, a model of clarity and convenience, has since been universally adopted. Celsius invented the centigrade temperature scale, and Gerhard de Geer produced the first absolute chronological scale in geology.

Sweden can offer the world an example of precision and orderliness, and sound planning in the social and economic fields.

André CAILLEUX

The 375 megawatt Stornorrfers hydro-electric power station, opened in 1959. Here, one of the huge generators is being assembled. SWEDISH INTERNATIONAL PRESS BUREAU

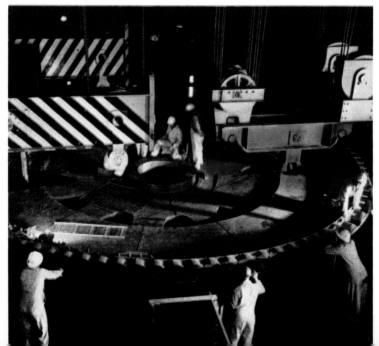

The Aulanko National Park in Häme from the air. A typical southern Finnish landscape: a gently undulating plain with numerous lakes, and a few clearings in the mainly coniferous forest. GAUTING, ATLAS PHOTO

FINLAND

NOWN to its inhabitants as Suomi, Finland is larger than Italy, less populated than Switzerland, and is mostly covered by the vast northern coniferous forest. The Finns have made agricultural clearings in the forest and exploit its resources to the full, supplying the world with timber, paper, plywood and prefabricated houses. The efforts of the people to find prosperity in so unpromising an area are commendable.

Finland is situated in the extreme north of the inhabited world. It extends beyond the 60th parallel and about a third of the country lies beyond the Arctic circle. With Iceland, it is the most northerly country in the world.

ON THE NORTHERN FRONTIERS OF THE INHABI-TED WORLD. In Lapland the sun shines for 57 days without setting. But the winter nights are interminable. Helsinki sees a total of 17 hours of sunshine in December. The rivers in the north are frozen from mid-October onwards, while even further south, they freeze at the end of November and remain frozen until May. By mid-December at the latest, ice covers even the largest lakes. From the same date a rim of ice lines the sea shores and connects the islands with the mainland.

Between January and April it is possible to reach the Aaland Islands (now the Ahvenanmaa Islands) and, in some winters, the Swedish coast across a bridge of ice.

Snow, which is permanent in certain parts of Lapland, begins to fall towards the middle of September, and its unbroken carpet covers the land from the end of October onwards. By Christmas the whole of Finland has donned the white cloak of winter that will not be shed until early April in the south-west and late May in Lapland. The country districts are the first to discard it; the surrounding forests keep it for another two or three weeks. The snow is thickest towards the middle of March, with 12 inches in the south-west, and from 20 to 30 inches on the higher ground of the eastern ridges. It rarely exceeds 23 inches in Lapland where the precipitation is lower. Thus for from three to seven months — depending on the latitude — fields, forests, rivers, lakes and roads, indistinguishable in their white uniform, are one vast skier's paradise. During the short, grey winter days, lumberjacks slide the tree trunks over the snow, to be carried away later by the impetuous torrents of the rivers when they are freed in the spring thaw.

Precipitation is comparatively light, for Finland is sheltered from rainy oceanic winds by Scandinavia. Snow accounts

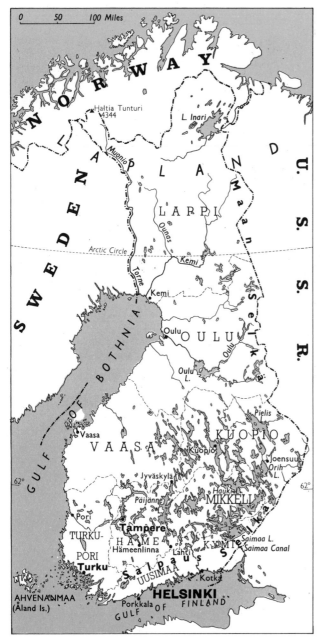

FINLAND. *Note the extremely broken topography, particularly in the south and east, where the coastline is deeply and closely indented and hundreds of morainic ridges enclose a myriad of lakes covering 20–50 per cent of the surface. The 55,000 lakes of Finland comprise 8 per cent of the total area.*

solar heat as the rest of the country. Vegetation in the north grows with surprising speed and strength, but the late frosts of spring (until early June) and early autumn frosts (from the end of August onwards) are often fatal to the crops.

With some justification Finland's climate is said to be one of the most temperate in the world, in relation to its latitude. January is 18° F. to 25° F. warmer than the average for the same latitudes. The lowest mean monthly temperatures never fall below 5° F., even in Lapland; nor below 28° F. in the south-west.

Drought and cold prevent trees from flourishing in the more northerly latitudes. The birch is the most northerly specimen, while the dark pines and spruces have withdrawn to southern Lapland. Slow growth and sparseness on the northern edge of the forest indicate that the trees here mark not an advancing front but a position retained with difficulty. On the higher ground there are no trees at all. The bare heights of the *tunturi* (similar to the Scandinavian *fjell*), are a wasteland of dwarf bushes broken only by light-coloured patches of lichens.

Finland's population, too, is sparser towards the north. In the north-east area, density is less than 25 per square mile and there are no towns; the only settlements are tiny hamlets lost in the middle of the primeval forest. Lapland has barely one inhabitant per square mile.

BETWEEN EAST AND WEST.

On the very edge of the inhabited world, Finland is also the meeting place of Western and Eastern civilisation. It occupies a sort of isthmus which joins the Scandinavian peninsula to the Russian continent. No point within its limits is more than about 190 miles from the sea. Civilisation reached it by sea from the south and west, but its first inhabitants came from the east.

This intermediate position, commercially advantageous in times of peace, is also at the root of the country's misfortunes. Linked with Sweden until 1809, Finland was then annexed to the Tsarist empire and became an autonomous Grand Duchy. Having proclaimed its independence after the October Revolution (1917), it has been able to preserve it only at the cost of heavy territorial losses and an unstable frontier line. By the Treaty of Paris (1947), it had to cede 17,698 square miles to the U.S.S.R., almost 12 per cent of the national territory. The ceded land included the region around the nickel mines of Petsamo (and thus Finland's outlet to the Arctic Ocean) and Karelia, with the town of Viipuri (Viborg). The naval base of Porkkala, also occupied by the Russians, was recovered in 1956. Finland has had to pay enormous war reparations. She has also had to rehabilitate 420,000 refugees from her ceded territory (11 per cent of the total population) and their livestock on her remaining land. This is the price she has had to pay to remain independent of Russia, with whom she has a common frontier of 792 miles. She maintains normal commercial and diplomatic relations with both east and west, but has not adhered to any of the blocs. She holds the·balance between east and west, an astonishing achievement.

AN ANCIENT LAND OUT OF THE SEAS.

Finland is a low-lying country, with altitudes exceeding 600 feet only in the north and north-east. The only mountains are in the north-west. The Haltia *tunturi* (4,344 feet) is a fragment of Norwegian *fjell*. The Gulfs of Bothnia and Finland are bordered by a coastal plain 30 to 35 miles wide and rising gently towards the interior in the region of the lakes, some of which are more than 200 feet above sea-level. Yet few plains have such a varied relief. The coastline is so deeply and closely indented, especially in the south-west, that certain parts of the country are inextricable tangles of strips of land and strips of water.

The lakes are an integral part of the Finnish landscape. They cover 8 per cent of the country's surface, are shallow, and very unevenly distributed. Comparatively rare in the

for 30 per cent of it in the south-west, and 40 per cent in the north. It rains frequently but only a little at a time. Summer is the rainiest season. Fairly high evaporation means that the rain is barely sufficient to meet the needs of the crops and the vegetation. In Lapland, some places receive only 8 inches a year.

In north-east Finland, the mean annual temperature is less than 32° F. The growing season, during which the daily mean is 41° F. or higher, is very short: 110 to 120 days in Lapland, 150 in central Finland, 170 to 180 in the south-west. The brevity of this period is to some extent compensated for by the length and brightness of the summer days. In June and July, Helsinki has 300 hours sunshine, and the lengthening days in the northern regions mean that they receive almost as much coastal plains and in Lapland, though it contains Inari — one of the biggest — they abound in the south-east, where they cover almost a quarter of the province of Mikkeli. The figure of 55,000 lakes is given for the whole of Finland, but in fact they defy counting because of their extraordinarily tangled outlines. The largest, Lake Saimaa (1,698 square miles), is also more accurately called *Satanen* (the Hundred Lakes).

Finnish rivers flow from lake to lake without any definite direction, like newcomers who have completely lost their bearings. They have no attendant alluvial plains. In the centre, a north-west to south-east axis emerges. Most of the lakes follow it, as do the long chains of hills called *harju*, which run across the country like roads and, in the south, actually rejoin two other west-east ranges, the Salpausselkä. These two ranges were left after the passage of a vast continental ice sheet which flowed down from the Scandinavian peninsula to the Baltic countries during the Quaternary era. In fact, they are terminal moraines marking the long front where the ice sheet stopped. A main road follows the ridge of the most southerly range, as does the Helsinki-Leningrad railway line.

A layer of alluvial soil covers the greater part of Finland, but it lies on an extremely ancient granite shield, for Finland is a fragment of one of the oldest known lands, Fennoscandia. In the strata formed by the granites and other hard rocks of the Archaean epoch, before the Primary era, geologists have identified the roots of two very old mountain chains, long since levelled down by erosion. Finland has none of the mineral wealth — coal, petroleum, bauxite — associated with sedimentary rocks.

Ten thousand years ago, at the end of the glacial period, the whole country, except for a few summits, was covered by the sea. Karelia was the first to emerge, then the upthrust continued progressively from south-east to north-west. New rocks emerged along the coasts. Passes became shallower. The islands increased in size and gradually joined up with the mainland. Much later, jetties built in the sea were gradually left high and dry. Towns situated on the edge of the sea, such as Vaasa, have had to be moved to keep pace with the sea's withdrawal. It is estimated that the country's surface area is

A ship caught in the ice at a temperature of 4° F. waiting to be towed away to the port of Turku by an ice-breaker.

PAUL POPPER, ATLAS PHOTO

increasing in this way by about 390 square miles per century. Hence the growing coastal plains of marine clay.

The thrust, which is not uniform throughout the country, involves a buckling of the surface sufficient to modify the outlets of some lakes. The formation of the Inari rapids in 1604 is an example of this action.

All these phenomena are the results of glaciation. The old Finnish shield subsided beneath the weight of many hundreds of feet of ice; it has not yet managed to regain its original position, though it is being raised rapidly enough for the result to be apparent in a single generation.

THE NORTHERN FOREST. The recent disappearance of the glaciers explains the vast expanse of peat-bogs which covers one-third of Finland. Their hillocks of turf interspersed with water are particularly common in the north. Elsewhere, many of them are wooded or even cultivated, for in the wake of the retreating glaciers came the advancing forest and its population of wild reindeer and furred animals. Later, came the hunters and trappers to occupy the still damp, soft land. Birches began to spread even when the glacier still reached down to the Salpausselkä. The subsequently warmer climate encouraged the introduction of pine trees, with hazels, elms and alders. Later still, the climate became more severe, and the pine abandoned Lapland to bushy scrub and the birch, which makes up 19 per cent of the forests today. Meanwhile, a newcomer, the spruce, encouraged by the cold, advanced from the east, worming its way into the forests of pine or birch, in whose shade it could grow. Today it forms more than a quarter of the forests, and its progress would have been even greater if man had not regained some of the best land from it.

Finland is the most densely wooded country in Europe. The northern forests are older than those in the south, for their trees are slower to develop. Seven per cent of the northern forests contain trees 200 years old, and more than fifty per cent are 100 years old or more.

The country's main activity, not surprisingly, is the exploitation of the forests. It supplies timber for building and fuel, and produces the woods in greatest demand on world markets: pine and spruce for timber and for the paper and cellulose industries, birch for plywood and cabinet-making, aspen for making matches. About two-thirds of the forests belong to private individuals or industrial undertakings; the remainder belong to the State, which has transformed many of them into nature reserves and national parks. The main occupations in winter are the felling and transport of timber. The tree trunks, usually made into rafts to avoid losses, are assembled and transported along 25,000 miles of waterways. In spring and summer floating timber gives work to tens of thousands of people.

The Finns are too astute to export their timber in its natural state. Timber processing and allied industries employ 70,000

The platform of a sauna bath. The Finnish sauna *is a room attached to a dwelling house in which the family takes a steam bath that combines elements of the Ancient Roman and Turkish baths. They beat themselves lightly with birch twigs to stimulate their circulation.*

IFOT, RAPHO

Left: *Finnish countryside in summer. Carts are in widespread use on the rough roads, whose surface is broken every winter by the ice.* FINNISH TOURIST ASSOCIATION.   Right: *The port of Inari, on Lake Inari, in Finnish Lapland. Lake Inari is one of the three largest lakes in Finland and is connected with the Arctic Ocean by the Paatsjoki.* WERNER BISCHOF, MAGNUM PHOTO

workers. Most important and longest established are the sawmills installed alongside the rapids and waterfalls, or at the mouths of rivers. In some years Finland has exported more cut wood than Canada.

The paper industry was a little later to develop. It utilises trees of smaller diameter whose stripped and crushed trunks are used in the preparation of wood pulp. Finland is the third largest exporter of paper, after Canada and Sweden. More recently new industries have begun to flourish: the manufacture of prefabricated houses (now one of the major export industries), plywood, furniture and man-made cellulose textiles.

During the last few years, forest produce has represented more than 90 per cent of the value of all exports. The forest is Finland's most precious possession. All owners are legally bound to ensure the continuous regeneration of their forests, and in all the rural parishes they are members of a forestry association. The Institute for Forestry Research at Helsinki,

the Forestry School of Helsinki University and six national Forestry Schools are dedicated to the study and improvement of the land's most valuable asset.

But man has not been satisfied with exploiting the timber only. From the second millenium before the Christian era, the forest was used as pasturage for the animals of Neolithic man, who created the first agricultural clearings by burning. In the Iron Age the ancestors of the Finns used to hunt animals in the forest and sell their skins to the Goths. And it is in the forest that, from the Middle Ages to the present day, agriculture has made steady progress, apart from occasional setbacks. The advance towards the north-east continues.

AGRICULTURAL ACTIVITY. Throughout the Finnish peninsula, between the two arms of the Baltic gulfs, the forest is dotted with bright fields and meadows. In the coastal districts, forest gradually gives way to cultivated countryside, with

A general view of Helsinki, capital of Finland and the only large city in the country (334,000 inhabitants). P. MOLINARD, RAPHO

villages grouped amid the fields, and towns situated on the coast. A line drawn from the north-east of Lake Ladoga to Kemi on the Gulf of Bothnia separates populated Finland from the Far North, the civilised from the uninhabited. The former contains nearly all the cultivated land, all the towns except Rovaniemi, and all except two of the railways. The line from Joensuu to Oulu and Tornio roughly follows the dividing line between the two Finlands.

The regions which have been longest occupied are the fertile plains of marine clay along the coast and on the shores of certain lakes. On them, vast expanses of unenclosed land were cultivated from the sixteenth century onwards, according to a system of collective rotation of crops. The villagers lived in houses tightly packed together in the centre of the clearing. Every man had a strip of land in each cultivated area proportional to the taxes he paid. The forests, fishing and pasture land were all communal. Successive re-allocations in the eighteenth and nineteenth centuries re-grouped the lands around newly built farms held by private owners.

Behind this coastal zone, pioneers scattered here and there along the waterways, or along the sprawling back of the *harju* burnt a few strips of forest and sowed the land enriched by the ashes. Their wooden houses, each with its barn, its granary, its *sauna* bath, its covered threshing floor, are grey, the natural colour the wood acquires with age. Each is arranged round two or three sides of a fenced-in courtyard. Near the towns, the houses are painted brighter colours: light brown, light yellow, or white. When they are grouped together, they are arranged in short rows, aligned along the edge of a road or a shore, or on the crest of a *harju*.

The slow encroachment into inland forest areas has accelerated with the demographic growth which quadrupled Finland's population between the middle of the eighteenth century and 1879, and has doubled it again since that date. From 1901 to 1931, the area under cultivation increased by two-thirds, although at the expense of the natural grasslands rather than the forests. After 1945, the need to settle more than 400,000 refugees from territories ceded to Russia entailed further land clearance in the centre and east (360,000 acres from 1945 to 1950), and the creation of more than 150,000 new farms. Finland is still a country of colonisation.

Even so, crops cover only 8 per cent of Finland's area. Before independence came, more than half the farmers were tenants. The agrarian reform of 1919 made them owners of the land they cultivated. Today, 95 per cent are owners. Three-quarters of them own holdings of less than 25 acres, which include a large proportion of woods. On most farms, the principal activity is not agriculture so much as the exploitation of the forest. This, together with the poor natural conditions — short summers that make it impossible to cultivate plants with a long growing season, and August rains delaying the ripening of cereals and interfering with the harvest — explains, in part, the nature of Finnish agriculture.

Its main purpose is to feed the inhabitants. Until 1940 winter rye was the main cereal for bread. Sown on unploughed land, it ripens as far as the south of Lapland. Today it has almost been overtaken by spring wheat. With State encouragement, the areas sown with wheat increased from 11,100 acres in 1930 to 452,500 acres in 1949. Winter wheat, which gives a better yield and ripens earlier, is more or less confined to the clay plains of the south-west. In spite of imported fertilizers, yields remain low: 6.8 cwt. per acre from spring wheat, 6 cwt. from rye. Nevertheless, before the Second World War, Finland had almost succeeded in winning the battle for bread. But since then she has had to start importing again. Potatoes are a valuable supplementary crop and, like the main Finnish cereal, oats, are also used to feed animals.

Finnish agriculture is turning more and more towards stock-farming, and more than two-thirds of the area under cultivation produces food for livestock. Forage crops are constantly on the increase. Oats, grown on the acid soil of the peat-bogs, covers one-fifth of the arable land, as much as all the other cereals put together. North of Oulu, it does not ripen, but is harvested while still green.

The products of stock-farming account for two-thirds of the total value of agricultural produce. About 500 dairies turn half the milk yield into butter. Before the Second World War, Finland managed to export butter, a little cheese, meat and eggs. Since 1930 she has developed fur-farming (mink, silver fox and blue fox). More than 1,500 farms are engaged in this industry and fur exports are considerable. Lapland has about 100,000 reindeer. Coastal waters are only slightly saline, and have no tidal ebb and flow. As a result they are not rich in fish. Five or six thousand coastal families, at the most, live by herring and salmon fishing. The salmon has been almost driven from the rivers by timber floating.

Since the end of the nineteenth century Finland has been a country with heavy rural emigration, particularly to America. More than 158,000 departures were registered between 1901 and 1910, and 58,000 from 1921 to 1930. Since World War II, about 100,000 Finns have left the country. New activities have had to be developed on the national territory.

THE NEW FINLAND. A people of farmers and lumbermen, the Finns have been able to consolidate the industries which they developed to pay off their heavy war reparations to the U.S.S.R. The food industries, for example, the flour mills and sugar refineries of Helsinki and Turku, now process national agricultural products and imported produce. Flax and some wool for the textile industry are home products, though the main textile demand is for fibres bought abroad. The principal textile centres are Helsinki, Tampere and Turku. The most remarkable advance of all has been made by the metallurgical industry, which today employs even more workmen than the timber industry (52,000 in 1958).

In spite of recent progress in prospecting (the majority of Finnish mines now being worked have been discovered since 1938), Finland, unlike her neighbour Sweden, is not an important mining country and is even less so since the loss of Petsamo. The Outukumpu Company extracts copper, iron and sulphur, and produces small amounts of lead, zinc, nickel and silver. The ores are smelted at Harjavalta, and refined in Pori.

But mechanical engineering employs the largest number of workers (slightly more than the timber industry) at Helsinki, Tampere, Turku, Pori and Kotka. This success is all the more meritorious in view of the number of obstacles: scarcity of raw materials; no coal; rapids with gentle gradients, and power per head of population half that of Sweden; shortage of ready capital; a comparatively small internal market limited to four million inhabitants; and, finally, a hostile climate. The interference of climate with traffic also had to be overcome. A network of modern roads 38,750 miles long, including 6,250 miles of first-class roads, has been substituted for the old forest tracks which radiated out around Turku. Snow ploughs keep about half of them permanently open to traffic.

These efforts in the field of production have not delayed completion of the railway begun in 1858, using the Russian gauge of 1.524 metres. Two of them reach as far as the Arctic Circle. More than half the railway goods traffic is timber. Ice-breakers keep the channels leading to the principal ports, Helsinki and Turku, clear, while the government has built a large winter port at Hangö, at the nearest point to the open sea.

Helsinki absorbs more than half of the Finnish imports, followed by Turku; Kotka comes an easy first for exports. Exports consist primarily of timber products and paper. Imports are more varied: fuel, fertilizers, cereals and foodstuffs, textiles, metals, factory plant and motor vehicles. The balance of payments, which displayed a marked deficit after 1940, is showing a tendency to redress itself. The United Kingdom

A winter landscape at Vuokatti, in northern Finland. The old insular shelf, worn down by glaciers, is now covered by lakes and vast fo

A young Lapp boy. FINNISH INFORMATION SERVICE

Finnish schoolchildren. The little girl has the true Finnish structure, while the boy is of Swedish stock. FINNISH EMBASSY

...mber being towed across a lake in bundle rafts. Tree trunks are collected and transported on 25,000 miles of navigable waterways, usually ...ped into rafts so as to cut down losses. During recent years, timber products have accounted for more than 90 % of the total export figures. Finland is the most wooded country in Europe. FINNISH EMBASSY

...e church in Rajamäki: an example of modern Finnish architecture.   The Pyhäkoski hydro-electric plant.   FINNISH EMBASSY

used to be Finland's main supplier and also her best customer, in some years buying nearly half of all Finnish exports, but first place has now been taken by the U.S.S.R.

Finnish sea trade followed a pattern of steady growth from 1917 to 1939. With the return of peace in 1945 the commercial shipping lines began to expand again. In 1958 45.7 per cent of the country's freight was carried by Finnish ships.

THE EXPANSION OF THE TOWNS. HELSINKI.

Development towards a modern way of life explains the recent expansion of the towns. In 1930 only one Finn in six lived in a town. In 1950, the proportion was one in three. It is true that the majority of Finnish towns are small. With their wooden single-storey houses, separated from each other by gardens, and their wide streets, which are not always surfaced or lined with pavements, they preserve a rural aspect. Only three have more than 100,000 inhabitants: Tampere (123,600), the main inland centre, where active industries are supplied with power by a waterfall and are served by a port on the lake; Turku (123,000), the old capital, which has become an industrial port; and, of course, Helsinki, the only large town in the country (453,000 inhabitants), a port, industrial centre and the capital of the Republic. Almost unique among Finnish towns, it has some tall modern stone and cement buildings, and is very proud of its enormous stadium in which the 1952 Olympic Games were held.

The economic, religious and intellectual capital (the old university of Turku has been transferred to Helsinki), it is even better known as the political capital. The residence of the President of the Republic, who holds the executive power and shares the legislative power with a single Chamber of Representatives (Eduskunta) elected every three years by direct universal suffrage, it is the symbol of national unity.

Anthropological research has made short work of the legend of the Finns' Mongol origin and has shown that they are closely allied to the European peoples surrounding them. Racially mixed, the principal stocks derive from Nordic and East Baltic races. Linguistically they belong to the Finno-Ugrian group. Although Swedish, the cultural language, is still an official language in addition to Finnish, only certain districts are officially bilingual, and the Aaland Islands are the sole region where Swedish alone is spoken. The Lapps number scarcely more than 2,000. Religious freedom has existed since 1923, though 95.7 per cent of the population are members of the Evangelical Lutheran Church, the national church.

Total population is 4,433,700 (1959 figures); density of population is 34 per square mile. The birth-rate, which was very high until the beginning of the century, fell to an average of 19.6 per thousand during the years 1930—1940, after which it rose again. At the same time the death rate fell. The demographic increase is likely to continue, and this is proving something of a problem.

However, the Finnish people, as a buffer between East and West, can ensure a safe future for themselves by making even better use of their country's limited potentialities, by improving still further their agricultural techniques, by mastering their inland waters more completely, particularly their lakes, and by introducing a still greater variety of industries.

François TAILLEFER

Fishing in winter through a hole in the ice. FINNISH EMBASSY

An Icelandic landscape, watered by glacial streams. In the foreground are typical Icelandic farm buildings.

ICELAND

ICELAND — *Ultima Thule* — is primarily distinguished by its geographical isolation. This Arctic island with an area of 39,758 square miles appeared at the end of the Tertiary era on the volcanic fault which fissured the Atlantic from Jan Mayen to St. Helena. It consists of a young granite shield, with very little metallic intrusion and a tough, nourishing grass as its only natural resource.

A very ancient civilisation has been in continuous existence there since the year 800. The Icelanders' natural insular character, the product of their complete isolation, has enabled them to preserve a language which is contemporary evidence of the sagas of the late Middle Ages. The re-establishment of national independence in 1945, after centuries of Danish rule, owed much to the retention of the language. Although its upper classes still spoke Latin only a century ago, Iceland is governed by one of the rare legal codes which owe nothing to Roman Law. Geographically and culturally it forms a little continent all on its own in the extreme north of Europe.

MANY OBSTACLES HAVE BEEN OVERCOME.
Iceland's inhabitants have had to triumph over the numerous obstacles of such harsh geographical surroundings. The temperature is alternately lowered by the action of the Arctic current and raised by that of the Gulf Stream, two opposing influences which give Reykjavik, the capital of the Republic, an annual temperature of 39° F., with a mean monthly temperature of 30.1° F. in January and 51.6° F. in July. These variations are bound up with the half-yearly variations in the duration of day and night which impose a certain pattern on human activity in the area. Such conditions make the island a seasonal meeting place for many kinds of birds and fish. Myriads of birds assemble there in the spring light, while its seas teem with cod in the winter and herring in the summer.

For nine centuries the tiny continent had nothing to offer men but its inland steppes disturbed by solifluction. Hurricanes blowing at more than 60 miles an hour discourage the growth of trees and shrubs.

The population is made up of a Celtic nucleus, which was soon submerged towards 860 by Scandinavian emigrants from Norway. Thus the Icelanders were the first Nonconformists to leave the Old World for the West, and later for America, which they probably discovered after they had colonised Greenland.

According to old maps the first cities were situated inland: the parliament of Thingvellir, which met in 930, was twenty-five miles from the Atlantic. The distribution of the population was determined by two main physical features: the twenty volcanoes aligned along a north-south axis, and the central glaciers which cover 13 per cent of the surface of the country. The extensive exploitation of pasture land has tended to disperse the settlements, which are not really villages so much as isolated farms animated only by the movement of the flocks or the cry of plovers. Stock-farming is conducted from a central farm, or *boer*, and spreads inland to make use of the remote communal pasture lands.

The *boer* is a conglomeration of small buildings with steeply pitched roofs, arranged in a straight line. It is generally situated on a hillside near a peat-bog. Its walls of violet dolerite and

Above: *A general view of Reykjavik, the most northerly capital in the world.* HANS MALMBERQ, RAPHO

Opposite: *An Icelandic pony. Iceland breeds more horses in relation to its population than any other country in Europe.* HANS MALMBERQ, RAPHO

Below: *Collecting seagulls' eggs in the Westmannaeyjar Islands.* HANS MALMBERQ, RAPHO

Above: *Barrels of herrings piled up on the quay awaiting shipment. Herring fishing is the country's main activity.*
HANS MALMBERQ, RAPHO

Opposite: *An old Icelander. Herrings are drying on the wall.* HANS MALMBERQ, RAPHO

Below: *An Icelandic girl in her gold-embroidered wedding dress.* HANS MALMBERQ, RAPHO

earth are cleft with narrow windows, and its roof is covered with sods of green turf. The interior is arranged to retain all possible heat. The stables are set apart. The hay loft plays an important rôle, for its fodder supplies the flocks during the winter. Above the rooftops, windmills turn in the strong winds. Gradually, though, the traditional *boer* is being supplanted by modern farm buildings of cement and corrugated iron.

URBAN GROWTH AND ECONOMIC ACTIVITY.

Urban concentration is a fairly recent phenomenon. In 1880 there were only three agglomerations, with a total of 3,630 inhabitants, or 5 per cent of the total population. For half a century now the industrialisation of fishing has been draining the countryside of its manpower so rapidly that in 1944 the island had ten towns — all fishing ports — with a total of 71,000 inhabitants (55 per cent of the population). The most recent figures (1959) show a total of 116,000 in 14 towns — or 67 per cent of the total population. In other words, the sea is still depopulating the land.

Towns and hamlets are connected by a network of horse tracks across expanses of pumice stone and moraine, signposted by cairns (*varda*) which often have legendary significance. Until quite recently transport was by pack horses formed into caravans. Because of the poor roads, the wheel was never used. Iceland is one of the few countries where transport has passed directly from horse-drawn traffic to aircraft. Internal airlines serve all the important points, and it is not uncommon for the farmer to fly to his hay fields behind the glacier line.

Urban economy depends on the sea, country economy on stock-farming and bird-catching. In spring, the eggs of migrant birds are collected in their thousands on the high cliffs, while the birds are caught in nets to supplement the food reserves. The herds and flocks are obviously of great importance. At the end of the Second World War, 622,000 sheep, 40,000 cattle and 61,000 ponies lived off the steppe; at the end of 1953 the figures were respectively 544,000, 45,000, and 38,000; in 1958, 774,814, 48,000 and 31,023. Iceland raises more horses than any country in Europe in relation to its population. Sheep supply meat, skins and — above all — their valuable wool, which is processed in the winter. That wool is considered a symbol of wealth can be seen from the fact that the Icelandic word for it is synonymous with 'silver'.

ICELAND COMES INTO ITS OWN.

In 1882, Iceland, freed from the Danish colonial monopoly, was at last able to sell wool direct for gold. With it she bought her first flotilla of old trawlers to exploit her deep-sea banks. As a result her economy underwent a rapid change. In 1958 she protected her fishing industry by proclaiming a 12-mile limit for foreign fishermen fishing near her coasts. Today more than nine-tenths of all exports come from fishing, while two-thirds of the imports are for fuels and building materials, and the rest for coffee, sugar and textiles.

The new fleet first exploited the spawning grounds of the cod off the southern coast in the winter, and it gained a sizeable share of Mediterranean markets. At the beginning of the twentieth century Iceland discovered the summer herring migrations along its north coast, and fishing became a national industry. Since then she has produced her own margarine, fish meal, fertilizers and canned goods. As in the other Scandinavian countries, trade unionism has played an extremely important rôle in this development. In 1944, the island was already industrially well equipped, with canning factories, cold storage factories and 40 electrical centres (21 using fuel oil and 19 hydro-electric power).

During the Second World War Iceland, occupied first by the English and then by the Americans, still managed to preserve the neutrality which geographical isolation had previously conferred on her in the course of history. Today it is one of the few countries which has no standing army, and this in spite of its strategic position. The current importance of its intercontinental aerodromes coincides with a new phase of aeronautical routing. Iceland is a sort of natural aircraft carrier, situated approximately halfway between Moscow and New York. Its grassland, a relic of an ancient pastoral civilisation, is losing its importance. Air and sea are rapidly helping to modify the economy, and even the age-old culture of this Arctic republic.

Marie-Magdeleine DEL PERUGIA

MAP OF ICELAND. *This 'Land of Ice' has a coastline deeply indented by fiords and in its interior vast expanses of ice contrast with powerful volcanoes (such as Hekla), the lava from which has covered part of the island. Evidence of volcanic activity still exists in the sulphur springs and geysers which spurt up like hot fountains. In spite of harsh living conditions and poor communications, Iceland has been populated for more than a millenium. Today aviation facilitates communications with this remote and misty island.*

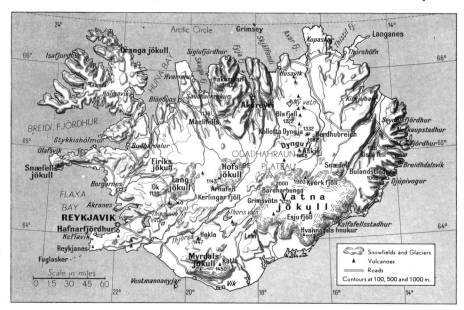

OCEANIC EUROPE

Above: *The austere landscape of mountains and barren earth on the Isle of Skye, the second largest island in the Hebrides, off the west coast of Scotland.* BRITISH TRAVEL ASSOCIATION

Below: *Megaliths near Waterville in Munster, a southern province of Eire. Such upright stones, which are Neolithic tombstones, are found in many places in Europe.* H. CARTIER-BRESSON, MAGNUM PHOTO

The Manchester Ship Canal in Lancashire. Thanks to this canal, which links Manchester with Liverpool and the Mersey, ocean-going ships can reach the centre of the industrial area. J. ALLAN CASH

THE BRITISH ISLES

OVER lies only twenty-two miles from Calais, and the crossing from Southampton to St Malo takes but a few hours. Le Havre is nearer to the English coast than it is to Paris. According to the geologists, the English Channel is a recent and minor feature, of no importance on the global scale, yet it is quite wide enough to isolate the British Isles completely. European but separated from the Continent, they consist in the main of two large islands: Great Britain with an area of 89,034 square miles, and Ireland with an area of 32,842 square miles. Small archipelagos are scattered between them and round their coasts. The country is 780 miles from north to south, and tends to be narrow — there is no point more than 75 miles from the sea. The sea, incidentally, varies vastly in its characteristics: in the west the deep waters of the Atlantic bring rains and storms; in the east the North Sea with its shallow continental shelf, though theoretically separating Great Britain from Scandinavia and Central Europe, in fact serves to link them rather than to divide them.

The fundamental feature of the British Isles is that they belong to north-west Europe. They do not possess a single important Mediterranean or Alpine characteristic. For the ancients, the frightening world of the Nordic countries began north of Armorica, and since the dawn of history no genuinely southern race of men or species of plant has ever penetrated into Great Britain, except perhaps in the extreme west. Its scenery often recalls the Dutch polders, the Danish grasslands, and the mountains and fiords of Norway, while its population

has traits that recall the tall blonde people of Scandinavia. This connection is of great antiquity; the oldest mountains, the Caledonians, which date back to the beginning of the Primary era, once covered the British Isles and Scandinavia without a break. During the cold Quaternary era, vast glaciers spread across the present site of the North Sea and over almost the whole of the British Isles.

The geography of Great Britain is explained by its dual association with a maritime and a Nordic world.

A SERIES OF BLOCKS. Far from the Alps, the British Isles have not been fundamentally upfolded since the end of the Primary era (600 million years ago). Over such a long period the ravages of erosion would have reduced them to nothing but a monotonous plateau today, had not three factors intervened.

First, the rocks of which they are composed are much less uniform than those of the old French massifs. Apart from the usual granites and gneiss, large areas are covered by extremely hard red sandstone, softer schists, soluble limestone pitted with caves, and complex volcanic lava. These different types have put up unequal resistance to erosion — which explains the features of the country's relief. In France, only the Armorican Massif is comparable.

The second original feature is that sediment has accumulated at the foot of the mountains in straits, lakes or seas. Throughout south-east England and in the broad depressed region of the

Midlands, the old shield is masked by Secondary and Tertiary limestone and clay.

Thirdly and lastly, the ancient massifs would no longer be mountains if they had not undergone comparatively recent minor upfolding into isolated blocks separated by regions which remained flat. What was the driving force behind this last act of structural history? A remote after-effect of the Alpine folding, or an unknown force issuing from the Atlantic, since the most elevated points are situated mainly in the north and west?

More recently (between 1 million and 10,000 years ago) glaciers from Scandinavia twice covered the North Sea and, with a few rare exceptions, swallowed up mountains and plains, making their mark in the form of valleys and leaving behind thick deposits of clay and pebbles (drift) when they melted. After they finally retreated isolated summits still had small glaciers which formed ridges and slopes. The majority of the lakes in England and Scotland were formed in this period.

THE ROLE OF THE SEA: AN OCEANIC CLIMATE.

The British Isles are generally reputed to have a mild climate, without excessive heat or cold but distinguished by prolonged rain and frequent fogs. There is some truth in this assertion. Extreme temperatures do not rise above 88° F. at Liverpool, or fall below 26° F. in the Scilly Islands; Krakow in the same latitude as the latter often registers —22° F. The mean January temperature of London (39° F.) seems delightfully mild in comparison with that of Winnipeg in Canada (—2° F.). Variations between winter and summer are small. Rain, which is more frequent than abundant, falls throughout the year with a definite maximum in autumn and at the beginning of winter, and a fairly pronounced minimum from February to April. Fogs occur for an average of 24 days in London during the months of November, December and January. The sun is sometimes covered in haze. In the south, it rarely shines for more than one hour in two on average (one in four in winter); in Scotland the average is one in three in summer, and one in seven or eight in winter.

But the pattern is by no means uniform. The climate of the archipelago is varied. The mountains in the west condense the rains, which exceed 80 inches on the most exposed heights in the south-west of Ireland and the Highlands of Scotland, with a maximum of 150 inches near Ben Nevis. A considerable proportion of the precipitation falls in the form of snow. In the plains of the east, the dry winds reduce the rainfall significantly; it is less than 40 inches in the Irish Plain, less than 30 inches in the English Plain, and a minimum of 23 inches (comparable to the figure for Paris) in the low country around the Wash.

Yet mean or annual totals do not accurately reflect the situation. The British Isles are situated in the path of the disturbance of the 'Polar front'. In summer the disturbances may withdraw further north, leaving the whole of the south open to warmer and drier air. Winds from the Sahara have been known to blow as far north as Scotland in mid-autumn. In winter, on the other hand, the zone of disturbance may move southwards to France or even Spain, allowing icy winds to dry up the Islands. Droughts also form a part of the complex British climate. Less common in the north and west — never more than 20 days in Northern Ireland and 30 in Scotland — they last longer in the east and south, and once persisted for two whole months at Hastings. The part they play in the country's agriculture can well be imagined.

No description of the English climate would be complete without a reference to its famous fog. Its distribution, heaviest in industrial towns, bears witness to the rôle which man and man-made smoke have played in its formation. Measures have been taken to combat it, and with improved methods of heating and the wider use of electricity the classical London 'pea-soup' fog is a thing of the past. It has been practically non-existent for thirty years.

The consequences of such a climate should not be underestimated. It excludes those types of vegetation needing heat but encourages certain plants thriving on prolonged cold. Grass grows rapidly and animal husbandry is more successful than crop growing; drought never lasts long enough to do the pasture land serious harm. But on the cold and humid heights the proportion of moors or peat-bogs to grassland is often excessive.

The heavy precipitation in the mountains feeds numerous rivers. After spring, however, their volume lessens. Although in January two-thirds of the rainfall finds its way into the rivers, in summer evaporation and vegetation absorb four-fifths of it in the mountains and nine-tenths in the plain. The July and September minima virtually deprive the rivers of water. Thus the mean volume remains low. The Shannon has no more water at its mouth than the Seine before it receives its large tributaries in the Paris district, and the mean volume of the Thames does not equal that of the Vilaine. If these two British rivers were harnessed, they would give little power.

Is it too rash to attribute many of the typical aspects of British life to this generally rather miserable climate? For example, the Englishman's preference for a house which is clean and cosy inside, and his attachment to his family and individual freedom? Many authors have thought that there was some truth in this theory.

THE ROLE OF THE SEA: POLITICAL ORGANISATION AND MIXED RACIAL ORIGINS.

Taine's simple, dogmatic statement: 'England is an island, now you know as much about it as I do', is no longer adequate, but even if the sea has not been sole master of England's destiny the English cannot be understood without reference to it. It was the sea which brought Britain's heterogeneous inhabitants to the archipelago: Celts from Central Europe, Romans from Gaul, Angles, Saxons, Scandinavians and, lastly, the Normans who arrived in the eleventh century.

A major part of medieval and modern English history revolves around the conflicts between these races and their tongues. The Normans and Saxons finally merged. The

Shipyards and docks at Newcastle, in Northumberland. Newcastle is important as a port for coal, as well as being one of the world's most important ship repairing centres. FAIREY AIR SURVEYS

English language, which triumphed at the beginning of the Hundred Years' War, has roots from both sources; but Cornish was not ousted for more than four centuries, and English still has not entirely conquered Wales, where a language similar to Breton is spoken. Although it is gradually losing many of its own special institutions, Wales still hankers for independence and puts up a spirited fight to preserve its native tongue. The Gaelic-speaking peoples of the north of Scotland kept their independence until the nineteenth century. The Scandinavians only managed to gain a foothold in the northern islands, the Orkneys, Shetlands and Hebrides. The union of England and Scotland in 1707 was never universally accepted and the Gaelic language, of Celtic origin, is still spoken by some Highlanders. The most determined opposition of all came from Ireland. Centuries of war and three hundred years of oppression have not overcome Irish resistance, aggravated by religious differences (Ireland is mainly Catholic, England Protestant or Anglican).

The consequences of this troubled history linger on in the political organisation. Three-quarters of Ireland (the Catholic South) has left the British Commonwealth and forms the independent Republic of Ireland. Nevertheless, legally, an Irishman is not an alien in England, nor an Englishman an alien in Ireland. The Protestant North of Ireland, together with England, Wales and Scotland, make up the United Kingdom, but a separate parliament for Northern Ireland (the Stormont) sits in Belfast. Scotland keeps its own institutions and has its own legal system; the Isle of Man in the Irish Sea, and Jersey and Guernsey in the Channel Islands have their own special forms of government. The only real bond between these territories, except in the Republic of Ireland, is the Crown, and few countries exhibit such monarchical fervour. The Royal Family's private life excites the interest and attention of the whole people quite as much as the pomp and ceremonial of a Coronation and other state occasions. This is all the more remarkable when we recall that the English were, historically, the first people to limit monarchical power and establish the prototype of constitutional and later parliamentary government. Imitated in Europe, it was spread by the English themselves in the New World, and has been copied by many states that have achieved independent status during this century.

The port of Grimsby, in Lincolnshire, is the biggest fishing port in the world, and its boats are found on every sea from the Arctic Ocean to Morocco. J. ALLAN CASH

Aerial view of Southampton. Southampton is the first passenger port and the fifth cargo port in the country. AEROFILMS LIMITED

THE ROLE OF THE SEA: ECONOMIC HISTORY.

Although England is insular she began to trade with the Continent at a very early date. We know how, in the Middle Ages, the fortunes of the feudal system linked her lot with that of Guienne, thus creating constant maritime traffic between the two territories, and how the Hundred Years' War arose partly from English commercial difficulties in Flanders. Time passed and the English ranged the seas and established colonies. Their merchant navy originally developed because of their geographical situation, but soon expanded far beyond the needs which brought it into being. After Dutch aspirations to supremacy had been crushed, England's Navy, until 1940, was the largest in the world.

This commercial success was the reason for the early influx of foreign capital with all its consequences. The money thus amassed was available for investment in new industries precisely when technical advances called for additional capital. England possessed mechanised factories long before other countries, and introduced the first textile machinery. English inventions included the flying shuttle, the spinning jenny, the Bessemer converter, and the Thomas process. The first railways, the first locomotives worthy of the name, and the first metal bridge were also English.

The profits derived from commerce were put to good use by the property-owning middle classes. Farm labourers flocked to the towns where ample employment in industry awaited them. Landed proprietors then acquired the plots and strips of land into which the open fields had formerly been divided. They enclosed them and suppressed the poorer hamlets; and since an archaic electoral system gave them practically unlimited rights, they were able to evict smallholders whenever they wished. Begun in the sixteenth century, this movement flourished most in the eighteenth and was completed in the nineteenth.

In this way Great Britain became at once a land of large towns surrounded by countryside on the one hand, and of large estates on the other. One-half of the land in England is owned by 8,000 proprietors; 91 of the biggest proprietors account for one-sixth. The big landowner normally tends to reduce his labour costs by keeping most of his land under grass. Despite a slight reaction which has been apparent since the Second World War, Great Britain is in the paradoxical position of being a green country where grassland predominates and every field is surrounded by a hedge, and a country with relatively few farm labourers: only 6 out of 100 Englishmen and 9 out of 100 Scotsmen live on the land.

The remainder are packed into enormous towns, sixty of which have more than 100,000 inhabitants. Some of the sixty stand side by side in vast conurbations. Red brick strikes a cheerful note in these towns but often fights a losing battle with industrial grime. The towns are composed of endless streets of identical houses with the same ground plan, the same roofs, and the same doors. In these enormous towns with tentacles like octopuses reaching greedily out for more space ancestral contact with the soil has been completely broken; even the garden is sometimes neglected and few of the 'de-ruralised' population have shown any desire to return to farming on a family scale. Moreover, the towns are often surrounded by uninhabited areas and within a few miles of the town centre the overpopulated, smoky, urban agglomerations have given way to the absolute solitude of hills and moors.

There is no denying the variety that these elements confer upon the English landscape. The plains contrast with the mountains, the humid west with the drier east, the urban ant-hills with the well-kept meadows and the uninhabited moors and heaths, the grassland with the arable land, England with Scotland and Ireland. In this way, like France, Belgium and Germany, Great Britain remains typically European, with small regional units displaying individual characteristics, often with their own vernacular names, features of which the New World is ignorant, at least on this restricted scale. Beyond the apparent uniformity of enclosed fields and monotonous houses there is a variety of scenery impossible to describe without carefully analysing the various 'geographical regions'.

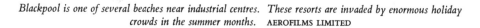

Blackpool is one of several beaches near industrial centres. These resorts are invaded by enormous holiday crowds in the summer months. AEROFILMS LIMITED

London. A view across the Thames to the Victoria Embankment on the north bank, showing a mixture of old buildings and new constructions, with the dome of St Paul's Cathedral on the right. J. ALLAN CASH

GREAT BRITAIN

SOUTH-EAST ENGLAND

A line from Newcastle to Exeter separates the plains, hills and plateaus of south-east England from the mountainous regions of the north and west.

To a large extent the south-east is comparable to the Paris basin. Here, as there, the beds descend in a gentle slope from the hills towards the heart of the basin. Hard (limestone and chalk) and soft (clay, sand) in turn, they appear alternately as hills and plains. These escarpments are markedly asymmetrical, rising steeply towards the mountains of the north-west but sloping gently down towards the south-east. Of the five structural belts of this type that can be identified, two are almost continuous: an escarpment of Jurassic limestone known as the Cotswolds in the south and the Lincoln Edge farther north, and a chalk escarpment, the Chiltern Hills.

The main rivers hesitate between a course following the general slope of the strata (the Thames, for example, cuts through the Chiltern Hills in this way), and the path of least resistance which, over the centuries, has turned them aside into the softer and more easily eroded beds. Thus at the foot of the Cotswolds-Lincoln Edge, the Severn flows southwards and the Trent northwards. These vacillations produce elbows and strange courses, even including a diffluence. The Waveney escapes from a tributary of the Ouse and reaches the North Sea, where its estuary is blocked by a long spit of sand. It is a river without a source and without a mouth.

As in the Paris Basin, structural arrangement is somewhat disturbed by geological foldings. The region south of London is an exact extension of the Boulonnais district in France. It was upfolded as a consequence of Alpine movements and its crest was attacked by erosion, with the result that it now consists of a depression, the Weald, flanked by two chalk escarpments, the Downs. The Isle of Wight and adjacent areas were upfolded in a narrower anticline which is an extension of the Bray axis in France.

There are two essential differences between the English Plain and the Paris Basin. While the latter's beds are disposed in a bowl-shaped depression with Paris or Orléans as centre, the English Plain is only a half-basin. Its strata descend from Wales towards the North Sea but do not rise again on the other side. The lowest points towards which the rivers converge are therefore situated near the sea. In addition, the Scandinavian glaciers once covered most of the plain, depositing boulder clay which often modifies the characteristics of the subsoil.

THE AGRICULTURAL LANDSCAPE. The south-east, the region south of a line running from the Cotswolds to the Wash, is the essence of rural England. There are very few districts which exhibit such a subtle and complete adaptation of agronomy to topography. With the aid of Dudley Stamp's excellent maps, a very accurate reconstruction of the

Opposite: *Canterbury, the cathedral. Canterbury is the seat of England's Primate and also a historic town which has kept its old-world appearance.* K. W. GULLERS, RAPHO

Below: *The Keep of Windsor Castle. Situated on the Thames near London, Windsor Castle was mostly built in the thirteenth century and is one of the residences of the Royal Family.*
FOX, ATLAS PHOTO

Right: *Cambridge, a university town which has been famous for 700 years.*
K. W. GULLERS, RAPHO

geological structure can be made from the land application. The clay plains, largely devoted to stock-farming, contrast with the limestone escarpments where mixed farming is practised. The originally wooded and marshy clay has gradually been transformed into grassland. Stock-farming, especially dairy farming, has swallowed up whole parishes, and arable land sometimes occupies less than one-tenth of the whole farming area.

On limestone and chalk, rich grassland, dairy farms, cereal crops and fruit are found alongside each other in every parish. The farmer follows the dictates of the soil down to the very last detail, abandoning completely as waste land only relatively small barren areas (the patches of sand in Dorset, and the excessively dry sand and chalk of Breckland around Thetford). Wheat and oats are the essential produce.

In spite of the continual contrast between the two types of agriculture, farming methods are similar. In both, the farms are run by large- or medium-scale farmers always watchful for new techniques, intent on improving yields, abandoning the less economical crops and developing others. In some fifty years (1884—1938) arable land in Northamptonshire decreased by one-third, yet the production level of wheat and oats remained the same. The high-grade specimens of seeds and breeding stock which English farmers have succeeded in producing are in world-wide demand.

Another development which goes hand in hand with the general economic conditions is noticeable everywhere: animal husbandry is gaining at the expense of crops. During the fifty years before the Second World War, arable land fell from 3,750,000 acres (excluding East Anglia) to 1,775,000 acres, whereas pasture land increased from 2,500,000 acres to 3,750,000 acres. The war reversed this tendency: arable land again spread at the expense of grassland and in many cases this appears to be a permanent feature.

SPECIALISED AGRICULTURAL DISTRICTS.

The picture is not altogether uniform however. To the south and south-east of London extend two strips of land devoted almost exclusively to fruit and vegetables, one between the North Downs and the Thames, the other at the southern foot of the North Downs, in the Weald, squeezed in on a narrow clay plain.

East Anglia, a vast protuberance sticking out into the North Sea between the Thames estuary and the Wash, is characterised by its flatness, its clayey soil, and its dry climate. Comparatively isolated from the main commercial routes and also from the paths of early invaders, it has known nine centuries of peace — a history undoubtedly unique in Europe — and adheres faithfully to the old ways of living. It is practically the only region in Britain which has retained open fields and compact villages, the only one where the area under crops is more than double the area devoted to grassland. Though Norfolk farmers travel little, there is nothing conservative about their agricultural methods. The Norfolk system of crop rotation revolutionised European agriculture in the eighteenth century by introducing root crops on land which had previously lain fallow. East Anglia alone produces one-quarter of England's wheat. Faced with economic difficulties, the large-scale farmers are developing the raising of livestock, while the smallholder prefers to grow more remunerative crops (vegetables such as peas and Brussels sprouts, seeds and fruit). The economies of town and country are interdependent. The towns serve as a market for agricultural produce, whilst their manufactured products are sold in the surrounding countryside. Norwich, the most typical, can draw on the largest radius for market supplies and for their retail sale. In addition, it is a financial centre for insurance companies, and a major manufacturer of agricultural machinery and shoes.

The Fens occupy an ancient marsh which was an extension of the Wash. Their drainage involves constant use of the world's biggest pumping station, which clears 2,595 tons of water a minute. A landscape of polders is replacing the old marsh with its chess-board pattern of oak saplings. It is the richest, most densely populated and most specialised of all the English agricultural regions. The crops, mainly potatoes and sugar-beet, are all grown commercially. There is no cultivation for home consumption.

TOWNS AND INDUSTRIALISATION.

Before the First World War, south-east England had the reputation of being rural and non-industrial. Its towns, often extremely picturesque — Canterbury, doyen of cathedral cities, and Salisbury, the seat of a bishopric, spring to mind — were generally little more than large market towns and county capitals. The most distinctive were the ancient university towns, Oxford on the Thames and Cambridge on the Cam, with their handsome colleges and quadrangles.

The last twenty years have wrought changes in this age-old state of affairs. Crisis in the West of England drove industrialists to seek fresh prosperity in a region which they had previously neglected. A new coalfield has been exploited in Kent. Nearly every old town has doubled in size with the building of new suburbs, and their populations have increased considerably. There is little to be gained by giving an exhaustive list, but new industries include agricultural machinery (Grantham), engines (Chelmsford), rail-cars (Colchester, which has grown from 30,000 to 60,000 inhabitants), refrigerators (Peterborough), and electronics (Cambridge). Cambridge, however, has not suffered anything like the same degree of industrialisation as Oxford, where the population has risen sharply from 50,000 to 110,000 and the city has become an important centre for the manufacture of motor vehicles, employing 12,000 employees in the engineering industry — a work force almost twice as large as the entire student body.

Lastly, since 1945, a start has been made on building 'New Towns'. Situated in the heart of the country, they are small enough to eliminate internal traffic problems, large enough to concentrate all the elements necessary for running one or more modern industries, and equipped with sources of power, transport systems, social institutions and schools. They are playing an essential part in the move to relieve congestion in the overgrown cities.

THE COASTS AND THE PORTS.

The English coastline follows the country's physical structure fairly closely. The chalk escarpments end at the sea's edge in vertical cliffs, indented and broken by dry clefts similar to those in the Caux district of France. The clay plains, on the other hand, terminate in a low flat coastline lashed by the waves. Often they have receded — in East Anglia as much as four miles since Roman times — leaving villages and even a town (Dunwich) high and dry. A general submerging movement has transformed the mouths of many rivers into estuaries and gulfs. It is still going on, and the South coast is losing ground fractionally but steadily every year. This movement, however, is counterbalanced by river and marine alluvial deposits. These fill up the estuaries and are shaped by the tides into ridges which gradually extend further and further into the sea, as at Dungeness in the Channel.

In the extreme west, the clay plain which stretches along the foot of the limestone escarpment has been much encroached upon by the sea in the Bristol Channel, the huge estuary of the Severn. For a long time, Gloucester, the lowest point at which the Severn can be bridged, served as port for the estuary. But it is accessible only to ships under 800 tons, and all the main traffic now passes through Bristol, where the difficulties involved in building a bridge are eased by the existence of a five-mile-long railway tunnel under the Severn. This is the longest underwater tunnel in England and connects Bristol with Wales. The city is sited a few miles from the Severn Estuary — its outport is in the suburb of Avonmouth — and has sent out a constant stream of expeditions and ships: to Guienne in the Middle Ages and later to the New World. John and Sebastian Cabot, the first to explore the North American coast, sailed from the quays of Bristol. Bristol men founded the Society of Merchant Adventurers in the fifteenth century and established a colony in Maine in 1620. Enriched by the slave trade, Bristol's fortunes declined when it was suppressed. The city assumed great importance again when Britain became industrialised. Half a million people live within its limits, and another six million within a radius of 75 miles. Apart from the usual traffic of an industrial port (imports of raw materials, motor fuel, oil, tobacco and foodstuffs), Bristol has become one of the main banana ports. In the city itself there are many factories engaged in a variety of industries (tobacco and aircraft construction are two), and a big packaging company has its headquarters there. Thus the port remains one of the busiest in England.

The south coast engages in two types of activity: tourism and trade. The first is encouraged by the fact that it is one of the sunniest regions in England, and by its proximity to London. The eastern beaches are only an hour's train journey from the capital. At weekends and in summer enormous crowds flock to the numerous seaside resorts, two of which (Bournemouth in the west and Brighton in the east) have almost acquired the status of regional capitals.

Cross-channel trade keeps a few medium-sized ports busy. Channel Island traffic sails from Weymouth; Dieppe is served by Newhaven. Southampton, one of the main centres of maritime trade, has grown up in the middle of this coast. The broad estuary of a minor river runs into the two straits to the north of the Isle of Wight, the Solent on the west, Spithead on the east. As a result, two successive tides reach the estuary at two-hourly intervals, creating a period of slack water at the flood which lasts for three hours. As it already combined the ideal conditions for establishing a port, its proximity to London (less than two hours by train) ensured its development. Southampton saves London-bound ships a fifteen-hour journey. Transatlantic liners sail from its docks, which were built by the big railway companies before the nationalisation of rail transport. Today Southampton is the chief passenger port and the sixth cargo port in the country. A few miles further down on the mainland side of Spithead is Portsmouth, formed by the fusion of four towns. Its functions are exclusively naval; it is a base, an arsenal, a provisioning centre, and a hospital. Consequently it suffered heavy damage during the Second World War. There are no comparable ports along the southeast part of the Channel coast, but here a new activity, fishing, has developed and makes a welcome addition to the cross-channel passenger traffic which is the main activity of the ports of Folkestone and Dover.

On the North Sea coast, fishing has become the principal activity of Yarmouth and Lowestoft, both important herring ports. Their commercial activity, on the other hand, has been on the decline since the silting up of the estuaries prevented ships from using them. Ipswich is the only town of southeast England's North Sea coast which retains any commercial

importance as a port, and this in spite of its position twelve miles inland. Passengers for Belgium and Holland embark at Harwich, at the end of the same estuary. Like all the other towns of the English Plain, these ports are developing industrially. Southend, the only really large seaside resort on this coast where the sea is colder than the Channel, is also becoming industrialised. It is already a kind of outpost of the London suburbs.

London

A POLITICAL AND ECONOMIC CAPITAL. The relative stagnation of the towns and ports in the east is partly due to London's excessive size. The city was built at the lowest crossing point of the Thames above the estuary. First there was a ford; later a bridge was built. London's early development was as a commercial centre but very soon it assumed political importance in addition to its economic rôle, because it was the centre of monarchical government and of the noble or popular resistance that established parliamentary government. Today London is known chiefly as the political capital, embracing the Royal Palaces, the Houses of Parliament, the Ministries, and the offices of the Commonwealth representatives. It is also a cultural capital, with its famous museums and galleries (the British Museum which is both museum and national library, the National Gallery, the Tate Gallery, and countless specialist museums), and the biggest university in England (23,000 students and a teaching staff of 1,700).

London is also the leading industrial centre in England, employing 21 per cent of British workers. Its industries are of the sort that need few raw materials and plenty of manpower. Statistics show that London employs one-half of all British workers making electrical equipment, one-third of those in the clothing industry, and one-fifth of the work force engaged in engineering and the manufacture of cars, bicycles, aircraft, food, leather and shoes. Add to this three large oil refineries with all the most modern equipment, and it is not difficult to see that London plays a vital rôle in English industry — except in its heavier aspects — considerably in advance of Paris's part in French industry, for example.

The capital's commercial and financial functions are even more important. All the wholesale houses have their head offices there. Futures markets deal in all kinds of goods, and the Stock Exchange in securities. There are centres for trading in tin, lead, zinc, copper, gold, rubber, wool, grain, cocoa and furs. The major banks and large insurance companies have no equals on the Continent.

ENGLAND'S CHIEF PORT. The port is the basis of all London's activity, although it has its drawbacks. The water is not deep enough in the heart of the city to take the largest vessels and it has been necessary to organise an extensive lighter service between the stretch downstream where the big ships moor and the wharves and warehouses up river. Canals and docks have had to be built, especially where a meander exists (e.g. West India Docks). At certain times of the year fogs downstream interfere with the regularity of the traffic. Lastly, the actual position of the estuary adds considerable extra distance to the voyages of transatlantic liners when compared with, say, Southampton.

In spite of these inconveniences, London remains the busiest of all English ports, importing half the country's raw materials and exporting half its manufactured goods, handling 18 per cent of British external trade and 16 per cent of its coastal trade. There is some lack of balance, however, because imports outweigh exports by nearly 50 per cent in value.

The port is one of the foremost in the world, though not as active as formerly in handling the entrepôt and re-export trade. Antwerp, Rotterdam and Hamburg compete with it in these fields, and Liverpool has taken over much of the

The River Thames from the top of the Monument, showing the Pool of London and Tower Bridge. J. ALLAN CASH

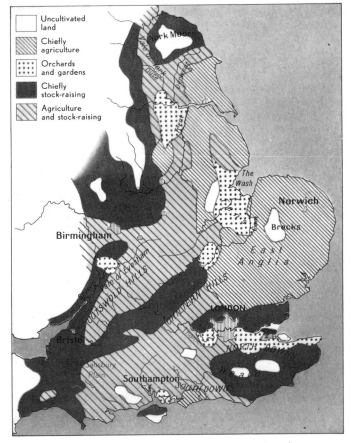

Above: THE DISTRIBUTION OF INDUSTRY AND INDUSTRIAL MANPOWER IN SOUTH-EAST ENGLAND. *The predominance of industry in London and the demands it makes on the labour force are striking. But the number of medium-sized factory towns processing all kinds of raw materials is on the increase. On this map, as on the following maps showing the distribution of industry and industrial manpower in various regions in Great Britain, the total number of workers is represented by inverted pyramids. The point rests on the town considered as the centre of the district, which does not necessarily mean that the workers live in the town indicated. These pyramids, whose dimensions are in proportion to the numerical strength of the labour force, also represent the distribution of workers in the principal industries, the white part of the pyramids standing for 'miscellaneous industries'. Industrial manpower in towns of under 20,000 inhabitants is not included.*

Opposite: LAND UTILISATION IN THE PLAINS. *This map showing the distribution of agriculture and stock-farming in south-east England indicates the regions which concentrate on growing cereals (wheat and oats), raising livestock, or on market gardening and fruit growing, and those where mixed farming predominates. Only the most barren soil has remained without cultivation.*

The Houses of Parliament, London. The left bank of the Thames was the site of the original city, but traces of the past have largely disappeared. It is also the site of the Houses of Parliament, a recent construction in Gothic style (1840—1850), with a terrace overlooking the Thames, and three towers. The clock tower houses the world-famed Big Ben, whose chimes are heard daily as radio time signals.

Daily delivery of bottled milk is a feature of every residential area.
UNITED DAIRIES LTD.

work of supplying English industry. London owes its importance today rather to its own industrial and commercial activities and to the extensive needs of a centre whose population equals that of Belgium and doubles that of Switzerland.

THE FIRST TOWN IN EUROPE. Until the outbreak of war in 1939 London was the first city in the world — in spite of statistics based on different data which awarded first place to New York. In fact, more than eight million people live in this enormous town. Very few live in the old, medieval 'City', now exclusively an office sector with a permanent population of only 5,000. After five o'clock in the afternoon, all activity here ceases and silence reigns in bank and office. But the City, as it is known, retains the prestige of history. Its numerous historic buildings include the Tower with the Crown Jewels and the Yeomen of the Guard. It preserves its administrative traditions, and elects its Lord Mayor, from whom the Queen must seek permission before entering the ancient precinct.

All round it, cities (Westminster is one) and boroughs have linked up as the capital grew and only a token municipal autonomy exists within the County of London, which embraces about 3½ million inhabitants. Although it stretches for 12½ miles from north to south and 15 miles from east to west, the county itself is now simply the heart of the city and as such is already affected by the inevitable depopulation of all urban centres, having lost more than a million inhabitants in twenty years.

London has extended far beyond these limits. Houses stretch continuously along the main roads for 15 miles north and south of the City, and for 25 miles to the west. More isolated suburbs lie even farther out, and a vast transport system of buses, underground trains and suburban electric trains is necessary to cope with the tremendous sprawl.

It is not easy to explain the variety of this vast agglomeration.

As in most other cities, there is a contrast between the metropolis with its overcrowded streets and its multi-storey flats, and the great collection of outer suburbs where the streets are blanketed in silence and lined with rows of small brick houses each with its small back garden and its still smaller front garden. As in most other cities, the different quarters are associated with specialised economic and social activities: Westminster with the Ministries and public services, the Strand and its vicinity with the law, Fleet Street with newspaper offices, and the City with finance and insurance. The residential West End houses a wealthier population than the industrial quarters of the East End, whose overcrowded slums were a favourite subject for nineteenth-century novelists. Even today they have not entirely lost their poverty-stricken character. In comparison with Paris, London's distinctive quality seems to consist, first, in a more dense general plan in which it is difficult to make out successive lines of growth; secondly, in the minor rôle played by the Thames in the city's aesthetic appearance — the river is too often concealed by warehouses, at least in the centre and to the east; and lastly in the large number of gardens for, in addition to the immense parks which form a veritable green belt in the west, there are countless gardens in squares or crescents. As soon as one leaves the centre,

Left: *Buckingham Palace. Built in 1703 but drastically altered on several occasions, particularly between 1825 and 1836, Buckingham Palace has been the principal residence of British sovereigns since the accession of Queen Victoria.*

PAUL POPPER, ATLAS PHOTO

Left: *Fleet Street, centre of the nation's newspapers, crowded with its usual mixture of cars, buses and goods traffic. Reuters offices on the right ; St Paul's in the background.* J. ALLAN CASH

Below: *Speakers' Corner, a well-known feature of Hyde Park, where anyone can get up to air his views and start a discussion. The audience listens without great conviction.*

the busy main roads tend to become increasingly isolated among the maze of quiet residential streets. Calm reigns over all; even the people who are in a hurry do not show it. Traffic jams are not marked by the horn blowing and cursing common on the Continent. Patient queues — the English grew used to them during the war — stand at stations, bus stops, theatres, cinemas, and sometimes even at restaurants. The Hyde Park orators with their *idées fixes* are symbolic of this social discipline, well aware that the crowd listening to their harangues would never dream of expressing disagreement in a violent or boisterous way, and that the only dissident voices will be those of odd hecklers here and there.

CENTRAL ENGLAND

To the north, the English Plain extends by swallowing up the Pennine Chain, pushing its way between the Pennines and the North Sea on the one side, and between the chain and Wales on the other, as well as along the coastline of the Irish Sea. It is still a plain, but a plain of very different character. It is flanked by mountains where the seams of coal basic to all industry and the salt strata indispensable to the chemical industry are found. The mountains are also the sources of springs of low limestone content that give the 'soft' water particularly suitable for the textile industry. Rainfall is heavier here because of the proximity of the mountains. Natural humidity in the textile factories is adequate at all seasons of the year, whereas in the south-east the atmosphere has to be artificially humidified to prevent dry threads from breaking during spinning and weaving.

But long before the industrial period, the central focal position of the humid districts gave them a key rôle to play in English politics. No other British region is so rich in historical memories. The medieval quarters and historic buildings of York, Chester and Lincoln attract many visitors. Sherwood

Lincoln Cathedral. This superb cathedral, largely rebuilt at the end of the thirteenth century on the foundations of the original Norman structure, is one of the finest examples of English Gothic architecture. BRITISH TRAVEL ASSOCIATION

Forest and Nottingham Castle were the legendary haunts of Robin Hood and his Merry Men. Rugby and Derby have given their names to two typically English sporting activities. The introduction of heavy industry resulted in the well-known 'Manchester School' of economists, and Rochdale was the cradle of the world-wide consumers' co-operative movement. Central England is unique for the intimate way in which the historical past blends with the industrial present.

The East: Yorkshire and Lincolnshire

In Yorkshire the two lines of the main chalk and limestone escarpments join. They are intersected by two gaps which connect the long north-south depression of the Vale of York with the sea. Only the more southerly contains a watercourse, the Humber, which receives the waters carried down from the Pennines and those of the Ouse and Trent. The present course of all these rivers is the result of a series of captures. The wanderings of the Don and Trent, which are now under control, have left the name of the Isle of Axholme as a souvenir to an area no longer an island. The last glaciation to fill the valleys deposited clay and moraines, and caused a westerly diversion of the waters of the Vale of Pickering which is separated from the sea by a moraine no more than a few yards wide.

THE MOST NORTHERLY OF THE LARGE CROP-GROWING DISTRICTS. Some of the land is unsuitable for growing crops. The tops of the limestone escarpments (the North Yorkshire Moors and the Yorkshire Wolds) are often uncultivated, the plains sometimes peaty. But many marshes have been drained, many rivers embanked, and the soil of the uplands improved by manuring. The climate is comparatively dry, especially in summer. The annual rainfall is less than 30 inches. Temperatures in July still exceed 59° F. — the most northerly point at which they are so high. Thus crops which had long been grown on very dry land have now conquered soil which has recently been brought under cultivation. The area of arable land exceeds 55 per cent, a proportion rarely reached in England. Moreover the importance of agricultural produce is more widely realised and accepted. In 1874, Yorkshire produced 7.6 per cent of England's wheat, in 1938 10 per cent. The establishment of two large sugar refineries has stimulated the growing of sugar-beet. However, this agricultural trend mainly affects the two big Vales of York and Pickering. Elsewhere, the open field system rapidly disappeared and enclosed fields have won the day. The Trent valley specialises in raising cattle for beef and veal, and in milch cows. The south produces early new potatoes, while mustard is grown on the banks of the Humber. But the sandy-soiled remains of Sherwood Forest (now protected) and the marshy strips of waste land on more humid soil are reminders of a past when poverty and insecurity were the general lot.

THE COAL AND WOOL DISTRICT. There was no shortage of ancient industries in Yorkshire. Wool from the sheep reared on the moors was woven in the dales. Metallic ores in the mountains supplied lead, baryta and fluorspar. But the Industrial Revolution proper was based on the exploitation of coal in the west and iron in the east. The exposed coalfield at the foot of the mountains extended for 65 miles, with a breadth ranging from 8 to 20 miles. The number of seams

Big Ben and the Houses of Parliament, London, by night. PAUL POPPER, ATLAS PHOTO   GREAT BRITAIN

is impressive; one is nearly 11 feet thick, a near record. Extraction began in the eighteenth century, and coal had been dug in small quantities many centuries earlier. In 1859 working was extended eastwards by sinking deep shafts through the upper strata. Gradually the centre shifted eastwards to the foot of the Lincoln Edge. In spite of some disadvantages (too many faults, too much flooding) it is by far the richest of the English coalfields. It has yielded a tonnage almost equal to that of all the deposits in France put together. Suitable as a source of power and for processing into coke (and therefore useful in metallurgy) coal is taken to southern England by rail and exported to other countries via the North Sea ports. For the present nothing seems likely to threaten the prosperity of the industry in this area.

The ancient woollen industries which were dispersed along the line of soft water springs were rejuvenated by the introduction of the steam-powered loom in 1822. Yorkshire supplies 86 per cent of England's woollen yarn and does as much as 90 per cent of her wool-combing. Other supplements to the textile industry proper were the manufacture of textile machinery, and the development of banking and financial houses and the wholesale wool markets — although some raw wool is still supplied through London. Built round the mines and mills, the old villages, now enormously expanded, are connected by long streets which are really suburbs. One could almost say that the area's textile industry is one vast oval conurbation, 25 miles long and more than 12 miles wide, containing more than 40 towns and nearly 2 million inhabitants. Most of the towns have their own speciality. Bradford is the chief centre of wool-combing and the manufacture of worsteds. To the south-west it almost merges with Halifax and to the north-west with Keighley, enclosed in the deep valley of the Aire. Supremacy in spinning and weaving is shared by Bradford and Huddersfield. Dewsbury concentrates on cheaper fabrics made of shoddy, Halifax produces carpets, and Huddersfield high-class cloths and tweeds. Leeds and Bradford stand out as the principal towns in population and in volume of trade. Rayon is being introduced in most towns, either alone or mixed with wool. Bradford, with 300,000 inhabitants, remains primarily a large·industrial town, producing textiles and machinery. Leeds is the fourth woollen town, engaging chiefly in the manufacture of ready-made clothing, but it has introduced more varied industries; mechanical engineering and the manufacture of steam and diesel locomotives. With its shops, warehouses, wholesale houses and university, it has more than half a million inhabitants and might be described as the industrial brain of Yorkshire.

THE STEEL INDUSTRY: SHEFFIELD. From the end of the Middle Ages onwards, metallurgy and cutlery manufacture in south Yorkshire were encouraged by local iron deposits, forests, numerous swift-flowing streams and the presence of a sandstone especially suitable for the whetting of steel. Just when local timber was on the point of exhaustion, the local discovery of coal solved the fuel problem and gave the decisive stimulus to the industry. Most of the iron ore today is imported. The blast furnaces have long been extinguished but the steelworks retain their importance. Sheffield is a town of contrasts. It contains highly concentrated factories employing the very latest techniques, such as the manufacture of stainless steel with new alloys like Britannia metal (an alloy of tin and antimony), and yet it still retains traces of the old ways of working. Grinding, for example, is still carried out by craftsmen. Although Sheffield manufactures a vast quantity of heavy steel equipment, supplying the steel industry as well as many others, its fame is based mainly on cutlery and special steels. This specialisation in the finer types of steel goods is due to the inherited skill of generations of workers, which has more than compensated for the city's inland position and its lack of local supplies of ore. Sheffield has more than half

THE DISTRIBUTION OF INDUSTRY AND INDUSTRIAL MANPOWER IN YORKSHIRE. *Coal-mining, which was first concentrated at the foot of the mountain in two areas, one around the estuary of the Tyne, the other in Yorkshire, is moving towards the east as the more westerly deposits become exhausted. The important textile industry is still concentrated on the eastern slopes of the Pennine Chain. The invention of new processes for treating phosphor-iron ores has given added importance to the deposits in the Cleveland Hills and around Leicester. (For key see map on p. 77.)*

At a Bradford textile factory in Yorkshire, centre of the wool industry. Here the wool is being examined by skilful sorters, on whose sight and sense of touch the quality of the finished fabric depends.

the country's output of alloy steel. With more than 500,000 inhabitants, it has grown enormously, and there are now large airy, well-lit suburbs on the hills lying cheek by jowl with the smoky monotonous districts in the valley.

NEW METALLURGICAL DISTRICTS. The progressive eastward shift of coal workings and the development of the Thomas process for treating ore with a high phosphorus content stimulated the growth of a new regional industry. The iron ore deposits in the Cleveland Hills in north-east Yorkshire and north Lincolnshire (5 million tons per annum) brought to life new blast furnaces which were soon followed by the introduction of industry and the growth of the old towns. Expanding metallurgical and other industries have doubled the population of Doncaster, the ancient Roman camp of Danum, in a very short time. The region had two other big

The inherited skill of generations of workers ensures the continued ame of Sheffield's cutlery manufacture.

Roman cities, Lincoln (Lindum) and York (Eboracum). The former now contains engineering works; York, the most densely populated town in the North of England in the Middle Ages, has to some extent been deprived of its functions as a capital by the breaking up of the ancient kingdom of Northumbria, by the division of the county into the North, East and West Ridings, by the growth of Leeds, and by the silting up of the Ouse. However, as well as offering the tourist attraction of its cathedral, city walls and historic buildings, it plays an important part as a railway junction (it is the headquarters of British Railways' Eastern Region) and has the biggest station in the district. In addition, it is the seat of an archbishopric, and is a military headquarters. Basically, however, it remains commercial rather than industrial.

FISHING PORTS AND COMMERCIAL PORTS. The whole of the region's North Sea coastline is low and constantly threatened by the sea. South of the Humber, it scarcely rises above the level of the high spring tides it has to contend with. To the north, its clayey cliffs with an average height of nearly 30 feet and no indentations are receding at the rate of 6 feet each year under the assault of the waves. Nearly thirty inhabited areas have disappeared since Roman times. But in summer enormous crowds from the nearby industrial towns flock to the beaches; in fact the fashion for sea-bathing was introduced at Scarborough. Several fishing ports situated opposite the rich North Sea banks have increased considerably in size since the opening of railway lines connecting them with London. The most important are Hull with about 170 trawlers, and Grimsby with a fleet of about 240, most of them smaller than the Hull vessels. With the gradual silting up of the rivers and increases in tonnage the up-river commercial ports have decreased in importance. The coal export traffic is shared between Goole (nearest to the mines), Grimsby (which imports timber, and is turning more and more to the manufacture of plastics), and Hull or, more correctly, Kingston-upon-Hull. At one time a whaling port, Hull has become the fourth port in England for imports and the fifth for exports (textiles, coal, metals) although it has not acquired the status of a major industrial town or a regional centre.

The South-West:
Lancashire and Cheshire.
The Cotton Country

On the other side of the Pennine Chain, Lancastria is divided into the counties of Lancashire and Cheshire. Like Yorkshire, its boundaries encompass both mountain and plain. The factory towns extend into the narrow valleys of the Pennines, while the countryside offers a contrast between barren, deserted moors and fertile plain. For more than two centuries the area's industry has concentrated on one textile: cotton. The westward boundary of the region is a coastline where crowded summer resorts (Blackpool, Southport) are succeeded by the busiest fishing port on England's west coast, Fleetwood.

There are many features which distinguish Lancashire from Yorkshire. Lying to the west, it is better watered. The sand left behind after the washing of the glacial deposits is covered with moors or poor pasture land. Clays are more often under grass (49 per cent of the total area) than under the plough (16 per cent). Farmers concentrate on potatoes and animal fodder crops rather than on wheat. But the principal activity is rearing pigs and the best milch cows and veal calves in England.

The poverty and decline in output of the coalfield contrasts most sharply with the vigour of the coal industry in Yorkshire. Criss-crossed with faults, and plunging too sharply beneath the plain, Lancashire's seams are shallow. Although the country still exports certain grades of coal to Ireland, it has to import it from Yorkshire and Northumberland for its own principal industries.

Like Yorkshire, it was once a woollen district. The almost total substitution of cotton for wool was the direct result of the absence of organised corporations at Manchester in the eighteenth century. This left industrialists with a free hand at the very moment when the demand for cotton was spreading. In the nineteenth century, Lancashire became the principal cotton centre in the world. Its towns lived by trading in cotton, spinning, weaving and calico printing. A vast conurbation has now grown up at the foot of the Pennine Chain, but there are very few enormous or comprehensive factories. Most factories and many towns specialise in a single stage of cotton manufacture.

For a long time the import trade was monopolised by Liverpool, and when the slave trade was suppressed at the beginning of the nineteenth century, cotton replaced it as the source of the city's wealth. Well situated for safe trading when England was at war with the Continent and for easy connections with the English Plain, Liverpool became the second port in England, a position it still holds. Constantly extending its operations, it now serves the metal industry as well as the textile trade, supplying both Lancashire and Yorkshire, and importing more wool than Hull. Nevertheless it faces competition in its own county. Manchester, nearly 21 miles away, disliked having to use a middle-man and in 1894 opened a ship canal from the coast to the city which has transformed it into the third port in Britain. But traditions are not so easily broken: docking facilities, commercial organisations, and a vast cotton futures market still ensure for Liverpool cotton imports twice as large as Manchester's, and yarn exports eight times larger.

Manchester, however, remains the brain behind the whole industry. Spinning and bleaching are concentrated in the neighbouring towns of Oldham, Bolton, Bury and Rochdale. Weaving is almost wholly centred farther north, in the basin of the Ribble and its tributary the Calder, in Burnley and Blackburn. There are some spinning mills, mostly downstream (Preston, for example), while Accrington specialises

in printing. The chemical industry, fed by the saline outcrops of the Triassic strata, provides dyes for cotton cloth and supplies the needs of manufacturing centres of all kinds, including Port Sunlight on the banks of the Mersey, a town created by Unilever (manufacturers of soap, fats, and allied products). The engineering industry born in Salford and Oldham to satisfy the demand for textile machinery now makes other products besides. Preston is one of the major engineering centres.

The cotton industry today is not as prosperous as once it was. Production has fallen by over two-thirds since 1913, the loss being greatest in the less urbanised districts. Most of the towns have ceased to grow. Other textiles have been introduced in an attempt to halt the decline, and today more than one-sixth of the yarn production is made up of rayon or cotton-rayon mixtures. New industries have been introduced: aluminium and glass at St. Helens, oil refining at Heysham and Stanlow, and gas engines at Blackburn. In spite of this, it is still proving difficult to employ the whole of the region's manpower — not surprisingly since it contains one of the densest urban populations in the world.

The two county towns are situated in isolation at the two extremities of Lancastria: Lancaster in the north, on the Lune, and Chester in the south, on the Dee. Both were ancient Roman strongholds and are virtually untouched by modern industry, rich in old buildings and scenic beauty. Their populations are less than 50,000.

Liverpool is one of the area's four vast conurbations. It first grew up on the north bank of the Mersey's estuary, and then extended to the south bank at Birkenhead, connected by ferry, later by railway tunnel, and finally by a tunnel for road traffic. The development of St Helens and other towns in the coalfield between Liverpool and Manchester has been somewhat cramped by the proximity of the two great cities.

Manchester is the principal town. Its administrative and trading centre fills to overflowing the old municipal boundaries, and its urban extension has had to encroach on Salford. To the south, towards Stockport, territories which separated it from the banks of the Mersey have been annexed; to the north, three or four suburbs connect it with the spinning towns. In all, some 1½ million inhabitants live there, most of them in brick houses of depressing uniformity, set side by side in characterless districts around the urban centre.

Lastly, the fourth conurbation, in the Ribble basin, consists of several towns, including Preston, Blackburn, Burnley, Nelson and Accrington. These towns are better spaced out, the linking suburbs are less continuous, and the close proximity of the mountains to some extent relieves the monotonous similarity of the towns. Strangely enough, except for Preston none is sited on the banks of the river.

The South: The Midlands

In the south the Pennine Chain dips beneath the Midlands which separate it from Wales. The Midlands, in the heart of England, is that region of England remotest from the sea. It is the centre of a drainage system and its waters escape to the Mersey, the Humber and the Severn. It forms a junction at which several plains meet. The region was formerly crossed by Roman roads whose place is taken today by canals, main roads and railways. Some economists consider the road running from north-west to south-east as England's real industrial and demographic axis (the country's axial belt).

Although the area is a plain, it owes many of its features to the mountains, which rise here and there in form of small massifs. Because of their low altitudes they are often wooded (Charnwood Forest, for example) and are favourite tourist spots. The uplifting of the ancient rocks has ensured that the coal seams are accessible.

Rural life in the Midlands is much the same as in south-east

Above: *Liverpool. Situated on the estuary of the Mersey, Liverpool is the most important cotton market in Europe. Its wet docks, closed by enormous lock-gates, and its busy shipping traffic make it the second port in Great Britain and one of the largest in the world. Its docks and enormous warehouses are considered the finest in the world.*
THE BRITISH TRAVEL
ASSOCIATION

Opposite: *A country scene in Lancashire. The rare fields and clumps of trees are found only in the bottom of the valleys, at the foot of the desolate moors. Stone is widely used to build houses and walls.*

BLACK STAR, RAPHO

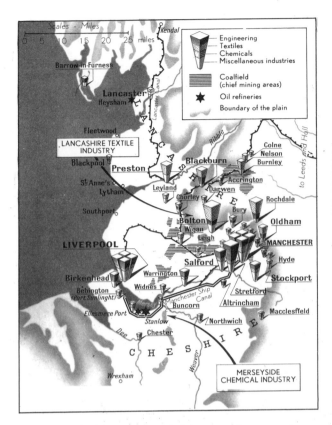

THE DISTRIBUTION OF INDUSTRY AND INDUSTRIAL MANPOWER IN LANCASHIRE. *(For key see map on p. 77).*

Reconstruction at Coventry, one of cities worst hit during the war. One of the notable features of the new plans is the ban on cars in the precincts of the flats. FOX PHOTOS

THE DISTRIBUTION OF INDUSTRY AND INDUSTRIAL MANPOWER IN THE MIDLANDS. *The Midlands form a shallow depression between the mountain ranges of the west and the south-eastern escarpments. The rivers flow into the Atlantic, the North Sea and the Irish Sea, and are frequently connected by canals which are, unfortunately, poorly maintained. The exhaustion of many deposits of coal has not harmed one of the most active industrial conurbations in Great Britain. The distinctive Potteries are situated in the north. In addition, a great many workers are employed in the metallurgical and textile industries. (For key see map on p. 77).*

England. Pasturage and animal husbandry find more favour with the farmers than crop-growing. Livestock for meat and milk are reared close to the main lines of communication. If reared solely for their meat, they are raised in the most luxuriant pastures farthest from the towns. The Leicester basin contains the highest density of cattle in England: 130 per square mile. Cattle are bought in the spring and sold in the autumn when fattened. A few drier, more sheltered sectors are still given over to agriculture. While on an average only 11—15 per cent of the area is cultivated, Shropshire has 45 per cent of its surface under cultivation, and the Vale of Evesham 61 per cent. The latter is noted for its fruit and vegetables.

As in the neighbouring regions, industry in the Midlands is considerably more important than agriculture today. It follows the old traditions, making use of the produce of local stock-farming, leather and wool, to which it has added mineral resources.

There are three coalfields adjoining each other in the Midlands. In the west is the south Staffordshire coalfield (the 'Black Country') which used to be very active but is now almost exhausted. Lacking up-to-date equipment and made up of tiny workings (28 of them employ less than 50 workers), it supplies scarcely one million tons a year. The Leicestershire and Warwickshire coalfields, however, have a combined annual output of nearly 9 million tons. A fourth Midlands coalfield, the north Staffordshire field, produces about 10 million tons annually.

The region also contains iron. Mines sunk at the foot of the Jurassic escarpment east of Leicester and Northampton

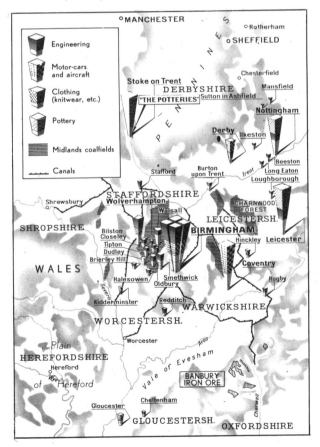

Land's End, at the furthermost point of Cornwall. The rocks are constantly split and eroded by the action of the Atlantic. J. ALLAN CASH

more than compensate for exhaustion of the Black Country's coal deposits, with a production of 15 million tons of ore annually.

Four large industrial and urban regions can be distinguished:

The Potteries in the north-west use the carboniferous clays which outcrop in the bed of an ancient glacial lake close to small coal mines. More than 500 factories manufacture all kinds of terracotta, earthenware and porcelain goods. In 1907 the six main towns, Tunstall, Burslem, Hanley, Stoke, Fenton and Longton, were fused into one vast city, Stoke-on-Trent (275,000 inhabitants), which also processes rubber.

The Black Country, without adequate supplies of iron or coal, has lost most of its blast furnaces. In 1850 it was the principal iron and steel district in Britain; now it has dropped to eighth place. But since the beginning of the century a wide variety of new products has been introduced, from heavy engineering to ironmongery, and Birmingham has been nicknamed 'the toyshop of the world'. Today industry is concentrating mainly on transport (motor-cycles, trucks, engines), electrical and hydraulic apparatus, man-made textiles, clothing and tyres. These extremely varied manufactures explain the flourishing state of a conurbation of 1,700,000 inhabitants.

Several centres have grown up in the south-east Midlands between Charnwood Forest and the foot of the limestone escarpment, near the fields of coal and iron ore. Coventry, although it suffered one of the heaviest bombardments of the Second World War, has resumed its rôle as the capital of cars,

trucks and tractors. It also produces turbines and equipment for jet aircraft. Leicester, celebrated from the thirteenth century for working up the high-grade wool of the sheep reared on the limestone ridges, has become a centre for knitted goods and for leather shoes, while still remaining an important market town. Northampton shares the same activities (together with Leicester, it manufactures 47 per cent of England's shoes) and is also a blast furnace centre. One-third of Britain's ore is extracted and much of her pig iron is produced in the neighbourhood.

To the north-east, a series of towns situated along the line where plain meets mountain indicate the proximity of Yorkshire. Derby, the most central town in England and as a result an important communications point, contains the main railway workshops for British Railways' Midland Region. Car manufacture is another important industry. An extremely busy town, Nottingham was originally determined by the strategic value of its isolated hill site, although its position slightly off the main routes resulted in its being neglected first by the Roman roads and by later main rail routes. The old city developed in the Middle Ages as a fort, a stronghold and — because of the charcoal from the neighbouring forests — a centre of ironworks. In the eighteenth century, when the flying shuttle was introduced it was one of the homes of the textile industry. An important hosiery and lace-making centre, it also has flourishing tobacco and bicycle factories and a large pharmaceutical industry. In the manufacture of hosiery it competes with its neighbour, Leicester.

The mountainous nature of northern and western England offers a vastly different landscape from the flat or gently rolling south-east. The mountains are never very high; the highest peak (Snowdon) is 3,560 feet. Yet these minor changes in relief are enough to create entirely different scenery. Arable land and forests are left behind. Population densities are very low, except when some workable deposit of iron or coal outcrops.

The mountains, hills and plateaus are divided by two depressions into three systems: the Bristol Channel separates Cornwall from Wales, and the Midlands separates the Pennine Chain from Wales. Within these three regions the characteristic features of the inhabitants vary widely. There is continual contrast between industrial districts and large expanses of territory without a single industry. The second are usually centred around high points covered with extensive moors. In the mountain areas men have become used to thinking independently, a practice indicated by their non-conformity. It is therefore by no means surprising that the Trade Union movement developed first in the west. Rural life plays an appreciable part in Cornwall and Wales, where proof of its strength lies in the long retention of the Cornish and Welsh tongues and in other features pointing to the resistance to English infiltration.

Cornwall

In south-west England a peninsula composed of Devon and Cornwall and a fragment of Somerset protrudes into the sea between the English Channel and the Bristol Channel. Its physical features are explained by its southern, maritime situation and its elevated relief. Not that the heights are very great. Four groups of high points, corresponding to four outcrops of hard rocks, are separated by broad corridors of soft rocks: Exmoor along the Bristol Channel, and its extension the Quantock Hills (1,708 feet); Dartmoor (2,039 feet); Bodmin Moor (1,375 feet); and Saint Austell (1,015 feet), composed of granite. Their appearance is one of a series of plateaus at varying heights decreasing from east to west, yet they are high enough to bring rainfall of more than 30 inches (58 inches on the heights) to the whole peninsula. They form a strange, deserted world of heaths and moors on which neighbouring communities have grazing rights. The farmers put out livestock to spend all summer there to economise on grass in the fields below.

Permanent settlements exist only below 1,000 feet. Although they differ considerably from houses in the English Plain — houses of granite, roofed with slate where this is available — they are dispersed into a multitude of hamlets and isolated farms. Most of these last are smallholdings, and more than half have an area of less than 20 acres. Land on the uplands is divided by a patch-work of dry-walling. Animal husbandry continues to increase at the expense of crops. In 1878 the peninsula produced 5 per cent of England's wheat against 2 per cent today, but 7 per cent of her cattle and 5 per cent of her sheep are reared there. The beasts often spend day and night out of doors all the year round; oats and barley are grown to feed them.

The mild winters have encouraged certain sheltered coastal sectors to specialise in early new potatoes and cauliflowers, while fruit is grown on the banks of the Tamar, and flowers in the Scilly Isles.

The ancient rocks contain a profusion of metalliferous veins which in ancient times made Cornwall a noted mining district. Centuries ago tin was extracted (the Scilly Isles were part of the *Cassiterides* where the Phoenicians came for supplies of metal); in the Middle Ages and after, copper and — more recently — tungsten were worked on a large scale. Today Cornwall is better known for its quarries than its mines, and its main products are kaolin or china clay, granite and slate. Well suited both for fishing and tourism, the peninsula has a rocky coast frequently escarped and indented by gulfs and branching rias along its whole length. Newlyn's small fishing fleet catches pilchards attracted by the warm waters in summer, and herring which arrive with the cold water of winter. Plymouth's main catch is sole and plaice; St Ives concentrates on herring and mackerel. But the fishing industry lacks the capital necessary for modernisation, and the vast numbers of summer visitors are inducing the fishermen to turn from their nets to the more profitable ventures of running pleasure cruises in summer.

The county possesses no big towns. Truro is small; Exeter, the administrative and commercial centre, has less than 60,000 inhabitants. Plymouth alone can really be called industrial, mainly because of its advanced position as a naval base, passenger port, and commercial capital of the peninsula.

Wales:
A peninsula and mountainous country

The Welsh peninsula, lying between the Bristol Channel, St George's Channel and the Irish Sea, differs considerably from England in its mountainous nature and its rôle as a place of refuge.

Heights frequently reach 1,200 feet, several ranges exceed 2,800 feet, and some isolated peaks top 3,000 feet. The highest summit, Snowdon (3,560 feet), is the skeleton of an ancient volcano disinterred by erosion. Eastwards, the Welsh beds dip beneath the English Plain but occasionally emerge again as wooded, dome-shaped hills amid more recent sediments. The Wrekin, the Malvern Hills, the Forest of Dean, and even the Mendip Hills east of the Bristol Channel are examples of such hills.

Along the coast the modest heights are enough to cause abundant precipitation. During some autumn months there is rain almost every day. Annual rainfall, which exceeds 40 inches throughout most of Wales, reaches about 200 inches on Snowdon. The duration of sunshine is short (about 25 per cent less than on the south coast of England). The permanent humidity modifies the cold, however, and on the top of Snowdon the mean temperature does not fall below 30° F. even

The Devon countryside. The gentle hills are capped with woods; in the valley pastures for sheep and cattle are interspersed with crops.
J. ALLAN CASH

Above: *Endless rows of miners' houses stretch along the bottom of the Welsh valleys which were once simple rural districts.*

COAL MAGAZINE

Opposite: *Miners in South Wales.* RAPHO

in the coldest month. Consequently snow is infrequent; 5 days a year on the coasts, 40 on the highest peaks.

A slight drop in the temperature during the Ice Age was enough to cover the whole country with thick ice-caps which have left their mark on every detail of the relief. Nearly all the valleys are glacial, with their upper ends forming corries. The ancient moraine-dammed lakes have been transformed into peat-bogs. Tongues of the early ice penetrated and deepened even the smallest cols, so that there are no insuperable barriers to lines of communication.

The mountains facing the English Plain have often served as a place of refuge. Wales, as a Celtic redoubt, has preserved its own distinctive civilisation longer than Cornwall or the Pennine region. The Welsh tongue is still in general use in the north and west. Nearly one-third of all Welshmen speak it habitually (87 per cent in the small Isle of Anglesey). They have also remained more faithful to their old rural way of life. Mostly smallholders, they practise stock-farming in preference to agriculture. Pasturage often extends over wide areas and the sheep are left to graze on the interminable upland moors, coming down to the farms only once a year for dipping and shearing. Frequently they lack the protection of sheep-folds and suffer heavy losses if the winter is harsher than usual. Only below the 1,000-foot contour line does pasturage give way to grassland or enclosed fields.

In a number of places signs of coal-mining — pit-head gear and waste heaps — stand out amid the fields where industrial and urban life has penetrated into the valleys and vast agglomerations of factories produce a landscape much more like that of England.

NORTH WALES. The two highest peaks (Snowdon, 3,560 feet, and Cader Idris, 2,927 feet) are in North Wales. On the coast, long depressions have wormed their way in between the massifs. Some of them (Conway, Clwyd) are covered with sediments and have become plains used for stock-farming and crops, others (Dee, Tremadoc) are still rocky defiles. The highest chain of mountains protrudes into the seas in the form of the Lleyn peninsula. The Menai Straits parallel to the chain and in places only 100 yards wide, separate Anglesey from the rest of the country.

The north is the most typically Welsh region. There is

a legend attached to every peak. Wales retained its independence here longer than anywhere else. University College, Bangor, one of the four colleges of the University of Wales, in which instruction is given in Welsh, is situated in the small town of the same name. The economy still preserves its upland nature. Pasturage and grassland are more common than arable land. Some degree of specialisation between the sheep-breeding districts on the highest land and the fattening districts in the valleys below has done little to modify the upland pastoral way of life.

Modern living has found a footing mainly along the coast and in the plains. The coastal plains and Anglesey send milk to Lancashire. The north-eastern coalfield was one of the early homes of the metallurgical and chemical industries. The first metal bridge in the world was built at Ironbridge. But now the field is nearing exhaustion (2.2 million tons in

Hot metal is poured into a modern LD/AC Convertor at a steel works in Ebbw Vale. RICHARD THOMAS & BALDWIN LTD.

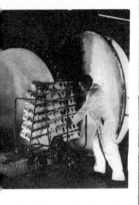

A view of Cardiff from the
ff is the largest industrial
ommercial centre in Wales.

1950) and the industrial towns, Wrexham (chemicals), Flint and Dolgarrog (aluminium) are of minor importance.

Seaside resorts such as Llandudno attract large holiday crowds from the Midlands. The port of Holyhead, at the tip of Anglesey, offers the most convenient boat service to Ireland.

CENTRAL WALES: FRUIT-GROWING AND PASTURAGE.
Central Wales is lower lying than North Wales though its relief is more distorted, is less wind-swept, and has higher-class crops including orchards and hop fields which carry the Midlands tradition over the border. Small coalfields and iron deposits, now exhausted, have established a series of towns built along the line where the mountains meet the plain, though these are often situated outside Welsh territory as far as administrative purposes are concerned. Mineral springs

The ruins of Tintern Abbey, a thirteenth-century Cistercian monastery. It used to be a centre of sheep farming in one of the most isolated districts in Wales.

explain the existence of a few spas (for example, Llandrindod Wells). Westward, the land becomes more rugged (only 5 per cent is arable) around Cardigan's vast bay. Peat covers broad valleys. The seasonal movement of sheep (transhumance) holds sway again. For many years this was organised by such abbeys as Strata Florida, whose ruins are one of the shrines of Welsh tradition. Aberystwyth, on the sea, is the seat of the University and the National Library, and a centre of applied agricultural research, and has claims to being the cultural capital. It is also trying to develop its importance as a seaside resort.

SOUTH WALES: INDUSTRY AGAINST ECONOMIC CRISIS.
The south comprises two mountain chains separated by a cultivated depression. The northern chain of barren red sandstone rises in a crest to the north and culminates in the Brecon Beacons (2,906 feet). The southern chain is intersected by the two large bays of Swansea and Carmarthen, forming three comparatively low peninsulas: Pembroke, Gower and Glamorgan. Natural conditions are rather more favourable here than elsewhere. The land is more fertile: wheat is still grown, and sugar-beet has been successfully introduced. All this would be of minor importance were it not for the mines. Strata of coal and iron in numerous beds — more than 100 coal seams often more than 3 feet thick — and easily reached by galleries driven into the sides of the deep glacial valleys enabled this region to flourish prodigiously at the very beginning of the industrial revolution. The mines are aligned along the valleys and connected by long streets of identical houses. Every valley has a railway line for easy transport of coal to the ports.

But the Welsh coalfield has seen its best days. Iron was exhausted first; many blast furnaces fell into disuse. Most of the iron ore for the blast furnaces of Wales is now imported. Nevertheless this is still the most important steel-working region in Britain. Now coal is threatened in turn. Extraction has fallen from 56 to 23 million tons and the coalfield suffers from unemployment. The expense of modernising the mines, only one-third of which are mechanised, was considered too much of a gamble. It became absolutely vital to find other occupations for the area's manpower. So, in 1936, for the first time in Great Britain, the State intervened to direct the establishment and location of new industries. A big drive was made in the metal industry. Swansea already contained enormous tinplate works. Continuous strips of steel manufactured according to the very latest techniques now make Margam, near Port Talbot, the biggest stripmill in Europe. But the main development has been the formation of 'trading estates' where everything has been done to encourage new industries by reducing the cost of equipping factories and rationalising work. Treforest, north of Cardiff, is an example. The list of industries introduced in this way is remarkable for its variety: coking plant, new metals (such as magnesium), light engineering, paper and packaging mills, and the production of rubber, fats, chocolate and wireless sets.

Although more than 140 new undertakings have been set up which employ more than 40,000 workers, they have not proved enough to keep the whole population from unemployment and migration. The inland towns have been hardest hit. Merthyr Tydfil, which once had the highest population, has fallen from 83,000 inhabitants (1939) to 59,000 (1958). The strangest example of all is Rhondda, established as a single urban district in 1898 by the fusion of a dozen towns strung out along the valley of the same name. It once had 170,000 inhabitants; now it has no more than 106,000.

The ports have suffered less, but they have not escaped altogether. To the east Newport, which falls in the English county of Monmouthshire for administrative purposes, exports coal from the valley of Pontypool. Llanelly, to the west, has copper and tin works. In the centre, Port Talbot has grown up side by side with the old town of Neath. The Port has become industrialised since the construction of a tunnel connecting it directly with the Rhondda.

Two large centres dispute the commercial crown: Swansea and Cardiff. To the west of the Glamorgan peninsula, Swansea has a name which recalls its Scandinavian origin — 'isle of Sweyn' (a Viking chief). Apart from its extremely important and long-established tinplate industry, it now possesses copper, zinc and nickel works. Even so, it has been unable to stay a slight fall in its population (1801, 18,000 inhabitants; 1931, 165,000; 1958, 163,000).

Cardiff, a newer town further east, had only 2,000 inhabitants in 1801. At first a small harbour for the export of vegetables, then a port of call for ships waiting for favourable winds to enter Bristol, it owed its prosperity to the export of iron and later of coal. But Cardiff exports very little coal today (6 million tons in 1913, 1 million in 1950). It remains a steel centre and factory town (oil refinery, paper mills, brewery and biscuit works), a minor fishing port and, more especially, the main commercial centre in Wales. With over 250,000 inhabitants it also has claims to being her intellectual capital, containing one of the University colleges and the National Museum of Wales. The business streets around the old castle are bustling and the city centre, built in a noble classical style, is worthy of a capital.

The Pennine chain: moors and lakes

Britain's spinal column, the Pennine Chain, stretches from the Midlands in the south to the Scottish border in the north. Its structure is simple enough: a broad Hercynian fold shaped into an immense plateau around the 2,000 and 900-foot contours. The loftiest peaks are not very much higher than the upland plateaus. Cross Fell in the north is 2,895 feet, and the Peak in the south 2,088 feet. The whole range is markedly asymmetrical. It dominates the coastal plain of the Irish Sea with abrupt slopes whereas its eastern flanks descend gently towards the North Sea. Narrow in the south, it spreads out in the north, finally covering the whole width of England beyond a line drawn roughly from Lancaster to Middlesbrough. The principal chain is repeated in the west by the dome of the Cumbrian Mountains (Scafell, 3,210 feet). To the east, in the counties of Durham and Northumberland, plateaus hollowed out of deep-cut valleys descend towards the North Sea.

There is a much greater variety of scenery than the Pennines' low altitudes would suggest. Underground water courses have carved out a strange world of caves and grottoes in the limestone escarpments. Throughout the region, glaciation has over-eroded the valleys to such an extent that in two places at least it has opened up easy lines of cross-communication, the Tyne Gap in the north and the Aire Gap in the south. It has shaped the Cumberland valleys into basins that are occupied by lakes. Over most of the region the rainfall exceeds 40 inches, reaching 130 inches at Seathwaite in Cumberland, the wettest place in England (excluding Wales). Snow lies on the ground for more than forty days. Strong winds blow across the broad treeless plateaus, and dense mists form on the hilltops.

Much of the south is covered by uninhabited moors and peat-bogs. Their sole function is to collect water for the insatiable agglomerations of Yorkshire and Lancashire. Further north the soil is less acid and supports a few flocks of sheep, but only the valleys under 300 feet offer a small amount of arable land, less than 9 per cent of the total area. Cattle are becoming rare on the pasture land. Sheep, on the other hand, abound; the Scottish black-faced breed has already interbred with English strains.

In other words, the Pennine region would be of minor

The atomic plant at Calder Hall, in Cumberland, showing the electrical sub-station which feeds electricity into the National Grid.

U.K. ATOMIC ENERGY AUTHORITY

Snowdon (3,560 feet), summit of the highest mountain range in Wales. J. ALLAN CASH

importance for the English economy if its northern edges did not enclose two coalfields.

NORTHUMBERLAND AND DURHAM: COAL AND SHIPBUILDING.

In the east the ancient Northumbria, now split up into several counties including Northumberland, which no longer touches the Humber in spite of its name, possesses the second largest coalfield in England. A wide variety of types of coal — steam coal in the north, and gas, house and coking coal in the south — and the ease with which deposits in the narrow valleys were reached were the factors which made this district rich. Although the best seams are nearing exhaustion today, those which remain are quite thick (from 3 feet to 5 feet) and are worked even when they extend under the sea. The production of nearly 40 million tons a year is sufficient to meet export orders and also to supply a wide variety of industries.

Inland, the least productive region is situated around Durham, a small ancient stronghold and a town rich in religious associations. Built on a spur, its picturesque old castle — now occupied by the University — is in marked contrast to the drab monotony of its working class districts. Aycliff, nearby, manufactures plastics.

Factories are located on the coast along three estuaries. In the north, the Tyne is about 90 feet wide where it flows through the plateaus. It is tidal for fifteen miles and can be used by ships drawing nearly 30 feet. Where the valley narrows on a spur ten miles from the sea, a castle (Newcastle) was built by the Normans on a site on the north bank which had already been occupied by the Romans (*Pons Elii*). Newcastle's residential districts have developed on the plateaus and its factories in the valley. By weight, coal represents all but one-twentieth of its exports but only one-half in value, for in addition to the shipbuilding industry, countless engineering works have been set up: marine engines, motors, wireless apparatus, cables and agricultural machinery are all manufactured there. The English co-operatives have their flour mills there. Newcastle's activity extends over the south bank to Gateshead, connected with the metropolis by monumental bridges. Here safety glass, steel goods and porcelain are made. In the estuary South Shields and the fishing port of Tynemouth complete this vast conurbation, which contains more than 800,000 inhabitants, 290,000 of them in Newcastle itself.

Further south, on the Wear estuary, Sunderland imports pit props and builds ships. Middlesbrough was built on the banks of the Tees close to the sedimentary strata of the English Plain. Since the Tees was not navigable, the opening of a railway line in 1829 decided the region's industrial future. The first railway line in the world ran from Stockton to Darlington. A second impetus followed the discovery of the Thomas process which made it possible to use the ore from the Cleveland iron beds close by. The proximity of strata of rock salt in the local Jurassic beds has encouraged the growth of the chemical industry at Billingham and Wilton (near Middlesbrough). The industrial population is divided between several towns. Middlesbrough (147,000 inhabitants) manufactures steel, possesses shipyards, makes cement, tar and steel wool, and even exports cloth from Yorkshire. The Hartlepools are both commercial and fishing ports.

CUMBERLAND: INDUSTRIES WHOSE MINERAL RESOURCES ARE EXHAUSTED. In the past a hand-weaving industry which made wool cloth for sale in America

flourished here, but it was ruined by the War of Independence. The output of coal, first worked in the nineteenth century, is declining. The presence of hematites and later of coal created the new town of Barrow-in-Furness near an artificial port. There is very little iron left today but metallurgy and ship-building continue. Carlisle, a railway junction on the borders of England and Scotland, has a few textile industries, while further south, near the coast, the first atomic energy station was built at Calder Hall. On the whole, with less than half a million inhabitants, Cumberland's fame rests mainly today on the delightful scenery of the Lake District.

SCOTLAND

Scotland, which covers an area approximately equal to half that of England and Wales combined, differs considerably from her southern neighbour. She owes her originality in the first place to nature. It is true that she has some English-looking physical features, such as high plateaus covered with moors and cultivated and industrial lowlands, but the Highlands reach altitudes unknown in English hills. They contain the highest peaks in the British Isles (Ben Nevis, 4,406 feet). Another difference is that there is no connection between the plains. Because of the layout of their relief all the English lowlands are intercommunicating and stretch between sea and mountain; the Scottish Lowlands extend from sea to sea, isolated by the Cheviots. One of these seas is the Atlantic, because Scotland is not screened from this ocean by the barrier of Ireland. She is open to the oceanic winds and has a higher rainfall than England — at least in the mountains — and more snow because she is at once further north, higher and more oceanic. On the other hand she is farther from Europe, the source of invasions. The Roman Emperor Antoninus strove in vain to push the Wall, which was his defence against the mountain clans, as far as the Lowlands. After the break-up of the Roman Empire, the Scots, who had fixed their frontier along the ridge of or at the foot of the Cheviot Hills, resisted English encroachment for centuries. Today they still proudly point out the battlefields which witnessed their resistance. Even after the union of the monarchies, it took a century of common rule and the decline of Scottish economy after the collapse of the Panama Company before Queen Anne could announce the union in 1707. Scotland still preserves many of her own institutions, her own administrative services, and

her own legal code. She had her own agrarian reform which dispersed the then concentrated dwellings and enclosed formerly open fields. The reform was not, however, universally accepted and traces of the old system still linger. Gaelic, the original language, has been slow to disappear. As late as 1842, biographies and poems were still being written in Gaelic; 90,000 Scotsmen still speak Gaelic as well as English, and over 2,000 speak only Gaelic. National costume is still worn by many, and even the army has preserved old traditions with its pipe bands. The Scots are a clan-conscious nation and remain deeply attached to everything evoking their earlier independence.

The Southern Uplands: the Tweed country

The Southern Uplands, of which the best known are the Cheviot Hills, form the first line of hills between the English border and the Lowlands. Although they are not very high (Merrick, 2,764 feet), the landscape is harsh and often desolate. Horned, black-faced sheep graze on the moors of the flattened peaks. They are kept primarily for breeding purposes and the lambs are sold in the valleys.

The valleys fall into two groups. In the west, as dales, they form a series of parallel north-east south-west corridors which are followed by the lines of communication between England and Scotland. The dales spread out into small peninsular and coastal plains which are less humid and fairly agricultural, such as the Rhinns of Galloway and the Machers of Wigtown. Despite the flourishing state of stock and dairy

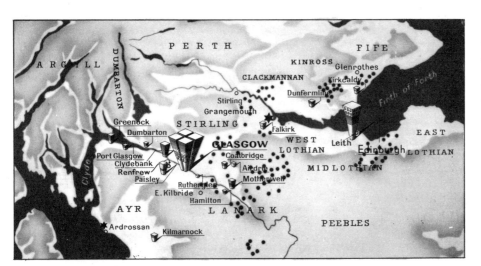

THE DISTRIBUTION OF INDUSTRY AND INDUSTRIAL MANPOWER IN THE SCOTTISH LOWLANDS.

Coal-mining, formerly mainly concentrated in the west around Glasgow, is being increasingly developed in the east around the Firth of Forth, where a more dispersed industrial region is being established, with more varied, modern industries. (For key, see map on p. 77).

farming which supply meat and milk to big towns as far south as Birmingham and London, the population continues to fall and the district has lost the individuality which ensured its semi-independence up to the fifteenth century.

Eastward the valleys are concentrated in the basin of the Tweed, the centre of the industry which produces cloth of the same name. Here the Cheviot breed of sheep (white faces and no horns) which gave Cheviot cloth its name, grazes on the grassland alongside the black-faced sheep from the mountains. Cheviot flocks are often reared on farms smaller than the mountain holdings (an average of about 200 acres against 5,000). Each farm employs from three to five labourers who, curiously, change their place of employment every year. Sheep-farmers specialise in judicious cross-breeding aimed at producing specific qualities of wool. Industry, far from the coalfields, has survived by concentrating on high quality goods. The region's woollen cloth is sold all over the world; so is the knitwear manufactured at Hawick. In addition, tourists are attracted to the Tweed by the district's literary associations. Sir Walter Scott lived and died at Abbotsford and used the local towns and castles as settings for his novels.

Towards the North Sea coastline there is a gradual change from the mountains to the Merse, a country of small glacial hills, or drumlins, with a north-east south-west grain which also dictates the orientation of the roads, villages and field boundaries. Here crops of oats and barley for brewing complement stock-farming, and the density of population is considerably higher (105 inhabitants per square mile). The small border town of Berwick-on-Tweed was lost by Scotland to England in 1649, producing the loop in the border between the Cheviot Hills and estuary of the Tweed.

Population in the Lowlands

The Lowlands were the home of unity and independence. Backed up by the flourishing state of agriculture and trade, the Scottish kings used them as a base when bringing the quarrelsome Highland clans to order and when resisting English attempts at encroachment. Today they form one of the richest, most varied, most industrialised and most urbanised regions in Great Britain.

The name 'Lowlands' does not mean that the region is a plain. On the contrary, the relief is much broken up, with hills following the line of geological folding, lines of glacial deposits, and impressive volcanic hills from which long tongues of lava have run down. The volcanoes look as if they had become extinct only yesterday, yet they are the remnants of activity in the Primary Era, 800 million years ago. Smothered with sediments, they were exhumed much later by selective erosion which had to give best to their basalt rocks and trachyte lava. The whole region is depressed in relation to the Southern Uplands and the Highlands whose almost rectilinear faults form a rigid boundary to the Lowlands. Because of this subsidence, the sea has made broad inroads into the Lowlands: to the east, in two big triangular gulfs, the Firths of Forth and Tay separated by the Fife peninsula, and to the west in the more tortuous and complicated Firth of Clyde. But ancient volcanic hills and moraines conceal a deep and varied structure dividing the coalfields into four basins: two to the west, in Ayrshire and from Glasgow to Stirling, and two to the east, in Fife and Midlothian, east of Edinburgh.

LARGE FIELDS AND SMALL MEADOWS. Consisting of a low-lying corridor in which rainfall decreases from west to east (about 40—60 inches in the west, 25—30 in the east) and virtually without snow, (it lies for 15 days against 100 in the Highlands), the Lowlands utilise all the lower ground for large fields and small meadows. Only volcanic outcrops and a few isolated massifs such as the Ochils in the north or the Pentland Hills in the south are abandoned to moorland and pasturage. However, high latitude, frequent fogs, and the short summer make growing certain crops a risky speculation. Wheat is grown on the driest soil, but the main cereal crop is oats. Around 1939 modern social and economic conditions were favourable here as elsewhere for successful stock-farming. Wartime needs gave a vigorous impetus to crop-growing, and it seems as if some lasting effects of this fortuitous development will remain. Whereas the reverse was generally true in 1939, arable far exceeds grassland in eleven counties.

The two types of climate are reflected in the agronomy. The west remains faithful to stock-farming, mainly for dairy produce. Permanent and temporary grassland covers 60 to 70 per cent of its surface. Co-operative creameries collect milk and cheese. The Kyle district of Ayrshire transformed its peat-bogs into grassland in the eighteenth century and now supplies milk to the towns. Potatoes are an important crop around Girvan. Various types of farming are practised in the districts around Lanark, radiating out from the steep valley of the Clyde. Land not used for cattle is covered with orchards, hot-houses for tomatoes, and strawberry fields for the jam factories of Carluke.

In the east, arable land is predominant: the plains and hills of the Lothians around Edinburgh, the Fife peninsula, the Carse o' Gowrie stretching along the coast between Dundee and Perth, and the straths at the foot of the Highlands are all regions where the soil is used to the full. Divided into fairly large fields by luxuriant hedges, it supplies a rich variety of produce. Wheat alone covers up to 16 per cent of the arable land, and oats from 30 to 50 per cent. The Second World War encouraged the cultivation of special types of potatoes along the eastern coast. Around the Tay estuary, raspberry and strawberry fields supply fruit for the jam and marmalade factories of Dundee. Sugar-beet has also been introduced and there is a refinery at Cupar. Although there is some stock-farming, especially round the towns, it is practised only as an ancillary to crop growing. Cattle are raised for their manure, sheep to eat up the turnips and to establish pasture on excessively steep slopes.

GLASGOW: FROM TOBACCO TO METALLURGY. Industrially, the picture is quite the reverse of the agricultural scene. The west has more active factories, ports and traffic than the east. Although this contrast is less marked today, and factories and new ports are being built in the centre, east and north-east, the west still remains the most highly industrialised sector.

In the past there was no shortage of old handicraft industries (mainly wool and leather) but the transformation of Glasgow from a modest borough of 13,000 inhabitants to a commercial metropolis dates from the Act of Union of 1707. The sudden acquisition of the right to trade with English colonies and the advantages of her geographical position which shortened transatlantic crossings were exploited to the full, and Glasgow became an important centre of the tobacco trade. The Clyde with its sand-banks soon showed that it was too shallow to give free passage to ships, and there is a good deal of literal truth in the words 'The Clyde made Glasgow, but Glasgow made the Clyde'. The maximum draught of the river was raised from $12\frac{1}{2}$ feet in 1820 to 18 feet in 1851. Today it is 36 feet 8 inches. At the same time, commerce adapted itself to the needs of each successive epoch. The rich tobacco princes were followed by cotton kings, and later by iron and steel barons. The metal and engineering industries, which employ half the workers in Glasgow, are devoted mainly to shipbuilding (42 per cent of British ships, including the *Queen Mary* and *Queen Elizabeth*, have come from its yards); they also produce boilers, locomotives, and all kinds of machinery. Other industries are wool- and silk-weaving, and chemical manufactures (dyes and explosives).

The Forth Bridge, near Edinburgh. This famous viaduct, which crosses the Firth of Forth at a point where the vast estuary is 1¼ miles wide, is only used for rail traffic.

THE BRITISH TRAVEL ASSOCIATION

Positioning the conveyor in a Scottish mine. NATIONAL COAL BOARD

A Scottish whisky distillery. The 'mash', a mixture of crushed malt and hot water, is dropped into the mash tun and stirred by this revolving rake: one stage in the manufacture of whisky.

SCOTCH WHISKY ASSOCIATION

Nevertheless Glasgow's future may not be completely assured. The output of the Ayrshire and Lanarkshire coalfields has declined: from 21.5 million tons in 1910 to 12 million tons in 1950. The mines are too rationalised and small, with an average of 300 workers. Many have had to close, and 6,000 miners have been transferred to the east Lowlands. Iron has to be imported and there is a preference for buying it in the form of pig-iron, so that the blast-furnaces are closing down. The Clyde, which used to hold second place among British metallurgical districts, has fallen to sixth place.

Glasgow has had serious unemployment problems — the result of clinging too closely to old industrial methods. Poverty is more obvious there than in any other town in Great Britain. For all that, Glasgow remains the fifth port and the third town in Britain. Imports consist of foodstuffs, iron, pig-iron and oil; exports of manufactured products.

The port installations stretch from the heart of the town, to the estuary of the Clyde. Its rôle as a point of departure for transatlantic passengers has to some extent been taken over by Prestwick airport, about 30 miles south of the port.

Glasgow was first built on the slopes of the right bank of the Clyde and then stretched down to the river itself in districts criss-crossed with long streets. Then new and rather monotonous suburbs began to cross the river and stretched downstream, connected by tramways and underground railways. Now they overspill into several neighbouring towns (Paisley, Dumbarton, Greenock) which are really no more than extensions of Glasgow and reach as far as the sea to the west and the nearest Highland lakes in the north. However, the population is no longer increasing; since 1951 it has been exceeded by Birmingham.

THE NODAL POINT OF THE LOWLANDS. A second group of industrial towns clusters round the upper end of the Forth estuary. This is the most central point in Scotland: to the north-west it is possible to traverse the Lowlands without crossing wide rivers or high hills; to the south-west, roads, railways and canals give easy connection between the Firth of Forth and the Clyde. It is also the region richest in Scotland's historical memories, containing the battlefields of Falkirk and Bannockburn and the fortress of Stirling perched on its volcanic rock.

Although Stirling was an important junction when rail communications were first introduced, its fortune has declined since the opening of the gigantic viaducts over the Forth and the Tay further downstream. The commercial centres have shifted towards Edinburgh and Glasgow. But round Stirling, industry is making great strides; the country is dotted with pit-heads and factories have been set up in all the small towns. There are foundries at Alloa in the north and at Falkirk in the south. The port of Grangemouth, on the Forth, was built to serve them. This town also handles imported oil in a vast refinery, and processes the by-products in large factories manufacturing dye-stuffs and plastics.

EDINBURGH: A MAJESTIC CAPITAL. A little further east, on the south bank of the Forth, is a series of volcanic necks parallel with the sea and separated one from another by small valleys running in the same direction. Edinburgh was built on these necks in the Middle Ages. It was then a small market town, with a castle and a few monasteries. First chosen as the Royal residence in the fifteenth century, it has been a capital ever since, even after the dissolution of the Scottish government. It has all the attributes of a capital city except ministries and a parliament. As the main business centre, it is a banking, insurance and trade headquarters. As the cultural and intellectual capital, its university has a teaching staff of 700, (a figure exceeded only by London and Oxford) and more than 5,500 students. At one time Edinburgh's industry may have seemed less active, boasting only a few large flour

Loch Alsh on the west coast of Scotland. In the foreground is Eilean Donan Castle, and the island of Skye can be seen in the distance. J. ALLAN CASH

A Scottish croft farm in the northern Highlands (Sutherland). The few small fields are surrounded by heather-covered hills. J. ALLAN CASH

Edinburgh, the capital of Scotland. Left: the Castle, an ancient fortress whose foundations date from the seventh century; centre: the station; right: Princes Street, the main thoroughfare.

THE BRITISH TRAVEL ASSOCIATION

Dundee from the air. The town is situated on the banks of the Tay, not far from its mouth. There is a marked contrast between the industrial districts near the harbour and the residential districts with their uniform houses neatly divided into blocks and crescents.

AEROFILMS, LIMITED

mills, paper mills and printing works, but the defect was soon remedied. The coal of Midlothian and of East Lothian is being increasingly worked (4 million tons). Its port, Leith, is the second biggest exporter of coal in Scotland and, together with the two small neighbouring ports of Granton and Newhaven, an important fishing centre. New factories of all kinds have sprung up in its suburbs, especially since the Second World War. But Edinburgh owes its unique character, above all, to its architecture. It is not a very large town; despite the accretion of its ports, its population does not reach the half-million mark. But it is admirably adapted to its site, being built entirely of stone, in contrast to the more usual brick of so many of Britain's towns. Princes Street, the main thoroughfare, stretches on a rise for more than a mile and is bordered by shops on one side and on the other by parks and gardens set in a ravine. The ravine also allows the railway lines to reach the very heart of the city without unsightly signs of mechanisation. To the north, spacious avenues lead to the ports. To

the south, the suburbs are built on the hill slopes and are interspersed with large parks. Fine civil and religious edifices, and the special quality of the light endow the whole city with a majesty that makes it one of the finest towns in Europe.

DUNDEE AND ABERDEEN: JUTE AND FISHING.
Perth, at the mouth of the Tay estuary, was the Scottish capital for a short time. Dundee, further downstream on the north bank, is a seaport and industrial centre. It first grew as a whaling port, then concentrated gradually on local hand-made textiles. In the nineteenth century it specialised in the manufacture of jute from British-ruled India and had a world monopoly of that trade until the rise of Bengal industry. It has been hard hit by Indian competition and has suffered heavy unemployment, although an attempt has been made to adapt the town to the new situation by switching some of its manufactures to linoleum, electric cables and shipbuilding, and by developing the traditional industry of jam and marmalade making.

A whole group of small and medium-sized towns in the neighbouring Fife peninsula, conveniently connected with Dundee by the enormous Tay bridge, produce 7 million tons of coal. Kirkcaldy reigns supreme among linoleum manufacturing towns, and Burntisland imports bauxite for processing into aluminium. Inverkeithing boasts foundries and paper mills. Burntisland and Methil export coal. St. Andrews, untouched by this industrial movement, is the seat of the oldest Scottish university, and its students still wear their traditional red gowns. A college of the university has been established at Dundee.

The Lowlands extend towards the north-east in a series of plains which separate the Highlands from the North Sea. Intensive drainage and stone clearing have made it possible to farm the indifferent soil of this district. Here the climate is harsher, with more than thirty days of snow a year. The crops best suited to it are oats and turnips, but the main activities are raising beef cattle and fat lambs for the London market. The ports go in for deep-sea fishing. Herring are fished from June to September, but trawling is tending to become the main activity. Haddock represents nearly half the catch. Apart from five or six medium-sized ports (Peterhead, Fraserburgh, etc.), the main fish trade is concentrated at Aberdeen. Originally a centre for the export of wool and furs to the Hanseatic towns of Germany, Aberdeen expanded as a direct result of the prosperity of its woollen and paper mills which used wood from Scandinavia; but it remains first and foremost a fishing port, six trawlers docking for every cargo ship unloaded. Unfortunately many of the trawlers are old and out of date, and Aberdeen, far from the big inland consumer centres, has lost some of its markets in Russia, Poland and the Baltic states.

The Highlands

The Highlands comprise the whole of the north-west of Scotland. The deep and narrow valley of Glen More separates two masses of high crystalline rock. It represents the scar left by a very ancient structural fracture which split the western from the eastern mass. It contains a series of lakes (including the famous Loch Ness) and is traversed by the Caledonian Canal with its eight locks that enable ships to reach its highest point.

The two masses, the Grampians in the east and the Northwestern Highlands, share a similar composition. They consist of plateaus worn down by erosion, dotted with volcanic outflows, cut into by deep cradle-shaped valleys (the glens) and often filled with long ribbon-like lakes or lochs. These features are the work of the ancient glaciers which also carved long estuaries branching out from lesser rivers. The coast has a fringe of long peninsulas and sheer columnar islands where

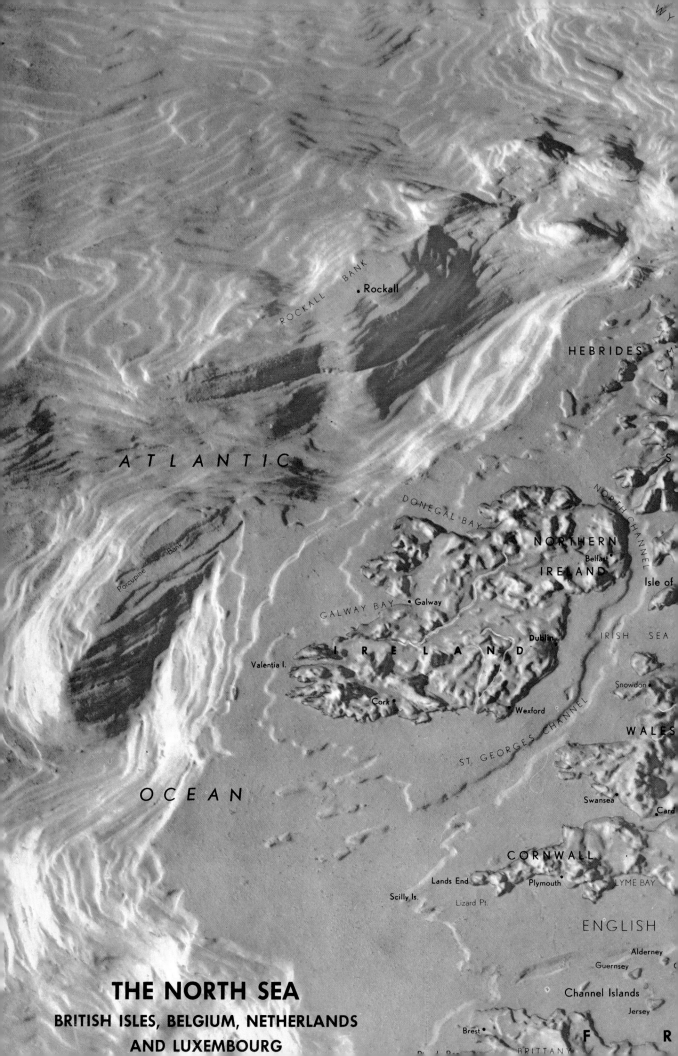

THE NORTH SEA

BRITISH ISLES, BELGIUM, NETHERLANDS
AND LUXEMBOURG

the waves have carved strange features at sea level, such as Fingal's Cave. The peaks are never very high but sometimes dominate the valleys with abrupt precipitous slopes. Ben Nevis, the highest (4,406 feet), was an ancient volcano. More often the heights resemble vast plateaus of roughly the same altitude, about 3,000 feet. Heavy rainfall, duration of snow-cover, and violent winds are more troublesome than the cold (which is insufficient to freeze Loch Ness). Centuries of over-cutting have destroyed the forests. The inhabitants of the Highlands live mainly by sheep-farming. Population is low, with 20 people to the square mile. In addition, vast regions which are absolutely deserted are privately-owned game preserves.

Pasture land and game preserves end abruptly a short distance from the sea or the principal rivers, where they are bounded by a continuous wall of stone known as the head dyke. Beyond it the narrow coastal plain is over-populated. Every inhabitant farms a small croft of a few acres on which he grows oats and vegetables in a primitive fashion (soot from his own home is often the only manure used), and raises a few sheep or makes short fishing trips with poor catches. For many years wool was home-spun and home-woven but this practice is dying out. Modern industry is almost unknown. However, since the Second World War the steepest torrents have been harnessed for the production of electricity, which provides power for a large aluminium factory at Fort William, at the foot of Ben Nevis.

The Scottish islands

Scotland possesses three archipelagos: the Hebrides, the Orkneys, and the Shetland Islands. The Orkneys, in the north, are an extension of the coastal plains and hills of east Scotland. They are tablelands of Old Red Sandstone, falling away into the sea in remarkable cliffs. The population of about 60 to the square mile cultivates about half the islands' surface. Experiments are being made to generate electricity by hydro-electric power. Scapa Flow, on the main island, is used as a base by the Royal Navy.

The Shetlands, on the other hand, lost in the ocean 60 miles farther north, resemble the Highlands, if not in height (900 feet) at least in their schistous and volcanic soil. Fiords divide them into long peninsulas and their scanty crops cover only 1 acre in every 13. One-third of the inhabitants live by fishing.

To the west, the Hebrides have preserved an archaic social structure. Drawing lots for fields and fishing grounds is still practised in places. Seaweed, now harvested mechanically, supplies the chemical industry. The main source of income is from the sale of tweeds, spun in the mills at Stornaway but woven at home. This trade does not yield enough money to modernise the islands' houses, which in some places are no more than black cottages with thatched roofs held down by rope. Nor can this modest craft provide an answer to the problem of over-population. The local people cling to their uncompromising land but are sometimes forced to admit defeat: the whole population of St. Kilda, the most westerly of the islands, left in 1930 after a thousand years of continuous occupation.

The Scottish problem

The basic problem is to strike a balance between the threat of overpopulation in the industrial districts and coastal crofts, and the lack of men and resources over whole counties in the Highlands. The development of sheep-farming, which would appear to be the natural use of the Highlands, is undesirable because existing farmers and weavers already find it difficult

enough to find a market for their products. A decision to utilise water power was opposed by coal-owners and salmon fishers. Almost £ 40 million has been invested in new factories covering more than 500 acres. The reforestation of waste land has begun and it is hoped to use the timber in new industries.

New activities often originate from abroad. American capital is making its way into Scotland. Scotsmen who emigrate are often replaced by Irishmen or Englishmen. Inevitable centralisation based on London is constantly removing more head offices from Edinburgh. It is easy to understand why the reaction of some Scotsmen is to demand a return to comparative independence and the establishment of a separate parliament. But is the present state of the world favourable for the subdivision of economic units? Does a Scottish problem really exist? Is it, perhaps, that it is rather an integral part of Great Britain's problems?

Freshly caught fish is packed on the quayside at Aberdeen, at the mouth of the Dee, on the North Sea. Aberdeen is the chief fishing port of Scotland. FOX PHOTOS

THE ISLE OF MAN

The Isle of Man (227 square miles) is a fragment of Ireland on which Scandinavian influence has left a deep mark. Its mountains (Snaefell, 2,034 feet, South Barrule, 1,585 feet) dominate uplands surrounded by low plateaus or plains. Mountain vegetation is scant: heather, gorse (burnt every year) and coarse grass. Local reforestation schemes have been successful. The plains, some of which have had to be drained, have excellent deep soil derived from glacial deposits. The climate is remarkably mild for the latitude.

Manx, a form of Gaelic, used to be spoken but has practically disappeared today. Place names, the agrarian structure, and various local traditions also have strong affinities with Ireland. The island is proud of its Scandinavian heritage which includes the parliament, or Tynwald, one of the oldest in the world. The Isle of Man does not form part of the United Kingdom; the Queen is 'lord' of Man and appoints a governor who, in conjunction with the Tynwald, administers the island.

The island has lost many of its ancient activities — fishing, mining and smuggling. But the Manxman has remained remarkably faithful to the plough, a rare fidelity in western Britain. The main crops are potatoes (harvested in June), oats and fodder plants, a small amount of barley for brewing and some hot-house tomatoes. The principal resource is tourism. Local agriculture is hard tested to feed the summer visitors.

THE CHANNEL ISLANDS

The fortunes of medieval history gave the Channel Islands (geographically and climatically a fragment of Armorica rather than Great Britain) to the English crown. They have nonetheless preserved their autonomous status, and their Assemblies are the sole arbiters of their laws. The lieutenant-governors who represent the Queen at Jersey and Guernsey (the governor of the latter has jurisdiction over the smaller islands of Alderney, Herm and Sark) have only very limited powers.

The whole archipelago is rich in archaic custom. For example, there is the Dame and her court at Sark, where cars are banned, and there are the vestiges of collective crops on open fields at Alderney. The islands have given up fishing and crop growing for home consumption and live by market-gardening and tourism. Guernsey is covered with hothouses and exports tomatoes, flowers and grapes. Jersey, more faithful to open field crops, produces early potatoes. The two islands raise cattle which enjoy a considerable reputation.

The islands' southern situation attracts vast numbers of English visitors; Jersey alone receives 250,000 annually, and is favoured by the French as well.

St. Helier airport (Jersey) is, after London, the busiest in the British Isles. The influx of money from visitors compensates for the adverse balance of trade. It encourages overpopulation (1,300 inhabitants to the square mile) and the hypertrophy of the towns (St. Peter Port and St. Helier) which contain nearly half the population and are further crowded by the annual influx of summer visitor.

The persistent English influence is gradually reducing the French language to the status of a dialect, although in Jersey at least it is still the official language. The way of life and eating habits, theatre and cinema entertainments, even the appearance of the streets, are moving farther and farther away from their counterparts in Normandy and making the islands thoroughly English in character.

Britain's problems

A quick glance at the position which Great Britain holds in the world immediately reveals paradoxes and apparent contradictions. She ranks as one of the great powers, with the biggest volume of external trade in 1938 and the second biggest in 1950. Her colonies and dominions are linked in the Commonwealth, the most extensive and most highly populated federation in the world. Her merchant navy is the second in the world and was for many years the first.

A shadow is cast over this impressive list of statistics by her large adverse trading balance, the fall of cotton from the list of her major industries, and the ruin of the export trade in coal.

There are further apparent contradictions between her admirable adaptation to the discipline and effort needed in wartime, and her relatively slow adaptation to post-war conditions. The long retention of rationing was one aspect of this adaptation: it was meant to ensure that everyone should receive a fair share of the essentials of life during a period of economic difficulties. When these difficulties had been overcome, a general rise in the standard of living accompanied an industrial expansion which progressed steadily if not spectacularly.

A study of Great Britain, then, reveals the causes of strength and weakness, both of which can be attributed largely to the changes that have made her lose first place in many spheres and to participation in two world wars, the second being particularly destructive.

Much of Great Britain remains virtually unused, devoted to moors, game reserves, golf courses, excessive pasturage, towns and factories. After 1914 the public authorities tried to counter this tendency by settling ex-servicemen in the country, allocating them smallholdings, regulating the price of agricultural produce, and introducing new crops such as sugar-beet. Really systematic development was first undertaken during the Second World

Herm Island, one of the Channel Islands, off the coast of Normandy. Rich vegetation leads down to rocky coves. G. H. BRENES, CAMERA PRESS

Castlebay — Barra, with the Kisimul Castle. J. ALLAN CASH

Reconstruction in the City of London. In the foreground is the new Bank of England building. J. ALLAN CASH

War, but the planning and controls which accompanied it — going as far as eviction for alleged incompetence — were repugnant to the idea of individual liberty which is so firmly rooted in the British mind, and the people found it difficult to accept them. The number of tractors has quadrupled. The production of wheat, potatoes and sugar-beet increased by two-thirds from 1938 to 1952, that of milk by one-third. Whereas in 1914 England produced only one-quarter of her annual consumption of food, in 1954 she produced approximately one-half. Nevertheless, she still has to import about one thousand million pounds worth of foodstuffs (wheat, butter, meat, vegetable oils, etc.), an expenditure which seriously affects her balance of trade.

SHORTAGE OF RAW MATERIALS.
Traditional major industries were based on local raw materials: wool, iron, tin. None of these meets the needs of industry today. English sheep meet less than one-tenth of the demand for wool; the shortage has to be made good by purchases from Australia, Argentina and South Africa. Iron, in spite of the providential discovery of the phosphoric ores of the East Midlands, no longer supplies more than one-third or, at the most, one-half of the amount consumed by the blast furnaces. It has to be imported from Spain, Sweden and Algeria. England has no more copper, tin or lead. She no longer extracts bauxite, and is forced to buy timber and rubber.

PRODUCTION COSTS.
For a long time excessive production costs were imposed on British goods by the high level of wages, the high standard of living — housing, clothes and entertainment being more important than food — and above all by her toleration of and, indeed, obstinate adherence to obsolescent organisation. Too many small undertakings with excessive overheads, incapable of adapting themselves to modern techniques of mechanisation, were her heritage. A coal mine used to extract 80,000 tons a year against a French mine's 300,000 tons. A blast furnace produced only 12 per cent of the yield of an American blast furnace. Many of these weaknesses have now been overcome. Today selling prices are comparable with Germany's, and often less than half those of France, but during the years of high prices many customers left England for other markets, and many of her competitors developed their sales territories; among them were Germany before 1914, Italy, Japan, the United States, and even the Dominions. Positions thus lost are not easily recaptured.

SOURCES OF ENERGY IN BRITAIN.
Coal, together with metals, was for long one of the solid foundations of English prosperity. Somewhat exaggeratedly the island has been described as a 'block of coal and iron'. In coal Great Britain had a cheap source of power and a product for export all over the world. In 1860 she met two-thirds of world coal consumption. The exhaustion of the seams, war damage, and the extremely high production costs of out-of-date mines have considerably reduced the exportable quota, which has fallen in 45 years from 76 million tons (1913) to 4 million tons (1958). Following nationalisation, a fifteen-year plan will at least make it possible for production to keep step with consumption. The success of hydro-electric development in Scotland will supply only a small part (3 per cent at most) of electricity production, which remains essentially thermal. Great Britain therefore has to rely on imported liquid fuel to complete her sources of power. To reduce the resulting expense she is buying more and more crude oil and refining it herself. With a refining capacity which has multiplied thirtyfold in fifteen years (1938—53) and has increased again since, she is able to sell petroleum products and so recover a part of the cost of her purchases.

THE COMMONWEALTH.
For many years England considered the colonies and dominions as inexhaustible suppliers of raw materials and insatiable purchasers of manufactured goods. But political independence and the desire for economic autonomy went hand in hand; overseas territories ruled by people of English descent (among them Canada, Rhodesia, Australia and New Zealand) are now self-governing and follow their own economic policies. The ex-British Dominion of India, too, has obtained equivalent autonomous status, while British sovereignty no longer holds sway in Egypt, the Sudan, Burma, or Ireland. In many places Great Britain has retained a place in the trade of her overseas territories only by agreeing to limitations on her own commercial independence. For example, she has to obtain Canada's agreement before modifying certain of her customs tariffs. Thus the development of trade with the rest of the Commonwealth is following a significant trend: the amount of trade of former colonies with Britain diminishes while Britain's trade with them increases. It is possible that the Commonwealth is becoming more necessary to Great Britain than Great Britain to the Commonwealth.

The solid bases of prosperity

THE MERCHANT NAVY.
The importance of British shipping dates back to Cromwell's Navigation Act which allowed foreign ships to unload only their own countries' products in England. From then on all colonial and transatlantic trade was the monopoly of British vessels. In spite of the enormous losses suffered during the Second World War, the Merchant Navy has exceeded its 1938 tonnage, though it has not recaptured the first place, now held by the United States. On the other hand, the United States tonnage decreased slightly from 1954—59, while the British increased by about 10 per cent. Favoured by a government lavish with subsidies and reparations for war-time losses, its flag still prevails on every

sea. Apart from the liners serving particular routes and run by a few very large shipping companies, it includes hundreds of tramp steamers, ships which roam the seas in search of cargo. The Merchant Navy is responsible for the major part of the country's trade. It carries cargoes between foreign countries and consequently earns a considerable amount of foreign currency. It created an entrepôt and redistribution trade now on the decline. It stimulated the growth of the largest insurance system in the world: freight, brokerage and maritime insurance bring more than 750 million pounds worth of foreign exchange into Great Britain every year.

BANKS AND CO-OPERATIVES. The deposit and investment of capital remains of primary importance. In 1930, deposits in English banks were almost four times those in French banks. Part of these funds invested abroad brings in substantial dividends every year. Although England had to sell about 45 per cent of her foreign share-holdings, especially in America, to finance the Second World War, she still has investments abroad worth more than £1,000 million.

In contrast with her laissez-faire banking system, England's internal trade is strongly and collectively organised. No other non-Communist country in Europe has so many members of consumer co-operatives, almost one person per family. Although these organisations handle only a part of the distributive trade, they perform a useful function as price controllers. There are few countries in which the difference between cost price and retail price is so small, with the result that in comparison with the Continent, the same amount of money purchases a larger quantity of goods and consequently offers a safer market for the goods produced.

Past and present

REORGANISATION. Geography and political economy alone are not enough when it comes to understanding and assessing England's achievements. Psychological factors must also be borne in mind. In the 'thirties the late André Siegfried gave a brilliant description of some aspects of the English psychology which appear to the foreigner to have made the country vulnerable to crises. He placed particular emphasis — somewhat exaggeratedly, the English thought — on the intellectual apathy which prevented the man in the street from considering serious problems, on the dual drug of the cinema and spectator sports (taken in much greater doses than in other countries), and on the remnants of Victorian pride which blamed crises on 'others' rather than on defects peculiar to the English system, with the result that the problem of finding remedies was shirked.

Conversely, certain other qualities have often helped the English to combat crises with particular success. These are an unostentatious tenacity, common sense which refuses to subordinate economic policy to ideological squabbles, and a marked consciousness of the higher interests of the nation.

England owes the reorganisation of her economy to this flexibility. Agriculture, as we have seen, is closely controlled by the State. Industry has been forced to accept rules made for the common good. It has had to adopt group purchasing, scrap old-fashioned plant, and introduce new methods. More drastically, in cases where it seemed necessary, nationalisation has put the State in control.

Thus the 117 railway companies were first reduced to four companies (1923) and then became a nationalised government organisation, just as London Transport and the inland waterways are. In 1930 a law was passed closing down 1,000 coal mines working at a loss, and in 1946 the whole industry was nationalised. In shipbuilding, 201 old-fashioned yards out of a total 684 were 'cleaned up'. In the textile industry, scores of old spinning mills were scrapped and the number of spindles

On the floor of the London Stock Exchange, which provides a market for the purchase and sale of about 10,000 securities valued at nearly £33,000,000 daily, affecting businesses throughout the world.
PETER ABBEY, CAMERA PRESS

drastically reduced. These measures, which mark a setback statistically, have resulted in increased productivity, lower selling prices, and better opportunities for sales. Moreover, no single rigid system has been imposed. England has not given up capitalism or liberalism; the big companies, even trusts, continue to function and prosper. Many such concerns in metallurgy, engineering, and chemicals spring readily to mind.

However, some of the traditional industries (particularly coal and cotton) are shrinking. In relation to the 1938 figures, the production of cotton yarn and cloth are respectively 59 per cent and 39 per cent of what they were. The woollen industry has been less affected, but even that produces only 90 per cent of its earlier total of yarn and of cloth. On the other hand, industries which were once unknown or rare are making great strides: aluminium (125 per cent compared with the figures for 1938), rayon and artificial fibres (800 per cent), plastics, isotopes. Also flourishing are industries manufacturing consumer goods: chemicals (phosphate manures, 230 per cent; sulphuric acid 200 per cent), cars (300 per cent) which have enjoyed the vast new markets created by the gradual replacement of trams and trains in densely populated countries; electrical and allied apparatus such as wireless sets and, more recently, television (more than a million sets a year are sold); the building and allied trades, stimulated by the enormous war damage, by the construction of new satellite towns and trading estates; clothing and shoes. The old 'block of coal and iron' has crumbled away and in its place a vast engineering workshop has arisen.

COMMERCIAL INSECURITY. And yet in spite of all this almost revolutionary progress there are still problems to be solved. There is an adverse balance of trade. The search for new markets abroad is not always crowned with success. Nevertheless, England has found ways and means of reducing her trade deficit below the returns she receives from non-commercial sources. The Merchant Navy, banking, insurance, the cinema, and even the tourist trade are sources of revenue. Europeans and Americans are no longer put off by the sea or air journey. About 1,400,000 tourists visited Great Britain in 1959 compared with 618,000 in 1950, and the numbers increase yearly.

THE POPULATION PROBLEM. It used to be thought that Britain's great industrial and commercial activity was still insufficient to ensure work for the whole population. The English worker was said to live under the perpetual shadow of unemployment. During the post-war years, however, the demand for labour has been at a high level — sometimes at an inflationary level — and the peak figure of unemployment, reached early in 1959, was still less than 3 per cent of the working population. At the same time, large numbers of immigrants have been absorbed from Commonwealth countries: over 50,000 annually, chiefly from Canada, Australia and the West Indies. Moreover, thanks to a free and comprehensive health service, the health of the workers has improved, and every year births exceed deaths by over 200,000.

In the nineteenth century emigration acted as a safety-valve to the pressures of over-population and unemployment. During the early years of the twentieth the flow of population from Great Britain was about 350,000 per year, with two-thirds of the emigrants bound for the Dominions. Later the numbers fell considerably, only to revive somewhat after the Second World War: about 100,000 to 150,000 have emigrated annually, chiefly to Australia, New Zealand, Canada, and the United States. There is thus still a considerable excess of emigrants over immigrants, and emigration may still be regarded as a safety-valve — though much less effective than in the past. Great Britain also has extensive areas of uncultivated land which might absorb thousands of workers on reforestation schemes or stock-raising, and bring a stimulus to the sometimes neglected occupations of forestry and farming.

English energy

Great Britain's steadfastness in World War II was admired by the whole world. Her struggle against economic crises, slow to gather momentum but increasingly successful, was less spectacular but just as courageous and not without its dramas. She has had to face hard facts. The bases on which her traditional prosperity were built were no longer adapted to modern conditions. In spite of her problems (often analysed better by outside observers than by her own government), she has triumphed over most obstacles. For this reason, if she is no longer premier world power, she is still a great nation.

André MEYNIER

Beachy Head. The Downs end in these impressive chalk cliffs overlooking the Channel.
K. W. GULLERS, RAPHO

A farm in County Kerry, in the province of Munster.   H. CARTIER-BRESSON, MAGNUM PHOTO

IRELAND

IRELAND is an island of 31,842 sq. miles situated to the west of Great Britain. It is divided into two states: the independent Republic of Ireland (Eire — 26,600 square miles) and Northern Ireland (5,242 square miles) which is part of the United Kingdom. The territory of the Republic includes the three provinces of Leinster in the east, Munster in the south, Connaught in the west, and three of the counties of the province of Ulster. Northern Ireland consists of the other six counties of Ulster.

THE MOST MARITIME COUNTRY IN EUROPE.

Ireland is the most westerly part of Europe, excluding Iceland, and is directly exposed to the winds and rains from the west. The continental winds hardly reach it. The outstanding climatic characteristic is rainfall — rainfall of all kinds, from heavy showers to fine drizzle. Over most of the country it rains for at least 200 days a year. Even during the driest month it still rains, on average, every other day. During fine weather, however, the atmosphere is clear and the western ocean takes on a deep tone of blue. The maritime influence results in an extremely mild climate; average January temperature in Dublin is slightly higher than that of Toulouse. Snow at sea level is rare. Some southern plants, such as the arbutus and Mediterranean heather, flourish in certain western parts.

PRIMARY ROCKS, GLACIAL DRIFT AND BOG.

The solid geology of Ireland consists of a great variety of Primary rocks, including limestones, schists, sandstones and granites. The most recent deposits occur in the north-east of the island; they are the Triassic marls, Secondary limestones and Tertiary basalts. Central Ireland is a plain floored with limestone, extending 120 miles from east to west and 100 miles from north to south. Its height seldom exceeds 300 feet; in places solution of the limestone has resulted in karst features including disappearing streams and, in particular, temporary lakes, locally known as 'turloughs'.

The mountain blocks, separated by broad valleys, form an intermittent low rim round the plain. These mountains are extraordinarily diverse: there is the high granite mass of the Wicklow mountains, the 'Appalachian-type' parallel ridges and valleys of Munster, the limestone plateaus of the Burren district in County Clare, the quartzite peaks of the north-west peninsulas, the basaltic plateaus of Antrim in north-east Ulster, and the schistose block of the Sperrin mountains in central Ulster. The mountain masses also show evidence of Quaternary glaciation — corries or cirques, and U-shaped valleys. The highest point of the island is Carrantuohill (3,414 feet) in the dissected range of the Macgillicuddy's Reeks which overlooks the lake of Killarney in the south-west.

The surface of the plain is for the most part uneven, as is the level of the mountain valleys. In fact, almost the whole island has been covered by a mantle of drift left by the Quaternary ice sheets. The weathering of the drift has given Ireland a much more fertile soil than would have been produced naturally by the weathering of its underlying rock. In the south the earlier drift has been eroded and levelled off, but in the north the later drift has kept its original forms. The Irish language has provided two words, now universally used, which describe the relief forms of certain glacial deposits — 'esker' and 'drumlin'. Eskers are irregular ridges, sometimes winding and frequently several miles long. Drumlins (literally 'little backs') are oval-shaped hills which are scattered over

IRELAND. *Two areas of moderately high land, one in the north, the other on the south, enclose a plain which is often boggy. The northern part of this plain is broken by gentle hills or 'drumlins' formed by deposition from former glaciers. The presence of large lakes helps to heighten the impression of humidity, which is emphasised by the predominance of pasture and the scarcity of arable land.*

almost all the northern lowlands. These recent and relatively undisturbed relief features have interfered with the drainage, causing innumerable shallow lakes. The Shannon, Ireland's chief river, in parts resembles a lake rather than a river.

Many ancient lake basins are today filled with peat-bogs, for the humid climate favours this remarkable growth, which covers nearly 5,900 square miles of the island's 31,842 square miles. The distribution of bog-land is an important feature of the physical geography. There are no bogs on the eastern plains in the provinces of Leinster and Munster; in the lowlands

of the Shannon and its tributaries, however, there are wide bog areas, separated by long sinuous eskers. In the north-east, the lowlands between the drumlins are often boggy, and in the west, peat-bogs envelop mountains and plains alike.

THE INVASIONS OF IRELAND. The first agricultural settlers of Ireland built innumerable megalithic monuments which can still be seen dotted about the countryside. Most of these people came from Brittany and Iberia, and this undoubtedly explains certain southern characteristics of the Irish. At a later date, invaders came from Gaul and Britain; some of them introduced Celtic speech — Gaelic, which made its appearance as the national tongue of Ireland at the beginning of historic times. In the days of their independence the Gaelic people remained grouped in tribes, leading an essentially pastoral life, ignorant of urban civilisations and cultivating a distinctive taste for poetry and music. Modern Ireland, particularly the west, has preserved part of this heritage. Medieval invasions, first by the Vikings and then by the feudal Anglo-French, failed to subdue the country, but they left their mark; the Vikings built the first towns — Dublin, Limerick, Cork, Waterford and Wexford. The Anglo-French built other towns and began methodical agricultural settlement in some of the bog-free lowlands. In the sixteenth and seventeenth centuries the English finally conquered Ireland. Wars caused much devastation, and the country suffered particularly from the 'plantation system' whereby a large proportion of land was confiscated and given to English or Scottish 'planters'

'Landlordism', with large estates owned by the English, now tended to replace the ancient tribal system, leaving the Irish as mere peasants. At the beginning of the seventeenth century the 'plantation of Ulster', on the other hand, drove the Irish population from several areas and installed in their place British farm workers of the Protestant faith. The majority of these came from the Scottish lowlands or from northern England — regions where rural conditions and farming methods were not very different from those of Ireland. Today the districts inhabited by their descendants are hardly distinguishable in their rural way of life from the older parts of Ireland; the great difference lies in their religions and the political allegiances.

DEPOPULATION AND INDEPENDENCE. In 1841, Ireland had a population of eight million. Most of the people subsisted almost entirely on potatoes. The potato blight of 1845—46 caused a terrible famine (one million people died) and the Irish have never forgotten it. The famine was followed by the eviction of thousands of farmers by the great landlords. Between them, these two scourges released such a flood of emigration that the population of the island declined continuously until 1931. The descendants of the emigrants form a considerable section of the population in many English-speaking lands. The peasants who remained in Ireland replied to the evictions with an agrarian revolt which finally compelled the British government to institute a system of land transfer to the farmers. The agrarian problem settled, nationalist activities received new impetus; finally Ireland proclaimed 'Home Rule', or self-government. This reform, passed by the British Parliament, was unacceptable to the Ulster Protestants who opposed it vigorously. The Great War then intervened and the reform was suspended. The Dublin riots of Easter 1916 stirred national sentiment, and in 1919—20 the whole of Ireland except the Protestant parts of Ulster ceased to recognise the British government. After a hard struggle a treaty was signed, acknowledging the Irish Free State with the status of a dominion and full jurisdiction over the twenty-six counties. In 1937 the state adopted an independent constitution, and the Republic of Ireland was proclaimed in 1948.

Ninety-four per cent of Ireland's population is Roman

A fair in a small town in the Irish Republic (Eire). In this land of pasture and stock-farming, local fairs are still important. Note the small, two-wheeled carts with shafts. D. LANGE, MAGNUM-PHOTO

Winding thread on to bobbins in a cotton factory. IRISH LEGATION

Above: *Peat cutting. This provides the cheap or free fuel used throughout rural Ireland.* H. CARTIER-BRESSON, MAGNUM PHOTO

Below: *Donegal Place, the main street of Belfast, capital of Northern Ireland (Ulster). Situated at the mouth of the Lagan, where it enters the Irish Sea, Belfast is both a great seaport and an important centre of industry and commerce.* CAMERA PRESS

The Guinness brewery, a major industry of Dublin. Cleaning a tun which can ferment 2,246,600 pints at one brewing and is the largest fermenting vessel in any brewery in the world.
ARTHUR GUINNESS SON & CO. LTD.

Spinning wool. IRISH LEGATION

Catholic. Northern Ireland sends members to the Parliament at Westminster, which is responsible for questions of defence, foreign affairs, trade, and the postal services. For domestic affairs, education, welfare and public works, the province has a Parliament which sits at Stormont near Belfast. Fifty-four per cent of the population are Protestants; the rest are Roman Catholics, most of whom would prefer to rejoin the Republic. In both countries the currency is the English pound sterling, but special coins are minted and notes printed for the Republic. English is the only official language of Northern Ireland, while English and Gaelic are both official languages of the Republic. Gaelic (or Erse) is the proclaimed national language, but English is the common tongue.

ENCLOSURES AND PASTURE. The basic territorial division of Ireland is not the parish but the 'townland' (366 acres on average) which has no administrative function but constitutes the foundation of Irish country life. In certain areas, farms may be grouped in small villages, one or two to a townland. Sometimes the arable or pasture land of these villages is still in 'rundales', that is, in small scattered strips in the open fields. Two centuries ago, the big landlords declared war on the villages and the rundales, enclosing them and dividing them into long parallel strips, giving one to each farm. Thus the farms were dispersed and the fields reorganised. In the Republic, the Ministry for Lands is continuing this policy of enclosure but has retained the villages. Now, the majority of farms in Ireland remain isolated in the midst of their fields, the oldest and most important occupying a compact territory, not in strips. The fields are enclosed, either with traditional banks or stone walls, or with hawthorn hedges, as in many parts of England.

Grass is Ireland's chief crop, for the mild humid climate suits it admirably. The growth of grass is hardly checked during winter or summer, and the best grassland is left as permanent pasture. Some of these lands have not been ploughed for more than a century and still show traces of the ridge and furrow made at the time of the famine or even during the continental blockade of the Napoleonic Wars. The less fertile lands are ploughed from time to time, and potatoes and oats grown on them. After two or three years' cropping, grass is sown and the land is given over to pasture again for a period of 4—8 years. This is typical 'ley' farming. Other resources which are turned to profit are the mountains and bog-land. Sheep, and even cattle, are grazed in the mountain districts, but the old practice of transhumance (booleying) which used to be carried on has just disappeared. The peat-bog provides a free or cheap fuel, and is generally used in rural Ireland. Even 'fossil wood' or peat is a valuable resource in a country almost totally deforested and without coal deposits.

NORTHERN IRELAND

Northern Ireland contains some lowlands — plains, river basins and large depressions, most of which converge on Lough Neagh — and these are divided by highland masses. The eastern lowlands are populated mainly by the descendants of Anglican and Presbyterian planters, whilst the old Irish Catholic population has tended to keep together in the western basins, especially in the glens of the Sperrin mountains and in the mountains of Antrim.

RURAL LIFE. Most of the 90,000 farms of Northern Ireland are very small (averaging 25 acres). One of the distinctive features of the countryside is the white-washed house with its neatly trimmed hedge, 'Protestant hedges' as they are often called. The normal Irish ley-farming system has been improved upon here for several centuries by the cultivation of flax, an exacting crop and usually grown in a seven-year rotation with other crops, but well suited to small-scale production. One-third of the farmers of Northern Ireland grow flax, but the quantity sown varies considerably from year to year. The mechanisation of agriculture is quite advanced (13,000 tractors in 1951). Farming is tending more towards the production of fresh milk for the industrial conurbations of England and Scotland, and towards specialised crops such as seed potatoes, soft fruit and, particularly, grass seed — all grown for export.

TOWNS AND INDUSTRIES. Although the towns and industries are only two or three hundred years old, they are of great importance today. The 'planters' founded nearly all the present-day towns, giving them a geometrical plan round a central market place, or 'diamond'. The linen industry was developed by the Huguenots after the repeal of the Edict of Nantes. Today it is the chief industry of the region, employing 50,000 workers and supporting many small towns. However, much of the flax has to be imported, chiefly from Belgium. Linen goods and yarn worth about £15 million are exported annually from Northern Ireland to all parts of Europe and to the United States. The textile and clothing industries combined give employment to about 84,000 people.

The dockyards of Belfast, built in the nineteenth century, are the third most important in the United Kingdom, after the Clyde and Tyne estuaries. Because these two specialised industries are subject to serious fluctuations, the government has encouraged the introduction of new industries — aircraft construction, electrical engineering, and the manufacture of optical instruments and leather. Aircraft construction has become one of the largest industries and alone provides employment for about 7,000 workers. The lowland valleys between Lough Neagh and the sea are dotted with small thriving villages — Newry, Lurgan, Lisburn, Ballymena and Coleraine — whose populations are between 10,000 and 16,000.

Unemployment nevertheless remains a serious problem and the Government offers special inducements to firms to establish new factories in Northern Ireland. This policy has had considerable success and by 1959 had provided employment for an additional 37,000 workers.

Situated on the estuary of the Foyle, the old settlement of Derry became Londonderry when it was given to the guilds of the City of London. It is a typical 'plantation' town with its central diamond, its Anglican cathedral and its city walls. It is also an industrial town specialising in the manufacture of shirts, and its extensive suburbs are mainly populated by Catholic workers who have come from the neighbouring counties. It has a University College, and with 52,000 inhabitants is the second largest city in Ulster.

Belfast, which has long been the industrial and commercial capital, became the political capital in 1920, and is also taking over the intellectual lead: it has an active university, especially notable for its faculties of geography and drama. It lacks only religious importance, for the sees of the Catholic and Anglican Primates of Ireland have remained at Armagh, although Belfast could claim to be the Presbyterian centre of Ireland. Belfast was founded on the estuary of the Lagan and grew up on the lower terraces near the foot of the great basaltic scarp of Antrim. To provide the city with a modern harbour the silted estuary has been dredged. There are few old buildings: the city centre, with its large public offices, is Victorian in character. The extensive working-class suburbs are monotonous but respectable. The whole city area contains 436,000 inhabitants; a little beyond, the small towns of Belfast Lough and the neighbouring hills are becoming residential suburbs or summer resorts: Carrickfergus (8,000 population), Bangor (23,000), Larne (11,000). The last is the packet port for Scotland.

The population of Northern Ireland declined after the famine until 1891, but since then has steadily increased. At the present time it is about 1,400,000.

THE REPUBLIC OF IRELAND

COUNTRY LIFE: A PASTORAL ECONOMY. Country life assumes conflicting forms in the Republic. In the western counties, in the mountain valleys, and among the bogs, many ancient customs have been preserved. It is here, in the peninsulas and islands, that the Gaelic language and the oldest folk-lore have been retained. These districts are always overpopulated, and the farms are often very small, averaging eight acres in the Rosses district of Donegal. Small plots of potatoes are cultivated with spades, in a manner similar to that of the mountain peoples of the Andes. Small quantities of oats and hay are also grown, and some cattle and sheep are raised on the mountains. The villages and rows of long narrow farms form islands in the middle of the brown and black peat-bogs. In the region of Rosses and in Connemara (part of Western Galway) comparatively poor ground is cultivated; farms are dotted among the morainic boulders, and garden spades probe between the rocks and in the thin soil above them. The thatched crofts are being replaced more and more by whitewashed houses roofed with slate. The Irish State has, in fact, done a great deal for the west: for example, farms in the centre of the island have been allocated to ease overpopulation, further enclosure has been effected by the Ministry for Lands, subsidies have been granted towards the building of houses and the construction of glasshouses for tomato-growing, roads have been opened across the bogs, and generous unemployment benefits and bounties have been paid to Gaelic-speaking families.

In the southern counties, overpopulation is less of a problem, and dairy-farming is quite well organised through the Co-operatives of Munster. In the northern counties, temporary emigration to Great Britain allows the people who remain to scrape a living. Connemara, lying between these two areas, is the poorest and most primitive part of Ireland.

From west of Munster to the frontier of Northern Ireland there is a belt where the farms are slightly larger, averaging 30 to 50 acres. In Munster and the northern parts of the provinces of Connaught and Leinster, the sale of milk to the Co-operative dairy forms the basis of the economy. In the greater part of Connaught stock-rearing is the main activity. These areas remain exceptionally backward in certain respects. The small villages lie tucked away, some distance from the roads, on the slopes of a drumlin or near a lake. Long, embanked bridle paths (boreens) lead to the isolated farms. Without intensive methods stock-rearing is hardly suitable on farms of this size, and depopulation continues. However, one of the less fertile regions, the Ox mountains, has been improved by the recent introduction of potato cultivation. The State has succeeded in establishing sugar-beet cultivation in Connaught and Munster, thanks to the national sugar company *Comhlucht Siuicre na Eireann.*

The south-eastern quarter of the island has farms whose areas average 50 to 100 acres. The largest and richest farms, 250 acres and over, are found to the east of the Central Plain in the counties of Meath, Dublin and Kildare. These are fatstock farms, buying store beasts in the markets of the west and exporting them as fat cattle to England or the Continent. The huge pastures cover the plain in an apparently geometrical pattern, whilst the farm buildings, often luxurious, are hidden behind a shelter of trees. The great estates with parkland surrounding old family residences give these parts of Ireland a similarity to the pastoral lowlands of the English Midlands.

There are, however, some slight regional differences; County Kildare is well known for its racehorse stud farms, and in the extreme south-east there are still some villages of feudal origin which grow a little wheat and malting barley. This prosperous countryside has suffered little decline in population, though it is sparsely populated. The size of its undertakings is well adapted to the pastoral economy, but problems still exist. Where the land is not naturally very fertile, the pastures have been encroached upon by thistles and reeds and need to be ploughed and resown, but there are many, representing the old pastoral tradition, who look askance on ploughing. Indeed, a conflicting attitude towards agricultural policy divides the two chief Irish political parties. One favours a 'natural' economy founded on grass and the fattening and export of cattle; the other fears that this policy will end only by jeopardising the independence of Ireland, forcing her to buy all her bread from abroad, simultaneously changing the country into a depopulated ranch engaged solely in raising cattle for the benefit of the English consumer. Those who belong to the second group recommend an 'arable' policy — a return to the plough.

Sea fishing is of little importance, although the State organisation *An Bord Iascaigh Mara* (Ministry of Fisheries) tries to encourage it mainly through the financing of modern vessels.

TOWN LIFE AND INDUSTRY. The Irish Republic has not the strong and active industrial tradition of Northern Ireland, but the Government has made considerable efforts to industrialise the country, particularly since 1932. The nationalised electricity authority has built hydro-electric stations with dams on the Shannon, the Liffey and the Erne, the last-named built in conjunction with Northern Ireland; a dam is also being built on the Lee, while additional peat generating stations are being constructed near the large bogs of Leinster. Peat is also available through *Bord no Mona*, the national peat authority.

The old industries of brewing, whisky distilling and bacon curing remain important, but various new industries, mainly light, have been introduced into most counties. However, these have not succeeded in checking the slow decline of the small towns of the West and the Central Plain — towns built by the great landowners of the eighteenth century and now serving as country markets. The medium-sized towns, on the other hand, are all growing. These are the ancient ports situated at the junction of diverse hinterlands. For example, Galway (20,000 pop.) is a market town linked with the Central Plain, Connemara and the Burren of County Clare; it is also a tourist centre and has a university college. Limerick (51,000 pop.), situated at the head of the Shannon estuary, is on a crossroad of the lowlands, profiting from the neighbouring transatlantic airport of Shannon. Waterford (28,000 pop.) is expanding since the introduction of a variety of industries (food, chemical and glassware). Cork (80,000 pop.) is the capital of Munster, a large regional market: it has a busy port with an excellent roadstead in Cobh, the port of call for transatlantic ships. The most noteworthy industries are those of butter-making, bacon curing, brewing, whisky distilling and motor-car assembly. The city also has a university college, which includes an important school for dairy farming.

The urban life of the Republic is centred in Dublin (540,000 pop.) which is the historical, political and intellectual capital of the country; there are two universities and a number of learned societies. It is the main port of the country, with a passenger outport at Dun Laoghaire, and a fishing port at Howth. It is linked by air with the chief cities of Great Britain, and to Amsterdam and Paris. It is an important tourist centre whose attractions include its buildings, its 'riviera' and the surrounding mountains. Moreover, it is becoming increasingly important for its industrial activity. The new industries have found here an environment more suitable than the small sleepy market towns of the interior. A belt of new industry is being created in the County of Dublin and the neighbouring districts. The small busy towns of Drogheda (15,000 pop. — cement works), and Dundalk (18,000 pop. — railway workshops), form a link between the Dublin region and the large industrial area of Northern Ireland.

The Dublin region is the only part of the Republic where the population is clearly increasing. Recently the increase has almost offset losses in other areas, and the total population of the Republic (now 2,898,000) has been decreasing only slightly.

In most of the counties the population is declining slowly because of emigration, which averages about 24,000 per year. Although birth and death rates have declined somewhat since the beginning of the century, there is a surplus of births. One of the great problems is to employ the increased population locally and to reduce the flow of emigration. Present industrialisation is still inadequate to attain this end. The other serious problem concerns the balance of payments. The balance of trade has shown a deficit since the Second World War. Invisible exports, which make up the balance, include interest payments on capital invested in Great Britain, and money payments by emigrants and tourist earnings; but this may not continue. Nevertheless, a real attempt has been made to try to solve the agricultural problem and to raise the standard of living in the western counties.

Pierre FLATRÈS.

O'Connell Street, one of the main commercial streets of Dublin, the capital of the Irish Republic. The liveliness of Dublin may be explained by its function as historical, political and intellectual capital; it is also the largest port of the country and a very important centre for industry and tourists.

The great 19-mile IJsselmeer Dyke, in the Netherlands. It separates Lake IJssel from the Wadden Sea (on the left). J. ALLAN CASH

The great industrial region of Belgium in the Meuse valley, above Liège: factories at Seraing and Ougrée. In the background is the edge of the Hesbaye Plateau, with its collieries and slag heaps. C. G. T. PHOT DÉDÉ

THE NETHERLANDS
BELGIUM and LUXEMBOURG

IT has been said that, given their distinctive physical features, their position in Western Europe, and their political and economic evolution, Belgium and the Netherlands cannot be completely separated from one another. These lowland countries had no difficulty in keeping their own political individuality, faced on one side with a deeply divided Germany and on the other with France tending to concentrate on her internal affairs. The vicissitudes of history have given good reasons for an alliance between North and South. Here were two small nations, divided, yet often with similar or identical interests; it was hardly surprising that they should be aware, albeit vaguely, of belonging to a single geographical unit. Their sufferings during the Second World War strengthened these tendencies which are now taking practical shape in an economic association, with Luxembourg as the third partner — namely, Benelux.

Belgium and Holland have no natural boundary separating them. The same low, swampy coastal plain, the same stretches of infertile sand, the same plateaus covered with a type of loam known as *limon* are to be found on both sides of their common frontier. The Belgian rivers, the Scheldt and the Meuse, have their outlets in the Netherlands, and Belgium's only communication by water with Germany is by means of the Dutch Lower Rhine. Yet there are differences. In the Netherlands, the sea penetrates inland in several places, but Belgium possesses only the head of the Scheldt estuary, while the Netherlands controls its outlet. Southern Belgium is more

continental; it is connected through the Ardennes with the Rhine slate plateau, that is, to the low mountains of Central Europe; southern Luxembourg is linked with Lorraine, and thence with the Paris basin.

All three countries are situated at a crossroads of traffic and trade routes. Nature, in fact, dictated it thus. The long sea coast, which is fortunately penetrated by estuaries with good harbours, brings within reach sources of raw materials and provides access to all overseas markets. Great Britain lies across a narrow sea which is the busiest in the world. By land there is no obstacle to the movement of traffic: the plain gives easy access to the Rhinelands, to the Paris Basin, and to the south of France: nor are the Ardennes and the Rhine slate plateau insuperable barriers, thanks to the valleys of the Meuse and Rhine.

Trade has always enriched the Benelux countries. In the Middle Ages, Bruges, a Hanseatic town, was the centre of the maritime trade of western Europe, and roads from Flanders to the Rhineland and to the fairs of Champagne were always busy. Antwerp took over the rôle of Bruges in the sixteenth century, and later Amsterdam. At the present time, the ports on the combined delta of the Scheldt, Meuse and Rhine control the most densely populated and industrialised hinterland of Europe.

Latin and Germanic civilisations, far from conflicting, fused harmoniously to make the Netherlands and Belgium cultural centres which at that time had no equal outside Italy.

Its central position also made Belgium the stake of political intrigues, the classic buffer state and, to her tragic cost, the constant battlefield of the Continent.

The historical development of the States

The total area of the Benelux countries is 26,268 sq. miles, comprised as follows: the Netherlands 13,514 sq. miles, Belgium 11,755 sq. miles and Luxembourg 999 sq. miles. The coast-line is 264 miles long. The intersection of the frontier of Luxembourg with France and Germany is only 186 miles from the sea, and no part of Holland is more than 124 miles from the coast. The frontiers are arbitrary boundaries which have been decided by conquest and treaty; hence the peculiarities of outline in the Rhine area between Nijmegen and Cleves, on the lower Scheldt in Flanders, and on the Meuse near Maastricht and Givet. The small feudal states bore only a remote resemblance to the present clearly defined nations. Within the Roman Empire and the Frankish kingdom, present-day Netherlands and Belgium formed only marginal provinces. Charles the Great, however, by virtue of his conquests, gave them the central position which they maintain today. The break-up of the Carolingian Empire at the Treaty of Verdun in 843 had serious implications for them; no longer were the 'Buffer States' objects of the envy of France and the Holy Roman Empire. Flanders, integrated with France, became increasingly self-governing. Lotharingia, which had been

attached to Germany after 925, was exhausted by internal struggles and in time broke up to form the Duchies of Brabant, Limburg and Luxembourg; the Counties of Hainaut, Namur, Holland and Zeeland; and the religious principalities of Liège and Utrecht. After the fourteenth century, these small states were more closely united by bilateral treaties. Soon they formed a single unit, the lowlands near the sea, 'Les Pays-Bas', or Netherlands. Political unity was only achieved by the dynastic marriages of the house of Burgundy. By 1467 at the death of Philip the Good, Burgundy and Franche-Comté, Flanders, Artois, Hainaut, Holland, Zeeland, Friesland, Namur, Brabant, Limburg and Luxembourg had all been brought together. The unification owed much of its success to sympathetic popular feeling, to the existence of similar economic interests, comparable institutions, and a common civilisation.

After the tragic death of Téméraire in 1477, the marriage of Mary of Burgundy to Maximilian of Austria converted the southern Low Countries into little more than an appendage to the distant Hapsburg empire, a status which was to persist for more than three centuries. Charles V completed the work of unification. He acquired Tournai, Utrecht, Overijssel, Drente, Groningen, and Gelderland; only Liège remained independent. He fixed the international status of the Seventeen States, which were henceforth reunited. The Pragmatic Sanction of 1549 stipulated that, united with France-Comté and Burgundy, they should 'be bound together forever' under the same monarch. Unfortunately, at the zenith of its prosperity, this splendid state was divided by religious wars and rebellion against Spanish

The Lys between Latem and Deurne, in Belgium. A broad, open valley with the rich pastures of the Flemish Plain.   C. G. T

The cheese market at Alkmaar. J. MEHL,
Opposite: *Tulip field in the Netherlands.*
RAPHO

Bruges, in Belgium, with its belfry and
aters. EDWARD HOLMES

rule. The Union of Utrecht, made up of the Protestant provinces (Holland, Zeeland, Utrecht, Gelderland, Overijssel, Friesland and Groningen), formed the beginning of the republic of the seven United Provinces whose independence was recognised in 1648 by the Treaty of Munster. The clauses of this treaty had serious consequences for the southern Low Countries (i.e. Belgium), which had remained Spanish: it allowed United Provinces to annex the Zeeland part of Flanders, northern Brabant and a part of Limburg, and closed the Scheldt to sea navigation, thus crippling the port of Antwerp.

The gulf between the United Provinces and the southern Low Countries was now immense, and soon the wealthy and powerful Protestant sea power in the north had nothing in common with the impoverished Catholic provinces in the south.

Sheltered behind the great rivers and protected by Belgium, the United Provinces had little difficulty in preserving their frontiers. On the other hand, Belgium lost to France: Artois, part of Luxembourg (Montmédy and Thionville), western coastal Flanders, Gallican Flanders (Lille, Douai and Béthune), Cambrai and Western Hainaut (Valenciennes and Maubeuge).

The French Revolution brought the formation of homogeneous states by sweeping away individual provincial institutions. The Congress of Vienna (1814) created a Kingdom of the Netherlands, uniting the North and South under the crown of William I of Orange-Nassau after two hundred and fifty years of separation. By the same treaty, Luxembourg was elevated to a Grand Duchy and became part of the German Confederation. The eastern boundaries were also modified; for example, the areas of Eupen, Malmédy (Walloon), Schlieden, Saint-Vith and Bitburg were ceded to Prussia.

The reunion of the Netherlands and Belgium was a great economic success; yet too many factors divided the two peoples, and the Belgian revolt of 1830 restored the partition. Belgium became an independent kingdom under Leopold I, but was obliged to cede the eastern part of Limburg, including Maastricht; from Luxembourg she succeeded in recovering only Walloon. Fortunately, the freedom of navigation of the lower Scheldt, restored by the French in 1793, was retained. With the dissolution of the German Confederation, the Grand Duchy of Luxembourg was recognised in 1867 as an independent and neutral state, whilst remaining within the German Customs Union (Zollverein). In 1920, the Treaty of Versailles allowed Belgium to recover part of the territory ceded to Prussia (Eupen, Malmédy and Saint-Vith). Luxembourg, having left the Zollverein, became reconciled with Belgium in 1921 and concluded with her an economic union which removed all customs barriers between them.

Today, Belgium and the Netherlands are kingdoms, and Luxembourg a Grand Duchy. In the three states the legislative power is exercised jointly by the sovereign and the parliament (in Belgium, the House of Representatives and the Senate, in the Netherlands, the States General, consisting the First and Second Chambers, and in Luxembourg, the Chamber of Deputies).

Belgium is divided into nine provinces, the Netherlands into eleven, and Luxembourg into eleven cantons. Their respective capitals are Brussels, Amsterdam and Luxembourg. The Dutch Court sits at The Hague, which is also the meeting place of the States General.

The physical outline

South-eastern Benelux is part of the Hercynian zone of Central Europe; it is a region of resistant, folded Primary rocks, eroded to form low mountains. Northern Belgium and the Netherlands, however, form a region of subsidence where great thicknesses of more recent and less resistant sediments have accumulated. Lying between the two zones are the low plateaus, undulating and rocky south of the Sambre and Meuse, monotonous and covered with loam (limon) in the north. In the extreme south are found parts of the Triassic and Jurassic arcs of the Paris Basin.

PLATEAUS OF HARD ROCKS. The Belgian Ardennes, like the Oesling of Luxembourg, is primarily a steep, forested region. A predominantly level surface is characteristic of these plateaus which reach a height of 1,300 to 2,000 feet. They culminate in the peaty massif of Hautes-Fagnes, but are deeply cut into by the incised meanders of the tributaries of the Meuse and Rhine. The weathering of the sandstones and schists produces a cold, damp soil. The climate is harsh and wet, and snow often lies for long periods. This region contrasts with Belgian Lorraine and Luxembourg's Gutland in the south, where the soils are often marly and more fertile, and the winters milder. Here one finds the extension of the Lorraine excarpments, notably the iron-rich Côte de Moselle.

To the north of the Ardennes the land descends rapidly. At first there is a narrow limestone plateau undermined with caves and riddled with swallow-holes which absorb the surface water. Then comes the slate depression of Fagne and Famenne which rarely exceeds 650 ft. in height. In the Condroz region the hills rise again (800 and 1,150 feet) and the sandstone ridges separated by limestone valleys run from east to west. The deep trough of the Sambre and Meuse, running north-east to south-west and incised in the coal measures, brings the undulating folds to an abrupt end. To the west, the trough is continued, after interruption, by the broad valley of the Haine, in the region of Hainaut; in the east it is continued in the picturesque valley of the Vesdre.

THE LIMON PLATEAUS AND THE SANDY PLAINS. Towards the north, the hard rocks disappear under more recent formations. Between the Meuse and the Vesdre the relief is surprisingly varied in the chalk and clay plateau of Herve (800 to 1,150 feet). On the other side of the Dutch frontier, the average height of the land is 300 to 650 feet, and the surface is without marked features. Towards the west the land opens out across the whole of Belgium, as far as the Scheldt and beyond. Here, the limon or loam almost completely covers a permeable subsoil — the Secondary limestones and gravel terraces of the Meuse in Hesbaye and in Dutch Limburg, where the country has a monotonous aspect; or the Tertiary sandstones in the region of Hainaut and Brabant, where green valleys give a more varied landscape. Towards the north, the subsoil becomes less permeable, beds of clay occur between the layers of sand, and surface drainage is increased. Hesbaye and Hageland are covered with hills, and between the Dendre and the Scheldt is an area of undulating hill and vale.

To the west of the Scheldt, hills are less common and gentler, and beyond the Lys, bordering the southern edge of the Yser basin, they give way to the Plain of Flanders with its sandy-loam soil in the south and its pure sand in the north. Relief seldom exceeds 65 feet and the rivers flow in broad, flat valleys. The same monotonous relief is seen in the sandy stretches of the Campine and Dutch Brabant. It is only in the east that there is a plateau, 80 to 100 feet in height, with sides that are steep and eroded, exposing the gravels laid down by the Meuse in Quaternary times. Further north the coarse alluvial gravels of the Meuse mix with those of the Rhine to form the underlying base of the Netherlands. In the south-east the subsoil conceals rich coalfields. In the lower parts of the Meuse and Rhine, the sands soon give way to recent alluvium which forms one vast, damp plain. In the dyke area it is difficult to see the slight hummocks made by older rocks as they protrude through the blanket of alluvium and the long natural levees.

North of the great rivers, the widespread fluvio-glacial sands and the boulder clays are evidence of Quaternary glaciers that descended from Scandinavia. Following the old north-

Aerial view of Wieringermeer, in the Netherlands. The land in this recent polder is divided into large rectangular fields, and the modern farms are spaced regularly along the straight roads. The drainage of Wieringermeer has allowed the clay soil to be cultivated, resulting in good crops of corn, sugar-beet, flax and fodder.

K.L.M. AEROCARTO

to-south routes, the glaciers removed and redistributed the sands and gravels of the valley sides. This has produced many morainic ridges in Overijssel, Gelderland, in the area between the Rhine and the Meuse to the south-east of Nijmegen, and especially between the Kromme Rijn-Vecht and the IJssel. Here, the curving sandy hills of Utrecht and Veluwe form the boundary of the huge amphitheatre of the Gelderland valley.

In Drente, in contrast, the morainic clays have been overlain with sand and undulate only slightly. Formerly the area was completely isolated by swamps whose existence has been almost obscured by peat exploitation.

AN UNSTABLE COASTLINE. The coastal plain is formed entirely of the accumulation of recent marine sediments. Towards the end of the Quaternary era the glaciers retreated; then followed submergence of the plain and the formation of an off-shore bar, surmounted by sand dunes between Cape Blanc-Nez and the island of Wieringen. The shallow lagoon thus formed slowly silted up and was then invaded by peat-

bog, except in the north. The return of the sea in the fourth century overthrew the first line of dunes, but the coastline immediately began to re-form, and a new chain of dunes emerged on another coastal bar, attached this time to the island of Texel. In the shelter of this bar, deposition of alluvium was renewed whilst the sea channels which had seriously eroded the peat-beds were finally silted up. In Holland the peat is level throughout and silting up of the hollows no longer occurs; in Friesland and Groningen, flooding in the Middle Ages prevented the completion of the silting process and preserved the shallow coastal water inside the bar — known as the Wadden Sea.

A MARITIME CLIMATE. The whole region has an equable climate, with prevailing westerly winds, though it is somewhat harsher in the Ardennes and in the extreme north. January has an average temperature of 35° F., July 64—66° F. There is no shortage of rainfall; 150 to 200 days of rain are spread fairly evenly throughout the year, and the total amounts to 25—30 inches, with rather heavier concentrations in the Ardennes region.

The conquest of the land

In the Ardennes, successive generations have tried to convert the forest into arable land, but with only partial success. In the *limon* zone Neolithic people had already opened up large clearings, and from Gallic-Roman times onwards, open landscapes were doubtless a familiar sight. As for the sandy and peaty plains, it seems that they were never more than sparsely wooded, so that the combined efforts of foresters and grazing sheep transformed them into cultivated land or barren waste. In Lorraine and Drente, hard work turned the land into an agricultural haven.

THE STRUGGLE AGAINST THE WATERS. In the coastal districts and along the great rivers it was first necessary to wrest the land from the sea. In parts the dunes give effective protection, but if it were not for the dykes bordering the estuaries and the Wadden Sea, the entire lowland would be flooded at every high tide. It is also necessary to ensure the escape of water from the interior: rainfall, percolating ground water, and rivers which the rising tides turn into lakes. This is particularly important in the south where the average tidal amplitude is 14.5 feet at Ostend and 11.5 feet at Flushing. Moreover, the land is constantly subsiding: since 1880 a rise of about one inch every ten years in the average level of the sea has been recorded.

The flooding danger becomes serious when an exceptionally high tide and heavy storm coincide. It has been estimated that during historic times in the Netherlands nearly 2,300 sq. miles have been swallowed up by the sea and that only two-thirds of this land has been retrieved. Even today, on the perimeter of the islands of Zeeland overhanging banks are continually collapsing. The Zuider Zee dates only from the thirteenth century, when the sea gradually invaded Lake Flevo, and Biesbosch from 1421, when the great flood of Saint Elizabeth swept away twenty-eight villages to the south of Dordrecht. In February 1953, a high tide accompanied by a violent and persistent storm forced the waves over the dykes where the unprotected inner slopes were worn down and destroyed. The flooding, serious enough on the Belgian coast and in the lands along the Scheldt, was catastrophic in the provinces of Zeeland and South Holland. Flood waters ruined 358,000 acres or 5.7 per cent of the arable land of Holland; 3,700 houses were destroyed, and 1,794 people perished. Since then still more careful watch has been taken for possible danger.

In spite of the continual attacks of the sea, reclamation of fertile areas has been continued. From the twelfth century onwards more and more of the muddy foreshores were reclaimed by means of embankments, in the provinces of Flanders, Zeeland, South Holland and Friesland. Before long the coastal plain was an irregular collection of dyked sections, called polders, crossed by drainage ditches. Conditions were particularly difficult in the bogs of Holland and southern Friesland, and it was not until the twelfth and thirteenth centuries that dykes began to be built around the Zuider Zee and along the banks of the main watercourses, including the Zaan, Amstel and Rotte. Barrages or dams were built at their mouths as tidal checks, and near them were founded the towns of Zaandam, Amsterdam and Rotterdam. By the end of the following century, small areas or polders had been isolated by dykes and as in the areas of tidal mud, the waters flowed away towards the sea at low tide, at first simply by gravity. But the combined effect of a further rise in sea level and subsidence of the dried peat soon made artificial drainage necessary. Since the fifteenth century the Dutch countryside has been dotted with windmills which constantly empty into the drainage canals the water collected on the polders.

Meanwhile large expanses of water persisted, floored with fertile clay; in Holland there were natural lakes in the north and in the south, excavations formed during peat extraction. In the seventeenth century, the wealthy citizens of Amsterdam took the initiative and drained the lakes north of the IJ, including Beemster and Schermer; these were enclosed by a dyke and drainage canal lined with windmills. However, it was not until the arrival of the technical innovations of the nineteenth century, especially the application of the steam pump, that a start could be made in reclaiming the huge flooded bogs (like the Haarlemmermeer) stretching between Amsterdam and Rotterdam.

Finally came the attempt to conquer the Zuider Zee, a shallow sea but liable to fierce storms which threatened to flood the low-lying river valleys. The drainage project was hastened to completion after a storm of unparalleled violence in 1916. After 1932 the dyke linking Holland and Friesland changed this huge bay into a freshwater lake, thereafter known as IJsselmeer. The smallest of the five projected polders, the 50,000-acre Wieringermeer polder, was the first under cultivation. The 120,000-acre North-East polder has been dry since 1942, and its development is well advanced. The embankment of the Flevoland East polder, 125,000 acres, has begun, and by the time the other two are completed, the Netherlands will have gained 550,000 acres, or nearly 7 per cent of its present land area. Thus the whole coastal plain is made up of a collection of polders, different in age and origin but with certain common characteristics: isolation by dykes, artificial drainage, and a controllable water table.

The threat of the great rivers must also be met. Nowhere is care more necessary than along the lower Meuse and Rhine, whose waters are normally above the level of the lands they

Aerial view of the greenhouses of Hoeilaart, to the south-east of Brussels. The area surrounding Brussels and Malines is the principal market-gardening region of Belgium; around Hoeilaart table grapes and peaches are ripened in more than 30,000 heated greenhouses. SABENA

A Dutch diamond polisher at work. NETHERLANDS EMBASSY

Fishermen of the island of Marken in the Netherlands.

G. VIOLLON, RAPHO

Above: *Villages clinging to the dykes of the IJssel in the South Holland Province in the neighbourhood of Rotterdam.* K.L.M. AEROCARTO

Opposite left: *The village of Bivels in Luxembourg, on the banks of the River Sure, which marks part of the frontier between Luxembourg and Germany.* H. HOLMES, CAMERA PRESS

Old houses in Ghent, with their intricate façades. Ghent is full of magnificent old private houses and public buildings, which bear witness to its ancient splendour as capital of Flanders. BELGIAN TOURIST OFFICE

cross. The enlarged winter floodwater channels, covered with grass and willow, are likewise bordered by high, strong dykes; these protect the Betuwe and other *waarden* (lands enclosed between the arms of rivers and brought under polders) as in the coastal plain.

The rural landscape

In Belgium, there is a southern region, with clustered settlement and open or unfenced fields, and a contrasting northern region with dispersed settlement and enclosed fields. This, however, is only a broad division, and there are many variants.

THE HIGH WOODED PLATEAU OF THE SOUTH.
In the Ardennes and in Oesling, forest and cultivated land merge imperceptibly. Formerly, the peasant grazed his cattle in the high forest, temporarily cultivating burnt out clearings in the undergrowth. However, the rights which allowed him to follow this practice have been abolished or have fallen into disuse, and the boundaries are now reduced to include only arable land and pasture. Grassland is increasingly replacing the poor crops of rye, oats, potatoes and fodder. The broad and squat stone farmhouses combine the living-quarters, the stable and the barn under the same huge slate roof. In the east one sees picturesque half-timbered white washed dwellings.

NETHERLANDS, BELGIUM AND LUXEMBOURG

In general the farms are grouped in villages and hamlets around which fields are scattered in small, narrow strips, often slightly curved to follow the contours of the slopes, and unfenced. Here, then, the open field system prevails, bound to old farming customs, dictating the same rotation for all the small plots in the same 'field' and prohibiting fencing of the land in order to allow communal flocks access to the ploughed land and stubble-fields.

In Belgian Lorraine and Gutland the forests emphasise the brows of the hills, extending more widely on the sandy soils. The countryside is altogether more inviting. Groups of unenclosed fields in strips spread to the plateau; pasture land and orchards bordered with hedges cover the valley floors. Crops vary according to the nature of the soil, and the Moselle valley, rich with vineyards, has an air of the South about it. The country house is built as a compact block, with a roof of slate or tiles, and walls of porous sandstone protected by roughcast. In the villages, which are nucleated in type, the houses stand in rows along both sides of the road.

THE UNDULATING PLATEAUS OF CONDROZ AND HERVE.
The valley of Famenne again shows, as in the Ardennes, a succession of woodland, arable land and pasture. However, in the Condroz, where the subsoil and relief features are more varied, forest is found only on the rocky soils. The better soils, those of the limestone depressions floored with *limon* (loam) produce wheat, oats and fodder. As elsewhere, permanent pasture-land is on the increase and spreads uniformly over the eastern and western limits of the region. The Walloon farm, with four blocks of buildings surrounding an interior courtyard, is an integral part of the countryside, as in the *limon* zone. Nowhere else does it look so imposing, with its huge structure of bluish limestone or yellow sandstone, and its large slate roof whose turret rises above a massive porch. It may be isolated in the middle of large fields, but more often it is found with smaller farms in the centre of a village. Around them, at one time, lay open fields divided into many small unenclosed strips.

In the region of Herve, pasture and orchards have replaced arable land. Each small plot is surrounded by a hawthorn hedge. The villages here are of little importance. The small farms, which produce butter and cheese, are scattered or grouped in small hamlets.

OPEN LANDSCAPES OF THE LIMON AREAS.
Across the Dutch frontier and westwards, and including a part south of the Meuse, the green countryside is transformed by the appearance of the *limon*. In southern Dutch Limburg and in Hesbaye wheat, barley, oats, sugar-beet and fodder crops are extensively grown. There is little pasture, but numerous cattle are stall-fed. Large rectangular or irregularly-shaped fields emphasise the private nature of land ownership, but it is also easy to recognise the pattern of the ancient system with its small fields subdivided into narrow strips. There are neither woods, hedges, fences nor dwellings in this bare and uniform countryside, but there are numerous villages surrounded by broad belts of hedged orchard. Square, brick farmhouses with large porches and high windowless walls stand beside more modest cottages. If the region of Herve is considered the perfect example of enclosed country, here one also finds some of the finest open country in Europe.

West of the Gette-Dyle interfluve, the landscape changes in Brabant and Hainaut: settlements are more dispersed, woods occur among the fields, and pasture increases in importance. The scene alters again towards the northern boundaries of the *limon* plateau, where it is dissected and merges into the plain. Hesbaye provides a green setting for its attractive half-timbered farmhouses, grouped in villages along the waterways. Hageland, with its wooded hill-tops, gives a foretaste of the Campine with its poor crops and its rows of houses close to the roads.

Finally, to the north of Brussels, and as far as the area round Alost, Antwerp and Louvain, market-gardening is tending gradually to replace the cultivation of cereals.

THE VARIED LANDSCAPE OF FLANDERS.

Beyond the left bank of the Senne, the characteristic features of Flanders gradually replace those of Brabant, and even before the Dendre is reached, the change is complete. The Flemish landscape is anything but uniform. In the hilly region between the Scheldt and the Dendre the countryside remains open, with strip-like fields, and the numerous houses cling to the close network of winding roads. In contrast, to the west of the Scheldt there are more divided fields but here plots are as broad as they are long and surrounded by hedges and rows of poplars. Everywhere, between the large villages and the small towns, there are farms; small elongated houses, or *hofstede*, with three separate buildings arranged round an open courtyard. The *limon* soils of the south produce wheat, oats and industrial crops; on the sandy lands of the north it is only possible to grow rye, potatoes and fodder (grown partly as a catch crop). The *bocage* character of the land persists everywhere: *bocage* is the French term for a type of country which is perhaps more familiar to the Englishman than to the Belgian or the Frenchman — meadows and cultivated fields separated by quickset hedges, together with patches of woodland. It is natural for the Flemish peasant to contrast the *houtland*, or wooded country, with the large clearings or *blote* of the coastal plain.

North of the Scheldt, from Eeklo to Antwerp, dispersed settlements are replaced by concentrations of one-street villages. The houses are built along the straight roads which broaden at the central market place. *Bocage* remains; in the east the long narrow strips are bounded by hedges or copses; in the west, in the region of Waas, the small square plots are grouped together into long, narrow fields by hedges and trees.

THE SANDY PLAINS; LAND OF HEATH, PINES AND POOR CROPS.

In the sandy regions of the Belgian Campine, northern Brabant and northern Dutch Limburg, forest forms the background. Over the past 150 years dark pine woods, deep and monotonous, have partially replaced the immense heathlands where the peasant used to graze his sheep and cut the heather for stable litter. Crops are poor; rye, oats, potatoes and fodder are grown. Meadowland, formerly confined to the alluvial plains, has increased. In spite of the recent growth of dispersed settlement, the original villages and hamlet grouping can easily be distinguished, and on the gentle hill slopes the long open fields, the *akkers* that were once collectively farmed. The agricultural regions have been extended: the heath which was under common ownership has been reclaimed, piecemeal, everywhere. Around the old centres, hamlets have grown up haphazardly amid irregular fields surrounded by hedges, strips of brushwood and sometimes oak trees. Modern reclamation has accentuated this pattern. The people, however, remain faithful to the old type of long farmhouse, which collects under the one roof the living-quarters and all the other farm buildings.

To the north of the broad alluvial zone of the Meuse and the Rhine in Drente, the three territorial elements of the old agricultural economy are found again: the heath, today often covered with plantations of pine, then the damp pastures divided by earth banks, and finally the arable land, or *essen*, in long, narrow, unfenced strips on the dry hummocks. Here, too, the old agricultural restrictions have influenced the open field system and the concentration of villages. The houses are distributed without system, separated from one another by spaces planted with trees; here and there they are found in a circle round a cultivated hillock. In this area the old Saxon type of farmhouse is still found, where dwelling and stable, joined as they were originally, enclose a central threshing-floor. Between the nucleated villages, there are numerous hamlets

and farms set amid pastures. However, the old customs of the countryside are slow to die, because the *marken*, or peasant societies, for long made sure that the inheritance should pass to one descendant and that the common heath land should be kept intact.

In Overijssel and in Gelderland, the *marken* have had less influence. For a long time now, small peasants have established themselves in fenced fields, or *kampen*, virtually punched out of the heathland. In Salland and Graafschap, the settlements have, from the beginning, had to be split up into numerous very small hamlets set in hedged fields.

In the extreme north of the sandy regions in Zevenwouden, to the south of Westerkwartier and Oldambt, there are one-street villages similar to those in the Waas region; their narrow plots stretching back behind the houses are given over to pasture and enclosed by hedges or earth banks.

Finally, in the high bogs of eastern Drente and Groningen the houses are arranged in tightly-packed rows on each side of the canals, and the narrow fields stretch out between the draining ditches. These 'bog colonies', the first of which dates from the eighteenth century, produce large quantities of rye, oats and potatoes.

THE COASTAL PLAIN.

On the oldest polders of Flanders and Zeeland settlement is closely linked with the old channel-banks which are slightly raised above the general level of the land. The farms are situated amid large fields yielding good crops; in Flanders these farms are mostly isolated, and in Zeeland grouped into villages. The low-lying fields of the area, damp and well pastured, are uninhabited, a medley of small irregular plots bounded by ditches. On the more recent polders the farms are scattered among the rectangular fields. In the Zeeland part of Flanders the houses are often built along the dykes and the banks of the Meuse and Rhine estuaries.

In Holland, along the old Rhine, the Lek, the Gouwe, and the Dutch IJssel, there are higher belts of land where settlements have existed since the twelfth century; here a succession of elongated villages is formed. In Western Friesland, the villages have also formed long roads, although not necessarily confined to the dykes and the edges of the polders. These boggy regions are essentially pastoral; the distant view is interrupted only by orderly rows of houses with their screens of trees, and by dykes and windmills. In contrast, the large drained areas of Wieringermeer, Beemster and Haarlemmermeer grow corn, sugar-beet, flax and fodder crops on their clay soils. The land is divided into large rectangular fields and the houses are regularly spaced along straight roads. Finally, at the foot of the inner slope of the Dutch dunes, is the region of early vegetables and flowers, often grown under glass.

In Friesland and in Groningen, settlement is confined to the *terpen* or mounds on which houses could be constructed as a protection against flood. To the west of Leeuwarden, in Westergo, *terpen* bear only small hamlets or isolated farms, whilst in Oostergo and in Groningen bigger villages are accommodated. Once dyke building had ensured reasonable security, the farms of the *terpen* were often dispersed, even in the lowest areas, and the old village was reduced to a mere religious and administrative centre, or disappeared altogether. The west of Friesland is now entirely pastoral; here, particularly, may be found the large Frisian farm, or *stelphoeve*, whose enormous thatched roof covers house and stable. Eastwards from the edges of the Lauwerszee, crops play a more important part, and great quantities of corn, oats, barley and sugar-beet are produced; on these farms, house and barn are often separate, linked by a third building.

On the alluvial plain of the Meuse and the Rhine, gradual changes in the level of the land influence settlement. The cultivated fields, divided into irregular plots, spread over the *donken* and the drained lands between the rivers. The marshy bottoms are left as meadows, intersected by numerous drainage ditches and edged with pollarded willows. Only the ridges are inhabited, with country dwellings strung out along the winding paths.

Urban settlement

Few of the towns in Belgium and the Netherlands are ancient foundations. In the Roman period, Tongres, Tournai, Arlou, Maastricht, Utrecht and Nijmegen were of some importance, but the fall of the Empire reduced them to rural settlements. After the tenth century, when the merchants set up wharves, warehouses and markets beside fortified towns, ecclesiastical palaces or abbeys, the cities of the Meuse region began to develop. These were Dinant, Namur, Huy, Liège and Maastricht, followed by the Rhenish centres of Nijmegen, Arnhem, Utrecht, Zutfen and Deventer, and finally the Flemish towns (Bruges, Ypres, Ghent and Alost), those of Brabant (Louvain, Brussels, Malines) and of Hainaut (Tournai and Mons). The cloth industry, in particular, increased the power and wealth of the towns which soon became city-states, defended by fortified walls.

In Holland, urban development was slower. Many towns owe their origin to the construction of dams across the rivers during the twelfth and thirteenth centuries. The necessity of trans-shipping goods from the lower reaches of the rivers which served the seaports to the upper reaches serving the interior determined the position of towns like Amsterdam, Rotterdam and Edam. Overseas trade also encouraged the growth of ports such as Vere in Zeeland, Enkhuizen and Hoorn on the shore of the Zuider Zee, and especially Dordrecht on the Merwede; industry enriched towns like Leyden, Delft and Haarlem,

Aerial view of the Cathedral of Tournai, one of the most beautiful churches of Belgium. SABENA

but even by the fifteenth century their influence was far less than that of the towns in the southern region of the Low Countries, and only in the sixteenth and especially the seventeenth century did they receive a real impetus with the increase in fishing and overseas trade.

In the extreme north, urban life is more recent in origin; apart from Groningen, the Frisian towns are growing very slowly. It was not until the beginning of the twentieth century that industry brought them new vigour, reviving the old towns and surrounding them with suburbs, creating the conurbations of the Haine-Sambre-Meuse trough, of southern Luxembourg, of Dutch Limburg, and of Twente.

URBAN SETTLEMENT IN BELGIUM AND LUXEMBOURG. In Belgium, the numerous cities contain about 40 per cent of the population. However, urban life never flourished where navigable waterways and embankments were lacking, as in the Campine, dry Hesbaye, and south of the Sambre-Meuse depression. Moreover, there are only six large cities, each with more than 200,000 inhabitants: Brussels, the capital, Antwerp, the commercial centre, Liège, Ghent, Namur, and Bruges. Only four towns have populations between 50,000 and 100,000: Malines, Ostend and Verviers and Louvain with their suburbs. Charleroi, the centre of an industrial region of about 450,000 inhabitants, could also be added.

Brussels, with about one million inhabitants, has all the appearance of a great cosmopolitan city. Its central position gave it political significance and spared it the decline which affected its rival, Louvain, at the time of the Dukes of Brabant. In the valley bottom of the Senne, the 'low' town, in spite of recent demolition for new road programmes, has kept its maze of medieval streets and the famous *grande place* and gothic Hôtel de Ville. The 'high' town with its palace and its ministries is more purely administrative.

To the east of Brussels, along the old embankment from Flanders to the Rhineland, are Louvain, well known for its ancient buildings and its university, Tirlemont, Saint-Trond, Tongres and Maastricht. To the north is Antwerp which owes everything to its port, where extensive docks stretch even further northwards along the right bank of the Scheldt. Old Antwerp, with its fine, historic houses over-shadowed by the slender spire of the Cathedral of Notre-Dame, is laid out in a large semi-circle, skirted on the west by the river. Having overrun the ramparts which replaced the sixteenth-century city walls, and then the zone fortified in 1859, the conurbation of Antwerp has now absorbed the neighbouring parishes and increased its population to over 750,000.

In the Campine, only Lierre, Turnhout and Herentals are really worthy of being called towns; Aarschot, Diest and Hasselt are more or less joined to the urban centre of Démer; but industry has led to the growth of a number of large garden-cities, particularly round Genk.

The cities of Flanders have undergone various changes. Ghent, at the confluence of the Scheldt and the Lys, whose branches divide the old parts of the town, was revived by the introduction of cotton spinning and weaving at the beginning of the nineteenth century. Like other Flemish towns, it takes pride in the large buildings which are evidence of its former grandeur: magnificent churches, the town hall, the belfry and many noble houses. The long streets lead out to the working-class suburbs which house a large proportion of the city's 450,000 inhabitants.

Industry, especially the textile industry, has invigorated other old towns like Grammont, Ninove, Alost and Termonde on the Dendre, and Courtrai and Menin on the Lys. It has led to the growth of centres such as Saint-Nicolas, Lokeren, Eeklo, Renaix and Roulers, but it has not succeeded in reviving the town of Audenarde. The once powerful medieval cities of the coastal plain are today only shadows of their former selves: ancient Bruges, the 'Venice of the North', is now little but a great museum. Ypres, Furnes and Nieuport have experienced even more rapid and complete decline. All activity now is concentrated in the seaside resorts of Ostend, Blankenberge and Knokke, especially during the holiday season.

The old towns in Hainaut and south Brabant have never been as prosperous as those of Flanders. Even today, Hal, Nivelles, Ath, Lessines, Enghien, Soignies, Binche and Thuin are centres of secondary importance. Only Tournai, on the Scheldt, clustered round its large cathedral, and Mons standing on a hill in the middle of a marshy plain, are exceptions. Mons owes its prosperity to its situation at the centre of a large conurbation based on the Walloon coalfields. One-seventh of the Belgian population is concentrated here. In the 'Borinage' to the west of Mons, around La Louvière, in the Charleroi basin, and in the Liège district, working-class houses in their thousands nestle among the huge factories.

Namur, at the confluence of the Meuse and the Sambre, and Huy — both attractively situated at the foot of a citadel — escaped the encroachment of large-scale industry. The city of Liège is equally fortunate. On either bank of the Meuse its pleasant, narrow streets intersect, and the old city is enriched by the wonderful ecclesiastical palace and the numerous old churches.

The conurbation of the coalfield has extended upstream as far as Seraing, and downstream as far as Herstal; it has climbed the valley sides and spread out on to the plateau. At the present time some 600,000 people are concentrated there.

In the Vesdre valley, Verviers is the most important of a series of towns (among them Dolhain-Limbourg and Eupen), which depend upon wool manufacture. In the regions lying south of the Sambre, Meuse and Vesdre, there are only small towns which have grown up in the shelter of a fortified castle or an abbey, flourishing in varying degrees due to their administrative importance (Arlon and Neufchâteau), their markets (Ciney, Bastogne and Stavelot) or their tourist industry (Dinant, Spa and Malmédy).

It is the same with the small towns of the Grand Duchy, like Wiltz and Vianden in Oesling and Ettelbrück, Diekirch and Echternach in Gutland. The only important town is Luxembourg, with its suburbs spread out on the edges of a dissected plateau falling steeply into the deep gorges of the Alzette and Pétrusse. Towards the southern limits of the country, at the foot of the Côte de Moselle, industrial towns comprising one-third of the population of Luxembourg extend from Rodange to Dudelange, and include Esch-sur-Alzette. This area is, in fact, part of the huge industrial region which includes Athus in Belgium, and Longwy and Villerupt in France.

URBAN SETTLEMENT IN THE NETHERLANDS.

The towns have increased considerably in size since the First World War, and this tendency has been most marked in recent years. At present, in the Netherlands, there are thirty-two towns of more than 50,000 inhabitants which alone make up 40 per cent of the population; among these, fourteen have more than 100,000. The most important are in the west, forming an urban girdle round the polders of South Holland. Here are to be found the three towns with more than half a million inhabitants (Amsterdam, Rotterdam and the Hague), two of more than 150,000 (Utrecht and Haarlem), and six of more than 50,000.

As in Belgium the contrast between the old town centres and the modern extensions is marked; there is the central maze of canals bordered by old gabled houses, and the outlying modern suburbs, often imaginatively planned and laid out. Amsterdam, with its 870,000 inhabitants, owes its distinctive character to its *grachten* (semicircular canals linked by transverse ones) and to its quays, many of them shaded and bordered by high, narrow brick houses with triangular pediments. The river IJ with its dock installations has checked the overspill to

The Town Hall of Brussels. The functions of large cities have always required the construction of important buildings which are an integral part of the urban scene. MICHEL HUET, EDITIONS HOA-QUI

the north, but in all other directions, especially the south, huge modern suburbs are encroaching more and more on the surrounding polders.

As in Antwerp, all the activity of Rotterdam (population 732,000) is based on its port, which is formed by the New Maas (Nieuwe Maas), and immense modern docks. The old town, its narrow streets cut by canals, was totally destroyed by fire after bombing in 1940; it has now been largely reconstructed. New districts extend all round, to the north along the Rotte, to the south across the river, and to the west towards Schiedam and Vlaardingen.

The Hague is the residential and administrative centre, divided by broad avenues round the *Binnenhof* where most of the government offices are housed, yet it has still preserved a large village atmosphere. Since the end of the last century, however, the town has branched out in the direction of the beach at Scheveningen and towards the polders, surrounding itself with a broad belt of garden cities. At present it has a population of more than 600,000.

Following a revival in industry, Haarlem, a beautiful city at the junction of the dunes and the polders, has extended far beyond its circular canals; so have Delft, Gouda and Dordrecht. Leyden, once the largest city of Holland after Amsterdam, has not benefited to the same extent from the impact of industry, and has remained pre-eminently a university city.

As for Utrecht, it too has benefited from modern economic development, but has kept its prestige as an ancient political, religious and intellectual stronghold.

Outside these large urban centres, there are still many old

towns, especially along the rivers. Gorkum has become industrial, but most of them — Oudewater, Schoonhoven, Kuilenburg — are attractive, sleepy, market towns. The same somnolence has affected the villages of Zeeland, of which only Middelburg and the port of Flushing retain some importance. As in Belgium, the coast is dotted with holiday resorts — Scheveningen, Noordwijk, Zandvoort — and fishing ports. In northern Holland, Zaandam has regained considerable importance as an industrial centre, Alkmaar as a cheese market, and Le Helder as a naval port; Edam, Enkhuizen, Hoorn, and Monnikendam, which have greatly declined in importance, exist now on a modest local trade and tourist patronage.

In the north-east of the country there are few towns of real importance. Parishes are often well populated because they cover large areas of land, and contain a large number of purely rural settlements. Leeuwarden, the capital of Friesland, is a large market town. Groningen is the commercial, industrial and intellectual centre of the north, and is linked by water to the port of Delfzijl. As for the towns of Sneek, Franeker and Bolsward, they are small but full of character. In Twente, not far from the old regional capital of Oldenzaal, a group of modern towns (Enschede, Hengelo, Almelo) has prospered rapidly with the development of the local cotton industry. These ordinary-looking towns have little in common with the ancient cities spread out along the IJssel, the great trade route which once linked the Rhinelands with the ports of the Zuider Zee: Kampen, Zwolle (not long ago a flourishing religious centre), Deventer and Zutfen.

Between the IJssel and the Vecht are some very old towns (like Amersfoort); large residential centres have also sprung up in this attractive region, such as Apeldoorn, Hilversum and Bussum (a neighbour of the ancient small town of Naarden which remains intact, secure behind its strong city walls). Further south, the old Rhenish towns of Arnhem and Nijmegen, both seriously damaged during the Second World War, owe their growth to industry. They boast some attractive modern residential areas along the slopes of neighbouring hills.

In North Brabant, Bois-le-Duc with its magnificent cathedral of Saint-Jean has not grown as rapidly as the series of industrial towns extending from Bergen-op-Zoom to Helmond; these include Roosendaal, Breda, Tilburg and Eindhoven. In Limburg, the very old centres are strung out along the Meuse: Venlo, Roermond and, most important, Maastricht.

Finally, coal-mining is responsible for the expansion of Sittard, Heerlen and Kerkrade, all of which are surrounded by mining villages.

LANGUAGE AND RELIGION. The Netherlands has no linguistic problem: Dutch is spoken everywhere, though there is a tendency to use local dialect in Friesland. The Grand Duchy of Luxembourg similarly has no problem; the official language is French. The situation is quite different in Belgium, a bilingual, sometimes trilingual, country; Dutch or Flemish is spoken to the north of the so-called linguistic frontier, French to the south of this boundary, and German near the eastern frontier. A large proportion of the citizens of Brussels form a French-speaking enclave in the Flemish-speaking area. French is the literary and official language south of the linguistic frontier, but the true local dialects are Walloon, Rouchi (a variation of the Picardy dialect spoken in the extreme west), and Gaumais, (similar to the Lorraine dialect and spoken in the extreme south). As for Dutch, it comprises a large number of dialects which can be related to the languages of the three main ethnic groups that took part in the settlement of the Netherlands and northern Belgium: Frisian, Saxon, and above all Frankish. The conquering Franks, issuing from the banks of the lower Rhine after the fourth century, succeeded in superimposing their tongue, but only as far as the borders of the regions strongly held by the 'Romanised' peoples, that is, as far as the present linguistic frontier.

The interior of a house in the island of Marken.   SERGE DE SAZO

The traditional dress of Vollendam, in the Netherlands.

Amsterdam. Large quantities of vegetables are still brought to the auctions by barge.   NETHERLANDS EMBASSY

Above: *Aerial view of the centre of Amsterdam. The semi-circular canals, linked by transverse ones, stand out clearly. In the background is the river IJ and a small part of the docks of this great city, which has been won from the water.* K.L.M. AEROCARTO

...*clists in the centre of Amsterdam.* B. I. P. S. RAPHO

The Brouwersgracht ('Brewers' Canal') in Amsterdam. A.N.V.V.

Numerically, the Dutch-speaking Belgians (usually but wrongly called Flemings) are more numerous: 42 per cent of the Belgian population speaks only Dutch, 34 per cent French, and less than 1 per cent German; 23 per cent speak both chief national languages.

Religion has created few problems in Belgium or in Luxembourg. The great majority of the population is Roman Catholic, although the law recognises and assists other religions — Protestant, both Evangelical and Anglican, and Jewish. The Netherlands, however, is divided over the religious issue. About 40 per cent of the population is Protestant, and some 38 per cent

The Netherlands and Belgium have very high densities, 922 and 773 persons per square mile respectively; but within each country there are marked local variations. For example, the sparse population of the rocky plateaus of south Belgium is in strong contrast with the swarming masses in the industrial belt of Hainaut and the Sambre-Meuse valley; and the relatively sparsely populated *limon* region and northern lowlands of the Campine are widely different from the densely populated banks of the Lys, Dendre and lower Scheldt.

The large towns tend to concentrate the population in the centre of the country; a circle of 30 miles radius around Brussels encloses only one-quarter of Belgium's area, yet it includes three-fifths of its population.

Luxembourg has moderate population densities, both in the Oesling and in Gutland, but in the metallurgical district in the south density is comparable with that of the industrial regions of Wallonia.

In the Netherlands, the population is particularly concentrated along the sea front of the Province of Holland. Nearly one-half of the population of the Netherlands is confined to the area between the sea and the towns of Amsterdam, Utrecht and Dordrecht. The highest densities occur here, though the industrial regions of northern Brabant, Twente, Arnhem and Limburg are also densely populated. The opposite is true of the sandy plains and the *polders* which are devoted exclusively to agriculture.

In Belgium the population has doubled in the last century. This increase is due primarily to the excess of births over deaths, and to some extent to immigration; there has been an influx of foreign workers, especially Italians. The countryside has remained populated because many of the agricultural labourers and smallholders who have been drawn into the factories have not left their own villages. The dense network of communications and the very low cost of season tickets on the railway produces a constant daily flow of workers between countryside and town.

In the Grand Duchy, the rural population has declined, and it was not until after the development of the iron industry, at the end of the nineteenth century, that an increase in total population occurred. Even this was due, in part, to the immigration of foreign workers.

In the Netherlands the recent rise in population has been surprising, even threatening to disrupt the economic and social balance. Since 1900 the population has doubled, and since 1830 quadrupled. About 1850 the population was smaller than that of Belgium, by 1933 the two were equal, and since then the Dutch population has forged ahead. The rate of growth is about 1.4 per cent, against 0.5 per cent in Belgium. The increase springs entirely from a very high birth rate coupled with one of the lowest death rates in the world. In order to find work for the continually increasing numbers, the Netherlands has speeded up its land reclamation projects, including drainage of the Zuider Zee, and has introduced new industries. Since the loss of Indonesia, which was able to absorb, albeit temporarily, part of the surplus, the pressure of population has found an outlet in emigration, especially to Canada and Australia.

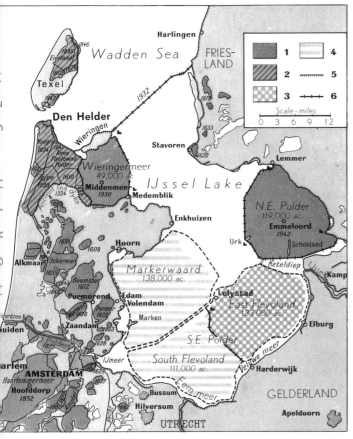

THE DRAINAGE OF THE ZUIDER ZEE AND THE SURROUNDING REGIONS.
1. Drained lakes (droogmakerijen), with the date of their completion. 2. Polders reclaimed from marine alluvium to the north of the old dyke of West Friesland. 3. Areas in the course of being reclaimed. 4. Proposed reclamations. 5. Old dykes. 6. New dykes of Lake IJssel.

Roman Catholic. The latter form a compact group south of the Rhine, and include more than 80 per cent of the local population; however, north of the river there are still strong Catholic minorities (except in the north-east), and in the large towns they may number from one-quarter to one-third of the inhabitants.

Population problems

At present the Netherlands has the largest population: in 1959 it was 11,346,000. At that period, the population of Belgium was 9,104,000, and of Luxembourg, 324,000. Thus Benelux has a total population of over 20 millions which, in view of the small area of territory, gives the high density figure of 810 to the square mile.

The agricultural economy

In few countries is there such intensity of economic activity as in Benelux. Each member state seems to have its own speciality, Belgium concentrating on coal-mining, heavy metallurgical industries and textiles, Luxembourg on iron manufacture, and the Netherlands on agriculture, shipping and commerce. These are, however, generalisations, for both Belgium and Luxembourg have a prosperous agriculture, the port of Antwerp is a rival of Rotterdam, and Dutch industry is rapidly expanding.

Vineyards on the slopes of the Moselle valley in the neighbourhood of Wellenstein, in Luxembourg.
H. HOLMES, CAMERA PRESS

IN BELGIUM. Agricultural land occupies three-fifths of the total area, though for a hundred years it has hardly increased. In the Ardennes and especially in the Campine, there has been land clearance, but very often this has resulted in the uncultivated land being replaced by pine plantations. In fact, the forest area has steadily expanded and at the present time covers about one-fifth of the country. Belgium is, above all, a land of small-scale farming; four-fifths of the farms are less than 25 acres. Tenancy predominates, and only one-third of the land is owner-farmed.

As everywhere else in western Europe, Belgium's agriculture has changed since the corn crisis of the years 1880—90; pasture land has continued to increase. The traditional food crops have been replaced by fodder cultivation, and sometimes by intensive market-gardening. In a few places, crops have disappeared completely, as in the region of Herve and the north-east of the Ardennes.

Cereals are grown on 30 per cent of the arable land. Although wheat always yields a good crop in the fertile areas of *limon* and polder, Belgium still has to import three-quarters of its wheat requirements. Oats are still grown, barley is replacing rye, and spelt (German wheat), which was formerly important in the Condroz, is now little more than a memory.

Of the industrial crops which were important until quite recently, only sugar-beet grown on the fertile soil of the coastal plain and the *limon* region has maintained any significance; chicory, hops, tobacco, and especially flax, have disappeared both in Flanders and in the north-west of Hainaut. The districts surrounding Brussels and Malines form a specialised market-gardening area, whilst around Hoeilaart, south-east of Brussels, table grapes and peaches are grown in 30,000 hothouses.

The area devoted to grazing cattle is enormous, roughly 70 per cent of all agricultural land. South of the Sambre-Meuse valley the area of pasture everywhere exceeds that of the arable land. Even to the north, grass is encroaching — more markedly in the Campine than in Flanders, where it is still profitable to grow rye and fodder crops, and more extensively in Hainaut

than in 'dry' Hesbaye, which has remained true to cereals and sugar-beet. Cattle are increasing rapidly, especially beef cattle. As for the rearing of the famous Belgian horses, so suitable for work in parts of the *limon* area, this has suffered severely from the effects of the mechanisation of farming.

IN LUXEMBOURG. Excluding the industrial region in the south, the land has remained agricultural, and forest covers more than a third of it. The rural economy has expanded here as well, especially since the First World War, but the Luxembourg peasant, usually the owner of his lands, remains nonetheless attached to his traditional crops: oats and rye in Oesling, corn, fodder and fruit in Gutland, and grapes on the valley slopes of the Moselle, around Remich and Grevenmacher.

IN THE NETHERLANDS. Agriculture is of paramount importance, accounting directly or indirectly for at least 45 per cent of the exports. Particularly since 1900, the country has done its utmost to increase the productive areas, clearing the moorland and draining the Zuider Zee. But the most remarkable feature of Dutch agriculture is its technical efficiency; it is surprising to find such extraordinarily high yields achieved in all branches of farming. There is a predominance of small-scale farms of less than 25 acres, and the farmers are usually owners of their land.

Cereals are grown on about half the arable land; wheat is most important on the marine clays, and rye on the sandy soils, whilst oats are grown everywhere. As in Belgium, the country has to import three-quarters of its grain needs. Potatoes are grown everywhere but especially in the bog colonies of Groningen, where the crop is the basis of an important starch industry. The country is also a large producer of dried vegetables. Finally, the good clay lands of the coastal plain produce sugar-beet and flax. But the Netherlands' fame lies in its horticulture. Although practised almost everywhere, it is most specialised in the zone where dunes and polders meet, between the mouths of the great rivers in the south, as far as

The vast oil refinery at Antwerp, in Belgium, with an oil tanker drawn up alongside. Oil supplements the fuel resources of Belgium which, though vast, are insufficient for the needs of its industry. RAFFINERIE BELGE DE PETROLE S.A.

Alkmaar in the north. In the extensive glass-houses of West-land early vegetables and table grapes are grown; in those of Aalsmeer flowers are grown for cutting. In the open fields, vegetables are grown over large areas; and the area devoted to bulb-growing comprises almost 22,000 acres.

Apart from horticulture, cattle rearing has been particularly successful. The rich pastures produce fine animals, especially in the provinces of Holland and Friesland; half the cattle are milch cows. The animals are reared for dairy produce rather than for beef production (butter in Friesland and in the sandy areas, and cheese in Holland); including pork production and eggs, dairy produce forms a large proportion of Dutch exports.

Fishing

Sea fishing is not very important in Belgium and employs only 2,000 people. However, the fleet of large Belgian trawlers is well equipped, and operates off the shores of Britain, Iceland and Spain, in contrast to the Dutch fleet which confines itself largely to the North Sea. Ostend and Zeebrugge are the main fishing ports.

In the Netherlands, the sea fisheries provide a livelihood for some 10,000 fishermen. The sea-going fleet catches mainly herrings. Mechanisation has induced it to concentrate on the ports of IJmuiden, Scheveningen, Vlaardingen and Maassluis. Off-shore fishing, with catches of anchovies and mussels, is divided among a large number of little ports on the estuaries of Zeeland, and on the shores of the Wadden Sea. The Zuider Zee, now transformed into a freshwater lake, yields only eels; some of its fishing ports, like Urk, still send part of their fleet to the North Sea, but other ports have fallen into decay.

Industry and communications

BELGIAN INDUSTRY. Industry is the basis of the entire Belgian economy, employing almost half of the working population. Mainly imported raw materials are used: minerals, textiles, potash, oil and rubber. Even home-produced fuel is insufficient in quantity, and a proportion of good coal for the metallurgical industry has to be imported, mainly from Dutch Limburg and the Ruhr. On the other hand, Belgium sells between 35 and 40 per cent of her products abroad. These include partly-finished goods, bulky and heavy goods (girders, rails, sheets of iron and zinc), cement, chemical products, fertilizers, glass, cables and textiles.

Her engineering works produce locomotives, machines and spare parts, but production is insufficient to meet domestic needs and she has to import precision instruments, electrical goods and motor vehicles.

Belgian industry is mainly concentrated in the coal-mining and metallurgical basin of the Haine-Sambre-Meuse, in the region of Verviers, in the west of Hainaut along the Senne-Rupel-Scheldt axis, in Flanders, and in the Campine.

She is pre-eminently a coal and steel power; annual coal production is about 30 million tons. The Walloon coalfield produces 20 million tons but is on the way to exhaustion;

Aerial view of the industrial region of Charleroi, showing the huge tip-heaps so characteristic of mining country. SABENA

Iron works at Esch-sur-Alzette in Luxembourg.
LUXEMBOURG TOURIST OFFICE

Assembly of television sets at the Philips works at Eindhoven, in the Netherlands. These factories occupy a special place in Dutch industry. They began in the last century as a small works for incandescent lamps, and have grown into a huge establishment producing large quantities of electrical apparatus, radios, television sets, records; 25,000 people are employed at these works, and another 15,000 elsewhere in the country. NETHERLANDS EMBASSY

the working of the thin, distorted coal seams is proving increasingly difficult. On the other hand, the thick, regular coal measures of the eastern Campine, worked since the end of the First World War, are producing more and more (10 million tons for industrial purposes).

Heavy industry is concentrated near the Walloon coalfields and along the great navigable waterways. Ten million tons of coal are used for coke, for lighting, and for chemical products. Except in Belgian Lorraine mineral ores are exhausted, and Belgium annually imports about 12 million tons of iron ore from France, Luxembourg and Sweden to feed some fifty blast-furnaces along the Charleroi-Brussels canal (Clabecq), in the Centre Basin (La Louvière), in Belgian Lorraine (Athus region), and throughout the regions of Charleroi and Liège. The steel works and rolling mills process approximately 5 million tons of pig iron. The biggest mechanical engineering works are in the Centre Basin and the Charleroi and Liège districts, but since engineering is less dependent on iron and steel production, factories tend to be more widely dispersed, as in the south of Brabant. In addition, there are the shipyards, the most important of which are at Hoboken, near Antwerp.

Belgium is one of the world's principal producers of zinc. Many zinc works have moved from the Meuse valley and the Liège region to the Campine, which is closer to the port of Antwerp and its imports of zinc ore from overseas.

Copper ore, tin ore, cobalt and radium are also imported through Antwerp and refined at Hoboken and in the Campine. Large quantities of cement are exported, the cement works being located on the clay in the Campine, and on the limestone and chalk around Tournai, Mons and north of Liège. Glass manufacture, of which Belgium once had almost a world monopoly, has remained important in the Charleroi area, but the white sand in the Campine has attracted it to that region. Glass-making is also still carried on in Hainaut and along the lower Sambre. This, too, flourished more in former years, although the famous glass-works of Val-Aint-Lambert, near Liège, continues to export fine glassware to all parts of the world.

Finally, a great number of factories on the Walloon coalfield, in the Campine, and along the navigable waterways between Brussels and Antwerp produce chemical products and artificial fertilizers. The textile industry is carried on, as in the past, in many towns in Flanders and in the region of Verviers, and has also increased in importance in Hainaut and Brabant. Flanders shows a high degree of specialisation in the choice

of raw materials: wool, flax (especially at Courtrai), jute and rayon are spun and woven, and Ghent is the chief of many cotton manufacturing towns. Verviers in its turn specialises in the preparation, spinning and weaving of wool. Also noteworthy are the huge brickworks on the banks of the Rupel and those of the northern Campine, the potteries of Hainaut, and the limestone, marble and sandstone quarries which are a familiar sight in the countryside of Hainaut and Condroz.

INDUSTRY IN LUXEMBOURG. Apart from a few tanneries, potteries and spinning mills, industrial activity is confined to the mining of iron ore and to iron smelting on a considerable scale. The Côte de Moselle produces about 7 million tons of iron ore annually, half of which goes to Belgium. The remainder is smelted in some thirty blast-furnaces situated beside the steelworks and sometimes near the engineering and cement works. The iron industry of Luxembourg suffers from three main disadvantages: first, there is no home-produced coke — all requirements having to be imported; secondly, it is hampered by a lack of navigable waterways, although the canalisation of the Moselle is intended to remedy this; finally, a good home market is almost non-existent.

INDUSTRY IN THE NETHERLANDS. There is not such a long industrial tradition here as in Belgium but nevertheless since 1890 industry has employed as many people as agriculture, and today there are two-and-a-half times as many workers employed in factories (about 41 per cent of the working population) as there are on the land. Several factors have contributed to the development of industry in the Netherlands. A large proportion of the country's agricultural products and imported raw materials are processed, and industry has had to play an important rôle in feeding a steadily increasing population. Furthermore, since the beginning of the century coal-mining in southern Limburg has stimulated all sections of industrial enterprise.

Although the concentration of industry is greatest near the ports, in southern Limburg, Twente and northern Brabant, it is also widely dispersed. There is not much heavy industry — certainly it is not comparable in area or in concentration with the industrial belt of Wallonia.

The Dutch food industry is traditional, and most of its products are exported. Agricultural products are usually processed in small co-operative factories; butter and cheese are manufactured in Friesland and northern Holland, starch from potatoes in Groningen, and sugar from the clay polderlands. Imported goods are processed as well; there are cane sugar refineries, factories for preparing rice, cocoa and chocolate at Amsterdam and Zaandam, vegetable oil refineries, margarine and soap factories; and there are the distilleries of Rotterdam and its neighbouring towns, Vlaardingen, Schiedam, Gouda and Dordrecht.

Numerous shipbuilding yards are concentrated near the great ports; Amsterdam, Rotterdam, and especially Flushing build large ocean-going vessels.

Mechanical engineering, which is important in the large towns, is primarily directed towards the home market, and the same is true of the blast-furnaces, steel works and rolling mills of Velsen near IJmuiden. On the other hand, the tin refinery at Arnhem, using ore from Indonesia, produces almost entirely for export.

The famous Philips factories at Eindhoven occupy a special place among Dutch industries. The original small factory for making incandescent lamps, set up in the last century, has developed into a huge establishment producing a whole range of electrical equipment. At Eindhoven alone, 25,000 workers are employed in the factories, whilst another 15,000 are employed elsewhere.

The textile industry is less developed here than in Belgium and is designed particularly to provide employment in the poorer, somewhat over-populated districts; there is a woollen industry at Tilburg in northern Brabant, and a cotton industry at Enschede and other towns of Twente and eastern Gelderland.

Other types of industrial activity include the manufacture of footwear in Langstraat to the west of Bois-le-Duc, rayon manufacture in the area of Breda and Arnhem, artificial fertilizers and petroleum refining near Rotterdam, the manufacture of cardboard in the peat-bog colonies of the north-east, and paper-making in Veluwe. Extraction industries produce salt in Twente, clay for innumerable brickworks along the Waal, peat in Drente, petroleum at Schoonebeek near Koevorden and, most important of all, coal in Limburg.

Of the three Netherlands coal basins, those of east Gelderland and Peel are being held in reserve. The south Limburg coalfield produces 12 million tons a year: it provides part of the country's needs and a surplus for export too. Only two mines were working in 1893; now there are eleven, of which the four most important are nationalised. The giant Maurits mine, the largest in Europe, alone produces 56 per cent of the total coal production; it also has important coking plant and factories for nitrate products.

COMMUNICATIONS IN BELGIUM AND LUXEMBOURG.
The Belgian road network is well developed and maintained, but planning in most cases relates to local needs; through motorways are still few and incomplete.

The railway network is extremely dense, totalling 3,100 miles (27 miles for every 100 square miles). This does not include various country lines, such as those which ended the isolation of such regions as the Campine and the Ardennes towards the end of the last century. The whole country is a focal point for the great international lines of western Europe. In spite of competition from navigable waterways and road transport, the railways continue to claim the larger part of the goods traffic, with 70 million tons against 60 million tons for canals and rivers.

Belgium is also at the crossroads of international air routes. In addition, regular helicopter services link Brussels with other Belgian towns, and with Paris, Lille, Rotterdam, Cologne and Bonn.

The network of navigable waterways is extensive, though only one-third as dense as that of the Netherlands. Most Belgian canals have been in existence for over a hundred years, but the Albert Canal has been completed recently. Skirting the Dutch enclave of Maastricht, it offers a short cut (via the Campine) between Liège and the port of Antwerp.

The only navigable waterway in the hilly area to the south of the Sambre-Meuse trough is the Meuse, above Namur. Elsewhere, communication by water between the Meuse and Scheldt basins was achieved only by means of several extensive and complicated engineering feats, like the elevation of the Centre Canal, and the huge cuttings of the Albert Canal to the level of Maastricht. Thanks to the deeper canals, sea-going ships are able to reach Ghent, Bruges, and even Brussels. Heavy industry is well served by the system of rivers and canals which link it to the port of Antwerp: the Scheldt, the Rupel, the Rupel canal to Brussels and Charleroi, the canalised Sambre and Meuse, and the Albert Canal. The last, which is navigable by ships of 2,000 tons, alone carries 40 per cent of the country's water-borne traffic. Linked with this important system of communication are the coal canals of Hainaut and the navigable waterways of Flanders in the west; in the east are the old canals of the Campine.

The Yser, Lys, Scheldt, and Sambre and their canals give access to north-west France and to Paris; the Meuse offers a route to the eastern part of France. Still more important are the communications with the Netherlands and through that country to Germany.

The lock of Lanaye, which is capable only of taking vessels up to 450 tons, forms a bottle-neck which still prevents the larger ships coming from Liège from reaching Maastricht. After Maastricht, the Juliana canal (capable of taking ships of 2,000 tons) joins the Dutch canals of the Meuse; this is linked to the Rhine at Nijmegen by the Mook canal. It is also possible to reach the Meuse and the Rhine by the Zuid-Willemsvaart canal, through Bois-le-Duc. To reach Rotterdam or the Rhine the largest barges travel via Antwerp, down the Scheldt estuary, across Zuid-Beveland using the Hansweert canal, and then through the coastal waters of Zeeland and south Holland. It is a difficult journey, sometimes dangerous in rough weather, and this fact has encouraged Belgian demands for a direct canal across northern Brabant, from Antwerp to Moerdijk.

The water traffic is colossal: 23 million tons of national and 32 million tons of international goods, with 2 million tons of goods in transit. Rhine traffic accounts for about half the international goods.

Luxembourg is practically without navigable waterways, except for the Moselle, which is accessible only to small ships and then only for part of the year. The railways are of much greater importance to the iron industry.

THE BELGIAN PORTS.
The port of Antwerp is an essential factor in the industrial activity of Belgium. As with Rotterdam, its hinterland extends far beyond the frontiers of its own country. It is excellently situated: it is the nearest port to the densely populated industrial sections of western Europe, the north of France, Switzerland, the Saar, Luxembourg and the Westphalian region of the Rhine; and it is connected with these areas by good navigable waterways and a close network of railways. These advantages, together with excellent outfitting facilities, have helped it to meet competition from Rotterdam and Hamburg with success. The navigation of the lower Scheldt is not without inconveniences: sandbanks, strong tides and an exit controlled by the Netherlands.

Antwerp has 27 docks with a total area of 1,000 acres. The docks are floating docks demanding delicate manoeuvres, a difficulty which Rotterdam does not experience.

Above: *The Cloth Hall at Ypres (13th century) in Belgium. It was completely destroyed during the First World War and afterwards reconstructed. The main front is 433 feet long; it is surmounted by a magnificent square belfry 230 feet high, flanked with turrets. 'Les Halles' of the old Belgian cities have the appearance of palaces, but as temples of trade they symbolise at once the love of work and the pride of wealth.*
BELGIAN STATE TOURIST OFFICE

The port of Rotterdam in the Netherlands. About 20,000 ships call every year at Rotterdam, the chief port of Europe and the second in the world (after New York).
NETHERLANDS EMBASSY

Antwerp has few advantages as a passenger port and devotes itself almost exclusively to goods. Every year 15,000 ships enter, with a capacity of about 30 million tons; 17 million tons of goods are unloaded, and 15 million loaded. Thus imports and exports balance fairly closely. Imports are mainly food and raw materials required by the industrial and densely populated regions in the hinterland of Antwerp; exports consist of manufactured products, especially of iron. Ships using Antwerp are practically assured of return freight. Whilst Rotterdam loads and unloads mainly bulk cargo, Antwerp handles large quantities of packaged goods requiring much and varied equipment, as well as numerous and specialised dock workers.

Of the goods discharged 75 per cent are solely for Belgian consumption. Belgium, in turn, produces 70 per cent. of the goods shipped from Antwerp. Transit trade therefore accounts for a large part of the tonnage, and this illustrates the port's international importance; along with Ghent, it handles one-quarter of the overseas trade of the Rhine area. Only a very small proportion of the total trade (about 9 per cent) is carried in Belgian ships, although there are regular services with the Congo; the greater proportion is carried in British, Dutch or Scandinavian vessels.

The port of Ghent is linked to the lower Scheldt by the ship canal to Terneuzen, which takes ships with a maximum of 9,000—10,000 tons. Ghent's hinterland includes the whole basin of the upper Scheldt and north-western France; here, however, there is keen competition from Dunkirk. Two thousand ships with a total tonnage of 1½ million enter the port of Ghent annually. They discharge, in particular, heavy goods in bulk (nearly 2 million tons) and load a slightly smaller tonnage (1½ million tons) of manufactured goods. Ghent is clearly much less important than Antwerp and her imports considerably outweigh her exports.

The other Belgian ports are of secondary importance, situated on a low-lying and unfavourable coast. Zeebrugge, mainly a passenger port, is the terminus for ferry boats from Harwich, and Ostend for the passenger steamers from Dover.

COMMUNICATIONS IN THE NETHERLANDS.

Water transport was once the chief means of communication, at least on the large alluvial plains; the broad waterways were a serious obstacle to land communication. Today the country has a fine network of roads; enormous steel bridges, like those at Moerdijk and at Nijmegen, have replaced the older crossings at many points. Railways, too, have developed slowly: in 1860 there were only 236 miles of track, at a time when Belgium already had 1,056 miles. Now there is a total length of 2,000 miles, about 15 miles per 100 square miles. Air transport has increased to a remarkable extent; from Schiphol airport, notably, the large transport aircraft of K.L.M. operate world routes.

In contrast to Belgium, the transport of goods by water greatly exceeds transport by rail: 115 million tons against 25 million tons. Several factors encourage this: the numerous navigable rivers, the relief of the land (almost sea level), and the absence of watersheds between the river basins. The total length of navigable waterways is about 4,660 miles (683 miles are the great rivers themselves); this gives the greatest density in the world.

Improved by artificial channels, the estuaries in Zeeland and in Holland give the ports access to the sea: from IJmuiden to Amsterdam the North Sea Canal with its enormous locks has taken over the functions of the Helder-to-Amsterdam canal; the New Waterway serves Rotterdam and its satellite ports; the Scheldt estuary connects Antwerp and Ghent with the sea, and also Flushing and Terneuzen.

The great inland waterways, the parallel courses of the Meuse and the Rhine's two distributaries (the Merwede-Waal and the Nieuwe Maas-Lek) branch off directly from the sea channels, the intercommunicating estuaries of Zeeland and

Aerial view of the quays along the Meuse at Liège. Rich in its cultural past, Liège has become a great industrial centre, and is growing from day to day. LIÈGE TOURIST OFFICE

south Holland. All are linked by important navigable channels, either improved waterways or canals, which include the new Amsterdam-Utrecht-Rhine canal. Rhine navigation is extended by the IJssel; the Twente canal is connected with it as far as Enschede and Almelo; the IJssel also gives access to the close network of small canals in the north. Here, the town of Groningen has a good connection with the port of Harlingen, in particular via the Eemskanaal with Delfzijl; from here, the way is open towards the sea, and towards the Ruhr by the river Ems and the Dortmund-Ems canal. In northern Brabant and Limburg, the canalised Meuse, extended above Roermond by the Juliana Canal, has not completely superseded the old Zuid-Willemsvaart canal which is connected with the canals of the Campine and linked by branch canals to Eindhoven, Tilburg and Breda.

THE DUTCH PORTS.

The seaports are more important in the Netherlands than in Belgium. Rotterdam, now restored after heavy damage in the war years, handles more than three-quarters of the total trade. Since the growth of Rhine-Westphalian industry over the last 130 years, it has formed, with its satellite ports of Schiedam, Vlaardingen and the Hook of Holland, one of the great dock areas of the world. The New Waterway, an artificial channel only 19 miles long, gives excellent connections with the sea; it forms an extension to the Nieuwe Maas on which are situated huge docks totalling 1,160 acres. There are excellent loading and unloading facilities on the quays, and ships moored to fixed buoys are able to discharge cargoes in the river itself or in the middle of the docks.

The hinterland of Rotterdam is similar to that of other ports at the mouths of the great rivers; its position is particularly advantageous in relation to Western Germany, and in spite of measures taken to encourage trade through Hamburg and

Above: *Dinant, in Belgium. Confined in the Meuse valley, Dinant is dominated by its famous citadel.* PHOTO SERGYSELS, BY COURTESY OF THE BELGIAN STATE TOURIST OFFICE

The reconstruction of Rotterdam. Badly damaged during the Second World War, Rotterdam is being rebuilt quickly and in a very modern style. A.N.V.V.

Bremen, Rotterdam continues to attract Rhine trade. It also handles half the tonnage passing along the river to the German frontier. Unlike Antwerp, Rotterdam's communication with the interior is mainly by water. About 20,000 ships with a tonnage of 40 millions now enter the port annually. The outgoing tonnage, however, is less than one-half of the goods discharged (52 million tons). This is because enormous quantities of cereals, petroleum, minerals, and other raw materials are imported from overseas, while from the industrial regions of the Netherlands and Germany much smaller quantities of raw materials and manufactured goods are received for export.

Transit business plays a considerable part in Rotterdam's trade, accounting for about half of the general movement of goods. As fewer than half the ships can be certain of a return freight, many have to take on more cargo in England or even at Antwerp. Because of this, Rotterdam is particularly sensitive to economic fluctuations in other countries.

The Netherlands has an important merchant navy of some 580 ships with a total tonnage of 4,000,000 tons. (Belgium has only 82 ships with a total tonnage of 500,000 tons.) One-quarter of the ships entering Rotterdam sail under the Dutch flag; United Kingdom vessels form the next most numerous contingent. Many shipping companies have their head offices in Rotterdam, and it is also the terminus for large passenger liners sailing regularly for America and the Far East. Other ports share the trade of Rotterdam: Vlaardingen, the third port of the Netherlands (annual tonnage 2 million tons), Schiedam, which has large dockyards, the Hook of Holland, an outport and the departure point for the packet-steamers to Harwich, and finally Dordrecht, the timber port.

Amsterdam is a very different type of port. Its functions are to some extent what they were during its 'Golden Age'. It is essentially a national port, and a great entrepôt for colonial products. Once the chief port on the Zuider Zee, it is still a North Sea port because of the North Sea Canal link, and is likely to attract more Rhine trade through the Amsterdam-Waal Canal. It imports more goods than it exports (6½ million tons against 3 million tons), mainly tropical products which are distributed to the hinterland after processing in Amsterdam's own factories. It is also the port for numerous shipping lines, in particular passenger services to the Far East.

Flushing, in Zeeland, although accessible to the largest ships, has not developed as might have been expected because of competition from Antwerp, and has become a packet port. Antwerp and Rotterdam compete for the markets of its hinterland, and Flushing itself is only kept going by the fast steamer services to Harwich. In the same way, the development of Terneuzen has been checked by the port of Ghent. In the north Harlingen and Delfzijl both import British coal, fertilizers, and timber from Scandinavia; they export some agricultural products.

Benelux
and its international trade relations

The overseas trade of Belgium, Luxembourg and the Netherlands is now entirely dominated by the agreements made between the three countries forming the economic unit of Benelux. These agreements, signed in London in 1944, stipulated that the three countries should have a common tariff for goods imported from other countries, and that they should remove all customs duties on goods of the member countries. But at the end of the Second World War there was a significant discrepancy between the productive and commercial capacity of Belgium and Luxembourg — linked economically since 1921 — and that of the Netherlands. Belgium, with its industrial plant almost unscathed by war, was soon able to resume production. The Netherlands, destroyed and impoverished, had first to rebuild and reorganise her plant. Imports were limited to the raw materials essential for the industries producing exports. Prices and wages were kept at the lowest possible level. The general prosperity of Belgium at this period was in contrast to the austerity practised by the Netherlands, and it was not until January 1948 that the pre-union agreements of 1944 actually came into force.

The balance has now been largely redressed. Both the Belgian-Luxembourg union and the Netherlands import large quantities of foodstuffs and raw materials for their industries, paying for them with manufactured goods sold abroad. Exports do not match imports in total value, but the deficit is mainly offset by the income from large capital investments abroad, from allowance made for the cost of transport of the imports, and from income earned by merchant shipping.

In no other country does foreign trade assume such importance as in Benelux. Together the three countries lie fifth in world ranking after the United States, United Kingdom, Western Germany and France. Western Germany and the Netherlands are the chief sources of imports for the Belgian-Luxembourg economic union. France no longer occupies first place but is still more important than the United States, the United Kingdom and the Congo. The Netherlands is far and away the most important customer, then France, followed closely by Western Germany, the United States, Great Britain and the Congo. The Congo, of course, helped considerably to strengthen the economic position. It has sent to Belgium a variety of goods which have stimulated industry: diamonds, raw copper, tin ore, gold, vegetable oils, coffee, copal, cotton and rubber. The economic effects of Congo independence will undoubtedly be considerable.

During the period following the Second World War, the Netherlands, while re-establishing trade with Western Germany, showed a tendency to return to her pre-war trading pattern. Western Germany therefore again became the chief customer, followed by the Belgian-Luxembourg economic union, Great Britain, the United States, France, Sweden and Indonesia. The Netherlands buys most of its goods from the Belgian-Luxembourg Union, then from Western Germany America, Great Britain and France, in that order of importance.

Benelux has brought about a fundamental change in the economic relations between Belgium and the Netherlands. The home market has been considerably enlarged, and the advantages will be even greater when the union is completely achieved. At international level, a fully implemented Benelux will be of economic and financial value to the three countries as well as having political importance. Benelux will, in fact, be a great power, with her 20 million people and control of the common delta of the Scheldt, Meuse and Rhine, in itself the busiest crossroad of trade routes in Western Europe. The three countries belong to the European Coal and Steel Community, producing about one-fifth of the total of coal and one-fifth of the steel.

It is only natural that such co-operation should present problems. Although they have different industrial structures, competition occurs in certain industries, notably in textiles and agriculture. The disparity which persists between prices and wages in the two countries (those of the Netherlands are always kept at a slightly higher level) presents difficulties for many Belgian industries. Rivalry between Rotterdam and Antwerp is another source of contention, and the improvement of the navigable waterways between the two countries still awaits a final solution.

The full union planned for July 1950 has not been achieved, mainly because of opposition from Belgian economic circles, and only at successive conferences will these differences gradually be overcome. It is better, however, that Benelux should be built up with caution and mutual understanding rather than with excessive haste. Its success will be the surer and its achievements a pointer to success to projected European union.

Frans DUSSART

The castle of Azay-le-Rideau, built in the
sixteenth century, and one of the famous
castles of the Loire country, in western France.
PAUL POPPER

FRANCE

IF Europe is considered as a peninsula of Asia, then France is its Finistère, for although the British Isles and Iberia extend appreciably further westwards, France is still the real terminal point of Western Europe. She alone faces the three seas which border Europe: the Atlantic Ocean to the west, the Mediterranean Sea to the south, and the partially enclosed seas of the north, the English Channel and the North Sea. France is the only European country to have three sea coasts. England, like Spain, faces two seas; most other European countries, only one; some have no coast at all.

The outline and position of France

THE THREE SEA COASTS. France owes much to each of her 'windows on the sea'. The Mediterranean brings her into contact with one of the most curious seas in the world, a sheet of water extending in a general east-west direction, whilst most of its basins face in a north-south direction; a sea which, as its name indicates, is not only in the middle of the land but in the middle of the mountains. Around it lie the highest mountains of Europe: the Alps, Pyrenees, Sierra Nevada, Atlas, Rhodopes, and Apennines. It is an enclosed sea, where the relief barriers have given rise to local climatic differences. The Mediterranean is the only sea to lend its name to a type of climate; a Mediterranean climate's main characteristics include mild temperatures, clear atmosphere, strong winds, drought in the hot season, and light rain occurring mainly in the unproductive cool season.

Such climatic conditions produce a rather specialised type of vegetation that is drought-resistant and shows little seasonal change. Southern France belongs to the Mediterranean lands, and here the Mediterranean climate extends farther north than elsewhere; olive trees are found as far north as Nyons, the evergreen oak as far as Lyons, and lavender up to and including the Pelvoux massif. The reason for the wide range of the Mediterranean climate is that elsewhere the sea is enclosed by high land; the only wide gaps are found in France. The Rhône valley gives access to northern Europe by routes which hardly rise above 1,000 ft., through the Belfort gap and the Burgundian Gate. The corridor from Languedoc is even lower (360 feet high at Naurouze) and leads towards the Atlantic. This is the only good outlet from the Mediterranean Sea; there are no such counterparts from the head of the Gulf of Genoa or the head of the Adriatic, nor along the Ebro into the Iberian peninsula. This is an important fact: as well as having a window on the Mediterranean, France possesses the best approaches to it.

Almost four thousand years ago, true civilisations had already made an appearance on these shores, complete with writing and alphabets, providing evidence of intellectual activity in the realms of literature, philosophy, religion and art far in advance of anything occurring in other parts of the world.

It was to France's advantage to look upon such a sea at this particular time. She derived the benefit of the first towns and ports, fine buildings, highways, Roman roads and, thus, many of the elements which helped shape her language, literature and philosophy. There is a good deal of truth in the claim that France was an 'extension' of Rome, whose influence was felt in many spheres.

Nevertheless, this was not the only influence: France's other windows brought equally important advantages. In the north, the English Channel and the North Sea are enclosed seas formed above the continental shelf and barely exceeding 100 fathoms. In terms of geological time they are recent, unstable extensions of the North Atlantic Ocean. Nevertheless, their influence on France is very important; from the physical point of view they allow the mild Atlantic waters to reach French shores; they have helped the development of the mild, damp climate which makes north-west Europe an unusually warm gulf. The value of this anomaly in temperature can be appreciated if it is remembered that Montreal, on the other shore of the Atlantic, lies in the same latitude as Bordeaux, and that the St Lawrence river is frozen for four months every year, whilst the Garonne has not experienced drift ice for a century and has never been completely frozen over. This thermal gulf is humid too. Such climatic conditions particularly favour the growth of vegetation. The area is one of green pasture and woodland; its flat fields and meadows are relieved by countless trees, primarily oak, beech, elm and hornbeam.

These seas provided exceptional opportunities of transport; since the Middle Ages they have attracted trade and encouraged the growth of European ports. Nowhere else in the world is there such a concentration of them: Rotterdam (Netherlands), Antwerp (Belgium), Dunkirk, Calais, Boulogne, Le Havre, Rouen, Cherbourg (France), London, Dover and Southampton (Great Britain).

The northern window has had a predominantly economic influence, whereas the Mediterranean has been of more purely cultural importance. The population density round the English Channel is exceptionally high, in fact among the highest in Europe. This great mass of people — there are nearly 100 million inhabitants on the coastal lowland of the North Sea and English Channel — earn their livelihood variously, in farming, industry and mining, and such activities have in turn fostered financial development. The fact that it faces the northern seas has thrown France into the main-stream of modern industrial and commercial life.

There remains the third and largest window: the Atlantic. For a long time it played a minor part, serving as a boundary rather than an influential zone. It was undefined and without known shores. For France, the west represented the frontier of adventure and discovery, of departures for distant 'islands', and the source of exotic produce; it was a rich fishing ground for whales, cod and seals. The ports here (Nantes, La Rochelle, Bayonne, and even Lorient) did not develop until modern times when their prosperity was sudden and rapid.

THREE SEAS: VARIETY OF COASTS. The 2,000 miles of coastline provide a great variety of scenery. There are the sandy beaches and cliffs of the Channel and North Sea, the deep groove-like rias in the ancient rocks of Brittany, the resistant headlands which project boldly into the sea from Cotentin to the estuary of the Loire, the great bay of Mont-Saint-Michel which is still invaded by the regular flood of the high tides, and the huge stretches along the shores of Vendée and Charente, no longer covered at high tide but silted up and reclaimed. Ridges of dunes extend south from the Gironde, breached fortunately at the Basin of Arcachon. In the south there is more sand, spits, lagoons, and fixed or shifting alluvial stretches which protect the shores of Languedoc and the Rhône delta. And there are the mountains reaching to the sea on both the Atlantic and Mediterranean coasts — on the Basque and Catalan shores of the Pyrenees, and the shores of the Maures, the Esterel and the Maritime Alps.

The diversity of all these coastal features is completed by islands whose outlines are sometimes barely visible above the waves. Bréhat, Batz and Sein are hardly above sea level. Ushant is the highest of these western islands (100—160 ft.); Belle-Ile and Yeu, and the northern part of Noirmoutier belong to the Breton islands, with their dark soil and characteristic shores. Southern Noirmoutier, Ré, Oléron, Aix and Madame, on the other hand, are seaward extensions of the flat outlines and clear colours of Aunis and Saintonge. Like the Mediterranean islands of Hyères, all are close to the continental shores. Corsica, the most easterly island, is over 100 miles from the shore. The large bays of this island, the gulfs of Calvi, Ajaccio and Sagone, Cap Corse, the colourful creeks of Piana, and the regular white terraces of Bonifacio, are a constant reminder of Corsica's separate origin; it is in fact a remnant of a submerged land mass.

THE CONTINENTAL LINKS.

The broadest of France's continental links is in the north-east towards Belgium, following the line of the rivers Oise, Sambre and Meuse, where the Cambrésis-Vermandois divide is scarcely noticeable. It is a traditional invasion route and the scene of many historic battles.

The second link, which is narrower, lies between the Vosges and the Jura. It corresponds with the curious gap at Belfort, called the Burgundian or Alsatian Gate, and links the two great north-south valleys of Europe, the Rhine and the Rhône, at a point where they are little more than 60 miles from the sources of Europe's greatest east-west river, the Danube. The latter opens the highway to the great continental steppe lands of the east.

The third continental link is more difficult for communications; this is the southern one to the Iberian Peninsula. The Pyrenees are considered difficult to cross, yet the two ends of this mountain range were originally inhabited by people on each side of the watershed — the Basques in the west and the Catalans in the east, and there has been continuous contact between the two regions throughout the course of history.

The effect of these high passes must not be exaggerated; a land frontier, even of high mountains, has never completely checked movement. The Alps, which are higher than the Pyrenees, offer proof of this: there was a Cisalpine Gaul even in ancient Piedmont; French is still spoken in the upper valleys of Aosta, Susa and Pinerolo on the Italian side; and even the old Italian dynasty was the House of Savoy. Continental influence on France has been almost as great as that of the sea.

CLIMATE AND VEGETATION.

There is no specifically French climate, but rather a struggle of climates. Sometimes the rain-bearing winds of Atlantic depressions invade France, at others the continental anticyclone which extends towards the Iberian peninsula, or the Mediterranean winds bringing the influences of the Sahara. In addition there are pockets of purely local climate, especially in the mountainous regions with their contrasting sunny and shady slopes, and their violent winds.

Considerable climatic changes occurred during later geological times, and the effects are still visible in the countryside. Mention is often made of the great primeval forest; in fact,

the forest cover of France is quite recent and has spread since the last Ice Age; some trees were evidently left in sheltered places and these were able to re-establish themselves. At the end of the Quaternary era, trees again took possession of the land. These advances of vegetation, which included more and more southerly species as the temperature increased, occupied different sites according to local conditions. This helps to explain the amazing variety of French woodland vegetation.

Most of France is part of this western European forest; the open spaces must have been small in area, either on the light powdery soil of the loess or on the very wet peaty soils along the coastal marshes or on the poorly drained high plateaus. The south-west and the west are most suited to the oak; the Paris Basin and the interior plateaus favour beech, while on the high peaks are the resinous trees: the fir and spruce. The Mediterranean region has kept its distinctive woodlands of evergreen oak (holm oak) and cork oak, with a dense aromatic undergrowth that merges into garrigue or maquis. Naturally there are exceptions; in the middle of the Mediterranean massif of Sainte Baume is an island of beech, preserved through the protection of the Church. In the Alps, there is a zone between the dry woodlands of the south and the damp forests of the north that is devoted to a type of pine adapted to the dry sunny mountains — the larch, which covers the region of Briançon and Haut Champsaur.

THE AGRICULTURAL LANDSCAPE AND NATURAL REGIONS.

The main changes in natural vegetation are primarily man-made. He began marking out his fields almost as the post-glacial reforestation was taking place; thus farmland and forest came into conflict. At first, the forest had its uses. Fields were occasionally cultivated on burnt out woodland and forest which provided the earliest form of fertilizer. The forest also provided secondary resources: food supplies, for example, the tunes of the Jura, hazelnuts, raspberries, bilberries, strawberries and mushrooms. Many a smallholder regarded the forest as a kind of common resource to be used without rights of ownership, as the fisherman regarded the sea. There was wood for fuel and building, branches for litter, pasturage for cattle. The fringes of large, forested mountains are frequently populated with hamlets which steadily encroach upon the woodland, as is the case around the forests of Grésinge and Perseigne. Thus, a forest with clearings has often formed the basis for agricultural colonisation.

The many variations of landscape have in large measure been due to the different ways in which trees and forests have been treated in different areas. Sometimes man has penetrated the woodland on his own, opening up his fields in the manner of the French-Canadians who made their land by felling the trees. When this was so, the population which settled there was usually dispersed; formerly, the only links were by individual or family clearings. The country is dotted with crofts and small farms of the kind known as métairies.

This was the common practice in the lands of the west, those which were most humid and best suited to tree growth, at least, deciduous trees; it is therefore paradoxical that these areas (Brittany and Vendée) are today the least wooded in France. Trees have not completely disappeared but they tend to flourish in relatively narrow strips round the fields or the estates, as enclosure. The woods have changed their composition; elm and hornbeam have prevailed over beech, but oak and ash remain in large numbers, the former providing timber for the carpenter, the latter wood for the wheelwright. Also, these trees took on a distinctive appearance; outside the high forest the branches spread out, only to be lopped off by the farmers, leaving a single trunk and small, easily removed branches — a kind of bushy stump. Treated in this way, the wooded borders offered the same advantages as the coppice of fully-grown trees; the bole was used for woodwork and the branches for fuel.

An aerial view of the cliffs at Étretat. The extensive plateau of the region of Caux in Normandy is almost level; it ends at the English Channel in high chalk cliffs. Certain more jointed, less resistant parts are eroded first by underground water, encouraging the formation of curved bays and headlands, and even huge arches; the Needle of Étretat is the pillar of a collapsed arch. A bathing resort has grown up in the small dry valley. RAY-DELVERT

Fields, meadows and woods on a plateau of northern France about 20 miles east of Rouen. The chalk plateau, today covered with limon, yield rich crops (corn and sown grasses). Once completely forested, it has been cleared in the course of centuries, and only woodlands remain on the less fertile parts, where they often form well stocked game preserves. RAY-DELVERT

The Forest of Les Landes, the largest French forest. Pines were planted in the nineteenth century between the Gironde and the Adour, on the huge stretches of infertile soil. Though they were intended only to fix the dunes and to produce some return from this region, once considered useless, the exploitation of the resin and the timber has brought real prosperity. Unfortunately, numerous hazards, such as repeated fires and invasions by crickets, have seriously jeopardised the exploitation of the pine woods and even their future. PAUL JOVET

A totally different method was followed in the east: for example, in Burgundy and Lorraine. Here the people settled in groups, felling a broad clearing around the common dwelling site, and gradually pushed back the forest. Here there was no confusion of *bocage*, but a kind of order where each feature of the countryside had a definite place; the houses were grouped into a village; the surrounding fields were divided into narrow strips but without enclosures. The forest was cut back to a point where it still covers quite large areas; it is a countryside of forests but has few scattered trees. This is the landscape called *champagne*, *campagne* or *plaine*. The boundary between *bocage* and *champagne* and their practices is difficult to determine; there was much intermixing as well as many transitional types, and in the south-west, the Mediterranean Midi, and the various mountain regions other rural landscapes prevail.

In many areas there has been more interest in growing trees than in farming; fields have made way for trees which have then become as important as crops. In the Mediterranean zone the olive occupies the place of honour, and more recently orange and lemon trees have been introduced. In Dauphiné, there are walnut trees; the whole of the Garonne basin has a type of agriculture which favours fruit-growing; Agen grows plums, peaches, apricots and grapes. In the Cévennes, lower Limousin and Corsica there are entire woods of sweet chestnuts grown for their nuts or coppiced for vine props and cooperage. The regions of the lower Loire and Anjou also have fields dotted with trees, including walnuts and pears; but it is Normandy, with its shady pastures and cider apple trees, that is the supreme fruit-growing region.

The French peasant has never been simply a pioneer; his attitude to the land, to the woods, rivers, animals, cultivated crops has been influenced by local conditions and by custom. Different methods of managing the land have produced different types of countryside, all with distinctive regional names. The names generally refer to very small areas.

The density and vitality of these *pays*, which more or less correspond to the cantons, vary according to district. There are large stretches which have preserved a certain unity but have not developed really distinctive names; and others where local names are prolific. The Paris Basin is a good example of the latter, unlike the Aquitaine Basin, where there is no local name with the ring of a Beauce, a Brie or a Gâtinais.

The small areas which gradually fashioned a way of life suited to their development often needed other areas to bring out their differences. A zone of stock-rearing by the side of a rich pasture region, wheat lands next to rye, the *pays* of the vine next to the *pays* of apples, the *pays* of the olive not far from that of the chestnut; slowly they formed themselves into complementary regional groups. A *pays* is distinctive because of its dissimilarities; variety not uniformity brought about unity.

In this fashion provinces were shaped, more often by history than geography. The province of Quercy included a small part of *ségala* with meadows, cattle and chestnut trees and part of the *causse*, or the *fromental*, with wheat, sheep, and walnuts; the province of Orléans included a district of Beauce, a stretch of the Loire valley, and a large part of Sologne.

These small units evolved earlier than the vast natural and geographical regions which came into being as a result of synthesis and research; Burgundy, Lorraine and Flanders were terms used long before the discovery of a Central Massif, a Rhône corridor, or a Paris Basin; these are new names, textbook names, the results of research in geology and geography, unrelated to the activities of the people who live there.

The population of France

The origin of the population is so diverse that, strictly speaking, there is no such thing as a French race. We have seen that France is a terminus of the continent, but not an isolated one; it is an isthmus rather than a headland, as Strabo pointed out, between the Mediterranean on one side, and the Atlantic Ocean, the English Channel and the North Sea on the other; an isthmus, serving as a bridge or a thoroughfare, which brought a continuous influx of new settlers. It is almost impossible to attempt an anthropological classification — so many and various have been the races in the Frenchman's ancestry.

THE STAGES IN THE SETTLEMENT OF FRANCE.
Settlement dates back to the first stages of early Palaeolithic man. For a very long time, certainly for thousands of years, small groups of men wandered along the river valleys without making any real technical advance. The whole of northern Europe was then uninhabited, as was most of the Mediterranean region. France, with its great river basins, was among the most settled parts of Europe at the dawn of Quaternary times. When the last glacial invasion occurred, man — in any case not very numerous in France — suffered great hardship and was threatened with extinction. He had to seek refuge in caves and concern himself with clothing and heating; however, this long, difficult period encouraged technical progress.

There followed an era when cold, steppe conditions prevailed and France became a great stretch of grassland similar to the prairies of North America. Like the prairies, it was overrun by large herds of hairy cattle or bison. Some of the limestone plateaus which contain a great many caves became the homes of the people who hunted bison, reindeer and mammoths; extraordinary drawings of animals have been discovered in the caves of Périgord and the foothills of the Pyrenees, on both sides of the Aquitaine Basin.

With the conclusion of the Quaternary era, the cold conditions came to an end. It was followed by the mild, humid climate which has resulted in the warm gulf now characteristic of north-west Europe, where the prevailing winds are from the south-west and the warm influence of the sea extends inland. Then, trees which had survived only in the more southerly, sheltered regions began to spread northwards; this is the period when the forest actually took possession of the land.

Such a fundamental climatic change had serious consequences for the fauna of the grasslands and for the men who lived there. As the forest advanced, the reindeer, bison and mammoth retreated northwards. The mammoth disappeared among the swamps of Siberia, probably not very long ago; bison are still found in some of the most remote parts of Russia and Lithuania, while reindeer are confined to Lapland. The hunters of the reindeer followed them, and their place was taken by other peoples from the south, who were used to the forest and the more humid conditions; among these people were the gatherers of snails, the hunters of the stag, and the fishermen of the rivers.

It was during this great migration that the first cultivators appeared. Cultivated crops and domestic animals were introduced from all sides; the most important seems to have been the route from the Danube lands. The new settlers established themselves in the midst of the forest and the centuries-old struggle between woodland and pasture land began. It was this struggle that resulted in the formation of the many types of countryside known as *pays*.

The era of Neolithic cultivation appears to have been a period of peace and prosperity when, judging by the extent of the clearings, the population must have increased very rapidly. Most of the sites suitable for settlement were then already occupied. It has been estimated that the population of France included some five million people at the end of the Neolithic period; it is estimated that in Palaeolithic times the population never exceeded one hundred thousand.

The size of the population remained substantially the same throughout the first thousand years of our era. The Iron Age, which followed the Neolithic, was marked in France by warlike invasions, mostly from the east, and the people were obliged to seek protection in *castella* built on the hilltops. This put an end to peaceful and prosperous agriculture. Then came the Roman conquest, followed by the long Pax Romana which saw a rapid decline in production, prevented any increase in population, and merely paved the way for new invasions.

THE DEVELOPMENT OF FRANCE.
Out of all this emerged a unified France. The scattered fragments were gathered around a new nucleus, centred on the Seine, which administered the Ile-de-France, a fairly small territory, originally extending from Senlis to Orléans, that is, from the Oise to the Loire. Consolidation was difficult. Until half-way through the Middle Ages, France looked on to the Mediterranean across the marshy coast of Languedoc; the great Mediterranean port of Louis IX was Aigues-Mortes. The Rhône formed the frontier; and groups of people who spoke the *langue d'oc* were settled on the Mediterranean shores, dreaming of their own land of Occitania. They were to become the ancestors of the peoples of Toulouse, Provence, Catalonia, and even of Majorca. The arrival in Provence of Charles of Anjou, brother of Louis IX, shattered these dreams. As for the Alps, they united voluntarily — Dauphiné, Savoy and Nice; and the frontiers advanced even further into the French-speaking valleys of Aosta, Susa and Pinerolo.

The provinces of the north and east, those nearest to the Paris nucleus, were bitterly disputed. There were attempts to include additional territories: Lotharingia, then Lorraine, Burgundy, the Low Countries and Spanish Franche-Comté. The present-day frontier is full of anomalies: the extension north to Givet, the bulge of Lille-Roubaix-Tourcoing, with the buffer states more or less neutral. The European Coal and Steel Community is perhaps as much an indication of this difficult frontier as it is the beginning of a European economic organisation.

The steady growth of French political unity was accomplished by the assimilation of different peoples with different ways of life. The people of the countryside were the first to be aware of belonging to a territorial community, the first to pay the costs of public administration, the *corvées* and *tailles*, the first to provide a militia. Not until later did the townspeople recognise their joint responsibility. Many towns long retained their extreme individuality; as *bonnes villes du Roi*, they were given privileges and often a special right or charter.

Others were slower to recognise communal responsibilities: the Breton or Basque fishermen took advantage of the common right of the sea to free themselves from all submission; and there were many forest dwellers who regarded the woodland as their traditional inheritance. Only severe regulations brought them to order, though they frequently led to rebellion and murder in doing so.

The marsh dwellers of the lower Charente and the coast of Vendée were for long regarded as beyond the law, and were neither included in the census nor taxed; the inhabitants of the Flemish marshes escaped similarly. Many mountain people lived in their remote cantons without acknowledging any central authority; the people of Vallouise preserved the old Catharian religion behind the fortifications at the entrance to their valley, and the people of the Upper Drac in the valley of Champoléon were called *Sarrasins* because of their customs. In other regions (Ariège and Périgord) miners gained a reputation for lack of discipline.

THE MIXED RACES.
The true assimilation of the peoples was brought about by natural rather than legal processes. France has an immense range of occupations and opportunities for considerable population movement. The country has always been criss-crossed by people continually on the move; inland migrations have stemmed largely from annual fluctuations in

Saint Malo, at the mouth of the Rance on the coast of Brittany. The site of Saint Malo is an ancient granite island attached to the mainland by a sand spit, which has been reinforced with a sea wall. The town, which was completely destroyed in 1944, has been rebuilt. Its ancient features have been reconstructed and the modern buildings harmonise with them. Saint Malo, with its neighbour Saint Servan, is the only important port on the north shore of Brittany for the import of coal and for cod fishing. Every year the traditional ceremony of the blessing of the Newfoundland fishing fleet takes place here; but the fleet is no longer composed of the great sailing ships of former times, but of trawlers that are mechanically equipped for fishing in distant waters. RAY DELVERT

the demand for labour. Certain products have been particularly instrumental in bringing people together; for example, the vine and wheat at harvest time. The gangs of grape-gatherers still enliven the countryside of the Midi, though the introduction of machines has almost checked the demand for extra labour for the wheat harvest; sugar-beet continues to attract the Flemish in the north. There are, too, irregular local needs for extra labour; for example, tree-felling and charcoal burning can only be done when the sap has stopped rising. The gathering of fruit and early vegetables along the Rhône valley, and the transplanting of new rice fields in the Camargue both require outside labour.

Intermarriage has tended to obscure distinct and separate racial movements. Research into the histories of families with different class backgrounds has frequently been carried out over large geographical areas, often revealing branches of the family scattered over several *départements*. On the other hand, geographical distribution of surnames shows very distinct localisations, indicating a certain stability. To this mingling of population within the national framework can be added a continuous and important influx of foreigners. Sometimes they are people with specialised trades: Italian bricklayers, Spanish or Majorcan traders in fruit and early vegetables. France has also been a haven for refugees and political exiles from numerous countries. These foreigners have seldom formed separate colonies; generally speaking, they have quickly been assimilated.

Craftsmen at Bayonne (Basses-Pyrénées) making chisteras, *used in the typical Basque game of* pelote. *Such regional games create their own industries.* FRENCH GOVERNMENT TOURIST OFFICE

Pyrenean landscape near Cauterets (Hautes-Pyrénées). Around the glacier-formed cirque stand the high peaks etched by ice, which streams and the alternate freezing and thawing are still eating away today. They make an imposing sight which attracts many tourists.

FRENCH GOVERNMENT TOURIST OFFICE

Breton costumes in Finistère. These traditional costumes are still worn in many fishing villages of Brittany.

FRENCH GOVERNMENT TOURIST OFFICE

Bagpipe players at Carnac (Finistère). Traditional or modern festivals are the opportunity for gatherings and processions. The musicians marching here are forming a band or kervenn *composed of bagpipes, large Breton pipes or* braz, *with* bombardes *(a local reed instrument) and drums.* MICHEL DE BUSSAC

A Basque house or Etche, *at Ustaritz (Basses-Pyrénées). It is a large building protected by a roof with two gentle slopes, which are covered by gutter tiles. The front of the house is the most important part, and has entrances to the various sections of the living quarters and the farm buildings. The large door leads to the combined barn and coach house. The timber work and the gallery are generally painted ochre, which gives the whole building a gay and smart look.*

A house in the northern part of the Upper Jura, to the south of Pierrefontaine, at Plaimbois-du-Miroir (Doubs). All the parts of the farm are gathered together under one huge roof. The main room, the tué, *ends in an enormous chimney where meat is preserved in the smoke. The barn occupies most of the first floor.*

The only problems concern the Italian and Polish communities in the Lorraine mining area and, recently, the North Africans.

Immigration has always been partially offset by emigration, and Frenchmen are frequently encountered far from their native land, engaged in a wide variety of trades and professions suited to their special skills and talents.

DEMOGRAPHY AND DENSITY. The constantly changing population has maintained a slow but regular increase in density. The birthrate declined perceptibly in the second half of the nineteenth century, and during the twentieth to the alarming point where births no longer equalled annual deaths. Since the Second World War, however, there has been an appreciable increase in the birthrate.

Nevertheless, France, one of the more densely populated nations of Europe at the beginning of the nineteenth century, has been outpaced by some of her neighbours — Great Britain, Germany, and — to a lesser degree — Italy.

VARIETY IN THE TYPES OF HOUSES. France is one of the most built-up nations in the world. The density of construction is among the highest anywhere in relation to the number of inhabitants and area of the country. Furthermore, it is estimated that nearly half the present-day buildings are at least one hundred years old. Such buildings were soundly built and are more often repaired than demolished.

Today, the west and the north still retain a preference for the self-contained house, as in Lille or Bayonne; even the industrial towns of the north have eschewed blocks of flats and have built instead semi-detached houses with yards and sometimes gardens. However, the towns of the east, from Strasbourg to Marseilles, have a well-established preference for blocks of flats. Paris seems to have wavered between the two alternatives, but apartment buildings have become increasingly popular.

In contrast, the individualism of the west has reached its peak in certain regions. Each dwelling is separated from the next by an alley (to prevent fire) and a narrow ditch or drain. Thus there are two main basic types into which urban dwellings can be divided.

FOOD. France's reputation in the world of food is second to none. No other country can boast so many different varieties of cheese or so extensive a list of 'specialities'.

The same variety is found in wines. France is, of course, the land of good wine as well as cheap red wine or *pinard*; the share of the latter has increased, although in average years the harvest is not sure of a market. Western France (Brittany, Normandy) is a cider-producing region, and beer is brewed in Alsace, Flanders and Lorraine.

Stone and wooden house in the Alps, at Molines-en-Queras (Hautes-Alpes). The house is built facing the sun rather than the street. Below are the living quarters, and at the back the stable where in former times men lived together with the animals in winter. The huge hayloft with its covered balcony is used for drying the crops.

Below: *An Auvergne house with barn and ramp near Mauriac (Cantal). The barn is above the cowshed; it is reached by a ramp, which the hay wagons can use. The stone gables are graduated; the huge roof is thatched. Here, the small dwelling is to the right, by the chimney, but today the house is usually in a separate building.*

The drawings on this page are by Pierre Deffontaines.

Aerial view of the Île de la Cité, the original city of Paris. In the foreground is the Pont-Neuf, the oldest bridge in Paris. It joins the two banks of the Seine, crossing the lower end of the island, today the square of the Vert-Galant. On the far side of the bridge is the Place Dauphine, with its Louis XIII houses and the Palais de Justice. Behind the latter is the Sainte-Chapelle, a jewel of gothic architecture. To the left is the Hôtel-Dieu. Then Notre-Dame, one of the finest masterpieces of the art of the Middle Ages, and indeed of all time. The scene illustrates well the geographical site and the history of Paris. LAPIE

Paris

Unlike London, which has always been the capital of England, even retaining its Roman name, Paris was not always the capital of France. At first, as Lutèce, it was a small and relatively unimportant town in Gaul. Bourges, Autun and Chartres were at the head of confederations and were able to put forward legitimate claims to leadership. The Romans established their centres alongside the Mediterranean; as movement occurred along the great European axis of the Rhine-Rhône valley, Narbonne, Arles, Vienne and Lyons were established, and Trèves became the capital. However, the Emperor Julian settled at Lutèce, mainly with the purpose of finding peace in pleasant surroundings rather than with a view to making it the chief town.

It was not until the beginning of the eleventh century that the king finally settled at Paris in his small castle. Though its fortunes have fluctuated, it has remained France's capital for a thousand years.

Since the eighteenth century, the highways have radiated from Paris like spokes from the hub of a wheel — the finest road network in France — and the arrival of railways linked her even more closely with all parts of the country.

A COMMUNICATIONS CENTRE. Paris occupies a position with many natural advantages, situated as it is in the centre of a great intersection of communications. One natural highway from the south-west to the north-east follows the line of the Oise, Sambre and Meuse towards the Rhine and Westphalia. This highway extends eastwards as far as the Russian and Asiatic plains. A second route intersects this diagonally, joining the English Channel with the Mediterranean by means of the Seine and the Rhône. This was essentially a commercial highway, pinpointed not with battlefields but with markets.

Paris, therefore, found itself at the meeting point of a number of vital strategic and commercial crossroads. Few capitals have been so vital in military history, for the city has often played its part in the country's defence. It is not the geometrical centre of France, but lies nearer the north, the more vulnerable section of the country. The buildings and plan of the city bear witness to its military function: the Arc de Triomphe, the Avenue of the Grande Armée, the Invalides, and the Grands Boulevards which have replaced earlier fortifications. Paris was the leading fortress in France.

PARIS AND THE SEINE. The Parisian merchants often traded by water, so that commerce benefited from the gentle gradient of the Seine. There are few towns where a river has played such an important part.

The bridges of Paris, too, have always had an important function. Paris was once a small bridge town, making use of the Ile de la Cité to facilitate the crossing of the earliest highway, the route from north to south, now the Rue Saint-Martin and Rue Saint-Jacques.

The Place de la Concorde, from the air. This well-known square, one of the largest and most beautiful in the world, was designed during the reign of Louis XV by Gabriel and was completed in the nineteenth century. Since 1836 the obelisk of Luxor (thirteenth century B.C.) has stood in the centre; it was given to Louis-Philippe by Mahomet-Ali. On the north side of the square are two beautiful colonnaded palaces (1760—75) which are occupied by the Hôtel Crillon and the Automobile Club to the left, and by the Admiralty to the right. Between the two palaces is the Rue Royale. At the end of this road is the Church of the Madeleine. In the distance is the highest part of Paris, the hill of Montmartre (427 feet high), dominated by the basilica of the Sacré-Coeur. LAPIE

The main commercial activity of Paris was at first concentrated on the left bank, but gradually this was transferred to the right bank, because of its more convenient communications with the economic centres in the north.

PARIS LANDSCAPE. The variety of the streams and rivers helps to lend diversity to the landscape. Assisted by the erosion of the former Seine, these streams have removed all the alluvium which once formed a monotonous landscape, rather like the regions of the Loire, where the Sologne or Brenne are still covered with poor heathland. The Ile de France has regained all the variety of its early landscape with the erosion of its former deposits.

Three attractive stretches of limestone opening fanwise join up in Paris itself: the coarse limestone from very old quarries that was used for the buildings of Paris; the limestone and millstone grit of Brie; and the limestone of Beauce.

Between the limestone regions are three layers of sand whose outcrops afford Paris an extensive area of woodland. More than 250,000 acres of forests extend around the conurbation of 5 million people. It is possible to travel more than 60 miles from Paris in the direction of Soissons without leaving the shade of the trees.

There are rich forests of beech and oak, particularly fine in the autumn. The woods even penetrate into the city itself; the Tuileries and the Champs-Elysées are not really artificial town gardens, but the sites of old forests which advanced as spurs and finally encroached right upon the heart of the city.

Fortunately, the surrounding areas have soils more directly useful than woodland soils. These are the loess-covered plateaus suitable for growing cereals. There are also some small well-exposed slopes, heating quickly in the sun, forming areas of microclimate, and encouraging the growth of vineyards and figs. Asparagus is grown at Argenteuil, haricot beans at Arpajon, strawberries at Chevreuse, cherries at Clamart, and peaches at Montreuil.

'THE CITY WHICH IS LOVED'. The Parisians have gradually discovered all these natural advantages and have organized them for common benefit. Paris was neither a natural nor inevitable capital city; but at certain critical junctures it exerted a unifying influence, as at the time of Saint Geneviève, Joan of Arc, and the battle of the Marne.

Its vital role throughout history in the political, economic, cultural and spiritual spheres helps to explain why there exists today an atmosphere so 'fruitful of ideas' as Paul Valéry has described it. Paris is a disseminator of ideas in the world of fashion, literature, drama — to mention only a few. Its influence on contemporary thinking and self-expression remains considerable.

The impetus and even the excesses of such a town can be understood. 'In every inhabitant of the world, there is a little of Paris', said Michelet, who rightly defined Paris as 'the city which is loved'.

The Place Vendôme with its column is an example of the architecture of the Louis XIV period (1687—1720). The Vendôme column (143 feet) in the centre is a copy of the Trajan Column. Built at the command of Napoleon I (1803—10), it is decorated in bas-relief made of bronze from Austrian cannon captured at Austerlitz. It is an historic square but also has commercial importance, as it houses some of the main luxury trades of Paris — fashion, tailoring and jewellery.

DENIS BRIHAT, RAPHO

Stalls of books and prints on the Seine embankment. These stalls are favourite places for browsing in Paris. A. MARTIN

Fishing in the Seine from the Ile St Louis, a typical Parisian pastime on Sunday afternoon. A. MARTIN

Aerial view of the Chateau-Gaillard, an ancient fortress overlooking the Seine near Les Andelys (Eure) RAY-DELVERT

The Old Port of Marseilles, the Lacydon of the ancient Greeks. RAY-DELVERT

FRANCE

The Arc de Triomphe in the Place de l'Étoile. P. ALMASY

The Seine from the Quai du Louvre. A. MARTIN

Boating on the great lake in the Bois de Boulogne. The Bois de Boulogne is a fine park, covering 2,154 acres to the west of Paris. Like the Bois de Vincennes to the east of Paris, it has grown on the gravel beds deposited long ago by the Seine. The beauty of the park consists in the elegant arrangement of the trees amid lawns and gardens. P. ALMASY

Part of the Place des Vosges, formerly the Place Royale. It was built in 1605 by Henry IV, on the site of the Palais des Tournelles. The houses, which have arcades at street level, all have facades in the same style — brick surrounded by white stone. Alone among Paris squares it has been preserved from the turmoil of traffic in the rest of the city. J. ROUBIER

The Place and the Arc de Triomphe du Carrousel. The latter was built between 1806 and 1808 to commemorate the victories of Napoleon I. To the right is the Pavillon de Marsan, built in 1659; it was destroyed by fire in 1871, along with the Palais des Tuileries, and afterwards rebuilt. Today it is an art museum. Behind the Carrousel lie the gardens of the Tuileries. In the distance can be seen the triumphal arch in the Place de l'Étoile. ROBERT DOISNEAU, RAPHO

Fontainebleau Palace, lying to the south of Paris. It was built for Francois I in the sixteenth century. J. ALLAN CASH

The towns of France

THE DEVELOPMENT OF FRENCH TOWNS. France has enjoyed twenty centuries of urban life. Before the days of Rome, ancient Gaul had no true cities, that is, no settlements without a means of providing for their own subsistence.

The first real towns were introduced from outside, and were located on the borders. First came Greek and then Latin colonies, whose inhabitants were by race and occupation quite different from the native peoples of the surrounding lands, in fact almost hostile; such was Massilia, the future Marseilles. In the interior of the country, the centres which already existed were military refuges, sanctuaries, or meeting places, often temporary sites, with no urban life. The conception of towns had been introduced by the Mediterranean colonists; throughout Gaul it took the form of a unit with a geometrical plan, an identical style of building and undivided houses. Even modern America has never reached such uniformity of urban growth.

By the end of the Middle Ages France had a considerable urban pattern. In fact there were almost too many towns. Some, built during the insecure feudal era, proved superfluous and even disappeared with the return of peace.

The later town dwellers provided few settlements; the sixteenth and seventeenth centuries saw fewer new foundations than earlier centuries. There were some residential towns, like those which developed around the chateaux of the Loire, or Versailles and Charleville; some were new ports facing the New World in the west (Le Havre, Lorient, Rochefort), and certain fortified places on the frontiers (Rocroi, Neuf-Brisach, Mont-Dauphin, Mont-Louis).

No further period of town development occurred until the nineteenth century. Revolutions in industry and transport resulted in a fresh growth of a new, dense type of town. First there were the colliery towns, factory towns, and mining villages. Then the railways caused the growth of a number of typical settlements connected with important junctions, and ports appeared, capable of providing the new navigational requirements of deep water and speed.

A new wave of urban development has more recently resulted from the organisation of leisure and the tourist trade: there are more than 350 resorts scattered along the 2,000 miles of French coast; there are the towns in the mountains, and the winter sports resorts in the Alps and the Pyrenees; there are long-established spas associated with health cures, and new springs which have attracted the growth of new towns. France has more than 100 spas, including those in the Massif Central, the Pyrenees, the Alps and the Vosges; finally there are the religious towns, the destination of pilgrims from all over the world: Lisieux and, above all, Lourdes, the second busiest railway station in France.

Today the urban population of France is 54 per cent of the total; though this is not as high as England's 70 per cent or Australia's 75 per cent, the population is nevertheless becoming increasingly gregarious. Paris has five million inhabitants; this is no more than a half of New York or London, but constitutes more than one-tenth of the population of France. This huge urban development has taken place in the last century.

THE SITING OF FRENCH TOWNS. It is important to recognise that it is not physical geography which has determined the situations of the towns; men chose particular sites according to their own movements and interests, which have varied enormously.

First came the requirements of defence and security. A town is a concentration of people, a centre of work and wealth; it is an obvious target for attack and must be protected. Concentration is a method of sheltering and taking refuge, and it is natural that towns should flourish in times of insecurity.

Concern over self-protection prompted the choice of sites that were easy to defend — high ground, islands (sea or river) and peninsulas. Many towns started on insular sites, for example Lille, (once spelt 'l'Isle'), Beauvais, and also Paris. Stagnant water, even more of a deterrent than running water, was often an important factor in defence. Many settlements arose in swamps and remain surrounded by marsh. Some were unusual sites, where people gathered together in places with difficult access — locations which were almost uninhabitable.

Considerations of trade have also played an important part in the determination of the sites of some French towns. Such towns preferred a place where trade was most useful and practicable, that is, where different regions converged. Often the urban centre lies near the edge of the natural region, on the perimeter rather than in the middle. Beauce, for example, has hardly any towns in the centre, but a ring of small towns encircles the boundary between the cereal country and the other regions which surround it, either pastoral, wooded or with mixed cultivation. Areas of marginal exchange are important in France, because the country has many regions with specialised activity and production.

The third factor which has helped to determine town sites is communications. Urban concentration is a centre of wealth, but wealth is of value only if it circulates. It was often the function of towns to promote circulation, and here communications played a part. Yet such towns were not necessarily sited where transport was easy; they tended to grow up in the places where the highways encountered difficulties.

Obstacles in nature are varied. First there is the the difficulty of relief; many towns lie at the foot of a mountain or a high pass. Typical foot-of-the-pass communities are Saint-Jean-Pied-de-Port at the foot of the Roncesvalles pass, and Briançon at the foot of Mont Genèvre. Other towns are located among forests, which are also natural obstacles.

The chief obstacle to road communications, however, is water. Rivers were the first highways, but quite often they present more dangers than advantages, with their threats of swamps and floods. In olden times tracks over plateaus and along ridges were preferred. In Aquitaine, for example, the *camis de la serre* is almost always older than the *camis de la ribière*.

For these old high-level routes the main obstacle was the water crossing; in the valleys the transverse routes generally developed before those along the valley. The easiest crossing places were sought, and these gave rise to ford towns like Limoges, and bridge towns like Amiens.

When it was possible to develop communications along the rivers, the town was usually built at an obstacle point or at a change in the flow of the water, a transverse valley, or a break in gradient. La Réole on the Garonne is the limit of ascent for the *barcasses* on the Gironde; similarly, Roanne is the head of navigation on the Loire.

MAJOR FRENCH TOWNS. The development of towns, both in time and space, gives an entirely inadequate picture of their complex growth in France, and of their diverse functions. There is room to give only a few examples:

Lyons, the town which should have become France's capital was the great link, firstly between the Kingdom and the Empire, at a time when the Rhône formed the frontier, and secondly and more importantly between the Mediterranean and the West. This undoubtedly avoided a division of the European continent and the formation of a 'Minor' part, paralleling the situation in Asia. Europe has not developed a 'Europe Minor' because its Mediterranean region was firmly welded to its northern part by the remarkable Rhône-Rhine corridor controlled by Lyons. The town has throughout its history been more concerned with European than with purely French affairs.

Marseilles is the only port on the Mediterranean which reaped the full benefit of its proximity to the mouth of a great river, the Rhône. The town is the chief continental gateway of the Mediterranean. Fortunately for Marseilles, the coastal currents flow westwards and bear away from the rocky shore in the east. Marseilles benefited at an early date from being the first safe inlet after the endless swamps of the Languedoc coast. Aix, which has remained the capital of Provence, is a quiet and peaceful town, a university town and a parliamentary and administrative centre.

The situation of Rouen on the English Channel is rather similar to that of Marseilles. For a long while Rouen, at the mouth of the Seine, existed quite separately from Paris, cut off by frontiers and fortified castles. The town was isolated from its mainland, like many such ports at the head of estuaries on the North Sea, and it was mainly concerned with its own trade and industry, as were London and Amsterdam.

It was steam shipping that showed the real value of the Seine and made Rouen into the port of Paris, even duplicating the activities of the outport of Le Havre. The town then managed to outstrip a number of neighbouring ports formerly almost its equal — Honfleur, Caudebec, Harfleur.

Lille, at the southern edge of the Flanders swamps, where all the traffic was borne by river in the heavy Flemish canal boats, was another town with a commanding site for navigation. It was the most southerly point reached by these ships, carrying the products of the industrial towns of Flanders: Bruges, Ghent, and Antwerp. At Lille the boats linked with the roads. This was the 'Isle des Flandres', where the change was made from waterways to roadways. All around was an exceptionally crowded working population, spread out in the countryside and employed by several small towns of textile merchants. Two of these centres, Roubaix and Tourcoing, in spite of their proximity to the Flemish capital, had courage enough to follow the example of England and start the factory system; the old rural crafts were concentrated into brand-new factories. Several large families became specialists, dominating the wool and cotton industries, especially wool carding. Today these towns are very prosperous.

Not far away are Dunkirk, Calais and Boulogne; three ports less than 60 miles apart, on an inhospitable shore but near the busiest strait in the world. To reduce competition each has succeeded in specialising in a particular field. Dunkirk is primarily industrial, and has become the third largest port for the import of goods; Calais is the leading passenger port and the railhead of many European expresses: Boulogne is the chief fishing centre and a transatlantic port.

Several French towns have recently undertaken the heavy task of restoration and planning; two world wars have tested them sorely. Repairs and rebuilding are now almost completed. It would seem, too, that the danger of severe congestion of population in the towns has been appreciated and in part countered. Modern transport methods ensure amenities to the countryside; new mobile services are supplying the most isolated districts; there are even mobile banks. It is impossible to tell whether France has yet reached the limit of her urban expansion.

Aerial view of the Château de Versailles and its surroundings. It is from the air that the formal plan of the gardens is most impressive. Only in this way can one see the whole facade, which extends for more than 1,312 feet, the small château of Louis XIII, the original nucleus now surrounded by buildings, the wings, the square building of the Grand Commun (today a military hospital), the Place d'Armes, and the Grandes and Petites Écuries. R. HENRARD, PILOTE-OPÉRATEUR

Left: Vine harvesters in Bordelais, in the Sauternes region. An unusual method of harvesting is practised, for each grape is picked individually and must have reached a certain stage of ripeness, to which the name pourriture noble *('noble decay') is given. The harvest begins at the end of September and can last up to six weeks. Right: Breton 'Bigoudens' in a fish cannery at Concarneau. Fish canning is an important seasonal industry in Brittany. The workers are mainly women. Here mackerel are being put into tins by women wearing the Bigouden cap which, like the Alsatian 'knot', has followed a fashion, and is now much higher than it used to be.* RAY DELVERT and GEIGER, RAPHO

French agriculture

Nearly 30 per cent of the French population works on the land; this is one of the highest proportions in Western Europe, exceeded only by Italy, the Iberian Peninsula, and Ireland. A country like Denmark, whose economy is considered essentially agricultural, employs only one-quarter of its working population on the land; in the Netherlands the proportion is still less.

However, with ten men for every 250 acres of cultivated land, the density of agricultural workers on the land is lower than in any other country in Europe, apart from Great Britain.

Another significant fact is the relatively restricted area of agricultural land (excluding woodland): 83 million acres, or 61 per cent of the national territory. This may be a little more than the United States with 59 per cent, or even Switzerland with 55 per cent, but it is much less than Italy (70 per cent), the Netherlands (73 per cent), and Denmark (75 per cent). Moreover, one-tenth of France is completely uncultivated. Although the general impression is of a relatively extensive type of agriculture, in fact, even allowing for recent progress, the gross produce per acre is hardly half that of Denmark, and less than a third of that obtained in the Netherlands.

SMALLER ACREAGE: MORE WHEAT. In spite of a decline of about 10 per cent compared with pre-war days, arable land still forms the greater part of the cultivated area (55 per cent). Almost half of this arable land is sown with cereals, and nearly half the cereal land is devoted to wheat, which therefore covers 10.6 million acres, compared with 12 to 13 million acres before 1940.

Wheat remains a vital part of the economy. A study of its production and yield help to delineate the effect of technical progress on productivity. In 1935—38, France's average yield was less than 12 cwt. an acre, while it exceeded 20 cwt. to the acre in Belgium, Denmark and the Netherlands. However, very rapid progress has been made in recent years — from 13 to 19 cwt. per acre, a yield that equals that of Western Germany.

Total production reached about 11 million tons in 1957; previously the peak of 10 million tons had been exceeded only in 1907, and then with an acreage half as large again. The spectacular increase seems to be largely due to the spread of more productive and disease-resistant varieties of corn. There has also been increased use of artificial fertilizers.

All the areas with high yields (more than 16 cwt. per acre) are situated north of a line from La Rochelle to Geneva, excluding Limagne, Saintonge and Lauragais; fifteen departments from Eure to the Ardennes and from Pas de Calais to Yonne form a continuous area which produces nearly half of France's corn, giving over 20 cwt. per acre. However, Brittany and the Armorican borderlands now form a second important wheat-growing area, with 15 per cent of the total production. Berry, Poitou and the Garonne Midi are also increasing in importance.

The general rise in the standard of living has naturally resulted in a decline in the consumption of bread, and France now has an exportable surplus of wheat which could easily reach two million tons a year. By supplying Europe and the French Union, France will probably play an important part in the world wheat market.

As for maize, the introduction of American hybrid varieties has brought a revolution in its cultivation; with increased yields and early growth, production is possible in the northern regions, and has already resulted in a heavy reduction in imports. Maize cultivation will probably be extended still further, for no other cereal provides such a high yield of food per acre; in Béarn the yield is 81 cwt. per acre.

Finally, rice cultivation allows some use to be made of the Camargue, which now provides about one-half of the country's home consumption needs. It is extending into lower Languedoc.

In balanced mixed farming, at least one field is reserved for 'cleaning' crops (usually roots or tubers), which require a weed-free soil with a good tilth. These are excellent for preceding cereals; maize, however, is both a cereal and a cleaning crop.

Left: *A peasant in the maquis of Corsica, going to collect hay, which he will load on to his donkey. The ancient forests of oak and pine have been stunted by felling and fire; the land has been abandoned. The main features of the landscape are now bare rock, scrub and wasteland.* Right: *The rich and extensive wheatfields of central France. France is gaining an increasingly important place in the world wheat market and already exports to many countries in Europe.* MARGO FRITERS-DRUCKER, RAPHO and FRENCH GOVERNMENT TOURIST OFFICE

Of the old textile crops, only flax remains; it is important in the agriculture of the Caux region and the Flemish plain.

FRUIT-GROWING AND MARKET-GARDENING.
Equal areas of land are devoted to vegetables, market-gardening and outdoor fruit-growing. Although only a small part (about one-thirtieth) of the agricultural area is devoted to them, their annual yield is estimated at about 11 per cent of all agricultural revenue. Vegetables are grown in alluvial valleys with a maritime climate (the Seine and its tributaries, the Loire and Garonne), the drained marshes of the Atlantic coast, and the irrigated plains of the Mediterranean Midi. There are numerous apple-growing areas, situated on sunny slopes which also suit the vine; Mediterranean areas are favoured by the early growth and the quality of both crops. The large urban centres of northern France have also stimulated the development of surrounding zones of market-gardening and fruit-growing. In this way the region around Paris provides about the same quantity as Brittany, where climatic advantage is offset by greater distances from the markets. Furthermore, production near Paris, which is stimulated by local consumption, is very varied.

The golden belt of Armorica specialises in early vegetables: potatoes, artichokes, green peas and cauliflowers; there is little fruit-growing, apart from the famous strawberries of Plougastel-Daoulas.

Compared with these two important centres, the other areas north of the Loire are insignificant. The only products worth mentioning are the market-garden crops of the Ill valley, the Mirabelle and Quetsche plums of Lorraine, the apples of Thiérache, the cauliflowers of Saint Omer, and the market-gardens of Amiens.

The Loire Valley and its neighbouring areas produce equal quantities of fruit and vegetables and fully justify the name 'Garden of France'. Anjou and Touraine provide salad crops, French beans and, above all, cauliflowers; Maine and Touraine have huge crops of pippin apples; Sologne is the most important area for asparagus; the market-gardening regions of Orléans and Nantes in particular send large supplies to the capital.

In the Aquitaine Basin traditional crops still predominate; there are the plums of Agen, the Chasselas grapes of Moissac, the peas and beans of Villeneuve-sur-Lot, and the tomatoes of Marmande. The market-gardening zone around Bordeaux provides asparagus; the Garonne valley, artichokes and onions; the Lot valley, strawberries, peaches and grapes.

In the last ten years or so there has been an important extension of fruit-growing in the Rhône valley, which now forms a huge orchard from Avignon to Lyons; peaches, apricots and cherries are the chief products. Walnuts have greatly improved in quality and there is a ready demand for the 'Grenoble walnuts' grown in the area of Saint-Marcellin.

Provence is the most important fruit and vegetable region, with a total of 650,000 tons a year, of which over half comes from the irrigated plains of the lower Durance. Around Avignon and Cavaillon there are early vegetables of all kinds: melons, spinach, tomatoes, peas, aubergines, artichokes, often giving two crops a year. On the unirrigated land, grapes are grown at Thor; fruit from the hills of Carpentras are destined for the confectionery factories of Apt. Higher upstream there are the other irrigated areas of the Durance, Pertuis (asparagus), Peyrolles and Manosques (early vegetables — tomatoes and potatoes). Still higher, around Sisteron and Laragne, apple and pear orchards now form small fertile islands in the solitudes of high Provence.

Towards the Côte d'Azur, the productive areas are split up into oases of a few hundred or at most a few thousand acres: Hyères, Solliès-Pont (cherries), Fréjus (peaches), Nice; and in Corsica there are the market-garden crops of Ajaccio and the artichokes of Bastia.

Finally, there are the valleys of Roussillon, where a Spanish type of climate produces the first of the early crops. These *huertas* are the only part of France to produce winter lettuce. They also export tomatoes and artichokes, while the well sheltered terraces provide two-thirds of the country's apricots.

In spite of the country's astonishing range of products, fruit

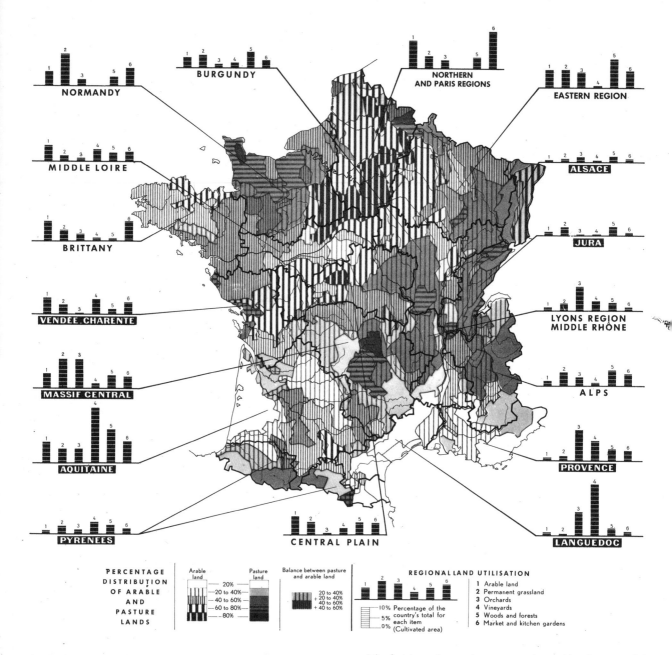

LAND UTILISATION MAP AND CHIEF AGRICULTURAL PRODUCTS OF FRANCE. *The first two columns of percentages show with reference to the map: — (1) The parts of France which are mainly arable (Paris Basin, Toulouse region in Aquitaine, etc.). (2) Where pasture is important (Normandy and some mountain areas, etc.). (3) Where neither of these two types of land use predominate (Provence, Landes in Aquitaine, etc.). The third column shows where the arable land and pasture balance, whether they cover between 20 and 40 per cent of the surface area each (in the Alps, Haute-Savoie), or whether they cover 40 to 60 per cent of the area (the region of Caux in Normandy). The arable land is usually devoted to cereals, potatoes, beet, and a variety of other crops, while pasture indicates cattle rearing with its products and allied industries (meat, milk, butter, cheese). In order to complete this picture of agricultural France, more detailed facts concerning regional land use have been added. The departments have been grouped into regions, and for each of these, the land is not merely divided into arable and pasture, but into fruit-growing, vines, woodland and market-gardening.*

and vegetables do not play as extensive a part in French economy as might be expected. In spite of the establishment of refrigerated fruit stations, old-fashioned marketing methods still prevail, to the disadvantage of both producer and consumer. Only organisation based on the experiences of the Netherlands and Germany, with agricultural exchanges, sales by sample, and good telecommunications — only these measures can abolish the distribution bottle-neck created so effectively by the Halles in Paris.

THE CRISIS OF 'VINS ORDINAIRES'. In contrast to the expansion of fruit and vegetable growing, the permanent

crisis of viticulture raises one of the most serious problems of French agriculture. Between 1871 and 1875, before phylloxera had attacked the vineyards, vines covered about 6 million acres and provided about 160 million bushels (worth at least 15 per cent of agricultural income at that time). Today the vineyard area has been reduced by more than a third, though in some recent years the crop has still reached nearly 140 million bushels; however, the value of the crop is about 8 per cent of agricultural income.

The bulk of French wine is for current consumption; only 15 per cent enjoys a name of origin. This latter category includes all the well-known wine localities: Bordeaux, Burgundy,

Champagne, Alsace, Beaujolais, Arbois. Most of these, concentrating on quality production, find that they have an expanding market with good export opportunities.

The reverse is true of wines for current consumption, which in metropolitan France often show a surplus of about 28 million bushels, or 18 per cent of the average crop. This is the result of three factors: competition from Algeria, reduced consumption, and a decline in quality that has come with larger yields. To sum up, the trends in production are quite the reverse of the trend in taste.

In order to reduce their risks, huge irrigation programmes are projected in some Mediterranean departments to allow the lowland cultivation of grapes to be replaced by intensive mixed farming similar to that adopted in Vaucluse.

The future of French viticulture will only be assured by reducing the growing area and transferring production to the hills where soils are drier and yields smaller but better.

THE GROWTH OF STOCK-REARING.
Before 1940, crops accounted for about 53 per cent af agricultural income, and livestock products for 47 per cent. Today the proportions are reversed: meat provides 28 per cent of this income, milk 21 per cent, eggs and poultry 8 per cent — in all 57 per cent. This development is related to a rise in the standard of living, as in other countries. The increase in livestock has had two important effects on agriculture: provision of good organic fertilization of the soil; better prospects for the mountainous regions which were unsuitable for arable farming.

The composition of French livestock today is quite different from that of 1935. Mechanisation has reduced the number of horses from 2.8 million to 2 million. Also the total number of sheep has fallen to 8½ million, although at the moment there is a tendency to increase, because this stock yields one of the steadiest incomes, both from meat and from ewe's milk. There are a million more pigs than before the war; cattle number 18 million (15.7 million in 1935).

It has been estimated that milk and meat production has increased by about one-third since before the war. The increase is due to improved weights and yields rather than to a rise in the number of cattle.

Technical progress is everywhere tending to reduce the number of breeds by the adoption of distinct and well-bred types instead of persisting with the innumerable crossbreeds which existed before the war. Increased selectivity in cattle breeding has been accelerated by the number of artificial insemination centres established since 1948. Artificial insemination is also being used in sheep farming. Finally, the local pigs have been replaced by the English Large White, which matures more quickly and gives a better return. Although French meat production may allow important exports in the future, dairy products are still handicapped by high production costs incurred through low yields. Hygienic conditions are often very bad (tuberculosis is common), there is insufficient modern equipment (except in the east, Lower Normandy and the Charentes), and the market is poorly organised.

Poultry farming has made marked progress since 1950; it is carried on in the traditional areas of Bresse, Gâtinais and Gascony, and on innumerable small, modern farms.

CHANGES IN FRENCH AGRICULTURE.
French agriculture is in the process of complete transformation. The years 1950—52 saw expansion and modernisation on a scale which had rarely been equalled in France, except perhaps at the end of the eighteenth century and the beginning of the Second Empire. It is estimated that agricultural production is now increasing at the rate of 4 per cent a year.

Progress in mechanisation is the most spectacular aspect of general modernisation; equally important factors directly influencing the volume of production are education in modern techniques, the equipping of agricultural industries, and the foundation of a rational marketing organisation. In particular, the traditional inadequacy of agricultural teaching is being remedied by the increase in technical courses and the establishment of winter schools, while test areas and study centres have spread modern methods of selection and fertilization into the most remote regions.

The rise in technical standards can be seen in the rapid increase in the use of artificial fertilizers, known to have a marked effect on yield. There has been a 40 per cent increase in the consumption of nitrate, phosphate and potash during the last few years. After a long period of stagnation, France is at last applying her natural aptitude and enormous resources to help remedy Europe's food deficiency, and thus contribute to the economic independence of the Continent.

The vineyards of Champagne stretch out across the sunny slopes of the chalk hills, which are often capped with woods. The vine has been grown in Champagne since the first century A.D., but it was only in the eighteenth century that Dom Pérignon discovered the method of making the wine sparkling. The stone houses clustered among the vines have an air of prosperity. COMBIER

A general view of Collioure (Pyrénées-Orientales). On the left is the old castle founded by the Knights Templar in the twelfth century and much altered by Vauban. In the centre, the old harbour, where the boats are hauled by pulleys on to the sand. On the right is the seventeenth century church, flanked by a picturesque round tower. Collioure is a fishing port (tunny, anchovy and sardine). In the background rise the foothills of the Albères, with their woods of cork oak and vineyards producing the wine of Banyules. POUGNET, RAPHO

CONVERSION OF FRENCH FORESTS. After that of Sweden and Finland the forested area of France is the largest in Europe; it covers over 27 million acres.

Since the pre-war period, the forest area has increased by over 1½ million acres under the auspices of the National Forestry Foundation, which finances reforestation of wasteland and planting of coppices with pines. On the other hand, fire has destroyed more than a million acres in the Landes. At the present time, the largest and most productive wooded areas are the limestone plateaus of the east, including the Vosges, Jura, Morvan, and the Alps.

Of the forests, 64 per cent are private, 22 per cent belong to the communes, and only 14 per cent to the State. Generally, only the last two enjoy a proper forestry system of sound exploitation and administration. Many communes in the east and in the Alps have a considerable income from their timber.

However, the composition of French woodland is not satisfactory. It includes too many broad-leaved hardwoods at a time when the trend towards the chemical rather than the mechanical use of wood favours coniferous softwoods. What is more, annual production includes up to 530 million cubic feet of firewood, more than the combined total for pulp, mines and industry, hardwood timber and softwood timber. The modern demand for wood fuel is declining (with competition from petroleum products), pitprops are being replaced by metal stays, and constructional timber is frequently being superseded by metal or concrete. At the same time the demand for wood-pulp is soaring (for paper, boxes, artificial wood, artificial textiles, plastics, cellophane, cellulose varnish, insulating panels). A conversion to pines and other soft woods is essential, especially in the forested areas of the Paris Basin, where the slump in the sales of wood for fuel has created serious problems. Significantly, the coniferous forests of the Vosges, the Jura and the Alps are an important factor in the prosperity of these regions.

UNDEVELOPED SEA RESOURCES. With 2,000 miles of coastline, France is one of the best situated European countries for sea fishing. Yet the quantity of fish landed is just over 520,000 tons, a total exceeded by Norway, Britain, Western Germany, and Spain, where considerable strides have been made during the last twenty years. Furthermore, when it is realised that even Portugal produces 390,000 tons, and Denmark and the Netherlands 340,000 tons each, it is evident that consumption is low and consequently production is relatively undeveloped in France.

With the size of the catch remaining more or less stable, and with the need for an improvement in productivity, the number of fishermen is continually dwindling. The size of the fishing fleet is less than before the war, though the value of the catch has risen.

Two-thirds of the fish handled by the trade is sold as fresh fish, the main types being the herring (which is also tinned in various forms), sardines (very irregular production), tunny (production could be doubled — there are many more potential markets for fresh or canned tunny), mackerel and whiting (fillets are in good demand).

Fishing for cod (especially from Fécamp and Bordeaux) provides one-eighth of the tonnage landed; one-third of this is exported to Brazil, Portugal and elsewhere. The shell-fish catch cannot be increased because the grounds are already over-fished; but shell-fish culture is expanding, in spite of the primitive methods often used. The chief districts are Cancale, Port des Barques, Marennes-Oléron, and Arcachon (for oysters); the bay of Aiguillon provides two-thirds of French mussels.

Sixteen fishing ports secure about 90 per cent of the catch (in weight). They are, in order of importance: Boulogne-sur-Mer, the best equipped of all; Lorient, now the chief Breton port; Concarneau, specialising in tunny fishing, La Rochelle, Dieppe and Douarnenez. Then come the ports of Saint-Jean-de-Luz, Guilvinec, Les Sables-d'Olonne, Quiberon, Cherbourg, Saint Guénolé, Calais, Port-en-Bessin, Arcachon and Fécamp. The Mediterranean accounts for only 3 per cent of all fresh fish caught.

Fishing is closely linked with the canning industry, which employs 23,000 in 2,500 canneries. Amalgamation is obviously necessary to reduce the costs of production, and probably two-thirds of the existing canneries should be closed.

The three indispensable conditions for the expansion of sea fishing are modernisation, more refrigeration, and reorganisation of the system of distribution.

The problem of power

When coal was the only source of industrial power, roughly during the period 1830—1920, France was considered an impoverished country, incapable of rivalling the other great economic powers. Around 1900, the French coal output of 33.4 million tons only amounted to 0.8 ton per head; at the same period it exceeded 5.2 tons in the United Kingdom, 3.4 tons in Belgium, 3.1 tons in the United States, and 2.2 tons in Germany. This was at the end of the Victorian era, during which England was the predominant industrial power, exporting large quantities of coal and ensuring economic domination over whole continents.

During the first half of the twentieth century there was a second industrial revolution as important as the first. In the face of competition from new sources of energy hydro-electric power, petroleum, natural gas coal has suffered a fairly rapid decline. Now nuclear power is adding to the competition. It would not be over-bold to envisage the eventual disappearance of coal as a source of power.

In this respect the power statistics of the United States are particularly significant. Between 1929 and 1954, the consumption of coal fell by 25 per cent, while industrial production increased by 110 per cent; solid fuel provided two-thirds of all energy in 1929, whereas today it provides less than one-third. On the other hand, the proportion of hydrocarbons rose from 21.5 per cent to 37 per cent, and that of natural gas from 9 per cent to 27 per cent.

In France, where technical progress is less advanced and where the national resources of petroleum are still small, the change has not been so rapid. Coal still constitutes nearly 70 per cent of the power used (92 per cent in 1929). Production (55 to 60 million tons) still leaves a considerable deficiency to be remedied by expensive American imports.

Oyster-breeding near Marennes (Charente-Maritime). The oysters are bred here according to old methods which date from the seventeenth century. They are placed in clear pools ('claires') like a honeycomb, where the famous marennes de claire *(flat oysters), and* portugaises de claire *(Portuguese oysters) are produced by the million every year.* RAY-DELVERT

REGIONAL COAL PROBLEMS. Before the war the Nord and Pas-de-Calais coalfield was the most important, and supplied nearly two-thirds of the French output. Today it supplies 53 per cent, and its prospects are declining with the increase of low-grade coal and because structural conditions are often difficult. The deep pits in the western part of the field (the Béthune area) are being steadily abandoned. In Pas-de-Calais the shortage of young men entering the industry is creating a serious problem. To overcome the difficulties, large central electrical generating stations have been built which can use the low-grade coal, and attempts are being made to attract other industries to the mining areas (for example, the chemical works at Mazingarbe, and the glass-works at Wingles). In the area of Valenciennes, where there is more manufacturing and where the coal measures are more accessible, the prospects seem reasonably bright.

Whilst the old coalfield of the Nord is being forced to stabilise production, Lorraine, which before the war was the poor relation, has been expanding since 1946. Reserves here are much greater, exceeding 5,000 million tons, or four centuries' supply used at the present rate. The seams are shallower and less disturbed, and since the war, processes have been evolved to produce coke from Lorraine *flambant* for the nearby blast-furnaces, and gas for piping to Paris by the East grid; at the same time by-products are recovered which provide raw materials for the chemical industry. Thus the Lorraine coalfield, where the yield exceeds that of the Ruhr, gives a very favourable return; it now produces twice as much as before the war, and nearly as much as the neighbouring Saar. The whole mining area of Forbach-Faulquemont-Carling has now been transformed with modern buildings and well-planned housing estates. The population has risen here by 30 per cent in twenty years.

The great expansion in Lorraine is quite unlike the rest of the French coal industry. In Burgundy, the Blanzy field is rapidly being exhausted; within twenty years it will probably have stopped working altogether. The Saint-Etienne field is better off because of the demand from industry close by, but it has had to reduce its labour force. The small fields of Auvergne are threatened. The Cévennes field of Alès and Graissessac produces such poor coal that it is hardly salable in face of competition from fuel oil. Carmaux and Decazeville, in Aquitaine, produce a good coal which is sometimes cokable, but the conditions for working the secondary seam are not promising, and there is a risk of unemployment. In the Alps, the small seam at La Mure is almost the sole producer of French anthracite, whilst in Provence, at Gardanne, and to a lesser extent in the Landes, lignite with a low calorific value is produced.

The total classified reserves of France amount to 10 or 11 thousand million tons, of which about half is in Lorraine. To this should be added a seam of coking coal recently discovered in the Jura, near Lons-le-Saunier, and the vast but little-known anthracite field from Tarentaise to Briançonnais. The Jura area will perhaps replace the coal supplies of Blanzy within five or ten years. The Tarentaise-Briançonnais appears to be easy to develop; at the moment some small mines extract a few tens of thousands of tons from close to the surface. Within reach of Turin, it could be of interest to the industry of Piedmont, particularly if it proves able to supply the latter with thermal electricity. Nevertheless, this coal which has raised hopes for half a century, today offers only limited prospects of local interest. This is the beginning of an era when coal will be used primarily as a raw material for the chemical industry, mined only where it is most readily accessible.

DEVELOPMENT OF HYDRO-ELECTRIC POWER. The first competitor of coal was hydro-electric power. It was in 1882 that Aristide Bergès installed the first head of water (1,640 feet) to produce electricity at Lancey, near Grenoble, at a time when industrial dynamos were being introduced.

However, electrical equipment did not really develop until 1897 with the introduction of the alternator and transformer. Progress was especially marked in the Alps because of local industrial activity. In the Pyrenees, in 1910, the power station at Orlu broke the world record with a head of water of 3,068 feet; this supplied the first electricity at 55,000 volts and allowed power to be transmitted more than 60 miles. In the same area, in 1921, the Compagnie du Midi started the first large-scale railway electrification.

Between the two wars, many large dams and power stations were completed; this was the beginning of the planned development of potential water power. In the Alps and the Pyrenees the heads of water are often very high with an uncontrolled flow; they supply industry and, to a lesser degree, the railways. In the Massif Central, on the other hand, because of its relief and geographical position, dams have been built to store and control the flow, and provide valuable power to the national grid. The first of these large dams was built at Eguzon on the Creuse. Then the Tarn (Le Pinet) was tackled, the Dordogne (Marèges), and lastly the Truyère where the Sarrans Brommat station was then the most important in France with 985 million kWh out of a total of 10 thousand million kWh of hydro-electricity produced in 1938.

Even so, the pace of construction had clearly become inadequate in the years immediately preceding the war. In 1945 the shortage of electricity was alarming, and it was not possible to foresee that eight years later there would be an insistent demand for thermal stations to utilise a coal surplus.

After 1947, an unprecedented programme of hydro-electric installation was undertaken within the framework of the Monnet plan. Many schemes were started, and eight years later the average annual output of hydro-electricity had already risen to 28 thousand million kWh. The production of thermal electricity, which was 8.7 thousand million kWh in 1938, reached 21.8 thousand million after the building of new power stations, often including units of 100,000 kW. In this way total production of electricity was raised by 1955 to 46.6 thousand million kWh, having doubled since 1946 (doubling of consumption every ten years is considered normal). By 1958 production had risen to 61.8 thousand million kWh.

The French hydro-electric power potential has recently been estimated; it totals 92 thousand million kWh for an average year, if falls below a certain size are excluded. If the small falls which are only just beginning to profit from technical progress are included, this potential is something like 100 thousand million kWh a year. This is the highest in Europe after Scandinavia; present installed capacity is about 30 per cent, so that scope for expansion is appreciably greater than in Italy or Switzerland.

Almost half of this potential is south of the line La Rochelle-Strasbourg, while most French industry is north of it. This situation involves heavy costs for distant transmission, and raises the cost of the power; it is one of the factors favouring industrial expansion towards the south.

The most northerly of the reserves of hydro-electric power is the river Rhine between Basle and Strasbourg. The flow of the river, which is diverted in the Alsace canal, should produce 6.5 thousand million kWh in seven power stations. The first three are those of Kembs, Ottmarsheim and Fessenheim.

The potential of the Central Massif is estimated at 21 thousand million kWh, of which 6.8 thousand millions are at present installed. The most important schemes of the last few years are the 'water staircase' on the Dordogne (Bort, 365 million kWh; the Aigle, 520 million kWh; the Chastang 540 million kWh), then the Couesque dam on the Truyère, and the complex scheme at Pouget, and finally the diversion of the upper Loire to the Rhône (with an underground power-house at Montpezat producing 325 million kWh). The constructions in the Central Massif have formed about thirty artificial lakes since 1925, some very beautiful and often of considerable size (Vassivière,

A coal mine in Lorraine. Typical landscape of a mining area, with slag heaps and numerous surface installations for the sorting and dispatch of the coal, or for the various processes that it may undergo. In the distance, the miners' houses, separated from the pit by a stretch of cultivated land but still bathed in an atmosphere of black dust and smoke.

CHARBONNAGES DE FRANCE

A view from the air of the Parentis oilfield (Landes). In 1954 oil gushed for the first time at Parentis, and since then several productive wells have been bored. The oilfield is mainly situated under the lake, at an average depth of 6,500 feet. The derricks — one can be seen here — are signs that drilling is in progress; these are later replaced by a control gear which is less obtrusive. The Landes has become an important petroleum region, and Parentis is already integrated into a huge industrial group. RAY-DELVERT

The dam at Montpezat, in the Massif Central where the Upper Loire is directed towards the Rhône. It serves an underground hydro-electric power station producing 325 million kWh. Hydro-electricity now provides 10 per cent of the total energy used in France.

FRENCH EMBASSY

Bort, Pareloup), which give these areas an additional tourist attraction. The dams themselves are often noteworthy for their fine architecture; Aigle and Chastang are particularly impressive.

The potential of the Pyrenees and the upper Garonne amounts to 11,600 million kWh. Already 4,350 million of this are produced. The main power stations are those of Aston on the Ariège (320), and Pragnières (the full development of the Néouvielle massif will yield 353 million kWh).

It is the Rhône Basin which contains the greater part of the classified potential. It can be divided into the following areas:

1. The Jura (Ain and Doubs) which could yield 1,850 million kWh, of which 580 million are already produced.

2. The Arve and the rivers of Haute-Savoie; 920 million kWh installed out of the potential of 3,220 million.

3. The Isère valley, noted for its large resources (16,600 million kWh, 6,770 million installed) and the high position of its large reservoirs. The first of these, at Tignes, was completed recently (at a height of 5,870 feet, capacity 8,120 million cubic feet); the two power stations at Brévières and Malgovert generate more than a thousand million kWh). The second reservoir is that of Roselend; two others, Champagny and Mont-Cenis, are under consideration. Meanwhile, the 'water staircase' on the Drac and installations on the lower Isère have been completed.

4. The Rhône itself (capacity 15,050 million kWh, 4,210 million installed). Since the war two of the largest hydro-electric stations in Europe have been constructed here; one is the well-known dam at Génissiat below Bellegarde (height 233 feet, capacity 1,690 million kWh), the other is the diversion and lock of Donzère-Mondragon where the Rhône enters Provence (a project with a capacity of 2 thousand million kWh per annum); above Donzère is the power station of Montélimar (capacity 1,670 million kWh).

5. The Durance, which should no longer be considered as a tributary of the Rhône, since diversion towards the Etang de Berre restored it to its ancient course. This diversion will produce at least 2,300 million kWh in five power stations, and will also allow modernisation and extension of the irrigated lands of the lower Durance. Flow will be controlled by a large earth dam at Serre-Ponçon (387 feet high) to the south of Gap; this will create a reservoir as large as Lake Annecy.

The basins of the Durance and Var have the lowest proportion of developed water power in relation to capacity, for though they have a potential of 15,520 million kWh, they generate only one-third (2,230 million kWh) of the output of the Isère basin. This wealth of power in south-east France again emphasises the difference between the present location of industry and the natural resources.

This last point will no doubt be modified by the building of the first tidal generator at Rance (640 million kWh). It seems, in fact, that the utilisation of tidal power will be expensive, and probably the scheme will be abandoned if nuclear power stations are able to provide western France with a cheaper source of power.

On a national scale, hydro-electricity now provides 10 per cent of all power consumed, against 6 per cent in 1929. This is a much higher proportion than in the United States, where it is 5 per cent, but much lower than Italy with 44 per cent.

DISCOVERIES OF PETROLEUM AND NATURAL GAS. If hydro-electric power has risen, there has been an even more significant increase in the use of petroleum products. In 1929 their proportion of total power, 3.3 per cent, was almost negligible. By 1937 it had doubled, and in 1954 it was five times the 1929 figure.

National production of petroleum was once virtually non-existent. But France's geographical position very soon provided it with an important refining industry; the estuaries of the Atlantic and the mouth of the Rhône corridor were very

suitable sites for importing crude oil and distributing refined products. The refineries, now extended and modernised, and the adjoining petroleum-chemical factories, have become huge works employing about 50,000 people.

Until 1950 French consumption was entirely dependent on overseas imports, apart from the insignificant oil field at Péchelbronn. A programme of systematic research was undertaken and in 1950 petroleum was found at Lacq, near Orthez. Another, more important field was discovered near the edge of the Etang de Parentis in the Landes. A survey is now proceeding in all areas of potential oil-bearing sedimentary rocks. The experience of other European countries in this respect is quite encouraging, for Western Germany now produces over 4 million tons of petroleum and the Netherlands over 1 million tons annually.

It is possible that drilling may reveal another valuable petroleum product: natural gas (methane). Natural gas deposits in the Po valley now yield more than 105 thousand million cubic feet, the equivalent of 4 million tons of coal.

French resources of natural gas are limited to the small field of Saint-Marcet (Haute-Garonne) discovered in 1942, which produces only 8,750 million cubic feet because of the limited reserves.

In 1954 there was the even more important discovery, below the oilfield of Lacq at a depth of 11,500 feet, of an extensive deposit of sulphurous gas most probably greater than 10 billion (million million) cubic feet. It is forecast that within a few years sulphur production will equal that of Italy, and that appreciable amounts will be exported.

NUCLEAR POWER. Coal, which is already threatened by the increased consumption of petroleum products, runs the risk of being completely eliminated from the power market when the atom has taken its place in the industrial world.

Uranium, the present raw material used in nuclear power production, is found in crystalline rocks. France is very well provided with these, and uranium deposits are already being worked in Limousin, the hills of Madeleine, the Morvan, and the *bocage* region of Vendée. The first atomic power stations have been built on the banks of the Rhône at Marcoule, and at the confluence of the Loire and Vienne. As far as is known, the cost of production per kilowatt-hour by atomic power should be comparable with that of a modern thermal station. Furthermore, the transport of the raw material does not influence the cost of production, for a pound of uranium will produce as much electricity as 500 tons of coal.

Well favoured geologically, France has at its disposal a wide and varied range of power resources. Water-power has been harnessed in different parts of the country; petroleum, natural gas and even solar energy are being tapped in the south-west; nuclear power based on the uranium of the old mountain masses will eventually equal and then replace the coal from the north. Power resources and consequently the scope of future industrial development are practically unlimited.

The basic industries

Basic industries are those which supply the processing industries with raw material or with semi-finished goods for further manufacture. They have a common characteristic: their locations are determined by mineral resources or availability of power. They can be divided into three main groups: iron and steel, non-ferrous metals, and heavy chemicals.

RESTORATION OF THE IRON INDUSTRY. Before 1890 France did not seem to have great potential as a steel producer. The iron industry was dispersed, it used low-grade ores, and it was still dominated by the traditional iron masters. With only 700,000 tons a year France's production seemed unimportant compared with the industrial areas of Britain (5.3 million tons in 1890).

After the Thomas process had been perfected, the situation took on a totally different aspect. The *minette* ores of Lorraine, then divided between France and Germany, became usable. They formed the largest iron ore deposit of the Continent. It is on this that present-day production of iron and steel is based.

The iron-bearing deposits of Lorraine are found in the Jurassic rocks; they include seven beds of iron ore, the main one being 24 ft. thick. Mining concessions cover some 320,000 acres, and stretch from north to south for about 60 miles, from the Belgian-Luxembourg frontier to south of Nancy. The mines are mainly concentrated in the area of Briey, which has the largest reserves of calcareous iron ore (self-fluxing); siliceous iron ore is less desirable because lime has to be added on smelting.

The *minette* ore has a low iron content (30 to 35 per cent) while Swedish ore often exceeds 50 per cent. This characteristic, although economically undesirable, has favoured local development of the industry; the production of one ton of steel requires 3 tons of iron ore and 1.4 tons of coal, so that it is obviously more advantageous to erect the blast-furnaces on the iron field and to bring the coal to it.

Lorraine mines annually about 40 million tons of iron ore, with a daily output per miner of 6.7 tons. This high rate enables France to export large quantities. Reserves are estimated at six thousand million tons, sufficient for about a century and a half, but the calcareous iron ore will be exhausted much sooner, and it is likely that a few decades may see a movement of mining activity towards the ore-field in the west.

This has considerable potential reserves, at least two thousand million tons, and an iron content of 45 to 53 per cent; and the geographical situation allows the ore to be distributed either by land or sea. The present mines are in Anjou, in Orne and, in particular, south of Caen.

Finally, the small Pyrenean field (the Canigou and Puymorens mines) has managed to keep going in spite of its remote position, because it produces very good high-grade hematite. However, the annual extraction rate does not exceed 300,000 tons.

The 120 French blast-furnaces use only 55 to 60 per cent of the national production of iron ore, the remainder being exported to the Saar, Belgium and Luxembourg. They produce more than 12 million tons of pig-iron, four-fifths of which is converted into steel. The steel works use an equal quantity of scrap-iron as raw material, this being equivalent to the richest possible iron ore, so it is to the advantage of the iron and steel industry to be surrounded by secondary industries which can provide it with scrap; in this respect the Lorraine field is not so advantageously placed as the Ruhr.

Nevertheless, the Lorraine iron and steel industry is fortunate in the local iron ore deposits and in the production of metallurgical coke from the Moselle coal. This explains why two-thirds of French steel is produced here: at Neuves-Maisons, Pompey, Homécourt-Joeuf, Hagondange, Hayange and Longwy. Within the framework of the Monnet plan, a continuous strip mill similar to those in America has been erected near Thionville. Altogether, the iron and steel industry employs about 80,000 workers.

Founded on the coalfield, the mills of the north make crude steel and some semi-finished goods, sheet metal in particular. Denain has a continuous hot strip mill, and at Montataire (Oise) there is a cold rolling mill. The other iron centres of the north are Valenciennes-Anzin and the Sambre valley (Maubeuge area).

Less important is the group of Mondeville-Caen; Basse-Indre and Hennebont manufacture tinplate. The reorganised mills of Saint-Etienne offset the disadvantage of their position by producing elaborately finished goods.

Two other groups of works are of particular interest. The first makes pig-iron, and this is supplied especially to foundries

The power station at Carling, in Lorraine, with the associated chemical works in the foreground. In the background are the four 260-feet cooling towers. This power station depends on coal from Lorraine, where production is increasing rapidly; this development has completely changed the face of the Carling area within the last few years.
CHARBONNAGES DE FRANCE

for further processing; it includes, besides six works in Lorraine, individual works on the coast or near local deposits: the Dunes (Nord), Isbergues and Outreau (Pas-de-Calais), Rouen (Seine-Maritime), Givors-Chasse (Rhône), Fumel (Lot-et-Garonne), Tarascon-sur-Ariège (Ariège) and Le Boucau (Basses-Pyrenees). The second group manufactures steel in electric furnaces (7 per cent of total production as compared with 5 per cent in 1938), which are often constructed in mountainous areas rich in hydro-electric power: Ugine-Moûtiers (Savoie), Allevard-Le Cheylas (Isère), Ancizes (Puy-de-Dôme), Saint-Chély-d'Apcher (Lozère), Pamiers (Ariège) and Imphy (Nièvre).

The iron and steel industry of France, apart from the huge production in the Lorraine region, includes a large number of works specialising in high quality metallurgy. Yet, in spite of a considerable attempt at modernisation and expansion which has more than doubled steel production since 1938, the industry remains appreciably smaller than that of its competitors, Britain and Germany. This backwardness is primarily due to the reduced growth of processing industries.

THE LEADING EUROPEAN PRODUCER OF ALUMINIUM.

Even though metropolitan France is the richest country in the world for iron ore in proportion to its area, it is one of the poorest in non-ferrous minerals. The sole exception, fortunately an important one, is bauxite, the aluminium ore. Bauxite is a red clay containing 50 to 70 per cent aluminium. First it is calcined to give alumina (1 ton of lignite and 174 lb of soda required for 1 ton of alumina). In the second stage, the production of aluminium needs per ton of metal: 2 tons of alumina, 1,100 lb of carbon for the electrodes, and 18,000 to 20,000 kWh. So the cost of the metal depends primarily on the cost of the electricity. This explains why electrolytic works are nearly always built in the main hydro-electricity producing area, far from the urban centres where electricity is required for other purposes.

Aluminium, the light metal of the second industrial revolution, is subject to a continually increasing demand. During the years 1934—58, world production grew from 160,000 to 3,530,000 tons, and it has more than doubled during the last ten years. With this startling increase France has kept her place as principal European producer, due to her wealth of hydro-electric power and her rich supplies of bauxite. Concentrated in the Midi around Brignoles (Var) and Bédarieux (Hérault), the bauxite fields have doubled their output compared with the pre-war period. The alumina works are situated near Marseilles,

The Shell-St Gobain chemical works at Berre. Petroleum derivatives have made the chemical industry very important in France. FRENCH EMBASSY

for they make use of Provençal lignite. The alumina is then taken by special trucks to the Alpine factories of the valley of the Maurienne, Rioupeyroux, L'Argentière and, to a lesser extent, the Pyrenees (Auzat, Beyrède). The most important and most modern works is at Saint-Jean-de-Maurienne. National production has increased nearly three times since 1938. Subsequent extensions, however, may take place in Africa, where hydro-electric power can be produced more cheaply.

Apart from special metals produced in very small quantities, the other non-ferrous metals, lead, zinc, tin and gold, have experienced a much more modest expansion.

BUILDING MATERIALS. Only one mineral product has been used in building up to now: asbestos; the development of its use in the form asbestos-cement is constant. France is not completely dependent on Canada and the other great world producers; since 1949 the development of the Corsican deposit of Canari has provided one-third of internal consumption.

The post-war resumption of building has also encouraged a marked expansion of quarry products. Modern techniques and the large building constructions have particularly favoured cement. World production has more than trebled since 1938 and that of France has more than doubled.

FRANCE IN THE CHEMICAL AGE. The great rise of plastics, chlorine products, and fertilizers has brought this complex industry into the limelight with a wide range of raw materials and a very rapid rate of growth. Between 1938 and 1958, French industrial production generally increased by nearly 70 per cent but the chemical industries in particular expanded production by 91 per cent. They now employ 200,000 workers. Chemical fertilizers have benefited from the recent expansion of agriculture. The production of synthetic nitrate, centred mainly on the north-east coalfield and at Toulouse, is two-and-a-half times as great it was in 1938. The phosphatic fertilizers have followed a different pattern as a result of the production of superphosphates; these are obtained from the phosphates of North Africa and the pyrites of Lyons which give sulphuric acid, or from basic slag, a by-product of the iron industry. Production from phosphates and pyrites is expensive because it is dispersed, and it has increased only slightly. On the other hand, basic slag is in strong demand by agriculture, and has grown by more than a half since before the war.

The Alsatian potash mines, modernised since 1945, have more than doubled their output, which now almost equals that of Germany. The deposit is situated north-west of Mulhouse, where model towns for the workers have been built in the forest itself (total population 36,000).

Farmers are demanding more and more mixed fertilizers containing nitrate, phosphate and potash, and these are made in a large number of factories.

France will be able to develop the vital manufacture of sulphuric acid from her sulphur deposits at Lacq. She is also well endowed for other manufactures which are expanding, largely due to her extensive salt resources. Most of the sodium chloride comes from the great deposit in Lorraine; Franche-Comté also has important saline deposits; and finally there is the salt from the Mediterranean shore, which provides one-third of total requirements.

From salt, limestone and carbon, sodium products are obtained — caustic soda and carbonate of soda; production is concentrated in Lorraine and in the Jura.

From salt, too, chlorine can be obtained by electrolysis; this basic product is perhaps the most important in modern chemistry. There is hardly any section of industry which does not require chlorine or its derivatives for some purpose. And it is from chlorine that polyvinyl chloride is obtained, nowadays the most commonly required plastic. This explains why the American production of chlorine increased by five times between 1937 and 1955; in France it has trebled. The centres of production of this key industry are in the Alps, or near the salt deposits. As chlorine is not easy to transport, there is some advantage in producing its many derivatives with it. At Saint-Auban (Basses-Alpes) it is produced with calcium carbide, an electro-chemical product giving acetylene and thus arising out of the manufacture of vinyl resins.

Electro-chemistry also provides silicon carbide, artificial corundum, phosphorus and its derivatives, electrodes, etc. With electro-metallurgy it forms the group of electrical industries linked to hydro-electric power which has brought economic growth to the Pyrenean and Alpine valleys.

While electricity has thus become a raw material as well as a source of power, coal remains the basis of a fully expanding organic chemistry. Concentrated in the northern coalfield and the Lyons area, with an extension into Lorraine, this industry produces in particular methanol, and in the field of plastics, nylon and polystyrene. Coal also plays a vital part in the dye-stuffs industry, which has, however, advanced little since 1938.

Some aspects of electro-chemistry and carbo-chemistry are in active competition with a fairly recent industry, that of petroleum chemicals. Of recent growth in France around the refineries (Etang de Berre and Seine Maritime), it now manufactures detergents, and will soon produce synthetic rubber, and will also find a vast outlet in plastics.

Mention should be made of synthetic textiles, usually obtained from cellulose or, more recently, from castor oil. Basic pharmaceutical products are also produced. Both these sections are particularly concentrated in the Lyons region.

Closely linked with chemicals is the glass industry, a large coal consumer and particularly concentrated in the north-east and Saint-Etienne areas. Its growth has been very satisfactory, for production has more than doubled since 1938.

PAPER AND PULP. One of the latest basic industries is the production of wood pulp, which is the raw material for some artificial textiles and plastics. France can now supply her own requirements of paper and cardboard, but still remains dependent on Scandinavian wood and wood pulp imports. An attempt has been made to develop national resources, and production of pulp has doubled since 1938. The factories have been extended; they are situated in particular in the valley of the Seine, the north-east, the Alps, the Landes and the Vosges. Large new factories have been built on the Seine (Alizay), the Rhône (Tarascon), and the Garonne (Saint Gaudens).

Secondary or processing industries

While the basic industries, including mining, employ less than 500,000 workers, the processing industries employ over 4 million. Fairly well dispersed apart from an excessive concentration in the Paris area, they have as a common characteristic almost complete geographical freedom. Power and transport usually add only slightly to production costs; rather more influential is the relative skill of the labour force employed.

On the whole, the processing industries are expanding, but technical progress and social development cause very important differences in rate of growth. To be more precise, the engineering, electrical, plastics, and certain food industries, and the manufacture of chemical derivatives (including pharmaceutical and beauty products), are developing faster than average. The old-established textiles, the leather industry and mechanical wood-working are gradually declining.

STAGNATION OF THE TEXTILE INDUSTRY. Around 1930, textiles employed 920,000 people; in 1936, after the depression, man-power had fallen to 700,000; now it is even lower. Production, however, has increased with the rise in productivity. This industry, which ushered in the nineteenth century Industrial Revolution, still creates serious employment problems in the old exporting countries, such as France and England, for today their markets are restricted by the industrialisation of the under-developed countries, their former customers. Demand has also switched towards lighter goods, and this has reduced the amount to be processed. The chief textile area is the north-east, with about 150,000 workers; here the factories are more concentrated than elsewhere. Roubaix is one of the leading wool centres of the world; the centres of Lille and Tourcoing specialise in cotton, and Armentières in linen, with the traditional retting in the waters of the Lys.

At the other extremity of France is the region of Castres, which has become the second wool centre. Its development can be explained by the proximity of Mazamet, an important region for the production of wool from sheepskins. Also in the south-west the small community of Lavelanet in Ariège is showing considerable growth. To complete the woollen areas of France the following isolated centres should be mentioned: Vienne, Cours (Rhône), Sedan and Elbeuf.

A loom at a silk factory in Lyons, the centre of the long-established French silk industry. FRENCH EMBASSY

In the cotton industry, the Vosges region has become most important since the industrialists of Mulhouse invaded the western slopes after 1871. Spinning and weaving employ more than 60,000 people. It is a valley-type industry, highly dispersed and often producing its own power hydraulically. This area often suffers from partial unemployment, because it is exclusively a textile area; attempts are being made to attract alternative industries.

The situation is not much brighter in the cotton manufacturing area of Normandy, which employs about 15,000 in the tributary valleys of the Seine. At Cholet the famous handkerchief mills have been superseded by engineering.

The silk industry, although made up of dispersed factories, is found in the region of Lyons. This town is also the centre for synthetic fibres, so that today both industries closely overlap. In this way the silk mills of the Ardèche and Dauphiné have found a new prosperity in processing nylon. The hosiery of Aube, strongly concentrated at Troyes, has been able to keep its labour force at about 25,000 through complete modernisation; the Cévennes form another important hosiery centre.

LEATHER INDUSTRIES. Leather is meeting strong competition from plastics for most of its traditional uses except footwear. At the moment only 240,000 people are employed in the treatment of hides and skins; 145,000 of these are in the boot and shoe industry.

Fortunately, the basic industries of hides and skins, tanning, tawing and furriery, are widespread and rarely form the chief occupation of a region. Glove-making, however, is distinctly localised: Millau has superseded Grenoble, Saint-Junien (Haute-Vienne), Chaumont and Niort. Footwear has also given rise to regional specialisation, as in the countryside around Cholet, the region of Hasparren (Basses-Pyrénées) and Mauléon, and the centre of Romans (Isère). There are active areas, such as Fougères and Limoges, but there are others which are suffering a crisis.

EXPANSION OF THE MECHANICAL AND ELECTRICAL INDUSTRIES. This huge sector of metal-working now employs more than 1,370,000 people. Production has doubled since 1938, and there is hardly a part of France where it is not represented.

Assembly line of 'Frégates' at the Renault factory outside Paris.
FRENCH EMBASSY

Some of the manufactures are directly connected with the building trade; for example, the cast-iron foundries produce heating and sanitary fittings. These employ about 50,000 people, of whom more than 10,000 are in the Ardennes where ironworking is a local specialisation. The rural area of Vimeu (Somme) is devoted to the locksmith's trade.

Agricultural equipment is another expanding section, at least for tractors and power-driven cultivators. This industry was virtually non-existent fifteen years ago; today its largest factories are at Le Mans (State-controlled Renault), Saint-Dizier, Marquette-lez-Lille, and Vierzon. Other equipment (ploughs, sowing and threshing machines) is usually made by medium-sized firms scattered all over France.

The greater part of the labour force of the mechanical engineering section is probably employed, directly or indirectly, in the manufacture of transport equipment. There are four branches: the manufacture of railway equipment, aircraft, motor-cars, and cycles (including motor-cycles). The first is not easily distinguished from general engineering. The chief builders of carriages and coaches are in the north. As for aircraft construction, it is almost completely nationalised, and the State is almost the only customer. The manufacture of piston and jet engines is concentrated in the Paris conurbation and at Bordes, near Pau. The construction of air-frames is much more widespread: Toulouse has become a large aircraft centre with more than 8,000 employees; other factories have developed in the Pyrenean region, near Nantes, at Bourges and Marignane.

The labour force directly engaged in motor-car manufacture now exceeds 130,000; but this figure should be at least doubled if account is taken of sub-contracting. Production in quantity of vehicles is almost five times the pre-war figure and, as concentration has reduced the number of firms, this comes almost wholly from a few concerns. The factories are for the most part in the Paris area, but there is a tendency to decentralisation; for example, Renault is expanding at Le Mans and now near Rouen; Citroën has works at Rennes and Strasbourg; Peugeot has grown at Sochaux (Doubs), and Berliet, in the Vénissieux suburb of Lyons. Moreover, the sub-contractors and accessory manufacturers are widely dispersed.

In contrast, cycle and motor-cycle manufacture is almost entirely provincial. However, since 1950, the industry has undergone a complete change in which the ordinary bicycle has lost ground to two new-comers, the auto-cycle and the scooter. Saint-Etienne, the main centre of cycle manufacture, was slow to adapt itself, and has consequently declined in importance. The chief manufacturing centres today are Courbevoie, Saint Quentin, Beaulieu (Doubs), and Vichy for auto-cycles; Fourchambault, Dijon and Troyes for scooters.

Electrical engineering, with 200,000 employees, has more than doubled its pre-war output, expanding with the consumption of electric power. The two main centres are the Paris area and the Alpine regions. However, other large factories have grown up at Belfort and Champagne-sur-Seine, where the new electric locomotives of the S.N.C.F. are built. In the Pyrenees, Tarbes and Bazet manufacture electro-technical porcelain.

The manufacture of domestic electrical appliances has benefited from a rapidly increasing demand, even greater than for electrical machinery. A policy of decentralisation has made Rheims one of the leading centres of this industry, manufacturing vacuum cleaners, washing machines and refrigerators.

The development of telecommunication and television has also given great stimulus to the electronics industry, which is no longer entirely confined to the Paris area.

Finally, the electrical engineering industries include two sections noted for the precision of their products and the skill of their labour force. The first is the manufacture of all types of cutlery in the traditional areas of Nogent-en-Bassigny and Thiers; then there are important factories producing razors and

THE WORLD

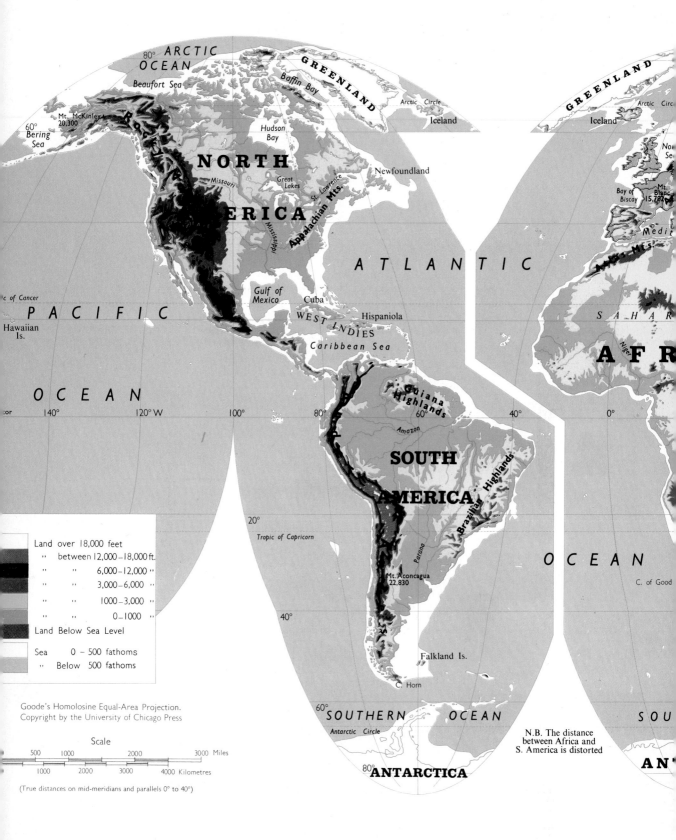

ARCTIC OCEAN

80°

GREENLAND

Beaufort Sea

Baffin Bay

Arctic Circle

Iceland

GREENLAND

Iceland

Arctic Circ

60°
Bering
Sea

Mt. McKinley
20,300

Rocky

Hudson
Bay

Great
Lakes

Newfoundland

Missouri

St. Lawrence

Appalachian Mts.

NORTH

ERICA

ATLANTIC

Bay of
Biscay

Mt.
Blanc
15,782

No
Se

Med

Mts.

Mississippi

c of Cancer

PACIFIC

Gulf of
Mexico

Cuba

Hispaniola

SAHAR

AFR

Hawaiian
Is.

WEST INDIES

Caribbean Sea

Niger

OCEAN

140°

120° W

100°

80°

Guiana
Highlands

60°

40°

0°

:or

Amazon

SOUTH

AMERICA

Brazilian Highlands

OCEAN

C. of Good

20°

Tropic of Capricorn

Parana

Mt. Aconcagua
22,830

40°

Falkland Is.

C. Horn

60°

SOUTHERN OCEAN

SOU

Antarctic Circle

N.B. The distance
between Africa and
S. America is distorted

80° ANTARCTICA

AN

Land over 18,000 feet
 "   between 12,000–18,000 ft.
 "   "   6,000–12,000 "
 "   "   3,000–6,000   "
 "   "   1000–3,000   "
 "   "   0–1000   "
Land Below Sea Level

Sea   0 – 500 fathoms
 "   Below 500 fathoms

Goode's Homolosine Equal-Area Projection.
Copyright by the University of Chicago Press

Scale

500   1000   2000   3000 Miles

1000   2000   3000   4000 Kilometres

(True distances on mid-meridians and parallels 0° to 40°)

Physical Features

The electric locomotive B.B.-9004 which broke the world rail speed record on a section between Bordeaux and Dax in 1955, exceeding a speed of 205 m.p.h. S.N.C.F.

razor-blades, the most modern one having been built recently at Annecy.

Watchmaking and precision engineering are definitely localised, as at Besançon in the Doubs valley, Haute-Savoie etc. The Arve valley, around the National Watchmaking School of Cluses, has recently become of prime importance in screw-cutting because of the ingenuity displayed by the innumerable small enterprises and family workshops. The increase in motor-cars and motor-cycles (requiring meters, clocks, precision-cut screws etc.) has brought direct benefits to watchmaking and precision engineering.

THE EXPANSION OF THE RUBBER INDUSTRY.
The growth of private motoring has encouraged the rubber industry to expand its production rapidly.

The main rubber firm, Michelin, has branched out from Clermont-Ferrand and built medium-sized factories near Orléans, Bourges and Troyes. Other tyre factories are at Montluçon, Montargis, Compiègne.

TOWARDS THE DISPERSION OF INDUSTRY.
This general survey makes it possible to note the effects of the 'neo-technical' industrial revolution, based no longer on coal and steam power, but on electricity, petroleum and, looking ahead, on nuclear power. The increased applications of electrical equipment, telecommunications and road transport controls the future development of the processing industries. It also explains how industries which require little heavy transport may very often be divided into average to small-sized units, provided that these units are specialised and able to undertake mass production.

These principles, postulated in 1925 by Henry Ford, are even more generally applicable today. Today two tendencies may be observed: one towards financial integration, with or without merging companies; the other towards specialisation and regional dispersal of the manufacturing units. Dispersal is assisted by the technical conditions of transport and power, and by new and rapid methods of vocational training. For example, it is very significant that the 'robot' installed in the first remote-controlled locomotive was made in a small factory of 40 employees in the Provence village of Lamanon (population 670), where no previous industrial tradition existed. So one can foresee an expansion of industrial activity throughout France, an expansion which is vital for the well-being of agriculture itself.

Transport and travel

The means of transport have multiplied enormously since the beginning of the twentieth century. To the railway and ship have been added the motor-car, motor-cycle, aeroplane and helicopter; the heavy service lorry for goods, and the pipeline for petroleum and other liquids.

However, the spread of electricity, the increasingly complex manufacture of raw materials, and the widespread search for lightweight products such as aluminium and plastics have resulted in a decline of heavy goods, and of coal in particular. Between 1930 and 1955, the total tonnage of heavy goods carried by rail and inland waterways in France decreased while industrial production was increasing.

The first apparent general trend is that the internal transport of goods by rail or water has increased little if at all, while expansion of private car travel has checked the growth of public passenger transport. In contrast, air transport has encouraged a rapid growth in foreign travel, and transport of goods by sea has continued to increase.

DECLINE OF TONNAGE AT THE PORTS. The statistical increase in tonnage loaded and unloaded at French ports is deceptive, being due entirely to petroleum products; other types of trade have sharply declined. The transport of crude oil and its by-products from refinery to tanker requires only a minimum of man-power.

In this respect, the picture is not so bright. In twenty-five years the total tonnage of entries and departures has fallen from 106 million to 85 million. The ports now handle no more than 55 to 60 per cent of external French trade instead of the pre-war 65 per cent.

With the end of imports from Britain and with the competition from oil bunkering, the coal trade has suffered a complete collapse in all ports. At Rouen, which was the chief port of the coal trade not long ago, the decline is already 80 per cent, while at Marseilles coal has practically disappeared from the wharves.

Trade in other products has declined appreciably, particularly imports: oils with the decline in soap manufacture; sulphur and pyrites with the decline of superphosphates and vine-growing in the south; cereals with the increase in home production; also wines and liqueurs. The last two groups show that a decline in sea-trade is often caused by an improvement in the national economy. The interests of the ports and the country generally do not necessarily coincide.

The present prosperity of the ports varies considerably according to whether they specialise in passenger traffic or goods, and whether or not they include refineries. The passenger ports are suffering more and more from air competition; while a certain degree of concentration has benefited Calais, Le Havre and Marseilles.

On the other hand, the ports serving the great refineries handle 84 per cent of all imports today instead of 76 per cent as in 1938. First comes Marseilles, with its subsidiaries Port-Saint-Louis and the new petrol port of Lavéra, which have superseded Genoa. In second place is Le Havre; third is Rouen, declining compared with pre-war years; fourth is Dunkirk, which is expanding; fifth Bordeaux with subsidiaries; sixth Nantes, with the subsidiary of Donges-Saint-Nazaire; seventh and last is Sète, which supplies the refinery of Frontignan. The other ports have only a restricted trade in spite of their very good harbours: La Pallice, Brest and Toulon have too scanty a hinterland to prosper, and the last two are only naval ports.

Shipbuilding is the main activity of some ports. Saint-Nazaire, whose trade is negligible, continues to exist because it has the largest shipyards in France; La Ciotat is in a similar position. The merchant navy of France had a tonnage of

Rouen (Seine-Maritime), the port of Paris. The town grew up at first on a slightly elevated part of the right bank, free from flooding. Now it extends all over the nearby slopes, and on to the left bank at Sotteville. In the old quarter of the town, the cathedral of Notre-Dame stands out. A city noted for its beauty, Rouen is equally important as an industrial town, and is surrounded by several other busy centres; above all it is a port. The part of the docks below Rouen which can be seen here has very modern equipment for handling both types of traffic, river and marine, which makes Rouen the port of Paris and one of the chief ports of France.

FRENCH GOVERNMENT TOURIST OFFICE

3,210,000 in 1934; it had fallen to 2,280,000 in 1947. Partly as a result of generous state assistance it now has a tonnage of over 4 million, about 4 per cent of the world total.

AIR FRANCE. Compared with the relative stagnation of maritime activity, the rise of air transport is astonishing. The French nationalised company possesses the most extensive network in the world, due to its African services.

Of the three or four large civil airports in metropolitan France, by far the most important is that of Paris-Orly; then come Marseilles-Marignane and Nice-le-Var, which are linked to Paris by internal routes.

The main air traffic is with Great Britain, Algeria and Morocco, then Switzerland and the United States. Sabena of Belgium also runs a Brussels-Paris helicopter service.

THE RAILWAYS. The railways secure the greater proportion of goods and passenger traffic (notably, 60 per cent of holiday travel). Therefore a modern railway system is vital for the growth of the national economy.

Rail transport has been revolutionised since 1920, with the replacement of steam traction by electric traction or diesel.

The French railway network was conceived under Louis Philippe as a political measure intended to secure relations between the capital and the Prefectures. The railway map of 1860 shows that most of the 5,880 miles of lines of the times radiated from Paris; cross-country routes were almost non-existent. By 1880 the mileage reached 14,750; then the Freycinet plan undertook the building of secondary lines, and by 1935 the length of line was 26,625 miles. It was evident that many of these secondary lines serving the economically poorer parts would not pay, and that road transport was competing seriously with rail over short distances. Between 1937 and the end of 1957, 7,688 miles were closed to passengers, and since the S.N.C.F. (Société Nationale des Chemins de Fer) was formed in 1937, 1,938 miles of line have been closed as obsolete. A few other closures have reduced the length of the normal rail to 24,300 miles. The rail density is therefore appreciably less than that of Germany or England.

The fact that total mileage has contracted only slightly has been due to intensive modernisation. Annual coal consumption was reduced by about 7 million tons during the 1929—57 period. For the same period, however, electricity consumption increased by some 1,800 million kWh and petroleum products rose from nothing to more than 35 million cubic feet. Steam power itself has undergone a number of improvements, for in spite of the large reduction of coal used it still carried more than 54 per cent of total traffic in 1957.

Between 1944 and 1957, another 1,400 miles of line were electrified. A revolutionary technique employing industrial current of 25,000 volts has reduced the cost of fixed equipment by half and allowed the speeding up of the electrification and equipping of lines carrying moderate traffic. First tried out on the Aix-les-Bains to Annecy-Annemasse route in Savoy, it has been applied to the Lille-Basle and Paris-Nord main lines, which carry the heaviest goods traffic on the S.N.C.F. There is also a continuous electric line between Paris and Rome.

Finally, the reorganisation of marshalling yards and depots resulted in outstanding installations (Villeneuve-Saint-George — the largest in Europe — Juvisy, and Gevrey-Chambertin).

La Rochelle (Charente-Maritime), an important fishing port, seen from the air. As an old fortified town, La Rochelle was surrounded by ramparts. Two large towers still guard the entrance to the harbour, which shelters part of the fishing fleet; this is dry at low tide because of the tidal range of the Atlantic Ocean. For larger vessels, wet docks have been constructed. La Rochelle is the busiest French fishing port south of the Loire. Beyond the town is the flat countryside of Aunis, with its crops of cereals, vines and early vegetables. RAY-DELVERT

FRANCE

Goods traffic has also benefited from many improvements, particularly the closer co-operation between road and rail. The most intensively used lines are Paris-Orléans, Valenciennes-Thionville, Paris-Metz, Paris-Nord, Paris-Lyons-Rhône valley. Productivity of the labour force and equipment have considerably increased, for both manpower and rolling-stock have declined in number since 1938, while in the same period the volume of traffic has risen.

THE NAVIGABLE WATERWAYS. Inland water transport, mainly of building materials, coal and petroleum, is almost entirely north of a Paris-to-Basle line. Beyond the plain of Flanders and the Seine-Marne-Rhine area, the relief of France is not suitable for the establishment of modern waterways. The link between Lille and Dunkirk for barges of up to 1,350 tons is an easy construction; but technical and economic studies on the Canal du Nord (Douai-Noyon) have shown that it would be far more profitable to electrify the railway between Paris and Lille.

All things considered, the only new waterway which is really profitable is the Alsace canal, which by means of locks combined with hydro-electric power stations allows Rhine navigation to reach Basle. Elsewhere it is advisable to concentrate on modernising the existing waterways.

The western motorway: dense traffic heading for Paris at the end of a Sunday afternoon. Access to the great conurbations is an acute problem everywhere. New motorways have been planned in the Paris area to ease the congestion and to 'canalise' the constantly increasing flood of vehicles. PIERRE BELZEAUX, RAPHO

In the interests of efficiency, 2,600 miles of small waterways with negligible traffic could well be abandoned, including the canals of Berry and Orléans; even the Midi canal carries a ridiculously small amount of traffic.

THE ROADS. While rail and waterway specialise in transporting relatively heavy goods, and cannot look for any serious increase in traffic, road transport shows increasing activity and is still unrivalled for the carriage of most types of goods over short and medium distances.

This development is largely due to the existence of an excellent road network, consisting of 50,000 miles of main highway, 165,000 miles of secondary road, and 235,000 miles of by-road (now usually surfaced). On the main routes by-passes avoid constricted urban areas, sharp bends are being straightened, and changes in level are avoided. These improvements have made it unnecessary to build motorways as in Germany and Holland. Only a few have been constructed and length for length the cost has been three times as high as double track railway line, which can handle a greater volume of traffic.

The revival of the roads has been more marked because of the continued increase of the important tourist trade. The rise in the standard of living has brought widespread travel during the last few years — organised journeys by train and motor-coach, private travel by car, motor-bicycle, scooter, and so on.

The extension and change in the character of travelling has had very important economic effects. When dominated by rail routes, tourist activity was closely restricted to the resorts so served — to the Côte d'Azur and large seaside resorts or spas. Today the tourist goes wherever he wishes and takes prosperity to the most remote areas.

Development here has been aided by the improvement or construction of roads giving access to the most beautiful parts of the French countryside: for example, the Alpine road from Evian to Nice, the *Corniche sublime* of the Verdon gorges, the coastal road of the Maures and Esterel, the route round the Corsican creeks, the Pyrenean road, the roads through the gorges of the Tarn and Vercors, and along the crests of the Vosges.

The poorer parts, like the southern part of the Central Massif, the infertile Alps, and central Brittany today enjoy a noticeable degree of prosperity; and Corsica is on the way to becoming a second Côte d'Azur. The tourist trade has already become the chief industry of the Alpes-Maritimes and of Var, and is very important in Savoy and the Basque regions, and even in the 'week-end zones' like the Loire Valley.

Altogether, France has over 4 million foreign tourists every year. They come mainly from North America, Britain, Belgium, Germany, Switzerland and the Netherlands.

In the same way, the internal tourist trade has continued to grow, and accommodation in parts such as the Alps or Corsica and regions of the Central Massif has been improved and greatly expanded in the last few years. In view of the national and local importance of the tourist trade and its continuous growth, modernisation of tourist facilities must be continued.

It is often said of France that it is an old land with an ancient civilisation, and this may imply that it is an exhausted country. It has wealth which is being expended; its coal deposits have not a very long life, while half its buildings are more than a hundred years old.

Nevertheless, the country possesses unexpected assets. Its agriculture has many natural advantages in spite of outmoded ideas; it possesses the most varied hydro-electric installations, which have allowed it to utilise unusual conditions. Its shores, particularly along the English Channel, provide the opportunity to develop tidal power, while huge deposits of natural gas and petroleum are just being discovered in the south-west, the very part which until now has been the least active. Raw materials for nuclear power are more abundant here than anywhere else in Europe. A redistribution of industry and population is occurring; the dominance of the north, the east and Paris is likely to be reduced in favour of the west, the south-west and, in particular, the south-east. The *bon pays* will have higher labour densities, especially the Rhône valley which is nearing completion of its development and which also provides France with the great land gateway to the Mediterranean. In communications France has the finest and fastest railway system; competition from the road and from the air has only acted as a stimulus. There is a traditionally high regard for the individual. Social changes continue to improve the laws and rights of all citizens, and there is ample opportunity for them to make the most of their talents. Resolute in purpose and bold in vision, France is still a progressive land.

Pierre DEFFONTAINES and Jean-François GRAVIER

The Tagus at Lisbon. Lisbon is situated on the coast of what is almost an inland sea, formed by the broadening of the Tagus estuary.
STUDIO LIMOT, RAPHO

PORTUGAL

PORTUGAL is one of the oldest countries in Europe and has preserved approximately the same frontiers since the thirteenth century. The original nucleus of this political structure was a small principality whose Christian population, driven back by the Moslems, afterwards set out along the coast to reconquer the south. At that time, Portugal could be distinguished from neighbouring principalities by its language, which had developed from the original Romanic language and was distinct from the Castilian tongue. Like the Castilians, the Portuguese became settled at a very early date, but their boundaries did not exactly coincide with those of their states, so that beyond the conventional frontier of the Minho, in the north of Portugal, Galicia (attached to Castile) spoke a Lusitanian dialect still surviving in country districts.

Although the Portuguese and Castilian peoples share certain traits of character and temperament (for instance, absence of racial prejudice and easy adaptation to diverse climates), there are important differences. Whilst the Castilian readily bridles at any affront to his dignity, for which he is ready to sacrifice himself and others, the Portuguese is more easy-going, more melancholy, and more tolerant of weakness.

Portugal preceded Spain in pioneering the great voyages of discovery which, at the dawn of the Renaissance, gave Europe temporary mastery of the world. After a century of great commercial activity, Portugal, by then part of Spain, shared its decline, especially rapid during the seventeenth century. The efforts of an enlightened minister, Pombal, did not prevent Portugal from remaining on the fringe of the great agrarian and industrial revolution in north-west Europe.

The reasons for this economic decline are not clear, but it is to this rather than to physical conditions that Portugal owes its present position as a small state with too large a population and too low a standard of living, depending for its resources upon a traditional agricultural system and, to a lesser extent, on fishing.

PHYSICAL DIFFERENCES. To understand fully the conditions of the life of the peasant and the fisherman, reference must be made to the fundamental difference in the physical features of northern Portugal (Minho) and southern Portugal (Alentejo), and then to the direction of the Reconquest, which took place from north to south, from an area with a high pressure of population.

The north is mountainous country. Parts of the plateau have been raised to 6,500 feet (the Serra da Estrela), though the main mass does not exceed 3,250 feet. Towards the coast the plateau is broken up into a great number of ridges, blocks, and wide-mouthed valleys like that of the Minho. Cultivated land is scarce, and is found especially in the enlarged valleys of the granite areas — excluding the schistose slopes where the soil is thin and infertile — and in the coastal region and certain interior basins like that of Viseu. Arable land is more extensive on the plateaus, but here severe winter conditions at such altitude limit the possibilities of cultivation. The only large area of lowland, the coastal triangle with the lagoon of Aveiro at its centre, is covered with sand and planted with the maritime pine. The whole of northern Portugal has the advantage of abundant rainfall and a short summer drought.

In contrast, southern Portugal is composed of huge plateaus between 300 feet and 1,000 feet high, where the winters are very mild, as in Alentejo. Here, however, the summer drought becomes serious and lasts from May to October, prohibiting continuous cultivation of everything except trees. The regions of the north-west, with mild winters and abundant rainfall, have a relief which is too rugged to provide extensive areas of soil. Again, the possibility of agriculture on the high plateaus

PORTUGAL

of the north-east is limited by the severity of the winter and by the beginning of the summer drought; drought is also the chief disadvantage in the low plateau lands of the south. The most favoured regions lie in the intermediate zone, especially the Tagus lowland, the Ribatejo, where there are large areas of cultivable soils and the climate is relatively humid. Here the mildness of the winter allows two consecutive harvests.

THE OVER-POPULATED NORTH.
The restricted granitic basins of the north-west have had the doubtful privilege of supporting the densest population. In Minho, the rural density

of population exceeds 500 per sq. mile though barely half the land is cultivable. It is only by tremendous human effort that so many people can be provided for. Intensive mixed farming is carried on, but the methods are old-fashioned and there is a lack of capital (chemical fertilizers are rarely used, for example). Tiny fields are surrounded by fruit trees or by climbing vines which yield a wine that is light and sharp. During the winter most of the land is sown with grass. Carefully irrigated by water from small springs or from wells dug in the sand, this yields four or five cuttings of hay. In spring, ploughs drawn by six or seven pairs of oxen break up the meadow lands which are sown with maize, the staple food. In spite of the relatively humid summer it is necessary to irrigate maize as it is sown late.

On the high eastern plateaus of Trás-os-Montes or Beira Alta, cold winters prevent continuous cultivation, and the range of products is much more restricted. The people live in large villages amid a misty countryside where rye alternates with fallow, and where potatoes, introduced relatively recently, can be grown only in the damp lowlands.

In contrast, the narrow incised valleys, the chief of which is the Douro, experience a dry, scorching summer, especially where the rock is schistose. This produces the concentration of sugar in the grapes of this famous vine-growing region. Viticulture here has required enormous effort on the part of the peasant. The steep slopes have been fashioned into a gigantic staircase of terraces which are covered with artificial soil carried there in baskets. Wine is made in the cellars of Oporto (Porto), and most of it is exported to Britain.

Industry in the north-west (Minho) is dispersed in a great number of small workshops, most of which are devoted to the manufacture of cloth or metal goods fashioned mainly by craftsmen. Industry does not provide sufficient opportunities for this over-populated countryside, and emigration is a necessity. Between 1880 and 1940, over a million people emigrated from the north-west, chiefly to Brazil, but the movement began as early as the sixteenth century.

The surplus population also moves naturally to the plains and the low plateaus of central and southern Portugal, where people from Minho introduced the practice of irrigation. However, irrigation still plays a relatively unimportant part, although summer drought makes it much more necessary here than in the north.

THE SETTLEMENT OF THE SOUTHERN PLATEAUS.
The physical features and economy of the southern part of the country in Alentejo differ radically from those of the north. The land is divided into huge estates, employing labour from the large villages, either tenant farmers who rent an area of land, generally for a year, or ordinary agricultural workers hired by the day. Wheat, oats and fallow alternate regularly, the last-named helping to feed great flocks of sheep. The ploughed land often lies between trees, evergreen oaks and cork oaks in particular. Portugal is the world's leading producer of cork. On the huge schistose peneplain, where the thin soil is sometimes too dry and sometimes too wet, wheat does not grow too well. Such agricultural activities are not enough to ensure regular employment for the skilled and semi-skilled workers of the villages, who are in competition with bands of temporary migrants from the north.

Conditions improve, however, where the rocks of the peneplain are less sandy, near Beja for example, or where they are covered with sediments of chalky marl in the Elvas region, and especially on the great plain of Ribatejo which is situated in a transitional position and has been strongly influenced by the northern system of mixed farming. This is particularly marked on the right bank of the Tagus, where the largest olive groves of Portugal are found. Olives provide an essential part of the nation's food, and are also exported to South America. The chalky marl and alluvial soils are

School for fishermen at Lisbon. P. ALMASY

Wolfram mines at Minas Cervas, in Trás-os-Montes (northern Portugal). ROSS MADDEN, RAPHO

Gutting sardines before drying them in the sun at Nazaré, a fishing village a few miles north of Lisbon. Mackerel, too, are treated in this way, then salted and packed in barrels. PAUL POPPER

A view of the centre of Oporto. The second town of Portugal rises like an amphitheatre above the right bank of the Douro, on two granite hills. In the foreground, barrels of port wine await shipment. P. ALMASY

A watering place in northern Portugal. The population is very dense in this part of the country, where intensive mixed farming is practised. Tiny fields are surrounded by fruit trees. P. ALMASY

The Square of Commerce in Lisbon, one of the finest squares in Europe, was built by the Marquis of Pombal, after the earthquake of 1755. In the centre is the equestrian statue of Dom José I. P. ALMASY

suitable for wheat, and the land is no longer left fallow. The low part of the plain, still within reach of the tides, is partially converted to rice plantations. Rice production entails considerable capital outlay, and the product plays an increasingly important part in the food supply of the townspeople: for example, in the lower Sado valley and in the region of Santarem. It appears, however, that the land is not yet being put to its full use. There are too many pastures in the Sado and especially the Tagus valley, which should be drained or irrigated instead of given over to bull raising. These rivers are no longer incised in the peneplains but flow on a level with the land, and during the summer a sufficiently large supply of water still flows, especially in the Tagus. This is the only part of Portugal where planning and improved equipment might lead to an important increase in agricultural production.

In the southern extremity of the country only Algarve has escaped the influences of Minho. Its limestone hills and tiny coastal plains, where snow and frost are unknown, are devoted to intensive mixed farming, derived from Kabylo-Arab methods of agriculture. Tiny fields have been carefully cleared of their stones, as is shown by enclosing walls sometimes a yard thick. On the red soils trees of all kinds are grown, producing almonds, figs (an important part of the food supply of the country), and carobs or locust beans which feed the enormous number of donkeys used as pack animals. On the small alluvial plains chain-pumps irrigate early vegetables which find their way to the Lisbon market.

Above left: Intensive cultivation on terraced vineyards at Cibio. These vines produce the best port wine.   Left: The Cabril hydro-electric dam. The development of Portuguese industries has long been held back for lack of fuel resources, but with the construction of hydro-electric stations the cotton industry, in particular, has doubled its output in the last 20 years. PORTUGUESE STATE OFFICE

The Dom Afonso Henriques Avenue in Lisbon. At the end is the Institute of Advanced Technology. This avenue is the centre of a new district built since 1940. The houses, with their walls painted in pink or green and with flowers on the balconies, have a fresh appearance. VIOLLET

A peasant family in the province of Estremadura eating their frugal meal. The floor of their dwelling is rough earth, and they wear no shoes.
P. ALMASY, CAMERA PRESS

The market by the Abbey Church of Batalha. The victors in the country's fight for independence from Castile built the church as a national memorial (14th—15th century). STUDIO LIMOT, RAPHO

A young shepherd standing in front of his roughly constructed stone hut. Shepherds in the hills behind Lisbon often wear this type of straw coat for protection against rain and cold. SEQUIERA, CAMERA PRESS

THE ROLE OF THE SEA. Fishing is an important part of Portugal's economy. It is estimated that about a hundred thousand people earn their living by fishing. Fish is a more important item of food than meat, especially among the poorer people of the towns, who consume large quantities of sardines. When salted, these are taken up to the mountain villages by the women. Cod, too, forms a large part of the average diet, but four-fifths of it comes from foreign fishermen. Sardine canning at Matosinhos and tunny at Portimão is a flourishing export industry. Mechanisation of the fleet is still incomplete (60 per cent of the total tonnage), and its methods and equipment are outdated.

Although the hinterland is mountainous, the northern coast is low, and except in modernised centres like Matosinhos, the fisherman lives like the peasant. He does not even move to the centre or the south to the specialist ports (Nazaré, Sesimbra, Setúbal and Olhão, etc.). He is part of a caste, isolated from the rest of the population.

The attraction of the sea is shown also in the situation of the large urban centres, which are all ports. The port of the north, Oporto or Porto (285,000 pop.), is an example of 'urban condensation in a region of over-population'. This medieval city, which originated where the coastal route from the south could cross the deep valley of the Douro, had very early trade relations with Flanders. Its industrial activities are varied; wines, fishing boats and textiles are produced but, like the rest of the Minho region, they are dispersed in small workshops. An outport has had to be constructed at Leixões because there is a bar in the Douro estuary.

Lisbon is much more favourably situated, on the edge of an inland sea formed by the broadening of the Tagus estuary. Its commercial importance has grown since the Moslem period, when the wild outskirts were only just beginning to be cultivated. But its national and international pre-eminence dates from the centuries when it became the capital of a colonial empire and an entrepôt for rare merchandise from the Indies. In spite of the loss of this function and the ruin of the political and economic system upon which it was based, Lisbon today has a population of 790,000, nearly one-tenth of the total. It is an international port of call for sea and air passengers, although the increasing range of modern aircraft is tending to limit its importance. It receives the bulk of the country's foreign and colonial imports, particularly heavy goods. Lisbon is also the chief industrial centre of Portugal; Barreiro, the suburb across the Tagus, has shipyards for naval construction, chemical works, jute mills, and soap and candle factories. There is, however, no comparison between Lisbon and the great industrial cities of north-west Europe.

A considerable proportion of the citizens contribute little or nothing to the economy: civil servants, small investors, and a great number of people who live by small trades. These have been drawn to the town by the attraction of a regular income, which they can no longer find in the countryside.

OVER-POPULATION AND INDUSTRIALISATION.
Portugal is undoubtedly over-populated in relation to its existing resources. Cereal production is insufficient and has to be supplemented by imports. Although manufactured goods form only a small part of family purchases, many are bought abroad rather than produced locally. The chief problem, then, is to develop industry. As the country's coal resources are poor (400,000 tons from San Pedro da Cova), and its iron resources (at Moncorvo) difficult to mine, the advisability of establishing heavy industry is doubtful. Since 1927 the government has been chiefly concerned with the development of light industry. A fine network of communications has been built, and a start has been made with the construction of great hydro-electric power stations on the northern rivers with their irregular gradients and fairly regular and abundant flow: for example, Castelo de Bode on the Zêzere, and Rabagão. The production of electricity has doubled in the last ten years, but the power installed still represents only about one-tenth of the potential reserve. The industries which have chiefly benefited from this source of power are those engaged in cotton spinning and weaving (at Minho, a small market town in the highlands, at Covilhã on the flanks of the Serra da Estrela, and at Lisbon). Their production has doubled since 1940 and is sufficient to meet the present needs of the country. Production in the chemical industry has increased by more than half during the same period. However, in total value and in value per head of the population, the figures do not bear comparison with those of countries with a higher standard of living. Industrial equipment has been restricted through lack of capital, the reluctance to borrow from abroad, and concern to maintain the value of the escudo, which in fact remains very steady.

Pierre BIROT

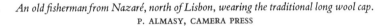

An old fisherman from Nazaré, north of Lisbon, wearing the traditional long wool cap.
P. ALMASY, CAMERA PRESS

THE PORTUGUESE ISLANDS
OF THE ATLANTIC

In the fifteenth century, the Portuguese occupied the un-inhabited islands of the Azores, Madeira and Cape Verde, on the route of the great voyages of discovery. These islands have played an important rôle as ports of call on the ocean routes and in spreading plantation cultivation to America. They are inhabited by peasants of Portuguese origin who brought with them many of the characteristics of rural Portugal which have been adapted to tropical cultivation. The islands form an insular province maintaining close ties with the parent country. Together with the Spanish Canary Islands, they are part of a group of islands of volcanic origin, some of which are very old and have been worn down by erosion, as in Madeira and Santa Maria in the Azores. In most of the other islands eruptions have occurred in historic times; one, in the Cape Verde Islands, took place as recently as 1951, on Fôgo island. Farming on the mountain sides is very difficult. All the slopes in Madeira are terraced to a height of 2,600 feet, the limit of cultivation. But variations in latitude and in the distances from the coast of Africa cause important climatic differences which influence agriculture.

The Azores (888 sq. miles), situated in mid-ocean in latitude 40° N., experience humid conditions throughout the year. Rainfall decreases only at the height of summer, and even then the decrease is restricted to a narrow coastal zone where the terrain resembles that of Minho in Portugal, but where the temperature range is much smaller because of the absence of winter conditions. (The average temperature for the coldest month is 57° F.). The chief areas of specialised cultivation are also confined to this lowland — pineapples under glass, chicory, tea and sugar-beet. Cultivated meadows are found higher up, and they provide food for the fine breed of Dutch dairy cattle. Milk production is highly commercialised, and the field is hardly used; the farmer is satisfied with growing maize and sweet potatoes. The chief islands are São Miguel, Terceira (where the capital, Angra do Heroismo, is situated), and Pico.

Madeira (302 sq. miles), situated in latitude 33° N. and nearer to the African continent, has a typically Mediterranean climate that particularly commends it to tourists. Rainfall is a little heavier on the northern slopes which are exposed to the trade winds, but it is confined to the winter months. Almost all the fields have to be irrigated. Specialised cultivation is carried out on the lower terraces. In the fifteenth century, the first large plantations of sugar-cane were started; today, banana plantations are replacing them almost everywhere. A special wine, produced with great care, is still exported, mainly to England. A dense population of peasants exists on corn, yams and sweet potatoes, cultivating the land assiduously and clearing the scrub from the higher slopes. Everywhere, stock-raising is closely associated with agriculture for the production of manure and milk, which is exported as butter.

The Cape Verde Islands extend over an area of 1,557 sq. miles; their chief island is São Tiago, which contains Praia, the capital. This completes the Mediterranean-Atlantic area, where journeying Portuguese found the same characteristics as in the mother country. It is a tropical archipelago with a short rainy season in summer. The cultivation of the staple food, maize, is restricted by shortage of water and backward methods. The only important export is castor oil.

The importance of these islands as ports of call on the routes to South America and South Africa is declining. Funchal, the capital of Madeira and the fifth Portuguese town in size of population, has seen its trade decrease. Long-range aircraft need no longer stop at the Azores, although cargo boats still refuel at the Cape Verde Islands.

Pierre BIROT

Terraced fields in the hills behind Funchal in Madeira, a Portuguese possession in the Atlantic, off Morocco. Madeira was first to have large sugar cane plantations, but today banana plantations have largely replaced these. J. ALLAN CASH

CENTRAL EUROPE

The ruins of the feudal castle of Aggstein on the Danube in
Wachau, Lower Austria. AUSTRIAN TOURIST AGENCY

The Matterhorn (14,701 feet). It is one of the peaks in the Pennine Alps and is situated between Valais in Switzerland and the Italian Piedmont. SWISS NATIONAL TOURIST OFFICE

THE ALPS

THE Alps occupy a vast area of Europe. Their length is 780 miles, measured along the outside edge from the Col de Tende to Vienna; maximum width is 165 miles, from the Karawanken Alps north of Ljubljana to the most eastern spur of the Wienerwald. With an area of 64,000 sq. miles, they are four times as extensive as the Pyrenees, and by reason of position as well as size they play a major part in the life of the continent. They form a barrier between two civilisations; on the one hand the Po valley and the northern Adriatic, on the other the Channel, the North Sea and the Baltic Sea.

Because of their open relief, they have been settled since earliest times. They are surrounded by a foreland, often fertile, which fosters a semi-mountainous type of existence complementary to mountain life proper. Their waters, swollen by melting snow and ice, flow off in all directions, feeding the Dutch Rhine and the Rumanian Danube, helping to create the Rhône and the Po, the two largest rivers (in volume) in Western Europe. The countryside, the way of life and the economy of the Alps have given rise to the term 'alpine' which is applied to mountain characteristics often far removed from the Alps.

ASYMMETRY OF THE ALPS.

Originating in a geosyncline of various strata, the Alps usually slope towards the outside of the curved line of folding. Lack of symmetry is very prominent in the western region, where the Piedmont Alps are less than a fifth as high as those in nearby France. It is even more striking between Monte Rosa, Lake Maggiore and Lake Thun. East of Lake Como asymmetry is less evident, because on the borders of the Po lowland the Alps are raised into many folds; yet the mountain mass of Triglav, to the north of Ljubljana, still reaches a height of 9,396 feet only 25 miles from Friuli. This arrangement of the mountain range has facilitated military attacks in the direction of Turin and the Ticino; it has also resulted in drainage being developed more on the external then the internal slope, with the exception of the Adige which benefits from a fold between Oetztal and the High Tauern. Finally, the lack of symmetry in the relief is at least partly responsible for some climatic characteristics; the exceptionally high rainfall in the Ticino area, and the strength and extent of the föhn winds are directly attributable to it.

THE HIGHEST MOUNTAIN RANGE IN EUROPE.

The Alps have faithfully recorded the buckling of the geosyncline from which they are derived, gaining in height what they lost in width; the mountains are high in the narrow sections, and lower in the broader parts. Between Annecy, Chillon, Thun and Lucerne on one side, and Lanzo, Ivrea, Biella and Varese on the other, the width of the Alps is reduced to between 78 and 85 miles, reaching a height of 14,022 feet on the Finsteraarhorn, 15,200 feet on Monte Rosa, and 15,781 feet on Mont Blanc.

Between Montélimar and Saluzzo, however, and between Vienna and the outskirts of Ljubljana, where the width of the mountains is more than 125 and 160 miles respectively, altitudes are lower. Here there are no peaks over 13,000 feet. The Aiguille de Chambeyron in the French southern Alps is less than 11,150 feet, whilst in the High Tauern, the most continuous section of the Alps, with nearly 100 miles between the Brenner and the Rastadt Pass, the Gross Glockner reaches only 12,461 feet. As for the eastern Alps, they only just exceed 8,000 feet in the Karawanken.

The supple folding of the Alps included longitudinal folds. In this way the high mountain masses of Argentera, Pelvoux, Mont-Blanc, Bernese Oberland, Ambin and Tauern are contrasted with the valleys of Lanzo-Susa (near Mont Cenis) and the Brenner. This type of buckling of the Alpine crest is largely responsible for the open character of the range.

The difference between the Pyrenees and the Alps is in part because the latter are composed of fewer recent Hercynian rocks (rigid and brittle) and of more flexible rocks that tend to yield into troughs. These are aligned along the axis of the range, presenting long zones of homogeneous formations, often very liable to erosion. The area occupied by rigid material is at least 38 per cent of the whole in the Pyrenees, compared with only 11 per cent in the Alps.

THE LONGITUDINAL VALLEYS.

The French longitudinal Alpine valley is at least 125 miles long from Champsaur to the Col d'Anterne; the longitudinal valley of Valais is about 75 miles from the Col de la Forclaz to the Furka; from Furka to Oberalp the Urserental stretches for about 12 miles, and the longitudinal valley of Grisons (Vorder Rhine) about 42 miles from Oberalp to Chur (Coire). Thus there is an almost continuous route of 250 miles from the approaches of the southern French Alps to Grisons. In the same way the Rienza valley (Val Pusteria), the Gail and the Drava open a direct route between the southern end of the Brenner Pass and Maribor in the Hungarian Basin. Also the trough of the River Inn extends diagonally from the bright countryside of Lake Como to the misty plateau of Bavaria. These longitudinal valleys are linked to outer limits of the Alps by transverse valleys, the most remarkable of which are probably those of Grenoble, the Rhine above Lake Constance, and particularly that of the Upper Rhône between Martigny and Lake Geneva. The dominant direction of the Alps and of the parallel valleys is roughly south-west to north-east; the valleys thus have one sunny, fully exposed slope which is suitable for the vine, and a shaded side rich with orchards, woods and meadows. The valleys are traversed by railways almost from end to end. Finally, the position of these longitudinal valleys in the Alps is an important factor in producing regional differences.

A MOSAIC OF MOUNTAIN CLIMATES.

The Alps would appear to promise a fairly uniform climate, because they are extended in the direction of parallels. Two-thirds of their area is enclosed between 48° and 46° 30', so that the spread of latitude between Thun and Vienna is little more than 100 miles. However, although there is not much difference between the precipitation and vegetation of Chablais and Salzkammergut, the reverse is true of the Styrian and Carinthian Alps and the opposite end of the range. In the former, the continental influences from Hungary penetrate deeply into the area. Here precipitation is sometimes reduced to less than 40 inches, and the difference in winter temperature is most noticeable in the Klagenfurt basin. In the valleys, the deciduous trees, pine copses and fields of maize give a more picturesque countryside than the Tyrol landscape. As for the opposite slope, it is typified to the east of the Val d'Aosta by

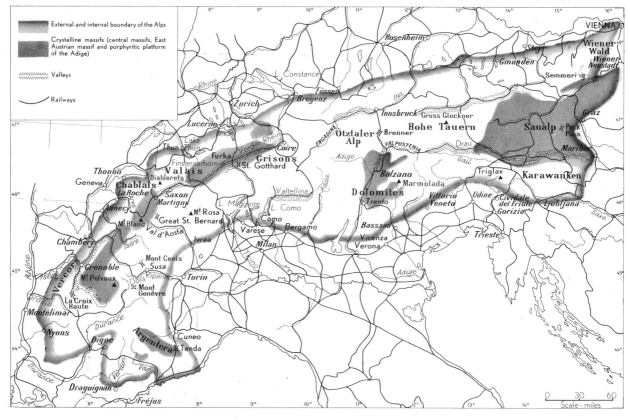

THE ALPS

very heavy precipitation brought by the Adriatic winds. The Ticino thus receives the quite exceptional annual average of more than 60 inches. With the blue sky, mixed crops on the lower slopes and the terraces of vines, one is strongly reminded of the Mediterranean landscape, though there are no olive trees.

Where the Franco-Italian Alps change to a north-south direction they naturally provide more contrasts. From Chablais to Draguignan, the difference in latitude is three degrees. The Mediterranean depressions let loose the northerly winds of the *bise* and the *mistral*, while the *marin* and the *levant* bring rain from the south and east. The southern French Alps are invaded by the drought of a Mediterranean summer as far as southern Vercors, the pass of La-Croix-Haute and the upper Drac, while there is a deficiency of summer rainfall in the Alpine interior, in the valley of the upper Durance, Queyras and the upper Ubaye.

In the southern Alps, the difference between opposite slopes is just as marked. Except to the west of Mont Genèvre precipitation is abundant, and the reverse of the normal French pattern, for the minimum rainfall is in winter, not summer, as it is to the north of the river Maira. The vegetation cover is always richer on the more exposed slopes; the forests look healthier and the pastures lusher. Sweet chestnuts are seen everywhere, but olives are rare.

In the most central parts of the Alps there are small areas of relative drought. In the centre of Tarentaise and in the area of Modane precipitation drops to about 26 inches. The Lower Engadine receives 28 inches, and the upper Adige and the centre of the Val d'Aosta less than 24 inches. In Valais, as will be seen later, rainfall is particularly deficient.

THE ALPINE TYPES. The French Alps, in the south, are larger and lower than those in the north, simpler in structure, but less accessible. The Pre-Alps here are three times more

extensive than in Dauphiné and Savoy; on the other hand, the central Alpine zone is only half as wide. The longitudinal valley is represented by isolated sections in the upper Verdon and Var. Only the valley of the Durance leading from the pass of Mont Genèvre (6,101 feet), the lowest of the trans-Alpine crossings this side of the Adige, resembles the great longitudinal corridors which are such a dominant feature of the central section of the Alps, between the southern French Alps and a line joining Lakes Como and Constance.

The central section includes, besides the northern French Alps, the greater part of the Swiss Alps, less the area to the east of Grisons. It is the most spectacular region. The Swiss Alps, which are the highest, feed 534 sq. miles of ice, three times more than the French Alps. Besides, the construction of this central section differs completely on the two sides of the river Arve. In the 'Grandes Alpes', the high limestone Alps such as Buet, Dent du Midi, Dent de Morcles and Diablerets are linked to the central blocks, and between the Mont Blanc group and the Bernese Oberland, the piling up of overfolds or nappes has raised Monte Rosa over 3,000 feet higher than the Levanna of Maurienne.

The western Dolomites and the Austrian Alps reveal further the diversity of Alpine scenery. Broader, and therefore lower (Marmolada is 10,965 feet), this area is complicated by faulting and volcanic extrusion. In the western Dolomites, to the east of Cima d'Asta and the porphyritic platform of Bolzano-Cavalese, a series of folds is aligned with impressive slopes, as for example the limestone Marmolada. In the extreme east of the Alps, the dense woodland and soft outlines of the Wiener-wald set off to advantage the rugged ridges and eroded limestone of Rax and the Schneeberg. The Alps of the Mur recall the crystalline plateau of the French Central Massif, but this impression is quickly removed in the Klagenfurt basin, by the sight of the rigid barrier of the Karawanken, where the Alps sweep towards the Hungarian plain.

The old quarter of Salzburg, on the banks of the Salzach,
dominated by the fortress of Hohensalzburg.   EDWARD HOLMES

AUSTRIA

The Simplon Pass, (6,591 feet) near the Swiss-Italian border. J. ALLAN CASH

THE GATEWAYS OF THE ALPS. There are a number of great passes across the Alps; all have played vital rôles throughout European history. The Col de Tende (6,143 feet) became part of Savoy, with the Comté de Nice, at the end of the fourteenth century, and until the French Revolution was the chief transalpine pass for wheeled transport. The Brenner Pass served as the axis of the Tyrol, and around Mont Genèvre was organised the strange republic of Briançon Escarton which was broken up in 1713, leaving a frontier which, with no consideration of human problems, simply followed the line of the watershed. For its part, Savoy, or rather the State of Savoy-Piedmont, founded its fortunes on the exploitation of several great Alpine passes, including the Mont Cenis (6,834 feet) and, until expelled by the Swiss in the sixteenth century, the Great Saint Bernard (8,110 feet). The State of Savoy had, in fact, its replica in the early Confederation of the Swiss cantons, bound together in the thirteenth century by the necessity of developing, exploiting and defending the route leading to the Saint Gotthard Pass (6,926 feet). The influence of the Alpine crossings is even felt at some remove: Turin, Venice, Trieste, and particularly Milan, Lyons, Basle, Augsburg and Munich are focal points of road and rail, and are also trading centres benefiting from transalpine connections and the hydro-electric power produced in the mountains. Along the length of the Alps, from Nice to Vienna and Ljubljana, from Coni to Gorizia, towns grew up at the points of contact between the mountains and the lowland.

THE TRADITIONAL ECONOMY. The salt in the Triassic rocks has played and often still plays an important part in Alpine economy; this is so in the region of Moûtiers, Tarentaise and in Austria. With certain metals, such as lead and copper, it encouraged early settlement, and has given rise to trade since prehistoric times. As for iron, coal and lignite, their development is located at La Mure, Aime in Tarentaise, La Thuile in the Val d'Aosta, and Gonzen in Switzerland, with several deposits in Styria and Carinthia; however, the present industrial centres are merely the survivors of an Alpine iron industry, once more scattered.

The Alps have a food-producing economy which, though somewhat chancy, is carried out wherever possible. Production is most effective in the heart of the Central Alps, with its warm spring climate, long periods of sunshine, and efficient irrigation. It is a countryside of patchwork fields, orchards, vineyards, forests and meadows on the lower slopes, and broad Alpine pasture above.

A VITAL AGRICULTURAL ECONOMY. The population of the mountain region is steadily decreasing, especially in the Southern Alps. This area, which had a population of 50,000 in 1806, including Briançon and Barcelonnette, had only 28,000 in 1946. In the Valais, where the total population has been increasing for a century, the upper valleys of the Dranse and the valley of Anniviers have shown an opposite movement. The downward trend will not necessarily lead to the inevitable doom of Alpine agricultural economy. In the southern Pre-Alps there is reorganisation of agriculture based on the use of artificial fertilizers and agricultural machinery, designed to give better output on a reduced acreage with less labour. The lean sheep have been replaced by fat lambs and milch-cows. Lavender and fruit have been introduced to enrich and give variety to the mixed farming areas, where the vine, olive and wheat continue to hold their own. In the Stubaital, close to Innsbruck, ploughing has been maintained by the widespread use of electric winches. In Tarentaise, the Bourg-Saint-Maurice area remains one of the most prosperous in the Alps, for here the high mountain pastures are used for grazing combined herds of several hundred cattle, selected for the production of Gruyère cheese.

The pastoral system of the French Alps is also changing rapidly. Jeeps give easier access to the pastures, motor-mowers save labour, and weed-killers, which are becoming generally adopted, clear the pastures. So the Alps are not necessarily on the way to becoming simply a summer reserve of hay. The French Alps remain an important agricultural region with 300,000 farm workers, more than 1,000 sq. miles of arable land, nearly 2,700 sq. miles of productive alpine pasture, 55,000 milch-cows, 260,000 sheep, and a valuable annual production of milk, butter, cheese, wool and meat.

HYDRO-ELECTRIC POWER. In the French Alps there were 54,000 industrial workers in 1900, and 153,000 in 1946 (123,000 of these were in the northern Alps). An important mining industry is based in the Alpine region, with a considerable production of lime and cement; leather-work and textile manufacture are also widely practised. Primarily, however, the Alps are a valuable source of electric power. In France, the Alps alone provide about 40 per cent (10,000 million kWh) of the country's total hydro-electric power. Installed capacity has increased two-and-a-half times since 1945. Present Swiss production is about 14,000 million kWh, that of Austria 8,000 million. Of the 28,000 million kWh of Italian water power, 21,000 million comes from the Alps, and much more still can be produced. Austria makes use of only one-sixth of its hydro-electric potential, though this includes the Danube; a further 24,000 million kWh may be expected from installations in the French Alps. Within the mountain region large electro-metallurgical factories benefit from local power. The French Alps produce alloys amounting to 80,000 tons of aluminium (three-quarters of the French output) and 139,000 tons of steel.

THE TOURIST INDUSTRY. Finally, the Alps offer magnificent scenery, mountain peaks, ski-slopes, and an invigorating atmosphere to the tourists who pour in almost all the year round. Briançon, Mont Genèvre and Serre-Chevalier are busy winter holiday resorts, as are Clavières and Sestrières in the Piedmont. In Dauphiné the Alpe-d'Huez and Villard-de-Lans are especially popular. In Savoy, the Val-d'Isère and more recently Courchevel in the valley of the Doron de Bozel are two typically attractive resorts; Chamonix, busy in summer and winter, typifies the larger Alpine resort.

It has been estimated that 10 per cent of the adult population of Haute-Savoie owe their living directly to the tourist trade. The Swiss Alps receive an annual average of nearly one-and-a-half million 'home' tourists and 2,800,000 foreigners. In the Austrian Alps, the corresponding figures are 3,800,000 and 1,500,000. There are also a number of urban centres in the Alps, such as Grenoble, both an Alpine border town, since its valley has become a great suburb, and an important centre of internal communications; Innsbrück, a regional centre like Grenoble, is a road and rail centre of international importance. There is also the collection of factory towns along the valleys of the Mur and Mürz in Styria, as well as many towns beyond the Alpine borders, such as Bolzano, Trento and Klagenfurt.

Henri ONDE

The remote valley of Hérens in the Swiss Valais. SWISS NATIONAL TOURIST OFFICE

The harvest in central Switzerland, above the Lake of Aegeri. Huge bundles of hay have to be carried up slopes too steep for machinery, and the whole family helps. SWISS NATIONAL TOURIST OFFICE

SWITZERLAND

THE Alps are the cradle of the early Confederation of the 'Waldstätten'. They helped to ensure the preservation of an independence which similar political organisations, such as Briançon, Tyrol and Savoy, eventually lost. Of all the present Alpine States, Switzerland is the only one which reaches the bordering plains on both sides of the range and, by reason of the height of its mountains, the most easily defended. The Swiss State, occupying nearly 16,000 sq. miles, is 220 miles long and 125 miles wide. Yet a population of 5,200,000 gives Switzerland a density of 325 persons per square mile. The world influence of this small state is even more remarkable, for, unlike the similarly small Netherlands and Belgium, it has never possessed overseas territories.

A COUNTRY OF DIVERSITY. Regional divisions as different in relief and climate as in language, religion and ways of life, are found side by side within a small area. Northern Switzerland, with its thundery summer climate, long winter snow cover, and mists over the peat-bogs, is related to central Europe. In the extreme south-west, the country falls within the sphere of influence of the Gulf of Genoa with its atmospheric depressions, and of the influence of the *bise* with its heavy autumnal showers; the slopes of Tessin (Ticino) are in the Adriatic part of the Alpine region.

Switzerland distributes the water which falls on its mountains by streams and rivers of very unequal catchments, (0.3 per cent for the Adige, 4.4 per cent for the Inn, 9.3 per cent for the Po, 18.2 per cent for the Rhône and 67.7 per cent for the Rhine). The Rhine is the great outlet because of the spread of its two branches and the Aar; however, the Rhône basin plays an important part as a source of power, having once formed a huge glacier to which western Switzerland owes some of its distinctive features.

The variety of the Swiss countryside is matched by its peoples. It has three languages, even four, since a popular vote made Romansch a national language. The Rhaeto-Romansch-speaking area suffered the intrusion of Italian and German during the Middle Ages when the German-speaking Walser migrated from Valais into the valley of the Hinter Rhein, and the region of Davos, Chur (Coire) and Prätigau. Further, language is often linked with religion. The people of Bivio, the village controlling the junction of the Julier and Septimer roads, speak three languages (German, Romansch and Italian) and practise two religions. The Romansch are Roman Catholic; the Italians — who came from the Val Bregalia (influenced very early by the Reformation) — are Protestants. The linguistic limits, however, do not coincide with the boundaries of the cantons, any more than with the political frontiers; eighteen cantons have only one official language, the other four have two or even three.

The religious variations are related to the historical conditions under which the Reformation spread, the differences of interpretation, and the religious rivalry that followed. This resulted in the individuality of the Roman Catholic cantons of Fribourg and Schwyz, and the Protestant centres of Zürich and Geneva. The Protestant canton of Vaud maintains a Free Evangelical Church, the established Church, and two schools of theology, while the State subsidises Catholic parishes of the

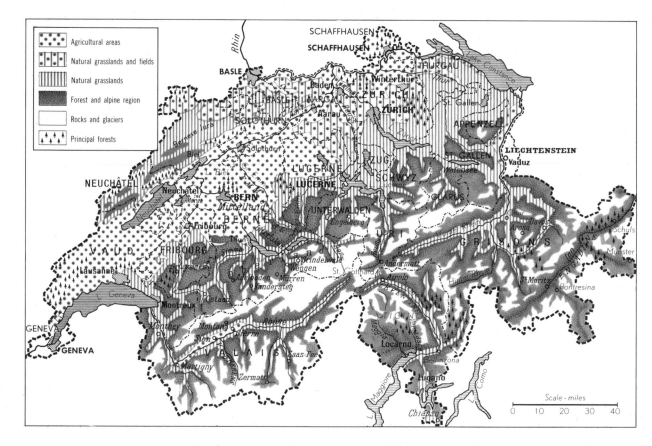

SWISS AGRICULTURE AND FORESTRY. *Note the importance of agriculture in the Middle Lands, especially in the central and southern parts, and in central Valais. Eastern Switzerland is devoted to forests and pasture, except around Lake Constance and in the Rhine valley above the lake.*

Echallens district. Religious boundaries are sometimes sharply defined, as, for example, in the transverse valley section of the Rhône, where the river separates Catholic Valais from the Protestant district of Aigle in Vaud.

Because of its relief and its historical and economic development, Switzerland lends itself to division into special groups; and within the Federation, each canton retains its individual framework, with its own institutions, authorities, local customs and extensive powers in education and religion.

COMMUNICATIONS. As an Alpine state, Switzerland has made good use of its privileged position in the network of European communications. The Great Saint Bernard Pass, much used in Roman times, and the Saint Gotthard made accessible by the early cantons, are situated in the narrowest and loftiest sections of the Alpine range. In the Grisons, the Julier, Splügen, Septimer and Maloja passes have been used since ancient times. However, the Great Saint Bernard and the passes of the Grisons were not centrally situated in a state which grew outwards from the area of Lake Lucerne (Vierwaldstätter Lake). The routes that they controlled towards the Jura and Dijon, Lake Constance and the plateau of Swabia and Bavaria were no longer as valuable at the end of the Middle Ages as they had been at the time of fairs of Champagne, and of the prosperity of Augsburg and Nuremberg. But the Saint Gotthard joins Milan and the industrial and densely populated lowlands of the Rhine by the shortest route. Other transalpine routes neglected the old historic passes and emulated the Saint Gotthard — via Berne, Lötschberg, Brig and the Simplon.

THE DIVISION OF SWITZERLAND. Switzerland may be conveniently divided vertically or horizontally. There

is a western Switzerland, a central Switzerland and an eastern Switzerland; or there are the longitudinal strips of the Alps, the Plateau and the Jura. It is not quite as clear-cut as that, however, for two of the largest cantons, Bern and Vaud, are closely associated with all three regions. Besides, the term Middle Lands is preferable to that of Plateau, for in the area between the Jura, the Black Forest and the Alps, plateau land is not the most typical.

The division into three longitudinal zones with reference to surface area and average height is as follows: —

Jura	10 per cent	2,920 feet
Middle Lands	28 per cent	1,903 feet
Alps	62 per cent	5,794 feet
Switzerland	100 per cent	4,396 feet

Thus the Alps cover nearly two-thirds of the land and tower over the other zones. Yet, while they form 42 per cent of the canton of Bern, they cover only 22 per cent of Vaud, which occupies more of the Middle Lands and benefits from a more southerly latitude and more sunshine. This accentuates the differences between the French-speaking Vaud and Bern, both of which belong to the even greater geographical unit of Western Switzerland.

WESTERN SWITZERLAND

Western Switzerland consists of the cantons of Geneva, Vaud, Valais, Fribourg, Neuchâtel and Bern, plus the southern part of the canton of Solothurn (Soleure). This area of 7,000 sq. miles includes the linguistic and cultural unit of French-speaking Switzerland.

Behind the morainic ridge in front of Wangen, left by a

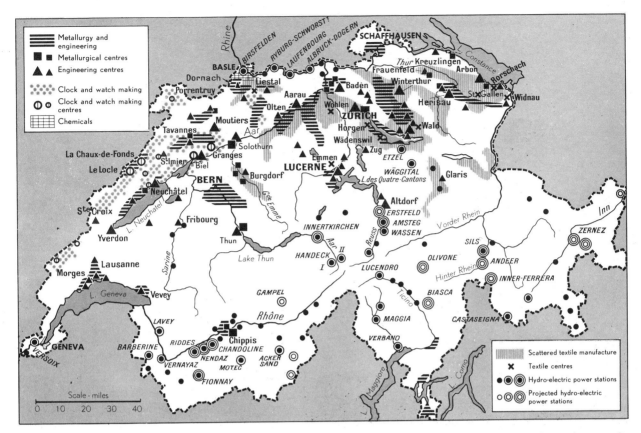

SWISS INDUSTRIES. *Note the industrial triangle of the Middle Lands in Central Switzerland (Lucerne, Basle, Winterthur), and the outstanding activity of the Jura; note too the lack of industry in Ticino and the extreme east of Switzerland. Valais is the leading power producing area.*

branch of the old Rhône glacier, was the former 'lac de Soleure' which, after silting up, gave rise to the plains of the Aar in Seeland, to the plains of the Broye, the Orbe and the Grande Emme. Thus a unique Swiss landscape extends from Lake Geneva (Lac Léman) to Wangen, with level stretches of land, broad horizons, slow and placid rivers, and extensive interlinking lakes.

Western Switzerland is a great cross-roads. The Great Saint Bernard route uses it, stretching along the shores of the lake to Geneva. From Vevey the Roman road runs to Payerne with its Benedictine abbey, Avenches with its Roman monuments, and Solothurn, the former residence of French ambassadors. The route along the sub-Jurassic trough begins at Lausanne and goes through the Col de Jougne towards Pontarlier and Burgundy. It was this section of the diagonal route joining Milan to Champagne and Flanders that the rulers of anche-Comté of Chalon tried to monopolise for their own ds, while the rulers of Savoy did the same with the section ossing the transverse valley of the Rhône through Saintaurice and Martigny.

In the Middle Ages western Switzerland existed almost as a political and religious unity. From the thirteenth to fifteenth centuries the territory of the House of Savoy extended to the gates of Sion and north as far as Morat. The State of Bern, successor to Savoy, strove in its turn to occupy this region. In the first half of the fourteenth century it gained control of the upper Aar and the Brünig and Grimsel passes. Then it established itself firmly on the highway along the sub-Jurassic rough; in 1475 it gained access to the Rhône route by annexing he Aigle region. Then came the occupation of Vaud until 1798, and finally a part of the Jura in 1815.

In western Switzerland, where there are numerous areas with moderate rainfall and rich alluvial soil, wine, wheat, tobacco and sugar-beet are important products. The region has 70 per cent of all the vineyards of Switzerland. Bern and Vaud are easily the main producers of sugar-beet as well as tobacco.

THE FRINGES OF LAKE GENEVA: Geneva, the centre of a mountainous semi-circle, breached by the Rhône at Fortl'Ecluse, is the smallest canton in Switzerland. Essentially urban, it has a population density of more than 1,850 to the square mile. The old town, with its cathedral of Saint-Pierre cut off by the ditch of the Bourg-de-Four (Roman Forum), grew up on a spur of alluvium from the old confluence of the Arve and the Rhône. Below it, the 'low' streets have been built over the Petit Lac. The island and bridgehead of Saint-Gervais was a former watchmaking centre. The parks encircling the Palais des Nations provide a green belt which includes the peaceful slopes of Collonge and Versoix. Geneva, the leading Swiss city in 1789 with a population of 26,000, and almost overtaken by Zürich in 1850, today has about 172,000. Industry is now more varied than in the days when watchmaking flourished in the small workshops of the *cabinottiers*. By 1950, the metal industries (turbines, motors, parts for electric traction) employed 4,000 workers, compared with 4,500 in the watchmaking and jewellery industry. The town is cramped by internal frontiers which leave only a very small free zone, but its international influence is widespread.

In the Vaud canton, the Middle Lands of Switzerland become more varied on the fringes of the Alps, where the conglomerates of Mont Pèlerin reach 3,585 feet. The sunny slopes and vineyards of the region fall steeply to Lake Geneva; they are among the finest in western Switzerland. East of Lausanne the vineyard of Lavaux, cut into terraces, bolstered by low walls rising one above the other, extends for nine miles and

Geneva, the third largest city of Switzerland. It has an international population, part of it United Nations staff. The town stands on two hills divided by the Rhône where it enters Lake Geneva, the largest lake in the Alps. J. ALLAN CASH

covers 2,224 acres. A good quality white wine is produced from chasselas grapes. In the nine viticultural communes of the Lavaux district, where population density is nearly 900 per square mile, grapes cover at least a quarter of the land. The harvest of an average year is about 880,000 gallons, almost a fifth of the whole canton's production.

Lausanne is a market and crossroads, situated at the junction of the fertile plateau of Gros de Vaud, the higher, wooded plateau of Jorat, and the valley of the Venoge at the outlet of the sub-Jurassic trough. The ancient cathedral city, perched on its spur of molasse, dominates both the lake and Ouchy. Lausanne is a hilly city, clinging to its gullies, which are about 800 feet deep. The *belle paysanne* of former times has become a residential and tourist centre, and even an industrial town. Its industries, however, are located mainly to the west of the town, scattered among many workshops and small factories (woodwork, paper, printing tools and measuring instruments), and have not affected the distinguished appearance of Lausanne. This is a common pattern in the region; the industrial enterprises of Nyon, Morges and Vevey merge into the countryside, which manages to preserve its rural appearance. Lausanne, a small town of less than 10,000 people at the beginning of the century, now has a population of 121,000, with at least 20,000 more if its suburbs are included.

DEVELOPMENT OF THE LAKE VALLEY. To the north of Mormont, the limestone hill between the Venoge and the valley of the Orbe, the sub-Jurassic valley widens. In this swampy valley, drainage has been satisfactory following the 'Waters of the Jura' improvement scheme, which lowered the level of Lakes Neuchâtel, Bienne and Morat. The plains of the Orbe, lower Broye and Bernese Seeland are intensively and scientifically farmed, producing cereals, sugar-beet, tobacco

and vegetables. The ridge of Vully, dominating Morat with its ramparts, is part of a group of hills dividing this longitudinal valley into two. At the very foot of the Jura is Lake Neuchâtel, 83 sq. miles in area, 25 miles long, and with its deepest point about 500 feet below the level of the plain. Once the frontier region between the Romanised Burgondes and the Alamans, the longitudinal valley is today crossed by the linguistic boundary, the Jura remaining primarily French-speaking. In Neuchâtel, the castle ruins and the old Collegiate Church dominate the lake. Although the town extends to the lower slopes of the Jura, it is essentially a lowland city.

Biel (Bienne), at the mouth of the Suze, a river from the Jura, has become a watchmaking town, as well as a centre for mechanical industries (car assembly, cycles, precision machinery, repair works for the Federal Railways), paper manufacturing and woodwork. This bilingual town saw its population grow from 5,600 in 1850 to 48,000 in 1950. Solothurn (Soleure) in German-speaking Switzerland has also felt the effects of the industrialisation of the lake valley. It was an old Roman town, a bridging point of the navigable Aar, with a wealth of nobly built houses and baroque churches; today, Solothurn is surrounded by factories: the von Roll ironworks of Gerlafingen, the cellulose factory of Attisholz, and the paper mills of Biberist.

THE PLATEAUS AND INCISED VALLEYS OF THE MIDDLE LANDS. The Broye above Payerne, the Saane (Sarine) from the dam of Gruyère or Rossens, and the Aar from Thun to Bern and Seeland, all carve a course into that part of the Middle Lands which most resembles a plateau. At Moudon, Fribourg and Bern, the rivers' deviations gave rise to town sites which, until the construction of modern bridges, were difficult of access. Agriculture consists mainly of cleaning crops and mixed fodder. Milk production is important. To

Above: *Lake Barberine in the Pennine Alps (Valais), an artificial lake formed by a dam 880 feet long.* SWISS TOURIST AGENCY

n experienced watchmaker superintends the nickel-plating of watches. SWISS NATIONAL TOURIST OFFICE

raditional methods, with individual processing and treatment during veral months in special cellars, account for the excellence of Swiss cheeses. SWISS NATIONAL TOURIST OFFICE

Aerial view of the old city of Bern, the capital of Switzerland. The loop of the Aar surrounds the promontory on which the city stands. SWISS TOURIST AGENCY

the north of the plateau of Schwarzenburg, the relief becomes more rugged and the valleys of the Bernese Middle Lands give a foretaste of the Pre-Alps. The Aar and Grande Emme flow from south-east to north-west, like the rivers of the Middle Lands of central Switzerland. The Emmental is bordered by the conglomerates of Napf, exceeding 4,600 feet; and on all sides are the scattered Bernese farms, with their curved ornamental fronts, their balconies and broad windows. This is a great cheese-producing region. The valley of the Aar above Bern is industrialised, and in the district of Konolfingen population density reaches 440 per square mile. The industries of the Bernese plateau and valleys include food products — chocolate, powdered milk, beer and preserved foods; in Bern and the surrounding area, they embrace metal-working, engineering, paper manufacture, clothing and printing. The Federal capital with its well-preserved historic centre enclosed by the river Aar contrasts vividly with the modern spacious suburbs on the plateau.

THE JURA. The Jura belong almost entirely to western and French-speaking Switzerland. The Jura in Vaud and Neuchâtel, the valley of Saint Imier, and the Chasseral (the southern part of the Bernese Jura) have an average height of 3,300 feet against 1,650—2,500 feet further north. Thus, towards the north the mountains become lower, and there are changes in landscape, in economy, and even language. Mont Tendre (5,520 feet) is the highest point of the Jurassic folds, which are aligned from south-west to north-east. The cool, damp heavily forested Jura are devoted to dairy cattle rather than crops. But it is the watchmaking industry which is pre-eminent here. The factories in the central Jura are neat and modestly proportioned, leaving the countryside unspoilt. Watchmakers are among the highest paid craftsmen in the country.

The Val de Travers is the first of many valleys devoted entirely to watchmaking. In 1752, there were fewer than

The Rhône glacier, with a clear view of the cirque and the sharp ridges of rock surrounding it. SWISS NATIONAL TOURIST OFFICE

Aerial view of the Sulzer factories at Winterthur, a large industrial town; the Sulzer factories produce diesel engines for ships.

500 watchmakers in the mountains of Neuchâtel, by the end of the eighteenth century there were 4,000, a thousand of whom were at La Chaux-de-Fonds. In 1941, the canton had 12,000 engaged in watchmaking and jewellery (nearly 16,000 by 1951), out of a total of 50,000 in the whole of Switzerland. In the Val de Travers, less than 150 of the 6,200 inhabitants of Fleurier and Couvet are farmers. At Le Locle and La Chaux-de-Fonds, watchmaking has been responsible for the rise of towns in the very heart of the mountains. In the middle of the fifteenth century the population of Le Locle was 260, nearly 8,000 by 1850, and in 1950 a little more than 12,000, of whom 3,000 were in the watchmaking industry. In 1656 the village of La-Chaux-de-Fonds had less than one thousand inhabitants, by 1850 the settlement had reached 13,268, and in 1950, 33,300. At this time some 7,400 people were engaged in watchmaking.

To the north of the Saint Imier valley, high relief gives way to plateaus. Through the barrier of the Jura, and still in Switzerland, several gaps link Basle with the Middle Lands. This relative ease of communication accounts for the spread of the German language in the extreme north of the area. The northern Jura is broader, with watchmaking, paper manufacture and metallurgy. In 1840, the valleys of the Birse and the Dünnern accounted for half the blast-furnaces of Switzerland; twenty years later the proportion was five in eight. This specialisation came about with the development of the iron ore in the Delémont basin. Since Switzerland ceased to produce pig-iron, its iron industry, consisting of further processing, has moved towards the Middle Lands, (mention has already been made of Gerlafingen). Instead of the blast-furnaces, there are now foundries and engineering workshops at Delémont, Rondez, Bassecourt, Courfaivre, Klus and Reconvillier.

The industrialised and populated valleys of the northern Jura contrast with the open countryside of the plateau of Ajoie (Porrentruy), where cereals are quite extensively grown. South of the Rangiers mountains, the plateaus of Franches-Montagnes are higher and are used for beef cattle and horses. Here only 17 per cent of the people are occupied in industry, and the density of population is less than 130 per square mile.

THE PRE-ALPS AND CENTRAL ALPS. THE REGION OF THE SAANE (SARINE). VALAIS.
In western Switzerland, in front of the central Alps, are spread the Pre-Alpine ranges of Chablais, Vaud, Fribourg and Bern. In no other part of Switzerland is the Pre-Alpine zone so broad and varied, though in the Saane region the landscape is somewhat similar. Here the medieval town of Gruyères is surrounded by mountains of over 6,500 feet (Moléson, Vanil-Noir), which produce heavy precipitation well suited for fodder. The farms

and chalets of the summer pastures, situated in the middle of forest clearings, are evidence of the pastoral activity of a region famous for its rich cheese. Gruyères and the upstream communes have rather more agricultural than industrial workers, and density of population is relatively high for a mountain area.

Above the Tine, the region of Enhaut, which is in Vaud and is Protestant, forms the boundary to Catholic Gruyères. Here, the valley of the Saane runs almost west to east, forming a series of gorges and open valleys, like that of Château-d'Oex. Once rather isolated, the region of Enhaut is now joined to Ormonts and so to the Rhône valley by the Mosses route and by the Bernese Montreux-Oberland railway.

From Saanen, Bernese Gessenay corresponds to the upper north-south section of the Saane. The language and landscape are typical of the Simmental. From the tourist centre of Gstaad a series of deep valleys leads towards the high Alps, whose steep slopes of grey limestone and glaciers contrast with the much lower mountains of flysch with their gentler outlines. The wooden houses assume large proportions, with overhanging eaves, tiers of windows, painted ornamentation and German inscriptions. The chalets seem literally sprinkled all over the Alpine pastures.

In the central Alps, the extensive anton of Valais is distinguished by the depth and uniformity of the Rhône trough. This distinction becomes more marked if the transverse valley section from Martigny to Lake Geneva is excluded, for, with an already Pre-Alpine climate and a higher basic standard of living, this region is not a typical part of Valais.

From Martigny to the Rhône glacier, Valais is the most clearly defined longitudinal valley of the whole Alps, with its double rank of peaks over 13,000 feet high and glaciers covering 330 square miles (almost twice as much as in the French Alps). Deeply cut into the mountain mass, the trough has a sparse rainfall, so that the clarity of the atmosphere and the colouring of the great slopes is almost southern. Central Valais has less than 24 inches of rainfall, and from November to January inclusive Sion has 112 hours more sunshine than Geneva. Valais, together with Vaud, is the chief producer of Swiss wine: 4,686 thousand gallons, almost all white wine. In good years the lowland produces 44 million pounds of fruit, of which a large proportion is apples and pears, and 11 million pounds of apricots; tomatoes, asparagus and strawberries are grown on a large scale. Frost precautions are necessary and watering is essential. There are at least 200 irrigation ditches, or *bisses*, in Valais, and spraying methods have made rapid progress. The aluminium factories at Martigny and Chippis, the chemical industries of Viège, Martigny and Monthey, the work in progress on the huge reservoir dams, and the construction of miles of tunnel occupy an ever-growing labour force. Valais has more available electric power than any other canton, including Bern. It has something of the air of a new land, and its population has doubled in a century.

Despite its physical unity, however, Valais remains a collection of dissimilar regions. Alongside a French-speaking Valais there is a German-speaking Valais a little above Sierre, a lower Valais in the transverse valley section of the Rhône, an upper Valais devoted to a pastoral economy, a central Valais with crops on the plain and the slopes, and a lateral Valais with many remote districts such as Lötschental, the valleys of Anniviers and Hérens.

THE BERNESE OBERLAND.
The Alpine basin of the Aar, or the Bernese Oberland, is particularly noted for its glacial mountains in the region of Grindelwald and Lauterbrunnen. Starting in a transverse valley in the crystalline rocks of the central mountains, at Innertkirchen the Aar penetrates the limestone of the high Alps through the gorge at Meiringen and then curves through Lakes Brienz and Thun. Along the valleys many lines of communication were built at great expense. The Susten, a very modern road, links Wassen to Innertkirchen, and the track and tunnel of Lötschberg link the Aar to the Simplon. From Interlaken the railways carry tourists to the foot of the Jungfrau, or even hoist them up the Jungfraujoch at 11,342 feet.

The district of Interlaken which includes, with Grindelwald and Lauterbrunnen, the whole of Lake Brienz and the eastern end of Thun, is relatively densely populated, and more people are employed in trade, catering and transport than in agriculture. The district of Oberhasle, thinly populated and little visited by tourists, is an important source of power. The polished rocks and the waterfalls and glaciers of the Unteraar and Oberaar, shut in by bronze-coloured granite walls, grace this harsh region. Today the Grimsel dam and others divert the torrential waters to the turbines of the hydro-electric power stations at Handeck and Innertkirchen.

CENTRAL SWITZERLAND

A GREAT ALPINE AXIS.
Central Switzerland, from Chiasso to Basle, includes, towards the east, lake Wallen and the Limmat and the cantons of Glarus and Zürich. The whole area is well served by communications. From Lake Lucerne, roads branch out in all directions. Aargau, the 'Gateway of the Waters', the region of the confluence of the Aar, Reuss and Limmat, has its counterpart on the southern slopes of the Alps in the lakes of Tessin (Ticino), winding and linked by gaps to the neighbouring regions. South-east of Lake Wallen, the bifurcation at Sargans offers a short cut across the curve of the Rhine. It was not without reason that the Romans selected the site of Windisch (Vindonissa) near Brugg, and the Hapsburgs that of the castle which perpetuates their name. At the end of the fourteenth century, seven of the eight cantons of the Federation were situated here, in the heart of central Switzerland.

THE REGION OF LAKE LUCERNE.
Nature has been kind to Switzerland with her many charms and reminders of the past. Lake Uri, from Flüelen to Brunnen, is a transverse glaciated valley, deeply gouged by the old glacier of the Reuss. On the alluvial lowland which extends upstream from the lake is Altdorf, immortalised in the legend of William Tell, a' prosperous village at the outlet of the road from the Klausen pass. At Brunnen the lake takes a right-angle turn and the mountain is divided into isolated blocks by valleys and sparkling lakes. The Mythen form a backcloth for the small town of Schwyz, where the original agreement of 1291, marking the

birth of the Federation, is kept. The mountains of Rigi and Pilatus provide tourists with magnificent views over the surrounding country.

The tourist industry has made the reputation of Lucerne, whose situation at the edge of the Alps on the outlet of a lake is very similar to that of Thun, and Annecy in Savoy. From the top of the wooded Gütsch the view embraces the bay with its tower, the Wassertor, the bridges over the Reuss, the fortifications of the old city, the Hofkirche on the site of a convent which was the nucleus of the city, and finally the new town, the station with its flower-decorated platforms, and the blue surface of the lake. Below the town, at Kriens, Emmenbrücke and Emmenweid there are metal works (von Moos), rayon and nylon factories, and mechanical engineering workshops (bridges, structural steel, turbines, funicular railways and lifts); industry occupies nearly 20 per cent of the population of Lucerne and its suburbs; the numbers employed in catering, trade and transport just exceed those in industry.

Old Switzerland has changed enormously. Yet it is not uncommon to meet the bearded and active mountain peoples, with their embroidered smocks, looking like characters straight out of a picture by Hodler. Pastoral life is highly regarded in an area proud of its cattle — the brown breed of Schwyz; but it is now the tourist trade which provides the main source of income. As for industry, it has advanced so rapidly that the numbers employed have almost trebled during the last fifty years in the Waldstätten and the Canton of Lucerne.

THE INDUSTRIAL MIDDLE LANDS.
Lucerne, Basle and Winterthur form an industrial triangle within which population density exceeds 520 per square mile of usable surface; the figure rises to 1,550 round Zürich and Basle. There is a busy network of railways, and the industrial towns with their brand-new factories crowd upon one another like some huge suburb.

Industry originated with the work of the early craftsmen of the surrounding regions. The linen industry came to Appenzell and Thurgau, cotton to St Gallen and the Oberland of Zürich, ironwork to the northern Jura, Fricktal and Schaffhausen. Many towns of the Middle Lands have put their capital into silk industries, or cotton, or printing. By 1949, the canton of Zürich had 30 out of a total of 55 Swiss silk-weaving mills; similarly, the two semi-cantons of Basle had 11 of the country's 17 ribbon factories. The development after 1836 of the rock-salt deposits of Schweizerhalle, Rheinfelden and Zurzach helped to develop the chemical industry. International railways and Rhine navigation have determined the position of many factories round Olten, Brugg, Baden, Lenzburg, Winterthur, Zürich and Basle. Finally, Aargau ranks third after Valais and Bern in the production of hydro-electric power.

In the cantons of Bern and Solothurn, there has been a fair amount of success in developing industries devoted to the

The diversity of the landscape makes Lake Lucerne the most attractive of the Swiss lakes. SWISS NATIONAL TOURIST OFFICE

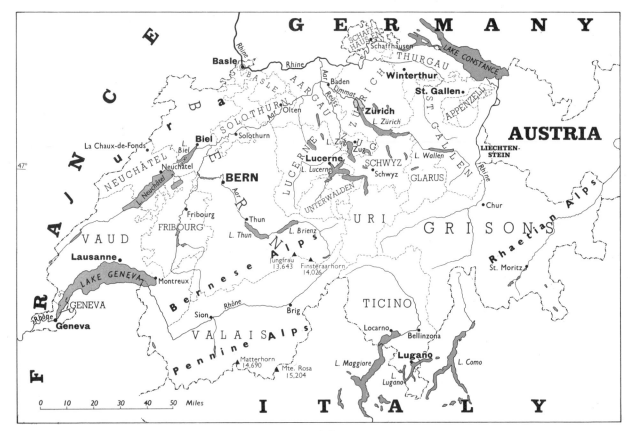

SWITZERLAND

processing of local raw materials: linen weaving and bleaching, pottery at Langenthal, footwear at Schönenwerd, braid for hats, and lime and cement at Aarau and Olten. Metallurgy and mechanical engineering are close to the Jura, as at Olten (railway workshops) and Baden (the Brown-Boveri electric generator works). In the Basle district there is a very important chemical industry (acids, the basic products of soda and chlorine, dyes from coal-tar), and also pharmaceutical production and heavy ironworks. At Dornach and Pratteln there are silk and cement industries. Basle, with a fine site on the concave bank of the Rhine, stands at the junction of three frontiers. The barges flying flags of various nationalities and the mountains of coal indicate the vitality of a port whose trade has increased from 25,000 tons in 1906—1910 to nearly 4 million tons today.

In the eastern zone of the industrial triangle, St Gallen (Saint Gall) and Appenzell are engaged in textile manufacture. In 1949, more than half the working population in the canton of Glarus (Glaris) were engaged in this industry, chiefly in cotton. But the area in general is especially noted for engineering and a variety of equipment. Winterthur produces locomotives, diesel engines (Sulzer), gas turbines and textile machinery. Zürich produces turbines; Örlikon, a nearby suburb, makes electrical equipment, ball-bearings and armaments; and Schlieren makes trucks. The population of Örlikon grew from 780 in 1870 to 12,500 in 1930. Since then it has been incorporated with several others into the city of Zürich. The old city centre which guarded the bridge over the Limmat has itself increased from a population of 41,500 in 1850 to more than 400,000. Zürich is Switzerland's leading city and its importance extends far beyond the country's frontiers.

ON THE ROAD TO THE SAINT GOTTHARD. Above Lake Lucerne, the valley of the Reuss reappears with fine Alpine scenery. The well-known gorges of Schöllenen and the road constructed without regard for cost by the early cantons, gives access to Andermatt and the valley of Urseren. This is a high pastoral valley reached by three passes, the Furka, the Oberalp and the Saint Gotthard. The canton of Uri has the highest proportion of Alpine pasture to cultivated land. The 'Corporation of Uri', consisting of all the communes in the canton, continues to manage the common property which covers a large part of the area. Pastoral life remains well established.

TESSIN (TICINO). The canton of Tessin tapers from the Saint Gotthard to the Plain of Lombardy, and is divided into two unequal parts by Monte Ceneri: in the north is Sopra Ceneri with Locarno and Lake Maggiore, in the south Sotto Ceneri with Lake Lugano. In the Sopra Ceneri, the valleys are deeply incised into a thick and relatively homogeneous mountain layer with continuous slopes; this is the prospect in the Leventine (Tessin Valley below Airolo) and in the Maggia valley. In Sotto Ceneri the relief has been cut into sections; broad corridors contrast with small mountains with abrupt slopes, as in Monte Brè and San Salvatore at Locarno. From avalanche-prone Airolo to Bellinzona in the gentler plain of Magadino, and to Locarno and Lugano, the main activities are tourist trade and commerce.

In this extremely rough countryside, where cultivation is rendered difficult by the steep slopes and the valleys are subject to flooding and swamping, there has always been every encouragement to emigrate. This accounts for the slow growth of population in the late nineteenth century, and for sizeable colonies of Tessin people abroad, especially in California. Emigration has least affected the district of Mendrisio in the south, but has emptied the high valleys of Maggia, Verzasca and Leventine. Part of this loss has been compensated for by immigration of foreigners and Swiss from other cantons. The region is popular with German-speaking Swiss.

Tessin's problem, therefore, is how to preserve its ethnic and cultural personality. The Saint Gotthard route has also influenced the economy. Industrial workers form 19 per cent of the total population; those in catering, commerce and transport make up 10 per cent, a proportion which increases appreciably during the tourist season, especially in Lugano and Locarno, where the hotel trade absorbs over a fifth of those engaged in trade, transport and catering. More people are employed in catering than in other local Tessin industries (tobacco, clothing and building); the sole exception is metallurgy. Although it is ranked as fourth producer of power, Tessin produces less electricity for itself than for other cantons. The city of Zürich has a share in the industries of the Maggia, and high-tension cables link the factories of the Aar, the Rhine and the Reuss to power stations in Tessin.

EASTERN SWITZERLAND

This area includes the cantons of Schaffhausen, Thurgau, St Gallen, Appenzell and the Grisons; thus the greater part of the territory is Alpine. As for the Middle Lands, they consist here of two distinct parts: the limestone plateaus and well-wooded upland of Schaffhausen, and the hills of Thurgau.

THE CANTON OF SCHAFFHAUSEN. The Rhine falls separate the navigable stretch of Lake Constance-Schaffhausen from the downstream section. Schaffhausen owes its past prosperity to compulsory trans-shipment as much as to its rapids and their motive power. The region of Schaffhausen is already structurally related to central Germany and, with Thurgau, forms that part of the Middle Lands most closely linked with German territory; in fact, the frontier is one of trust, with the German bridgehead of Constance (Konstanz) and the enclave of Büsingen. The region of Schaffhausen tends to concentrate on woollen products and metal-working. The iron ore deposits and the forests on the limestone plateau of Randen attracted an iron industry very early; today there are such enterprises as the wrought iron works of Fischer, and the rolling-stock and armaments workshops at Neuhausen. The aluminium industry has always been located at Neuhausen. This highly industrialised urban area is encroaching on a rural region where large villages stand isolated in the fields.

VALLEYS AND ORCHARDS OF THURGAU. On the other side of the Rhine lies Thurgau, a land of east-west valleys between hills formed partly of material left by the old Rhine glacier. Thurgau is a pleasant region, especially as the waters of Lake Constance bring a moderating influence on the climate. It is less wooded than the canton of Schaffhausen, with lush meadows and orchards of apples and pears. Its settlements are dispersed in small hamlets, giving it a character all its own. The cotton industry of St Gallen has invaded the whole southern part of the region. Embroidery has often given way to knitwear, hosiery, or the manufacture of voile and muslin. The engineering industry today employs more of the remaining manpower than the textile and clothing industry. On the edge of Lake Constance, Romanshorn produces aluminium, as does Rorschach in the canton of St Gallen. Arbon manufactures lorries, textile machinery and ballbearings; Alteinrhein in St Gallen makes aircraft and various vehicles.

THE TEXTILE REGION. South of the gentle landscape of Thurgau, the Middle Lands become higher and steeper. The valleys are incised into conglomerate rocks, and the region passes imperceptibly into the Pre-Alpine zone where farms are isolated or, occasionally, huddled together in the middle of open countryside devoted entirely to pasture. The delightful village of Appenzell is reminiscent of a colour print, and Säntis, often obscured by clouds, juts boldly out towards the

Zürich, the most populous and most important town in Switzerland. It is built on the banks of the River Limmat and beside Lake Zürich.

Basle, from the air. Owing to the advantages of its position on the frontier of three countries (France, Germany and Switzerland) and as a Rhine port, the second city of Switzerland has rapidly become an important commercial and industrial centre. SWISSAIR

The Tremola valley. The construction of the zigzagging St Gotthard route (the pass is 6,930 feet high), makes it possible to travel from northern and central Switzerland to Ticino.
SWISS TOURIST AGENCY

Rhine valley. In Toggenburg (the Thur valley), the linen industry supported some 40,000 people in the seventeenth century; in the eighteenth century it gave way to cotton. In 1750 St Gallen manufactured muslins, and the new cloth spread to Inner and Ausser Rhoden, to the Rhine valley and to Schaffhausen. St Gallen also introduced embroidery in the eighteenth century, an industry which reached its peak in 1910 but has since declined in the face of mechanisation and foreign competition. Since then the dense population of these areas has remained stable and prosperous. In 1926, Ausser Rhoden supported about 340 cattle per square mile of productive surface, a figure unequalled by any other canton. The canton of St Gallen remedied the decline of certain textiles by developing the metal and engineering industries and the manufacture of equipment for silos, flour-milling, brewing (Uzwill), cables (Herisau), and artificial silk (Rorschach).

FROM THE RHINE VALLEY TO VALLEYS OF THE GRISONS.

The Rhine valley, its lowlands comparable to the sub-Jurassic trough, is today fertile agricultural land since the embankment and straightening of the Rhine and the systematic drainage of the lowland. It gives access to the principality of Liechtenstein and Austria. Upstream, the ridge at Fläscherberg guards the entrance to the Grisons. This canton has been by-passed by the railways and not a single transalpine line crosses it, though formerly its passes were heavy with traffic. Chur (ancient Curia) controlled a circle of routes. The Grisons League in the sixteenth and seventeenth centuries engaged in politics with France, Tuscany and Venice and with Spain, ruler of Milan. Grisons is a huge canton, occupying a sixth of the country; this land of a 'Hundred Valleys' has long been a replica in miniature of Switzerland itself, with its federal organisation, its distinctive politics, and its dependent territories such as Valtellina.

Today, the network of narrow roads in the Grisons, although extended, serve only a part of the country, and the main rail routes stop at the edge of the canton. Nor has it developed in proportion to the country as a whole. Population has certainly increased during the last hundred years, but it can show a rise of only 34 per cent compared with almost 100 per cent in Valais. In this way the Grisons are more like Tessin, although differently placed on the transalpine routes. The people of Grisons speak more German than Rhaeto-Romansch. The appearance of the countryside remains distinctive, with innumerable north-south valleys (whose slopes are very liable to avalanches), rich vegetation checked by the lower rainfall in the east, and a Dolomitic character in its mountains beneath which nestle imposing whitewashed and painted houses.

The snowy winters, hard but sunny, have made the Grisons the leading health centre and one of the chief tourist areas of Switzerland. It is the region of 'winter sports' — Saint Moritz, Davos, Arosa, Pontresina — the names are famous. The canton has remained agricultural, with 12 per cent of the inhabitants living off the land and Alpine pastures; the same proportion is engaged in industry. Electricity production is important in the Grisons, one of the sources of supply for Zürich; it should have more than 4,000 million kWh to sell after completion of the schemes of the Lower Engadine, Greina-Blenio, and the valley of the Lei-Hinterrhein.

SWITZERLAND'S PROSPERITY.

The prosperity of Switzerland needs little emphasising. Everything proclaims it: the towns with their carefully maintained properties, the building sites bristling with cranes and scaffolding, and the volume of traffic on roads and railways. This prosperity stems partly from internal factors, from the Swiss virtues of orderliness, hard work, attention to detail and community spirit. Switzerland, a land of refuge in the centre of an agitated Europe, owed some of her past industrial prosperity to Huguenot immigrants. Her policy of neutrality enabled her to escape the drain of two world wars on population and national purse. The Swiss franc, although devalued, has maintained its purchasing power. Finally, she has been a refuge for capital as well as for people, and this has helped the expansion of the Swiss economy.

A mountain state crossed by important international routes, Switzerland concentrates on the type of production best suited to her land and skilled labour; costs of transport and of raw materials, which the country lacks, are absorbed in the higher value of the finished product. Thus the Swiss economy is very deliberately directed towards specialisation, to continued research into higher yields and quality of traditional specialities, to watching fluctuating demands or future potentials in the international market. Switzerland has a merited reputation for efficiency in all matters, whether they touch on wheat yields, milk production, watchmaking, the manufacture of machines, clothing or textiles. She has to cover more than 60 per cent of all power requirements by imported fuels liquid fuel. In addition, she has developed her hydro-electric power, and more than four-fifths of her railways are now electrified.

With an abundance of available capital, Switzerland uses it for foreign investment and loans. Interest yields from such sources improve the country's world position and help to secure the necessary supply of raw materials and food. She has consented to making loans to finance railway projects of her neighbours, and some of her own industries are largely international, and Swiss capital investment has its place in the balance of payments. In 1954, when the balance of trade showed a deficit of 320 million Swiss francs, invisible items showed a surplus of 1,360 million francs, of which 460 million came from the tourist trade, 80 million from transport charges, 95 million from insurance, and 500 million from interest and dividends. With exported goods exceeding 5,000 million francs (1,500 million for machinery, appliances and instruments, 1,000 million for watches, 800 million for pharmaceutical products, dyes and basic chemicals, nearly 500 million for cotton, embroidery and cheese, and a tourist industry whose gross revenue was estimated at 750 million) Switzerland, within its mountainous and small territorial limits, is an important economic power.

Henri ONDE

LIECHTENSTEIN

THIS tiny pleasant country of 62 square miles and a population of 15,000 (mainly Catholic and German-speaking) is tucked away in the broad, transverse alpine valley of the Rhine, on the right bank of the river. It is situated between the crossroads at Sargans and the valley of the Ill, that is, between the routes from the Grisons (Switzerland) and the Arlberg (Austria) to Zürich and Basle. It is encircled by the cantons of St Gallen and Grisons, from which it is separated by the ridge of the Fläscherberg and the foothills of the Rhätikon, and finally by Austrian Vorarlberg, with which it shares the Samina valley.

Liechtenstein originated as the Roman Rhaetia; Vaduz is its capital. It still has ties with the episcopal town of Chur (Curia) in the Grisons, though it was established as a principality at the beginning of the eighteenth century for the benefit of the House of Styria. A member of the Holy Roman Empire, and then of the German Confederation until 1886, Liechtenstein formed a customs union with Austria from 1852 to the end of the First World War. After the war, this constitutional and hereditary principality concluded a currency and postal customs union with Switzerland, which is also responsible for Liechtenstein's diplomatic representation abroad.

Liechtenstein is made up of two regions of unequal size. The Unterland, the smaller, includes the flood plain of the Rhine (average height 1,500 ft.), and the alluvial fans from the Schellenberg ridge (2,065 ft.). The plain has been healthier since the embankment of the river, and bridges have taken the place of ferry boats. However, the Unterland is still not completely safe from the incursions of the Rhine. The Oberland, which includes the eastern slope of the Rhine valley, rises to more than 8,500 feet on the Grisons side, and to over 7,500 feet on the Vorarlberg side. It is Alpine in character and has become a tourist region.

The population and the economic activity of the country are concentrated on the edge of these two regions, in an area influenced by the warmth of the föhn, and covered with fields, gardens, orchards and vineyards.

The towns of Vaduz, overlooked by its castle and rich in artistic treasures, Schaan, on the route from Buchs to Feldkirch and the Arlberg, and Triesen, support various industries, such as the manufacture of textiles and precision instruments; they are related to the neighbouring Swiss and Austrian localities.

Henri ONDE

Castle Vaduz, the residence of the reigning prince of Liechtenstein, high on the slope above the town of Vaduz. This small country is tucked away on the right bank of the broad valley of the Rhine, between Switzerland and Austria. SWISS NATIONAL TOURIST OFFICE

Innsbruck, the capital of the Tyrol, situated on the Inn at an altitude of 1,884 feet, in a wide valley surrounded by mountains.   FOX PHOTOS

AUSTRIA

THE Austrian Republic is, politically and geographically, rather like Switzerland; both have federal governments and both are Alpine — Austria more so than her neighbour. The Alps occupy 71 per cent of Austria's 32,000 square miles compared with 62 per cent in Switzerland. The forelands of the Danube and Hungarian basin, the counterpart of the Swiss Middle Lands, cover 20 per cent of the total surface, against 28 per cent in Switzerland, and the Bohemian massif, whose position is comparable with that of the Swiss Jura, 9.8 per cent (Swiss Jura 10 per cent). Thus Austria is a more integral part of the Alps and overlaps less on to the Alpine forelands. This fact has important consequences.

The people of the forelands have revived the Alps with their towns and investments, constructing, for example, many hydro-electric power stations in the mountains. Austria controls only a very small part of the Alpine foreland (8.3 per cent of her territory), and though it includes part of the Hungarian Basin, this fails to yield the same advantages. Exposed by its valleys to Eastern Europe, Austria lies on the fringe area of the economic current which unites the lowlands of the Po and the Rhine through the centre of Switzerland. Carved up by treaties, Austria is now broad in the east, narrowing towards the west. The Brenner route is the main artery of the eastern Alps. However, the political and population centre is far to the east of this axis; the triangle of Linz–Vienna–Graz contains four-fifths of Austrian industry and two-thirds of the population.

WESTERN AUSTRIA

VORARLBERG, RHINE PROVINCE OF AUSTRIA. This province, which is almost as far from Vienna as from Paris, is situated 'before' the Arlberg Pass, almost wholly in the basin of the Rhine. Many of its features recall Switzerland: the high mountains and the Rhine lowland, the frontage on Lake Constance, the nature of the economy, the advanced development of hydro-electric resources, the cotton industry, and the proportion of the working population employed in manufacturing (51 per cent, the highest proportion after Vienna). Austria owns less than one-twentieth of Lake Constance, but Bregenz, capital of the Vorarlberg province, is situated on its shores. Here Austria incorporates a small part of the Rhine foreland, the Rhine valley, the large village of Lustenau surrounded by its orchards and market-gardens, and the textile centre of Dornbirn. Feldkirch and its castle lie in an area of glacial ridges at the end of the transverse valley section of the Ill through the Pre-Alps; this is the real gateway to the Federal

INDUSTRY IN AUSTRIA. *The Linz–Vienna–Graz industrial region is further from Innsbruck and the Brenner route than the corresponding Swiss industrial region is from the St Gotthard route. This comparative isolation from the main routes of European trade is one of the handicaps of Austrian industry in the face of Swiss competition, but it is offset in part by Austria's possession of far greater reserves of timber and of mineral deposits, in particular oil, iron ore and magnesite. Industries follow the relief and are strung along the valleys.*

AGRICULTURE, STOCK-FARMING AND FORESTRY IN AUSTRIA. *Agriculture is the chief occupation in the Alpine foreland along the Danube, and in the Styrian foreland to the east and south-east of Vienna (Burgenland and the Graz district), as well as in the Mur valley and Carinthia (Klagenfurt). These agricultural districts cover little more than twenty per cent of the total area of Austria, but the intensity with which they are cultivated varies greatly: in the Burgenland district the soil benefits from volcanic outcrops and supports a very high rural population. Climate, as well as relief has determined the concentration of agriculture, for these districts are on the fringes of the Hungarian Plain.*

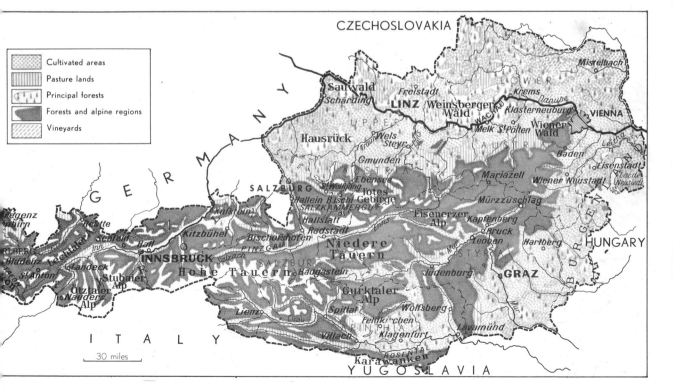

Republic from the west. With the forest of Bregenz, the Ill basin includes most of the Alpine Vorarlberg and can be divided, apart from the Grand Walsertal, into two main valleys: Montafon and Klostertal.

Montafon is the upper valley of the Ill, and its chief town is Schruns. Very remote, like Walsertal, the Montafon region has produced a steady flow of emigrants from the mountains. After the Union, Germany constructed a reservoir dam in the valley to form Lake Silvretta. The power station at Rodund in lower Montafon receives the impounded water of the upper Montafon with a head of 1,300 feet, and produces almost 300 million kWh. Together with Vermunt and other power stations, the Montafon has an output of 1,000 million kWh, most of which is sold to Germany. When the projected installations are completed, including the reservoir at Lünersee, it will supply some 2,000 million kWh.

Eastwards, bare, harsh Klostertal provides a direct route which is, with difficulty, followed by the railway. The Arlberg line has the steepest gradient of any of the main Alpine railways and was intended to weld the Rhine Province of Austria to the rest of the country, and to encourage communications between Switzerland and Western Europe and the old Austro-Hungarian Empire. It was also designed to divert some of the Saint Gotthard traffic towards Trieste. Apart from a tunnel over six miles long, it has required much work in avalanche protection. In Vorarlberg snow is abundant, and on the Tyrolean side of the pass Saint Anton is well known as a winter sports centre. The Arlberg road, the Flexenstrasse, serves many resorts, and the little Walsertal accommodates at least 350,000 foreigners each winter. However, avalanches are dangerous and have caused many accidents in a mountain region where traffic lacks the natural facilities afforded to neighbouring Tyrol with its many gaps and passes.

TYROL, THE ACCESSIBLE REGION. Since the inclusion of its southern part into Italy, Tyrol and East Tyrol have been separated, and in this volume East Tyrol will be considered with eastern Austria. Taking its name from the château of Tirolo, near Merano, it grew up as a State on the crest of the Alps, controlling the Brenner Pass. The pass is only 4,495 feet high, but it would hardly have succeeded in founding the fortune of a political organisation without the exceptionally good approach routes along the Adige and Inn valleys. Completely Alpine, the Tyrol stretches from west to east along the Inn, which bends in the opposite direction at each end, at Landeck and Kufstein. Halfway between these points and to the south of the Inn, is the junction with the Sill valley, or Wipptal, which leads up to the Brenner; this is framed on both sides by the glaciated valleys of Ötztal and Zillertal. These valleys on the south side of the Inn have developed because of a typical lack of symmetry in the Alps. To the north of the Inn the calcareous and schistose Alps, including the Karwendel (9,013 feet), rise in a steep, defensive wall. Fortunately there are several breaches opened up by former glaciers, the Fern Pass (3,965 feet), Seefeld (3,871 feet), and the Achen Pass (2,877 feet), so the Tyrol is easily linked to the Bavarian foreland, much as it is linked to the province of Salzburg by the glaciated passes of Saint Johann and Kitzbühel.

Now that the Austrian Tyrol no longer bestrides the Brenner, the east-west axis of the Inn valley has become more important than the north-south axis. The Inn valley forms a very good natural region. It is over 80 miles long and is part of the longitudinal valley which starts in Klostertal at the junction of the crystalline mountains and the Pre-Alps, and extends eastwards along the Salzach and the Enns. Its height fluctuates between 2,600 and 1,600 feet. The föhn, particularly noticeable at Innsbruck, and the sunny aspect of the northern slopes help to make the Inn a warm, sheltered valley, although the winters are severe. Above Innsbruck, the upper Inntal adheres faithfully to a three-course rotation of rye, barley and potatoes,

and industry is scattered; Landeck produces electro-chemicals and numerous textile workshops make *loden* (thick local woollen cloth), cotton and ribbon. The broad alluvial lowland of the lower Inntal dotted with wooden haylofts and stooks at haymaking time, is the region of the 'pounds', a system whereby the fields are put to grass for a number of years. Around Innsbruck the important industries are engineering, metal-work and optics; at Wörgl and Kufstein they include the production of pharmaceutical products, timber and cement. The copper, silver and salt industries were once responsible for the wealth of the Tyrol, and the small towns of Hall, Schwaz and Rattenberg with its strange *talweg* roofs, are evidence of this erstwhile prosperity.

Electric power is one of the foundations of the economy of the modern Tyrol. The Ötztal should, in time, produce more than 2,000 million kWh, part of which will be exported to Bavaria and Italy. The wonderfully blue Achensee above the Inn valley supplies a large power station. The upper Inn should also supply a considerable quantity of power, but fulfilment of projected schemes is linked with Swiss and Italian plans. The Prutz-Imst section is awaiting development. With the power stations of Zillertal, the Tyrol has available at the moment more than 1,000 million kWh.

Finally, tourist trade is important in the Tyrol in summer and winter alike. Innsbrück, in a valley where population density is 260 per square mile, is a popular centre. The town controls the Brenner and the Arlberg passes. The alluvial fan of the Sill has pushed the Inn against the valley side at Hötting, and thus determined the site of the bridge to which the town owes its name. From the cable railway running to the Hafelekar the whole outline of this Alpine capital can be clearly seen, in many respects similar to Grenoble but in a higher position and more deeply embedded in the mountains; it is a ski-ing resort, a tourist base, a commercial and residential town, and a university centre.

THE PROVINCE OF SALZBURG. Before the construction of the Tauern tunnel (5.2 miles) and the opening of the Gross Glockner tourist road, the ecclesiastical State of Salzburg controlled the longitudinal Alpine valleys. At the beginning of the eighteenth century, the Archbishopric was linked to the Inn valley by the upper Salzach, the Gerlostal and the Zillertal; by the upper Mur to its enclaves of Friesach, St. Andrä and Sachsenburg. It was well stationed along the routes to the south, in the direction of Klagenfurt and the Drava, and also controlled the Alpine crest by means of the Radstädter-Tauern pass (5,700 feet), which is still part of Salzburg today. The province is shaped like an inverted T, the horizontal line of the T formed by the Salzach and the upper Enns, with part of the upper Mur, and the vertical line consisting of a strip of territory between the German re-entrant of Berchtesgaden and the Salzkammergut in Upper Austria.

The high limestone Alps of Salzburg, with those of neighbouring Salzkammergut, belong to a particularly rugged section of the mountains. The Steinernes Meer, the Hochkönig (9,639 feet), and Dachstein (9,827 feet) whose tremendous south-west slope falls within the province, are partly Dolomitic mountains and are excellent bastions. The snowline here lies at about 9,000 feet; the limestone conceals wonderful caves embellished with ice cascades, such as those at Dachstein, and especially the Eisriesenwelt, 'The Ice Giants World' of the Tennen mountains. The wild beauty of these mountains is enhanced on the northern slopes by a series of lakes recalling Lake Lucerne, which include the pleasant lake of St Wolfgang and the deep and forbidding-looking Lake Hallstatt at the foot of the Dachstein.

The longitudinal valley of the Salzach is not so varied in shape or coloration. Differences in height are greater than in the Salzburg area. From Krimml (3,468 feet) to St. Johann in Pongau (1,860 feet), the Pinzgau or valley of the upper

posite: *The Rhine*
St Goar.
EDWARD HOLMES

low: *The harbour at*
mburg.
LOUIS, RAPHO

Salzach stretches for about 50 miles. Some dozen tributary valleys pour in water from the melting glaciers of the Gross Venediger (11,008 feet), the Gross Glockner (12,461 feet), Sonnblick, etc. This valley, regular in size throughout its length, was covered by the Quaternary ice. The Salzach glacier, which was over 6,000 feet high, escaped partly through the Thurn Pass (4,176 feet), and by Zell am See, where the huge gap indicates the size of the glacier that passed through to the Saalach.

The railway now runs through Pinzgau, formerly one of the most isolated parts of Austria, linking Salzburg and Innsbruck via Zell and Kitzbühel with its schistose highland; the road from Kitzbühel to St. Johann in Pongau and beyond goes via the Thurn Pass. Smoke from its aluminium factories draws attention to Lend some distance away, recalling again the fact that this is the land of hydro-electric power. The steep, ice-covered High Tauern are very suitable for hydro-electric development, well demonstrated by the great installations at Kaprun. The valley of Kaprun, with the power station of the same name, began to operate under the German occupation, and today includes two large reservoirs: the Wasserfallboden, nearly 400 feet high above its foundations, supplies the factory at Kaprun; the Mooserboden feeds the factory at Limberg. Together they hold more than 5,650 million cu. ft. of water. A smaller dam on the southern side of the Tauern collects the water from the Pasterze glacier, which is then diverted through a seven-mile tunnel to the other side of the watershed and into the Mooserboden reservoir. Even now the province of Salzburg is a big producer of power for the Federal Republic.

It is also one of the most popular tourist areas. The Gross Glockner road, opened in 1935, has the advantage of crossing a section of high mountain where there was formerly no route for cars between the Brenner and the Radstädter-Tauern passes, nearly 100 miles as the crow flies. It also forms a link between the two parts of the Tyrol, and between western Carinthia and the north slope of the Alps, which were previously able to communicate only by means of a long detour through Italian territory. The Gross Glockner route is a fine road which shortens the journey between Venice and Salzburg by 94 miles, and rises to 8,212 feet amid glorious mountain scenery. The salt mines of Dürnberg, near Hallein, and the copper mines of Mitterberg are important industries around Salzburg.

Salzburg presides over the destiny of an extensive Alpine hinterland. Its rivers have descended from the mountains, and Mönschberg is part of an old consolidated delta of the Salzach. The castle looks down on this handsome town of over 100,000 inhabitants, enhanced with squares and buildings in the baroque style; and every year music-lovers from all over the world gather for the festival which is devoted chiefly to the works of Mozart.

EASTERN AUSTRIA

East of Salzburg Austria extends nearly 190 miles from north to south, but less than 65 miles from east to west. With East Tyrol, Upper and Lower Austria, the federal area of Vienna, Burgenland, Styria and Carinthia, this part of Austria covers 24,450 sq. miles out of a total of 32,000 sq. miles, and includes 87 per cent of the population of the Republic.

THE EASTERN ALPS. In eastern Austria the Alps widen out and lose height. The Styrian mountain mass of Totes Gebirge, though structurally the same as the limestone mountains of the Salzkammergut, barely exceeds 8,200 feet. The well-named Nieder Tauern is nowhere higher than 9,500 feet. And unlike the rest of the Alps, the southern slope is broader than the northern slope which, once beyond the bend in the Enns at Hieflau, has only a small share of Alpine wealth and population.

Whilst the economy of Salzkammergut is dependent on the development of salt mining and cattle-rearing, plus the income from the tourist industry, the transverse valley of the Enns concentrates in particular on metallurgy. The factories at Steyr, producing armaments, cycles, motor-cars and pressed steel, owe their development to the rich iron ore of Eisenerz, well-known for its remarkable open-cast mining in the valley of the Erzbach. This river joins the Enns at Hieflau, an old centre for the processing and trans-shipment of Styrian ore. The combined resources of iron ore and wood encouraged the development of the iron industry in this region of Steyr, from which Styria derives its name.

The Tauern hydro-electric scheme in the province of Salzburg. In the foreground is the Margaritzen Reservoir with the Möll Dam on the left and the Margaritzen Dam on the right. They form part of a network of dams serving several power stations. AUSTRIAN EMBASSY

Stift Klosterneuburg, buildings of the twelfth-century Augustine canonry. To the left is the church, dedicated to the patron saint of Austria, St Leopold. AUSTRIAN EMBASSY

The Trisana railway bridge near the Arlberg Pass. Austrian railways have been rapidly improved and electrified since the war.
AUSTRIAN EMBASSY

The Enns also provides some of the electric power of Upper Austria, on the northern Alpine slopes, producing nearly 700 million kWh per annum. Still more is anticipated of the Enns (2,500 million kWh), and the power station under construction at Hieflau marks the beginning of complete control of the river.

On the southern side of the Alps, East Tyrol is fairly isolated. The lands of the Drava begin here — a series of east-to-west valleys, including the lower Möll, the Gail, and the Drava itself, bordered by the magnificent ridges of the Austrian Dolomites south of Lienz. The rampart of the Carnic Alps, passable by way of the Plöcken Pass (4,461 feet), checked erosion in the direction of Friuli; all drainage is directed towards the Hungarian Basin. The valleys are quite low (about 1,700 feet at Spittal, on the Drava) and the area has an almost southern appearance along the lakes of Millstatt and Wörth, which are very popular in summer. On the upper Drava, above Lienz, the landscape takes on more of the appearance of the Grisons than the Hungarian Lowland. At Sillian, not far from the Italian frontier, the trough leads towards the Brenner by way of the Dobbiaco Pass; here the peaceful green valley of the upper Drava with its granaries and large rough-cast houses brings to mind the Rhaeto-Romansch regions.

The countryside of southern Carinthia has an unusual region in the 47-mile-long Klagenfurt basin and lies at the foot of the high wall of the Karawanken separating Austria from Yugoslavia. The railway to Ljubljana and Gorizia overcomes the obstacle with a five-mile tunnel. This was an important area in Roman times but is rather isolated today and devoted mainly to agriculture. Industrial activity is represented by mining in the Villach area and by lead and zinc processing between Bleiberg and Kreuth. However, industry is expanding more rapidly to the north, as much in Styria as in Carinthia, in a network of valleys bordered by rounded mountains that lack distinctive Alpine appearance.

In the north-south valleys of Görschitz, Lavant and the middle Mur, and in the south-west north-east trough of the upper Mur and the Mürz, local resources of timber, iron ore and lignite have been developed. Various industries exist in the towns of Voitsberg, Köflach and Oberdorf to the west of Graz, in Wolfsberg, St. Andrä in the Lavanttal of Carinthia, and in Leoben, Seegraben and Fohnsdorf to the south-west of the iron ore field of Eisenerz. Iron works are important in the valley of the upper Mur around Leoben and Donawitz,

where there are blast-furnaces, steel works and engineering workshops. At Köflach, St. Andrä and Wolfsberg lignite is used in the glass and cellulose industries and in the production of electricity. Finally, paper is manufactured all along the Mur, from Judenburg to Graz.

Such industrial development gives a high density of population to the valleys on the south side of the eastern Alps. The longitudinal valley of the Mur and Mürz has a string of small and medium-sized towns from Fohnsdorf-Judenburg, through Knittelfeld, Leoben, Donawitz and Bruck to Kindberg. The dense population and multiplicity of industries have had little effect on the rural charm of 'green Styria', whose proportion of woodland is nearly 50 per cent, compared with 37 per cent for the whole of Austria. From Semmering with its frontage of large hotels to Bruck, the valley floor of the Mürz is under grass. Fields and barns increase in number towards Mürzzuschlag; there is a succession of villages of rough-cast houses, where timber is seen only in the roof shingles and the odd hay lofts. The slopes are covered with mixed broad-leaved and coniferous forest, and close-felling leaves inoffensive gashes, for the relief is relatively gentle when it is not levelled off into flat-topped mountains, as at Pack Pass. From the steep and isolated hill of Schlossberg, at Graz, the view includes the Alpine fringes of the Hungarian Basin in the east, a hilly rather than mountainous landscape; the valley of the Mur and the town are also visible, the latter with its high brown-tiled roofs and onion-shaped steeples. At night the activity in the streets resembles that of a Mediterranean town. Graz, a market town, communications centre and second city of Austria, is also an industrial area with factories for motor-cars, shoes, paper and engineering.

THE BOHEMIAN MASSIF. Part of the south side of the Bohemian Massif is shared between the Provinces of Upper and Lower Austria. These borderlands of Hercynian Europe reach 4,521 feet in the Blöckenstein, an extension of the Bohemian Forest. Both above and below Linz, the Massif extends in places beyond the Danube, as at the gorge of Grein and the gorge of Wachau in Lower Austria. In this province the Waldviertel is contrasted with the Weinviertel, the region of fertile hills east of Krems, where the ancient bedrock is concealed under Tertiary sands, clays and loess. Sheltered by the Bohemian Massif and the Alps, the Weinviertel has a light precipitation. It concentrates on intensive wheat production, viticulture towards Retz and Eggenburg, and raising stall-fed cattle, encouraged by the proximity of the Vienna market.

THE ALPINE FORELAND. The Hausruck (2,625 feet), an old alluvial fan of the Salzach and Traun, recalls on a smaller scale the Swiss Napf. As the glaciers here hardly reached beyond the Alps, the softer Tertiary formations make a large extension into the hills of the Innviertel, between the Inn and the Traun. In this rural area industry is gaining ground. The Austro-Bavarian power stations of Ering and Obernberg on the Inn, and that of Braunau supply huge quantities of power to the large aluminium factory of Ranshofen. The lowlands of fluvio-glacial gravel between the Traun and the Enns have been cut up into terraces and used for arable farming. Orchards surround the villages. Linen is manufactured at Lambach, glass at Wels, and there are paper works along the Traun. Finally, east of the Enns the forelands stretch between the Bohemian Massif and the Pre-Alps. In this strip, with its hot summers, the arable land extends over the loess and Tertiary rocks right up to the lower slopes of the Pre-Alps. Between Durnstein, on the Danube, and the approaches to Vienna the countryside has a prosperous look. The vineyards and plum orchards are replaced by open fields with strips where maize and cultivated grass are grown in rotation on the arable land. Apple and walnut trees are everywhere. In the broad valley

The ammonium sulphate plant at the Austrian nitrogen works at Linz. 180,000 tons of ammonium sulphate are produced annually at this factory. Chemicals are an important industry in Linz.
AUSTRIAN EMBASSY

of St Pölten, parallel to the Wachau, the villages are close together, and the large farmhouses with their closed yards are surrounded by small houses. St Pölten, a communications and industrial centre (artificial textiles, paper manufacture, milling, etc.), precedes the plain of Tulln, which is the first of the Danube plains before the Vienna basin is reached.

Vienna and the valley of the Danube

THE UNITY OF THE NORTHERN FRINGE. The stately Danube is not entirely free from disadvantages. Between Linz and Vienna the river cuts into the spurs of the Bohemian Massif, and its speed is between 7 and 10 feet per second. The average flow of the river at Linz is 53,000 cu. ft., with a winter minimum of 35,000 cu. ft. in December and a maximum in June of 76,000 cu. ft. Unfortunately, this June maximum can coincide with the violent storms of a continental summer, resulting in disastrous floods like those of July 1954. Linz, with Urfahr on the opposite bank, is a bridge-town which grew up at the end of the Ottensheim gorge. It controls the confluence of the Traun with the Danube as well as the crossing leading, via Freistadt, to Budejovice in Czechoslovakia. The capital of Upper Austria is also an important industrial town. Linz has blast-furnaces, steel works, coke ovens and a thermal power station in the former Hermann Göring Works, now the Vereinigten Österreichischen Eisen und Stahlwerke. Its factories also produce synthetic nitrates, sulphuric acid, matches and footwear, and distil lignite. Along the quays there are docks with silos, petroleum equipment and shipbuilding yards.

The descent of the Danube by boat is of most interest below the confluence of the Enns. The low terraces of the Enns are

followed by the most recent Tertiary formations, then comes the crystalline gorge of Grein-Ybbs, covered with a mixture of beeches and conifers. Leaving Pöchlarn, the feudal ruins conjure up thoughts of the legend of the Nibelungen. St Florian, between the Traun and Enns, recalls the Babenbergs, whose capital was moved downstream, first to Tulln and later to Vienna. However, it is in Wachau that the Danube valley is most like the gorge section of the Rhine. The ravine with wooded slopes, crowned by medieval ruins, runs north, conforming to the trend of the Hercynian structure. The vines on the terraces at Spitz and Durnstein lend a more colourful touch to the austere scenery.

The Danube is a rich source of potential power. The plant under construction at Ybbs-Persenbeug will provide nearly one million kWh, and is being jointly constructed by Austria and Germany. A further twelve stations already planned between Jochenstein and Hainburg, situated below Vienna, should produce more than 11,000 million kWh, and will assist in controlling the river.

THE EASTERN LOWLANDS OF AUSTRIA. A series of rivers descending the Graz Alps to the south-east have dissected the Styrian foreland into hills, and their sands and clays form part of the infilling of the Hungarian Basin. In the steeply undulating country between the Raab and the Mur, sweet chestnuts and vines are plentiful, the wine being particularly excellent around Halbenrain, at the most easterly point of Austria. The prosperity of this region is based on maize, orchards, poultry, cattle and horses. In the area next to Burgenland, near the volcanic outcrops of Güssing, which is crowned by one of the castles which have given their name to the province, the density of rural population is so high and large properties are still so widespread that there is constant emigration. In the region of Eisenstadt, to the west of the Neusiedler lake, the vine is exceptionally important. The lake itself is very shallow and fringed on the north and west by heathland and reed-covered pools; there are also stretches of farm land, with the former manorial demesnes. All enjoy a burning summer climate like that of the Hungarian Plain.

Although the lowlands of the Leitha and the Marchfeld, to the south and north of the Danube respectively, are aligned in a south-west to north-east direction, the Vienna Basin nevertheless belongs to the sphere of Hungarian subsidence. It is bordered by a fault-line and a thermal line running from Mödling and Baden as far as Burgenland. To the south of Vienna and along the mountain slopes, the plain is edged with gentle and highly cultivated hills. It ends in a kind of gulf which spreads out between the Alps and the hills of the Leitha around Wiener Neustadt and Neunkirchen. The alluvium distributed by the streams descending in the south-west is covered with pine woods. The metallurgical industry is important at Wiener Neustadt, and other industries include engineering and tyre manufacture. To the north of the Danube, the alluvial lands of the Marchfeld form the granary of Lower Austria. In the north of the plain, in the hills of the depression of Moravia, an oilfield, Zisterdorf, extends from the neighbourhood of Vienna to Breclav in Czechoslavakia. Pipelines link this field to the refineries of the Danube, particularly Lobau and Floridsdorf.

VIENNA. Vienna (Wien) owes its name to the modest river Wien, partly covered over as it traverses the built-up parts of the city, but by Schönbrunn opening a route toward the west, through the lonely forests of the Wienerwald to Linz. The Wienerwald is part of the flysch zone on the northern edge of the Alps which projects like a spur towards the Danube. It is not very high (less than 3,000 feet) but is notable for its numerous valleys and dense forest cover, preserved in the past by the landed gentry. Thus the capital has at its gates a huge natural park, invaded every week-end by crowds of

A general view of Vienna with the Wiener Burgtheater (Vienna Civic Theatre) in the foreground. AUSTRIAN EMBASSY

Oil derricks at Zisterdorf, the centre for oil production in Lower Austria. Pipelines connect the area with the refineries on the Danube.
P. ALMASY

Factories at Donawitz, in Styria. Metallurgical industries are carried on in the Upper Mur valley, round Leoben-Donawitz, where there are blast furnaces, steel works and engineering workshops.
P. ALMASY

its citizens. At the foot of the Wienerwald, to the east, they sip the local wine and enjoy the music in the gardens in the 'Heueringen' of Grinzing and Neustift, while Mödling and Baden are famous for their thermal waters. In Vienna itself, which is not a bridge-town like Linz, the Danube is divided into three branches: the Canal, the boundary of old Vienna on the north side; the Old Danube, suitable for aquatic sports; and the Danube proper, straightened after 1868 and confined between the high banks of its larger bed. Between the Canal and the Danube, to the south of Leopoldstadt, lie the fields and trees of the Prater. The famous Ring was constructed in the second half of the nineteenth century on the site of the fortifications and glacis which surrounded the 'Innere Stadt' and was dominated by the bold spire of St Stephen's Cathedral. With its public buildings and gardens bordering the Hofburg, the Opera House and its avenues, the airy and peaceful Ring contrasts markedly with the early eighteenth-century suburbs found between the Ring and the Gürtel, the encircling avenue on the site of the old defensive wall. These suburbs include the very busy districts of the West Station and the Maria-hilfstrasse. From the height of the Kahlenberg there is a fine view of the town which brings two worlds together: the western and Alpine world, and the eastern world with its characteristic lowlands. Formerly a communications centre and today a frontier town, Vienna's buildings and its guide books recall the city's past. However, Vienna has overcome what can only be called its earlier 'Imperial complex'. It has a variety of industries: engineering (motor-cars), textiles, (linen, hemp and jute), factories for footwear, glass and petroleum. With its artistic wealth and its cultural influence, all these contribute to the active life of an outstanding city. With more than 1,700,000 inhabitants it concentrates within its limits one-quarter of the population of Austria, a capital all the more authoritative because the country is so small. In spite of economic crises, civil war, the fighting at the end of the Second World War, which damaged it severely, and a long military occupation, the noble bearing of this great city augurs well for the future of the Austrian State.

The future of Austria

A SOUND ECONOMIC BASIS. The economy of Austria rests on solid foundations. The heart of a former political organisation which had had a balanced economy but which was weakened by internal discord, Austria had, after 1918, to cope with the inevitable difficulties of becoming a neighbour to the successor States which were now its rivals. This situation was aggravated by the misfortune of having to support a capital too large for the rest of the country, which was almost entirely Alpine in character. A complete readjustment was necessary, and this was interrupted by the 'Anschluss'. The Second World War and the occupation weighted the scales still further against it. After the collapse of the Third Reich, as after that of the dual monarchy, Austria had once again to face fundamental reorganisation. Uneven distribution of the most densely populated and prosperous areas in relation to the Brenner axis cannot wholly explain the difference between Austrian and Swiss economies.

Austria is more capable than Switzerland of feeding itself. Of the working population, 32 per cent (against 21 per cent in Switzerland) are engaged in agriculture. With a total population 40 per cent greater than that of Switzerland, Austria produces slightly less milk and almost the same amount of wine; on the other hand, she harvests twice as much wheat, three times as many potatoes, even more barley, oats and maize, and four-and-a-half times as much sugar-beet. Agricultural equipment increased considerably after the Union and after the abolition of customs barriers between Austria and Germany; more recently, in the post-war years, it was helped by Marshall Aid.

Austria is still more fortunate than her neighbour in power resources. She produces six million tons of lignite, two-thirds of which come from Styria. Nevertheless, she still has to import coal from Germany and Poland. The coke ovens of Linz, although they have a capacity of 1 million tons, are inadequate to cover Austrian requirements, and German coke has to be imported. But if the lignite forms a rather small industrial basis for Austria, it is mainly because she has a heavy industry that requires large quantities of coal and coke. She also has petroleum resources which make her the third most important European producer after Russia and Rumania, and superior to Germany. With a production of some three million tons, Austria produces twice as much mineral oil as Switzerland imports. Oil refining has become one of the major industries, and processing the by-products and the natural gas is of obvious interest for the conurbation of Vienna. Austria has an annual hydro-electric production of 40,000 million kWh, which represents only about one-sixth of the capacity available for development. Omitting salt, which is also produced in Switzerland, Austria has more raw materials available than her neighbour. The iron ore production of Styria and Carinthia of about three million tons is huge compared with the 100,000 tons mined by Switzerland. Besides magnesite (she is one of the world's main producers) and several non-ferrous metals, Austria has more timber in her forests. Austrian woodlands are exceptionally dense. Forest covers 37 per cent of the land, as compared with 24 per cent of Switzerland, and forest production is almost three times as important as in Switzerland.

Because of her iron ore and a very old tradition of iron working, Austria is provided with a heavy iron and steel industry in Styria and at Linz. Yet for the most part this has not developed much into secondary industries, and a large proportion of its products are exported; these include pig-iron, crude steel, refractory bricks and slabs of magnesite, paper, fertilizers and electricity. No doubt this type of economy supplies Austria's need for foreign currency, but it also has its origin in historical conditions. Austrian industry was intended to supply the requirements of the old Austro-Hungarian Empire, then the Third Reich; it was not developed with the object of competing in world markets.

Unlike Switzerland, Austria lacks a solid financial foundation. From its inception the Republic has had monetary difficulties. With the Anschluss, three-quarters of the firms became German property; then petroleum was considered as coming under reparations and was put under Russian control until the signing of the peace treaty. American help was necessary after the Second World War, similar to that of S.D.N. in 1922, to enable Austria to achieve a sound financial position and to develop her industrial equipment. For the years 1950, 1951 and 1952, the contribution of the European Recovery Programme reached 1,756 million Schillings for the construction of hydro-electric power-stations alone; including the high-tension lines it was 2,200 million Schillings, twice the sum of the national contributions.

A FUTURE OF PROMISE. The progress already achieved by Austrian economy encourages justifiable hopes for the future. Financial stability was achieved as a result of certain measures which included nationalisation of all electricity undertakings producing for distribution, certain banks, transport companies and mines. The three-year investment plan introduced in 1950, which was partly financed by funds from the Marshall Plan, also helped to stabilise finances. Austria has had to find work for several hundreds of thousands of refugees and displaced persons. New industries have been started, notably the glass industry; factories have opened using the newly acquired manpower. The returns on the Federal railways have increased. Electrification has been completed on 22 per cent of the system, totalling 3,750 miles and carrying 45 per cent of the traffic. Already the line has been electrified

between the Swiss frontier and Vienna. The production of hydro-electric power has increased nearly four times since 1938. The nitrate industry of Linz, developed during the period of the Anschluss, and the engineering industries have made good progress; however, this success has not been shared by the textile and paper industries, which are influenced by world conditions.

Finally, the tourist industry is one of Austria's most important resources. Statistics show that in 1928—29 there were 4,203,000 tourists, including 1,832,000 from abroad; this fell to 2,772,000 including 618,000 foreigners in 1933—34, following restrictions introduced by the Reich against certain nationalities staying in Austria. After the Second World War, the tourist trade, at first almost non-existent, quickly developed again and exceeded the figures for 1928—29. The receipts from the tourist industry cover an important part of the balance of trade deficit. Industrial production has doubled since 1937. Agricultural production has improved to the extent that the import of foodstuffs accounts for only 20 per cent of total imports compared with 30 per cent in 1937.

Because of its position in Europe, Austria can only prosper in an atmosphere of good will with its neighbours. It remains a transit country for movements from north to south. Besides, any improvement in east-west relationships could only be to its advantage.

The Austrian tourist industry depends very much on Germany, whose people find the natural wonders of a high mountain region more or less at their very door. Increasing quantities of electricity are exported to Germany and Italy, for power produced in western Austria exceeds local requirements and is available for export. The Vorarlberg sends electricity to the thermal power stations of the Rhine and Bavaria; the same is true of the Tyrol. Lienz is linked to Italy by a high-tension cable. These are the possibilities which the Austrian potential of hydro-electric power offers to Europe, and this is the part that she should be called upon to play, after the harnessing of the Danube.

Henri ONDE

The elegant town hall of Vienna. AUSTRIAN EMBASSY

Foundries and copper works along the Lower Rhine, at Duisburg Hochfeld. GERMAN GOVERNMENT INFORMATION OFFICE

GERMANY

GERMANY occupies a northward-sloping region of Central Europe. With the exception of the Bavarian plateau, the whole country drains towards the North Atlantic and its gulfs. Of all the great national units Germany is the most exclusively European. Although in relation to the central spine of the Alps it occupies a situation comparable with that of Italy, there is this important difference: Germany does not jut into an inland sea towards Africa or Asia.

Since 1918 Germany has had common frontiers with ten different States; a Germanic country with Latin or Slav neighbours. German history has been played out within a continental framework — from the Rhine to the Vistula and from the Alps to the Baltic. The brief colonial period — between 1884 and 1914 — when only 7,000 Germans emigrated to the ephemeral African possessions, is negligible in comparison with the thousand years of Germany's continental history. Nevertheless, few countries down the centuries have furnished a greater number of migrants and emigrants. During the tenth, eleventh and twelfth centuries, Germany (or the Holy Roman Empire, as it was from 962 to 1806) waged a struggle of varying fortunes, and ended by reconquering beyond the Elbe the Germanic peoples' original homeland which had been abandoned to the Slavs at the time the Germanic tribes pushed westward. From the thirteenth to the fifteenth centuries, the Germans penetrated still farther eastwards and carried their arms, often with great savagery, beyond the Vistula. Thus, in the history of the West's developing influence and civilisation, we may consider Germany as a type of colonisation intermediate between the Roman, which was solely Mediterranean, and that of modern times, which is world-wide.

The German 'Push towards the East' (Drang nach Osten), which during the eighteenth and nineteenth centuries assumed largely the shape of an economic and technical domination, had before its ebb in the twentieth century determined that the German lot should be very different from the future offered to the maritime nations by the ocean.

ACHIEVEMENT OF UNITY (1871).

Germany has always had shifting frontiers except in the essential regions of the Rhineland and the Hercynian massifs which formed its cradle. Furthermore, within the linguistic and ethnic mass of the German lands, the country was continually being subdivided into an ever-changing mosaic of units of different degrees of political importance. Among these units, the most numerous, the most unstable and the smallest were to be found in the essential German regions, where physical conditions too are the most diversified. These small States, although they enjoyed various political constitutions (kingdoms, principalities, ecclesiastical fiefs, free towns, Hansa cities, Länder) have always been held together by a succession of links — leagues, confederations, empires. A federative tendency is a typical factor in German political conceptions.

Although the idea of a specifically Germanic 'area' assumed more definite shape after Luther had fashioned and unified the language, and although the concept of one unified nation, das Deutschland, was making headway as early as the end of the eighteenth century, matters came to a head with the French Revolution. Between 1802 and 1806, Napoleon's action in reducing the number of sovereign German States from 300 to 39 gave practical effect to some of the nationalist aspirations. The tendency toward national unity was further strengthened in 1812 when Prussia led the reaction against Napoleon's domination. The Germanic Confederation of 1815 was the first effective step towards unity. From 1828 to 1854, the Customs Union (Zollverein) obliterated most of the economic frontiers inside Germany. Nevertheless, a final internal conflict took place in 1866 between victorious Prussia and the southern German States. The opponents were ultimately reconciled and with the alliance of 1870—1871 German unity became an accomplished fact in the form of the Second German Empire.

After forty-seven years of smooth-working unification in which local susceptibilities were respected, Germany, after her defeat in the First World War, was thrown once more into a period of confusion. After the so-called 'Weimar' Federal Republic (1918—33) came the era of the Third Reich during which the nation was first swept up in a whirl of triumphant expansion and then cast down into the abyss. Now, under the regime of the Bonn Federal Republic, West Germany has effected an almost incredible revival.

During the last half-century Germany has undergone the following changes in area and population: in 1909, 208,934 square miles and 64 million inhabitants; in 1929, 187,835 square miles and 69 million inhabitants; in 1939, 226,299 square miles and 79 million inhabitants; in 1946, at the end of the Second World War, 137,063 square miles and 66 million inhabitants. By 1959 the population had risen to 72 million

DISSECTION IN 1945.

Although the territorial modifications brought about by the Second World War (and by the 'Cold War') have not been recognised or confirmed by international treaty, Germany is today dissected after a period of division into occupation zones by the victorious Allies in 1945 — the British zone in the north-west, the American in the centre, the French in the south-west, and the Russian in the east. The Prussian provinces beyond the Oder and the Neisse have been detached from Germany, their populations have been displaced and the regions annexed to Poland or the U.S.S.R. (39,758 square miles to Poland, and 4,246 square miles to Russia). In the West, the Saar territory was constituted an autonomous area and linked economically with France; it is now re-united politically and economically with Germany. What remained of Germany was in 1949 split into two States for an indefinite period, and the frontiers determined by the arbitrary boundaries of the military occupation zones. These two States, situated in the heartland of German territory, are linked together by a common past, a single nationality, and a firm hope of reunification, yet they are at the same time divided by the most diametrically opposed economic and social policies. The German Federal Republic (the Bund) in the west is a federal and conservative State basing its policy on liberal capitalist ideas and practices, while the German

Democratic Republic (*Deutsche demokratische Republik*) in the east is a centralised, State-controlled unit developing along socialist lines. Moreover, Berlin, the old capital of the Reich, is in part an enclave joined (under certain suspensive conditions) to the *Bund*, though the city is situated in the middle of the German Democratic Republic's territory.

The landscape and regions of Germany

FOUR GREAT NATURAL REGIONS. Germany is a central European transition zone in which continental and maritime climates are almost evenly balanced, though there are marked local variations. In the north the influence of the sea in summer combines with the latitude to produce isotherms which decrease regularly from south to north, allowing for differences in altitude. Thus the July average temperature is 60.5° F. on the coastal plain, while on the southern plateaus the average is 61.5° F., and exceeds 66° F. in the mild Rhine valley. In January, the Rhine and Moselle valleys, Westphalia and the Frisian area are the only regions with temperatures above freezing-point. The 30° F. isotherm follows, generally speaking, the 10° meridian. In the Danube basin temperatures of from 29.5° to 23° F. occur, especially near the source of the river and in areas near the Alps.

In Schleswig-Holstein and on the Great Plain (particularly where these regions face the stormy North Sea), cool winds and a misty atmosphere lend the landscape a rather greyish 'western' colour all the year round. Rainfall is fairly regular at all seasons (198 rainy days at Hamburg). The autumns are mild and long. The springtime is chilly and comes late; in mid-April there is not a bud to be seen, whereas along the Rhine fruit-trees are already in flower. On the Baltic slope and in Brandenburg the weather is drier. Beyond Hanover snow is more frequent and lies longer. The Hercynian heights in the north have from 200 to 230 days of precipitation (60 to 100 of which are of snow).

Over the hills and up the deep valleys of the Rhine or the Weser a very different climate prevails. In summer rain is heavy on the heights, and both warmth and cold are more marked because the low-lying areas sheltered from the westerly winds are relatively dry. These rains are often stormy, and white cumulus clouds piled up against a rather harsh blue sky hover over southern Germany during the summer. After a fine autumn, the brilliant winter sun — except when masked by the frosty Danube fogs — shines for hours on end over the snowy expanses. In the sheltered middle valley of the Rhine, Mainz especially and even Cologne (which enjoys the highest average temperatures of any place in Germany and boasts air that is soft from the sea and warm from the river) present skies, landscapes and a flora that are almost southern.

Four great natural regions (of unequal area) make up the land of Germany today: (1) The narrow fringe of the Bavarian Alps. (2) The Subalpine plateau of Bavaria and Swabia, south of the Danube. (3) The most ancient massifs (Hercynian massifs) north of the Danube and the basins they enclose, including the middle valley of the Rhine and the valleys of the Moselle, the Neckar, the Main, the Weser, the Saale and the Elbe. (4) The western extremity of the broad, low, alluvial glacial plain of northern Europe, lying between the Hercynian massifs and the North Sea and the Baltic.

THE NARROW ALPINE FRINGE AND THE BAVARIAN PLATEAU. In the extreme south and stretching for some 160 miles (drained throughout by the Danube), the Bavarian Alps are no more than an Alpine fringe. This narrow northward-looking slope, some ten miles wide, is made up of a succession of short 'links', thickly wooded up to 5,200 feet and at some seasons of the year exposed to extreme cold. The links are intersected by grassy corridors, with three deeper

indentations: the Allgäu, the upper valley of the Iller; the Garmisch basin on the Amper, and the Berchtesgaden basin. Above the forests, they are blocked by the steep sides and stony wastes of the frontier summits, picturesque peaks when viewed from the plateaus of Bavaria and Upper Swabia.

The Bavarian plateau is a fairly uniform glacis, or slope, pierced by rivers that fan out on its surface. Here the moraines of the most ancient Alpine glaciations have left a jumble of low hills whose rounded surfaces are covered with grassland. Round the ten long lakes, filled-in plains with damp bottoms, like that of the Inn, are of the same glacial origin; so are the peat-bogs and the regions strewn with drift boulders. Wide clearings surrounding the villages cut into the mantle of huge spruce forests. Generally speaking, this region is rather poor.

Farther north, as far as the Danube, where the plain was not subjected to glaciation, the landscape is drier and more rolling, and its dales more densely populated. Little clumps of trees covering a few acres alternate with terraced fields often covered with fertile loess. This, however, spreads out more extensively in the Danube valley, especially in the Dungau with its brown, open fields. The towns here serve mainly as markets for farm produce.

The river Lech running from south to north through the middle of the subalpine plateau is, if not a political frontier — for the *Land* of Bavaria reaches as far as the Iller — at least an ethnological and natural one between Bavaria and Swabia. Bavaria has something eastern European about it, with its monotonous landscapes, its Danubian, essentially peasant and but slightly modernised character; Swabia, more varied in appearance and more attractive, is definitely Western and very much like the Rhineland. Upstream, in a rolling country of recent moraines and molasse, the attractive Allgäu Pre-Alps are covered with rich meadows and dairy-farms. The damp valleys of the Danube's tributaries are enclosed by long, well-wooded ridges and terraces covered with loess, while from Ulm to Donauwörth the Danube runs through marshes in a denuded valley. Westwards, beyond the Iller, the Upper Swabian plateau in Württemberg spreads out in open fields and peat-bogs. In the south lies a jumble of grassy 'molehills', with clumps of firs, and a sprinkling of high-perched farms. Then, lower down, at a height of about 1,300 feet, stretch the shores of Lake Constance, or *Bodensee*, the 'Swabian Sea'. To the east and south of this immense, deep reservoir of the waters of the Upper Rhine rise the ranges of the Austrian and Swiss Alps. The northern shores of Lake Constance enjoy a mild climate and are dotted with gardens and villas set among orchards and even vineyards. This is the 'German Riviera'.

To the north-west of the lake, the fertile Hegau basin, bristling with basalt peaks, backs on to the limestone hills of the Swabian Jura, which are cut by the imposing gorges of the upper Danube.

ANCIENT MASSIFS. The ancient massifs of the Hercynian zone present the most typical of German landscapes — gently rounded, well-wooded hills stretching away as far as the horizon. In the vales neat fields and villages are surrounded by orchards. It is a landscape which, although made up of quite different elements, in many respects resembles the Ile-de-France. As it enters this region, the middle course of the Rhine runs between two massifs, the Vosges in France and the Black Forest in Germany, like two pillars of a collapsed arch.

The Black Forest, or Schwarzwald, raises its loftiest bare granite summits in the south (about 4,900 feet), the highest points in Germany except in the Alps. It is scored by steep, narrow valleys with numerous glacial terraces. On the Baden side, towards the Rhine, there are very small fields, meadows with cheerful farms and terraced villages at the edge of white fir forests. On the Württemberg slopes, to the north-east, the Schwarzwald is nothing but an immense, silent, solid mass of fir forests. The landscape is slightly undulating, without

GERMANY

any striking features, and drops down gently to Pforzheim.

In the neighbourhood of Karlsruhe, on the right bank of the Rhine, the mountains give way for about 30 miles to an attractive and fertile region of low hills and rounded hillocks tilled or planted with vines. This is the Kraichgau, which offers an easy route to the Neckar and the Danubian lands. Before reaching Heidelberg the ground rises, though nowhere exceeding about 2,000 feet, to enclose the sinuous course of the Neckar and its outlet on to the plain. Then the great beech forest, interspersed with growths of fir, makes its appearance as the Odenwald, slopes gently down to the Darmstadt plain and, beyond the Main, continues along the wide, beech- and oak-covered Spessart massif. It is a lonely region but a sportsman's paradise, and the woods are the finest in Germany.

Opposite Karlsruhe, on the left bank, or Palatinate side, is another sandstone plateau of the same height, covered with pines and beech — the Haardt, the northern extension of the low Vosges forests. The Haardt, however, is hillier and is thickly populated. The western side drops very gently down to a cultivated plain dotted with villages, the natural border of Lorraine.

Still farther west and abutting on Lorraine, is the Saar, a district of rolling pastures and hills that rise to the foothills of the Hunsrück. A beech forest that covers just over one-third of the province cuts diagonally across the Saar from Neunkirchen to Saarbrücken.

THE RHINE. About seven miles below Lake Constance the Rhine enters German territory, which the river first skirts and then traverses for about 540 miles through four natural and well-defined regions. First there is the narrow passage through which the great torrent pours at the foot of wooded hills to border or cross Swiss territory as far as Basle, harnessed en route for the production of hydro-electric power at the roaring Schaffhausen Falls. Beyond Basle comes the mid-Rhine basin, 188 miles long and some 25 miles wide, through which the waters flow less turbulently as far as Bingen. Beyond Bingen the river passes through the 'Heroic Gorge' where the deep, swirling waters have cut their way for about 62 miles through the schist massif. For the final 95 miles of its course the Rhine, majestic and calm, flows slowly over an immense plain to its estuary in Holland. The twofold contribution of its tributaries — on the one hand Alpine waters swollen in summer by melting snows, and on the other Hercynian waters increased by winter rains — make the flow of the Rhine remarkably even and allow navigation all the year round, except for a few days of fog or ice-jams each winter.

THE WEALTH OF THE MIDDLE RHINE BASIN. The *Oberrheinische Ebene*, the splendid alluvial plain of the Rhine's middle course, is enclosed and sheltered, warm and with clear skies, though liable to winter frosts. The level of the plain drops from 820 feet at Basle to 460 feet at Kehl, and then, more gradually, to 260 feet at Bingen.

This plain is the heart and the crossroads of northern Europe, and one-quarter of it belongs to France. Here the river's course has been regulated and from this point on it is navigable. Old meanders and arms of the river are hidden under aquatic plants and thickets of trees. Long strips of woodland, called generically *Hardt*, clothe stony ground with oaks and sand with firs, yet fields of grain and orchards are abundant. As early as 1870 the density of population in this region was more than 380 to the square mile and now — in the northern part — exceeds 750. The built-up areas are prosperous, urbanised

The fertile Middle Rhine basin, seen from the edge of the Schwarzwald. GERMAN TOURIST OFFICE

townships set in the dry, narrow and attractive Breisgau to the south (Freiburg) — centred round the volcanic and ice-covered Kaiserstuhl facing Upper Alsace — and they are found again in the damper plain of central Baden (Karlsruhe) with its crops of maize and colza, its walnut-trees reminiscent of the south, and its chestnut woods. The *Bergstrasse*, noted for its plums, cherries, almonds and peaches, as well as the neighbouring plain, is covered with lively little towns surrounded by industrial crops and market-gardens. The left, or Palatine, bank is not so flat, is less well watered, and has fewer towns and villages. The plain is well wooded but the region's main feature is a slope of loess and of wheat fields rising to meet a long row of low hills, the *Weinstrasse*, which enjoy an eastern prospect and are, like the Burgundy hillsides, covered with vines that come right down to the river bank farther north.

Finally, the Rheingau terraces from Wiesbaden to Rüdesheim (on the right bank) look across the river to the fertile market-gardens of the Mainz area, while on the Rheingau slopes, sheltered by the Taunus, ripen the famous grapes that yield the golden Rhine wines.

THE COMPACT BLOCK OF THE SCHIST MASSIF.
The Rhine schist massif is composed of a fourfold block of monotonous, wild and barren plateaus, rising to heights of from 1,600 to 2,600 feet under a harsh climate. This schist massif containing some of the most out-of-the-way parts of Germany separates the lively Rhine plain and the busy Rhenish-Westphalian region. On the right hand the barrier of the Taunus raises its beech-covered summits as high as 2,885 feet above the urbanised area of the Rhenish Hesse towns. Opposite, on the left bank of the Rhine, the Hunsrück, although offering a less definite outline and shape, is still more harsh and forsaken. It rises in a succession of tree-clad ridges to a high, grassy plateau (2,585 feet). Beyond the course of the Moselle, the Eifel, a wind-swept moorland with rocky roads winding among copses and scrub, pushes upward to a height of 2,490 feet. The Eifel was formerly a military area and played a considerable part in frontier strategy. Its most fertile stretches are those near the Moselle and those approaching the Rhine.

On the other side of the Rhine (the right bank), downstream from the Lahn, the Westerwald is more inviting, less monotonous and more populated. Facing Bonn, rise the picturesque and volcanic *Siebengebirge* (Seven Mountains), though most of the Westerwald consists of pasture land with great herds of cattle on its basalt plateaus and extensive beech-covered schists, especially in the Rothaargebirge (2,625 feet) and in the Sauerland (56 per cent forest). The landscape becomes more inviting downstream in the green hills of Bergisches Land.

THE BUSY RHINE GORGE.
Between these lonely heights the highways of human activity follow the natural corridors of the rivers Rhine, Moselle, Ahr, Lahn and Sieg. The rocky Rhine Narrows were produced by an abrupt fracture of the plateau, and through them, below the old castles and walled vineyards, winds and twists a heavy volume of river-traffic. Downstream the Rhine broadens out at Coblenz, where it is joined by the waters of the Moselle and the Lahn. The Moselle, which has not yet been regulated (at least not below its 'industrial' stretch in France) reflects in its lazy loops downstream from Trier (Trèves) steeply sloping vineyards, flourishing orchards and quiet but cheerful old villages.

At Bonn the Rhine flows into the Cologne basin which retains some trace of a mild southern climate even as far north as Düsseldorf. To the west, between the Rhine and the Meuse, there lies a fertile agricultural region round Düren and, farther north, another round Krefeld. In the Cleves area stock-breeding and dairy-farming conducted on Dutch lines occupy most of the plain. On the right bank, three rivers (the Wupper, the Ruhr and the Lippe) serve to mark the gradations of the great coalfield as it descends to the Westphalian plain. The heart of this plain is markedly Western in character — it is an almost flat region of *bocage* dissected by hedges, clumps of trees and ditches, and strewn with fields of heavy cretaceous marls, fertile meadows and many farms.

The gently undulating Lower Rhine countryside, near Cleves, largely devoted to dairy-farming and stock-breeding. PAUL POPPER

THE SWABIAN-FRANCONIAN BASIN, AND THE BORDERLAND OF BOHEMIA. Beyond the screen of wooded sandstone massifs which border the Rhine trough to the east, the Swabian-Franconian basin opens out. It is situated in the heart of the Hercynian area and forms a crescent. Linked, farther north, with the Thuringian basin, it forms the *Mitteldeutsche Senke*, or Central German Depression, that is drained towards the Rhine (in a direction opposed to that of the strata slope), the Swabian part by the Neckar, and the Franconian part by the Main.

The Neckar, Württemberg's principal river, rises only a few miles from the Danube, but dug a deeper bed more quickly than the latter, so that in Tertiary times the Neckar had already captured a number of tributaries. The Neckar's source lies between the Black Forest and the Swabian Jura, or Swabian Alb. The *Gaue*, open and cultivated areas contrasting with the dark forests of the sandstone massifs, extend from west of Stuttgart to north of Würzburg. This open country (divided into districts with fanciful or descriptive names — Korngau: 'Wheat District', Strohgau: 'Straw District', Bauland: 'Farming District' — is the granary of the region, but on the slopes of the Neckar, the Rems and the Main there are also numerous vineyards. For 110 miles the skyline of Württemberg is dominated by the diagonally ranged Swabian Alb, a tall façade of rocky ridges and isolated peaks, dotted with proud castles and rising to heights between 2,300 and 3,280 feet.

Lower Swabia is very hilly and divided into attractive little districts by a tangle of valleys. The region was once Romanised for it lay within the defensive wall that marked the Empire's limits. It presents a contrast with neighbouring Franconia which, although it has the same substratum (except quite near the river Main), has a harsher climate, poorer soil, lower and less diversified hills, and a less gracious landscape than that of Lower Swabia.

The Swabian Alb comes to an abrupt end at the flat, fertile and circular basin of the Riess. Beyond, the Franconian Jura, less distinct and less compact than the Swabian, raises its spurs and peaks and isolated hills in a wide semi-circle round the gloomy, sandy countryside and pine-forests of Nuremberg. The beech woods and stony moors (numerous in the north, especially in 'Franconian Switzerland', a region of picturesque rock-formations) reach south as far as the Danube which cuts into them in the Weltenburg gorge.

The upper Main, near Bayreuth, and the Naab of the Upper Palatinate, run through a transition region with a complex subsoil. The Fichtelgebirge (3,445 feet), an area of bare fields, fir forests and cold winters, is the water-tower of the Hercynian ranges and lies quite close to the triple frontier of the two Germanies and Czechoslovakia. The Furth-im-Wald corridor, linking Bavaria with Bohemia, runs between the Upper Palatinate and the double range of the Böhmerwald (at the frontier) and the Bayrischerwald, cut by the Danube near Passau. The region is entirely covered with the most deserted and wildest of all the German fir forests. Rainfall is heavy, and the population, whose life is hard, is concentrated in the long fissure of the Regen that runs through the middle of the area.

The bright, mild valley of the middle Main through which the river meanders in lazy loops, is set with vines and plum orchards. This valley occupies more or less the position of a transition zone between northern and southern Germany — much as the Loire valley does in France. Northwards, the whole of Hesse lies in the Hercynian zone. Two great dead volcanoes covered with peat-bogs and rain and snow-soaked meadows surround the verdant basin of Fulda. They are the Rhön (3,115 feet), dotted with little volcanic pimples, and the star-shaped Vogelsberg (2,625 feet). This area is one of the poorest in Germany and one from which emigration is among the heaviest. Between the Vogelsberg and the Taunus, the fertile, well-tilled depression of the Wetterau offers by far the easiest natural line of communication between south and north

Germany — one of the reasons for Frankfurt's prosperity.

To the north of Kassel, the curved ridges of the Weser, crowned by beech forests, descend gradually through a countryside of ancient little towns till they meet the borders of the great northern plain.

To the east of the broken Weser ridges, two tall Primary massifs rise as horsts, or elevated blocks, and surround the sedimentary basin of Thuringia, drained and open only on the south-east side. First comes the Harz (3,610 feet above the northern plain) with the legendary granite promontory of the Brocken enveloped in clouds and fogs. Fir forests and peat-bogs cover over one-half of the Harz plateau, while on its broad slopes lies a belt of busy little industrial towns. Then, to the south, juts the slender spur of the Thuringerwald (2,950 feet high, 63 miles long from south-east to north-west, and about 6 miles wide). It is a wooded barrier, but highly industrialised and thickly populated throughout its maze of branching valleys between the Werra (the main branch of the Weser) and the Saale (the main affluent of the Elbe). The Saale itself drains all the waters of the Thuringian basin but touches the area only as it follows a winding course through a deep valley from Saalfeld to Jena and Naumburg. It is the Saale's tributary, the Unstrut, that is the main artery of the oval, rain-sheltered area. Here, the countryside is wholly agricultural, dotted here and there with residential towns.

To the south-west the indeterminate outline of the gorge-pierced Vogtland plateau (1,640 feet) links the Thuringerwald to the Saxon Erzgebirge. This last is a crystalline massif (2,855 feet) on the Bohemian frontier and, of all the Hercynian secondary ranges, was the first to be cleared, cultivated and worked. It is an over-populated region; towns, villages, workshops and factories jostle each other right up to the round, blunt summits. There is little woodland until the deep valley of the Elbe in the 'Saxon Switzerland' (Dresden), beyond which are the well-cultivated, granite hills trickling with rivulets, of Upper Lusatia (Lausitz).

The great Northern Plain

The vast plain of northern Germany (it has no boundaries to the east) lacks the diversity of the Hercynian zone but, despite its apparent monotony, it divides (according to the epoch and the intensity of the former glaciations) into large areas of different characteristics, where agricultural land gives way to forests, and forests to moors or marshes.

THE FERTILE ZONE. The first of these zones, strewn with loess in post-glacial times, stretches like a foundation of uncovered soils along the length of the Hercynian heights. This zone can be seen from Dresden and the Leipzig-Halle depression at the foot of the Erzgebirge and the outlet of the Thuringian basin, as far as the Weser heights beyond Hanover. It is a region without charm but one of the most fertile in Germany, and one that has been long established and is still densely populated. Towns are numerous, and land is extremely expensive, especially in the rich *Börde* between the towns of Magdeburg and Brunswick.

THE HEATHLANDS. Northwards, this fertile zone gives way to another that overlies the accumulations of ancient moraines. This is a region of moors, with pink or red heather and juniper bushes covering immense areas of the middle course of the Elbe. To the east of this region are the wooded hills of Lower Lusatia (Lausitz) and the rather desolate heights of the Fläming. To the west lies the Letzlinger Heide (a reforestation area) and the huge Lüneburger Heide (Lüneburg Heath) stretching over some 2,315 square miles between Celle and Hamburg. The heath is being replanted with pines in a number of places.

Neustadt, a small Protestant town in Holstein. The houses are built of brick and tile to withstand the northern climate.

FRANZ HOCH, ATLAS–PHOTO

BRANDENBURG AND MECKLENBURG. To the east, and in the middle of Brandenburg, early glacial valleys left deep furrows (from the Oder to the Elbe) through which the Spree and the Havel flow. Most of the soil is sandy or peaty, and at times marshy. Here and there are stretches of gently rolling, fairly fertile land that is well cultivated and populated. But for the most part the landscape is one of vast pine forests and is rather monotonous.

Farther north, beyond another forest zone, the middle of the Mecklenburg plateau (655 feet) presents innumerable sheets of water, where the extremities of the frontal moraines lie. Some of them are of considerable extent and are surrounded by woods of beech and pine. Müritz, for example, covers forty-five square miles. On the site of the ground moraines or sub-glacial drift there are flat, cultivated expanses of argillaceous or silty soil. Along the Baltic shores, where the landscape is more lacustrine than maritime, there runs a coastline of bays and spits of sand, with the chalk cliffs of the island of Rügen standing out against the sea.

THE GEEST. THE MARSCHEN. SCHLESWIG-HOLSTEIN. To the west of the Elbe and Lüneburg Heath, there is a land of quite different character. It is the melancholy countryside of the Geest. This huge, sandy plain was once glaciated and subsequently eroded. It now remains badly drained. Sterile peat-bogs extend interminably, flecked here and there with the waters of reed-ringed meres. The bogs — some low-lying and spongy under a covering of rushes, others drier and with convex surface — are worked for fuel, but more and more, they are being drained, cut into squares, covered with small farms, and cultivated as in neighbouring Holland. Here and there a few remaining clumps of the former oak and birch woods can be seen.

Between Geest and the sea-silts of the *Watten* there are a number of argillaceous polders along the coast and the estuaries, from Emden to the Danish frontier. They are extremely fertile and in marked contrast to the lands of Geest and *Watten*. The polders were protected by dykes as early as the eleventh century and are known as the *Marschen*. They are from 7 to 10 miles wide and make up a number of distinct little areas,

some of them cultivated (to the west of the Weser and in the Dithmarschen) and others used for grazing and stock-breeding. The string of high dunes of the Frisian Islands from Borkum to Sylt forms a protective screen and cuts off the *Watten* and the *Marschen* from the waves of the North Sea.

Lastly, Schleswig-Holstein has portions of each of these eastern and western landscapes on both sides of its isthmus. On the North Sea are *Marschen*; in the middle, the Geest and sterile moors; on the Baltic side, the same agricultural and lacustrine landscape as in Mecklenburg (with the Wagrien or 'Holstein Switzerland' beech woods and Eutin and Plön lakes) and the Angeln of Schleswig, whose low-sided fiords penetrate far inland.

Population and habitat

The German people, who since 1945 have been squeezed between the Oder and the Ardennes, do not today include any ethnological minority except for a small number of Danes in the Flensburg area and, eastwards, the 60,000 Wends or Slavs of Lusatia. There are few surnames which are not of Germanic origin. Most of the non-Germanic names that do exist are of Polish derivation and come from the old Prussian provinces of Posen and East Prussia or from Polish miners in the Ruhr who have been Germanised. Other non-German names have a French look about them, and stem from descendants of middle or upper class Huguenot refugees; they are found particularly in Brandenburg and Frankfurt. Again, other French-sounding names are of Vaudois (Waldensian) origin, and form tiny groups in villages with French names in Württemberg or Main-Hesse. Only a very small proportion of the population (0.9 per cent) is of foreign nationality, chiefly Polish or Dutch in Bavaria and the Lower Rhineland.

As a people, the Germans are hard-working and tenacious, serious and eager to learn, filled with ideas of grandeur and expansion, always in a state of 'development' (*Werden*). At the same time they are conventional, respectful of social and official position, and of rather solemn disposition. They like orderliness and are ready to accept orders and to submit to what seems in the general or national interest. In the past, this characteristic has led at least some of them to confuse the superhuman with the inhuman. Although attaching much importance to town-planning, the Germans are also great lovers of the unspoilt countryside; they are attached to their homes, yet ready to travel and settle in other lands. Enjoying the most modern equipment and employing the most advanced techniques in a highly traditional setting, they are, generally speaking, of bourgeois behaviour — though 75 per cent are, in fact, proletarian. One is tempted to ask whether the rise in the standard of living does not sometimes hinder their enjoyment of life.

The German population is a uniform one, still displaying, however, signs of the divisions between the old great Germanic groups, divisions which were perpetuated in the duchies of the early Middle Ages and which perhaps to this day are the real internal frontiers rather than the political borders of the Länder and districts — or the limits of the many principalities of post-medieval times.

On the North Sea coasts, the Frisians are bold sailors and have always been jealous of their independence and individual liberties. Their neighbours on the great northern plain, the Lower Saxons (Eastphalians or Westphalians) are energetic and hard-working, uncommunicative, undemonstrative, and trustworthy in their social relations. The southern and western limits of their settlement are well marked — from Göttingen and Brilon to Wuppertal, Gelsenkirchen and Bocholt. Thus, in the heart of the Ruhr, the taciturn, sound and hard-working Westphalian contrasts markedly with the vivacious, enterprising Lower Rhinelanders, who are slightly Latinised Ripuarian Franks. In Hesse, along the course of the Main, and especially in the plain of the middle Rhine, the Franconians (many of their characteristics remind us that they were formerly in contact with the Romans) are sharp-witted, open-minded and talkative. South of a line running from Baden to Heilbronn and thence to Nordlingen, Nuremberg and Bayreuth, are to be found the two great groups of southern Germans, peoples whose substratum is Celtic. To the west of the Lech are the Swabians (who came formerly from the north), hardworking, reflective and practical. They are subdivided into Alemans, or Alamanni, (in the Black Forest and on the banks of the Rhine) and Swabians (properly speaking, on the Neckar and the Danube). To the east of the Lech are the Bavarians, originally from Bohemia, a cheerful and exuberant peasant people, but often also coarse and violent.

In eastern Germany, the Thuringians, related to the Franconians, are sensitive, relatively carefree and deeply musical. The Upper Saxons, ingenious and hard-working, display a combination of mysticism and shrewd commercial sense. To the east of the Elbe are what may be called the 'east-Elbians', a mixture of peoples that conquered the territory from the Slavs who had long held it. These people from beyond the Elbe are energetic, punctual and well-disciplined — a little slower in Mecklenburg, hard-working and inclined to be waggish in Berlin.

Differences of origin are reflected in the houses, in tastes and, particularly, in dialects. Though the High German of the south has become the official language (albeit marked by varied accents and other pecularities from the Danube to the Rhine), 'Middle' German is spoken from Saxony to the middle Rhine (between Speyer and Düsseldorf), and Low German in the north.

THE VILLAGE. The earliest form of German habitat we can discover is the village agglomeration (*Haufendorf* or *Gewanndorf*), with houses set down haphazardly in the middle of a piece of land (with triennial crop rotation) divided equally among the inhabitants. Communal lands, or commons (the *Allmende*), once marked these groups but they no longer exist. Such villages are almost the general rule in all western Germany

(as in eastern France) up to the Elbe and the Saale. Names ending in -*ingen* (in the south-west), in -*ing* (in Bavaria) and in -*heim* and -*dorf* (in the centre), all indicate the oldest of such villages. Other, more recent villages — the *Wald* or *Marschhufendörfer* (twelfth or thirteenth centuries) strung out along a single street, with fields stretching out in strips behind each house — mark forest-clearings in the Black Forest, the Odenwald, the Spessart, Saxony and the Frisian marshes. Beyond the Elbe, the villages or little towns built by settlers follow a regular plan: the *Strassendörfer* wind along the sides of roads; the *Angerdörfer* set on an oblong common surround the church, the pond and a few trees (Anhalt, Brandenburg are examples); the *Rundlinge*, formerly fortified and more or less of Slav origin, are rounded and enclose a central square, as in Saxony and Mecklenburg.

There are fewer dispersed settlements; yet in agriculturally backward regions hamlets (*Weiler*) are common on the Swabian and Franconian plateaus, the outskirts of the Black Forest and the Upper Palatinate. Over the whole of eastern Bavaria they lie between the villages, and in Mecklenburg were grouped round country houses (*Güter*) which have since been deserted or destroyed. Near the Dutch frontier, on the grasslands of the Frisian area, Westphalia and the Lower Rhine, as well as in the Baltic region of Schleswig-Holstein, there are isolated farms here and there. They can be seen, too, in the south, on the Allgäu pasture-lands, on domains which were reconstituted in the eighteenth century, or in the Bavarian Pre-Alps.

TYPES OF HOUSE. The typical German dwelling is a house with a visible wooden framework that is painted or, more often, blackened, and walls of white-washed brick or cob. Its form has been kept unchanged throughout the centuries in little towns, villages and farms alike. Each storey has a row of small, shuttered windows set close together. There is no balcony. The high, pointed roof (perhaps with eaves in the front) has tall dormers and cowled chimneys, and is covered with Flemish-type tiles or, in the south, with fishscale shingles. There are, of course, local variations on the basic type. The brickwork used in the northern plain is generally left bare. In contrast, in Upper Swabia and Bavaria the houses are given an over-all coat of white- or ochre-wash. In Franconia, Rhenish Hesse and Lower Swabia the walls are more elaborate and are covered with a criss-cross of wooden strips. In Hesse and Hanover (except for the constant recurrence of Renaissance shell motifs), in Thuringia, Brandenburg and Saxony, the wall sections are more regularly shaped and form large squares. In southern Germany and in the oldest buildings the gables generally give on to the street. Bavarian chalets are often decorated with mural paintings. Stone houses are found only in parts of Swabia and Franconia and from Frankfurt to Cologne and Trier in the schist massif, where the houses are roofed and faced on their upper parts with slates. White windows and green shutters are found in the Bergisches Land.

Farms with open yards and separate outbuildings are rarely found, except on the Lüneburg Heath. The Franconian type, with enclosed yards, closed gateway and blocks of buildings forming three sides of a square (dwelling, barn and stalls), is the commonest all over central Germany, from Basle to Brunswick and from Cologne to Görlitz and Berlin. In Lower Bavaria and on the Danube, four wings form a square. The 'unitary' house that shelters men and beasts under the same roof assumes a variety of forms. In the Frisian polders we meet it as a ground floor under a huge two-storey, thatched attic-granary, the dwelling in front and the stalls for the animals behind. Then there is the *Diele* of Lower Saxony, Westphalia and Mecklenburg. This type has a ground floor, also extending far back, but with a lower roof than in the Frisian version; there is a gabled entrance-gate, the barn and stalls are on the side and communicate through a central space, and the living accommodation is at the back. In the Black Forest we find a stone-built ground floor containing the stalls with the barn behind, surmounted by two wooden storeys with balconies. In Swabia the houses are long and roomy and divided up cross-wise, with side entrances, barns and stalls at the back and living accommodation under the eaves. To the east of the Lech, in Bavaria, there are wooden chalets with several storeys, balconies, and low roofs that project far beyond the walls. In the region of Trier the Lorraine-type houses have flat roofs, while in the south there are the vine-growers' houses, tall with two or three storeys above the ground-floor-cum-store-room. Dutch-type dwellings are seen in all the towns north of the Ruhr, Belgian styles can be met with as far as Cologne, and Danish-type houses as far as Kiel.

The houses, repainted periodically, are admirably cared for and the windows decorated with geraniums. A venerable lime-tree usually casts its shade over the village square, while birches and weeping-willows adorn the flower-gardens.

THE SPACIOUS TOWNS. In the towns, the character-istic picture of Old Germany is of a market-place surrounded by houses with four or five projecting storeys (or, in the north, with Flemish gables of brick), a fountain and a sixteenth or seventeenth-century *Rathaus* (town hall). Since war brought destruction to the central districts, such towns are now rarer. Elegant oriel windows dating from Renaissance times — coarsely imitated in the bow-windows of over-decorated, late nine-teenth-century houses — project from the frontages; watch-towers, turrets, lanterns and belfries are numerous, and in the smaller places the old entrance gates of the towns are often preserved while the Romanesque towers of the Rhineland

Lobster fishers in Heligoland, an island in the North Sea facing the estuaries of the Elbe and the Weser. PAUL POPPER, ATLAS-PHOTO

churches, the tall green copper spires of the northern towns, the onion-bulb belfries and the eighteenth-century pepper-pot roofs all add to the old-world appearance of towns and villages. The 'Wilhelm II' period — coinciding with the ex-pansion of the larger towns — was one which showed con-tempt for the harmonious classical and romantic traditions, so the pretentious buildings in the *Neustyl* of 1890 are to be seen everywhere. However, the towns are imposing with their numerous monumental public offices, fine business pre-mises, parks, shady avenues and general spaciousness. The working-class suburbs with airy *Siedlungen* (garden-cities) are modern and extensive.

All the larger towns (*Kreisfreie Städte*) — which are no longer administered by the 'Circles' — annexed suburban communes, green belts and woodland in 1937. Essen, for instance, in the heart of the Ruhr, includes wooded districts.

With the exception of a few Roman foundations (such as Trier, Mainz, Coblenz, Cologne or Regensburg) there were no German towns before the eleventh century; then they sprang up as market-places or settlements round castles or monasteries. Many towns, however, were founded during the recolonisation of the east. Then, in the eighteenth century came a number of others, some built on a regular plan as resi-dences of lay or ecclesiastical princes. The industrial towns date from the nineteenth century.

The German towns were much more detached from their countryside than the French ones and soon won their liberties. In particular, the Hanseatic cities in the north and the Imperial cities in the south supplied in opposition to the paramount rulers an enterprising class of patricians and a body of skilled and experienced craftsmen who laid the foundations for modern Germany's commerce and industry. The towns of today have developed extraordinarily during the last century. The largest of the cities have kept their individual character, and their inhabitants regard them as real capitals even if they do not enjoy that rank. None, however — especially since Berlin has been isolated — claims to be a real metropolis, not even Hamburg. But the cities have their own financial, cultural and artistic life; they contain the head offices of great businesses, they have their specialised institutes, their important news-papers, their famous orchestras. There is no single one which can claim to be the sole arbiter of taste and fashion or the natural and inevitable leader in the political sphere.

THE IMPORTANCE OF RELIGION. The strong religious feelings of the Germans have been noticeable throughout their history. It was during the struggle between Emperors and Popes and, later, during Luther's Reformation (which was brewing long before Luther's time) that a certain awareness of the existence of the German 'Community' came into being. It was the seventeenth-century religious wars that broke up this 'Community' into little principalities with differing religions. Today, the geographical tangle of Catholic and Protestant areas is very often the only perceptible remaining trace of those vanished States. Whereas France is, from so many points of view, the favoured meeting-place of the European north and south, the area of contact between the dominating Catholicism of the south and the Protestantism of the north has, generally speaking, been transferred to the Rhine (owing to the banish-ment of French Protestants in 1685). The two Churches — and especially the Protestant Church because of the number of its adherents in East Germany — form at the present time the only permanent link between the two Germanies.

In the Germany of 1937 the Evangelicals constituted 64 per cent of the population. Now, in West Germany (since the scission between East and West) the figures for Protestants (51 per cent) and Catholics (45 per cent) almost balance. How-ever, in East Germany the Lutherans form 81 per cent of the population and, in consequence, the Protestants in West Ger-many are particularly anxious to see Germany reunified. The professed free-thinkers (3 per cent in all) are numerous only in the large cities (Berlin has 18 per cent and Hamburg 15 per cent). In the Federal Republic there are now no more than 25,000 Jews as against 280,000 in 1930.

The four *Länder* of the north-east (beyond Rhenish Hesse and the lands of the Weser) are Lutheran. Hamburg is the most thoroughly Protestant city in the whole continent of Europe (80 per cent). Hildesheim, Fulda and Duderstadt are the only three Catholic 'islands' in the north. The northern Rhineland from the Moselle and Mainz to the Ems, and West-phalia from Münster and Paderborn, are mainly Catholic, as is Cologne, their influential metropolis on the Rhine. But the Ruhr is divided between the two religions and has three Protestant strongholds: Wuppertal, Dortmund and Soest. The Main, except at its source (Bayreuth) and its mouth (Frank-furt) flows through a Catholic countryside. The Neckar and the plateaus of Lower Swabia and Franconia — from Baden and Mannheim to Nuremberg and Hof — are Protestant. The Middle Rhine valley presents a religious mosaic but with Catholics in the majority in Baden, and Protestants in the Palatinate. Bavaria as a whole and Upper Swabia are 75 per cent Catholic, but the percentage is much higher if we consider only the Danube valley or the shores of Lake Constance. There are innumerable exceptions to this general rule in the enclaves developed by historical circumstances (*cuius regio, eius religio*). Most of the old Free Towns and Hanseatic Cities have remained strongholds of Protestantism.

Religious observance is, generally speaking, customary — especially in the Catholic districts of Westphalia, Upper Swabia and Bavaria where almost all the members of the Church attend Mass on Sundays. However, with the exception of the reformed sects, church-going is less general (from 20 per cent to 50 per cent) in the Protestant areas. The two religions, although steadfast in their adherence to dogma, provide mutual stimulus and exist side by side without clashes. Indeed, many ecclesi-astical buildings are used jointly by Catholics and Protestants.

Out of the 27 provincial Churches for the whole of Germany (8 in the East zone) which, since 1945, have been co-ordinated into two groups under the 'Evangelical Church in Germany', 24 are Lutheran or 'United'. The small Calvinist minority (half a million) is concentrated mainly in Bremen, Hesse (Kassel), Hanover-Lippe, Brandenburg and Anhalt. At Wuppertal and Reutlingen many pietistic sects flourish.

The Catholic Church (whose dioceses are in many cases of great extent) is made up of six archbishoprics and sixteen bishoprics, with four apostolic vicariates in the north. The monastic clergy is numerous. Crowds of devotees are attracted every year to famous places of pilgrimage. The Church is strongly conservative, but under present political conditions there is no anti-clericalism.

The social activities of the Churches are notable. There are 6,000 hospices supported or staffed by the Catholic association *Caritas* or by the Protestant home missions. Noteworthy, too, are the Catholic Youth Centre at Altenberg, near Cologne, and the Protestant academies at Loccum, Boll, and other places.

In the economic sphere in southern and western Germany, Protestantism is especially associated with industrialisation and modernisation. Factory owners tend to inhabit the Lutheran towns and villages, while even in the Catholic areas business leaders, organisers and independent workers are very often Protestant. The Catholic towns, on the other hand, are mostly agricultural and residential centres.

THE GERMAN FEDERAL REPUBLIC (WEST GERMANY)

The territory of the *Bund*, the German Federal Republic, covers 95,683 square miles. Whereas the old Reich at its widest point, from west-south-west on the French frontier to east-north-east on the Lithuanian border, measured about 845 miles, the *Bund* is only some 138 miles in width. On the other hand, at its longest point north-south from Denmark to Switzerland or to the Tyrol, the extent remains the same (500 miles) and has become the country's main axis, so that the Federal Republic's 'Atlantic' character has been markedly accentuated.

In 1939 39.3 million inhabitants lived on this territory (410 to the square mile). At the present time, with a population of more than 55 million (578 to the square mile), West Germany swarms with people. Even the casual visitor cannot help but notice how densely populated the land is. Out of 418 rural administrative areas ('circles') only twelve (eight in Bavaria) have less than 150 inhabitants to the square mile; there are but two (in the impoverished regions of the Eifel and the Upper Palatinate) that have less than 130 to the square mile. On the other hand, in Rhineland-Westphalia — an area of 13,125 sq. miles, which is considerably larger than Belgium — there are 1,080 inhabitants squeezed into each square mile.

Besides possessing such a densely populated region, the *Bund* also has the largest population of any Western European country. In matters of population Germany may indeed be compared with Great Britain. There is the same north-south axis, with a similar number of people and roughly the same excess of births over deaths. But the *Bund* is a Great Britain without the support of a Commonwealth or the supplies from overseas territories. The Rhine basin occupies almost one-half (44 per cent) of West Germany's total area, but the area's relative importance is still greater from historical, demographic (55 per cent of the pop-ulation) and economic points of view. And, all due allowances being made, the new Germany, since its restoration and revival, has increased its resemblances with German Switzerland and Holland by means of the Rhine link: the same federalist spirit, the same religious composition, and the same economic structure to ensure that output, markets, business and trade assume more importance than politics.

Organisation and problems

THE TEN-STATE FEDERAL REPUBLIC. The German Federal Republic (*Bundesrepublik Deutschland*) is governed according to the Fundamental Law of May 8, 1949, by a Chan-cellor (*Bundeskanzler*) who is chosen by the Diet (*Bundestag*) and assisted by nineteen federal ministers appointed by the Federal President (*Bundespräsident*), himself elected for five years by the Federal Diet and the Federal Council (*Bundesrat*) combined. The Chancellor is responsible to the *Bundestag*, whose members are elected for a term of four years by general election. The *Bundesrat* is composed of forty-two members appointed by the local governments of the ten States making up the Federation. A Federal Constitutional Court sits at Karlsruhe.

Bonn was chosen as the federal capital in 1949. This uni-versity and residential town (where the wide windows of the Parliament building give on to the Rhine) was chosen in pref-erence to Frankfurt (larger, more central and traditionally more important) because Bonn is nearer to Cologne and the Ruhr, and because it was sought to stress the temporary character of the makeshift capital.

The ten federated States (*Länder*) are: Schleswig-Holstein, Hamburg, Bremen, Lower Saxony, Northern Rhineland-Westphalia, Hesse, Rhineland-Palatinate, Baden-Württemberg, Bavaria and the Saar.

Schleswig-Holstein (capital: Kiel), to the north-east, is an

essentially agricultural land, with some Danes in the extreme north, Frisians on the west coast, Saxons in Holstein, and today overcrowded with refugees. From 1459 to 1863 the region consisted of two Danish duchies. In 1863, however, Schleswig (to the north of the Eider and Kiel Bay) and Holstein were annexed by Prussia (with the Free City of Lübeck in 1937) and remained Prussian until the break-up of that country. In 1920 four districts in Schleswig were returned to Denmark.

Hamburg, first an ancient Hanseatic city and then, from 1474, an Imperial Free Town, was the main heir of the Hansa after its disappearance. Hamburg was never (except for three short periods) able to enjoy its own liberties and its own constitution within the German Empire. In 1937 the city was enlarged by the incorporation of its suburbs lying in Prussian territory. Despite its rather out-of-the-way position, Hamburg remains the richest and most important town in West Germany.

Bremen, a point of departure in the Middle Ages for a stream of missionaries who set off to evangelise northern Europe, has had a history which mirrors that of Hamburg. Bremen's inhabitants have displayed a similar spirit of liberty, although their city never had such great importance and prestige as Hamburg.

Lower Saxony (*Niedersachsen*) is, with the exception of a string of industrial towns in the south, a predominantly agricultural State, although the soil is not very fertile. Lower Saxony is made up of the old kingdom of Hanover (which after lengthy resistance became a Prussian province in 1866), the duchies of Oldenburg and Brunswick (Braunschweig), and the principality of Schaumburg-Lippe, all three of which remained autonomous in the German Empire until 1918. The capital is Hanover.

The North Rhineland-Westphalia State (Nordrhein-Westfalen) comprises the *Ruhrgebiet* and contains one-quarter of the *Bund's* population and two-thirds of its industry. This is, then, Germany's 'Empire State' and was formed from the Rhine Province, assigned to Prussia in 1815, and Westphalia (also Prussian from 1815). The whole region has, however, undergone continual political transformation from Carolingian times through the centuries. The capital is Düsseldorf.

Hesse (Hessen) is a central State, situated on the crossroads from north to south, and includes the old State of Electoral Hesse, part of Nassau, the old Free City of Frankfurt and that part of the Grand Duchy of Hesse (swept away in 1918) that lay across the Rhine. There is strong contrast between the rich slopes of the banks of the Main and Rhine in the south and the relative poverty of the Weser's slopes to the north. The capital is Wiesbaden.

The Rhineland-Palatinate (Rheinland-Pfalz), inconveniently grouped on the left bank of the Rhine, is made up of bits and pieces and includes the southern part of the former Prussian Rhineland with Coblenz, Trier, the western part of Hesse (including Worms and Mainz but minus the latter's industrial suburbs on the right bank of the Rhine), and the old Bavarian Palatinate with Kaiserslautern and Speyer. Each one of the Rheinland-Pfalz's neighbours would jump at the chance of taking over one of these parts of its territory. The capital is Mainz.

Baden-Württemberg is composed of three Länder (until the referendum of 1952 separated by the different zones of occupation): North Baden-Württemberg, Württemberg-Hohenzollern and South Baden. Württemberg, an ancient duchy raised to the rank of a kingdom by Napoleon in 1806, received from the Emperor certain Catholic principalities and free cities of Upper Swabia as well as some Austrian territory. The Grand Duchy of Baden, an oddly-shaped crescent of territory running from the Main to Lake Constance, included lands of very varied character (the right bank Palatinate, margraviates, bishoprics, Austrian possessions and free towns). The former principality of Hohenzollern was annexed to Württemberg in 1937. The capital is Stuttgart.

A procession in Bavaria, with the whole village following. Bavaria, like Westphalia and Upper Swabia, is strongly Catholic.
GERMAN TOURIST OFFICE

The Rhine at Bacharach, in Rheinland Pfalz. On either bank the hills drop steeply into the river, and vines are grown intensively on terraces. The town is crowded into the narrow space between hillside and river bank. GERMAN TOURIST INFORMATION BUREAU

An aerial view of Cologne in Westphalia. The city was badly damaged in World War II: almost three-quarters of the houses were destroyed, but the Gothic cathedral with its twin spires survived and is now surrounded by new buildings. KEYSTONE PRESS AGENCY

Bavaria (Bayern) was, even in the eighteenth century, the largest of all the south German States, entirely Catholic by religion, and geographically a part of the Danube area. Napoleon doubled the size of the country by adding to it the bishoprics of Bamberg and Würzburg on the Main and part of the archbishopric of Mainz, the principality of Bayreuth-Anspach, Nuremberg, and a few other Protestant free towns. Bavaria therefore extends, rather oddly, right up to the gates of Frankfurt, though the Bavarian's unswerving individualism looks rather to the Danube and the Inn than northwards. Bavaria has remained exceptionally rural. The capital is Munich.

The Saar (Saarland), is made up of five 'circles' of the former Prussian Rhineland together with two 'circles' of the Bavarian Palatinate. Subjected for forty years to be the international see-saw of France and Germany, the Saar was returned to the latter in October 1955 and was constituted the tenth *Land*. The very dense population is concentrated in small towns and large villages. The inhabitants include a number of Germans from other parts of the country who were attracted to the area by the coal mines in the nineteenth century. About two-thirds of the population is made up of workmen, miners, and small landowners, who depend for their foodstuffs (except beef and potatoes) on imports from neighbouring regions. Three-quarters of the industrial output must be exported. This, coupled with the Saar's reunion with Germany after a number of years in the French economic plan, has raised a number of readjustment problems. The capital is Saarbrücken.

INCREASING POPULATION. SOCIAL AND FINANCIAL PROBLEMS. The great rise in the German birth-rate after 1940 has now dropped to 17 per thousand (about 800,000 births a year), with maximum figures in the Catholic regions of the Moselle, the Münsterland and Bavaria, and the minimum figure in Hamburg. The death-rate (10.9 per thousand) is hardly greater in the south than in the north (about 550,000 deaths in all per year), and the infant mortality rate is 36 per thousand. However, despite war losses (amounting to 4,600,000 persons) the population has increased by 26.5 per cent (10,600,000 persons) since 1939. This increase has been due in great measure to the influx of people expelled from the east, of refugees from the Communist zone of East Germany, and of Germans who have returned from abroad. Even after the repatriation of prisoners-of-war the female population still exceeds the male by 6 per cent.

The destruction of the towns brought a temporary rise in the rural population, but at the present time the flight from the countryside is more marked than ever. In fact, today the towns have regained, and even surpassed, their pre-war population

The Rhine at Bacharach, in Rheinland Pfalz. On either bank the hills drop steeply into the river, and vines are grown intensively on terraces. The town is crowded into the narrow space between hillside and river bank. GERMAN TOURIST INFORMATION BUREAU

figures. Only one-quarter of Germany's inhabitants live in communities of less than 2,000 people, 6 per cent in villages with less than 500 people (the corresponding figures for France are 38.5 per cent and 13.5 per cent), 29 per cent crowded into towns of more than 100,000 inhabitants, and 15 per cent in huge cities of more than 400,000 inhabitants — the corresponding figures for France are 17 per cent and 9.5 per cent.

The population actively engaged in work is 46 per cent of the total. The number of independent workers continues to decrease while that of persons with private incomes, living on pensions and retired pay, continues to increase, as does the number of employees and civil servants. The number of employed persons has risen considerably. For instance, between 1948 and 1956 it rose from 13,800,000 to 18,600,000 wage-earners, 36 per cent of whom were women (a much higher proportion than before the war). Unemployment is on the whole slight and unevenly distributed. The number of unemployed fell during 1959 to 187,000 — the lowest figure since the end of World War II. There are few unemployed in Württemberg, whose social and economic structure was strong enough to withstand even the great crisis of 1931. On the other hand, there is a fair amount of unemployment in Bavaria and Holstein. In the latter the unskilled refugees are the greatest sufferers, for skilled and trained workers can get jobs anywhere in a country short of such men.

During the same period (1948—56) there was a movement, both technical and financial, towards economic concentration by selling cartels and *Konzerne* (a movement first among the big industrial concerns and then among the banks). There was a widespread 'paternalistic' attitude among employers (dating back as far as 1880) that in some measure anticipated the social progress with social security legislation of the twentieth century, thus averting much of the bitterness of class conflict. This paternalistic spirit, reinforced by an all-powerful technocracy, has survived and exists alongside the social legislation since effected. Workmen and employees of all sorts are realistic, concerned with the efficient running of the enterprise they serve and of which they are generally very proud. First, the workers' reasonable claims were confined to a participation in management. Despite opposition from the Employers' Confederation, the *Deutsche Gewerkschaft Bund* (D.G.B.) which comprises about six million trades-unionists was able to secure, in 1952, the enactment of a law establishing joint management.

Reutlingen. In the distance, the abrupt escarpment of white rocks and one of the hills of the Swabian Alb (Jura) rise above the fertile plateaus of Württemburg, with their forests, their broken fields and their busy industrial towns. NÖHER

Freiburg-Günterstal at the foot of the Schauinsland mountain in the Schwarzwald. GERMAN TOURIST INFORMATION BUREAU

The Karlsplatz at München, capital of Bavaria. In the centre is the Karlstor, relic of the medieval town walls.
GERMAN TOURIST INFORMATION BUREAU

CULTURAL ACTIVITIES IN THE LÄNDER. Cultural activities (education and the fine arts) are — if we exclude a department of the Cultural Affairs Ministry in Bonn which deals with inter-regional questions — still entirely in the hands of the individual *Länder*, though the position has given rise to much discussion. Five-and-a-half million children are educated in 30,000 public elementary schools divided almost evenly between the 'Christian community' schools, and the schools that are wholly Catholic or Protestant. Fifteen per cent of the children go on to secondary schools (20 per cent of these in private establishments) or complete their studies in the 9,000 technical schools.

The seventeen universities (in addition to the six in East Germany) enjoy a considerable degree of autonomy. Some are in large cities while others have been for centuries the pride of certain smallish learned towns, *Universitätsstädte*. Three of these — Heidelberg, Freiburg and Tübingen — date from the Middle Ages. The universities, plus seven polytechnic institutions, have 130,000 undergraduates of both sexes, 25 per cent of whom receive scholarships and many of whom manage to continue their studies only by taking on an outside job.

The libraries and museums are heavily subsidised and, in addition, scientific research is strongly supported by the industrialists. Academies, institutes and large special schools of national importance are scattered all over the country. The activity of the publishing trade may be judged by the figure of some 15,000 titles issued every year (Stuttgart and Munich are the main publishing centres). There are 500 daily newspapers in Germany, seven of which have circulations over 200,000 (15 million copies in all); 600 different magazines sell 45 million copies.

PRESERVATION OF HISTORIC MONUMENTS. There are very strict rules against disfiguring natural scenery and urban areas with advertisement hoardings and unsuitable buildings or façades. Again, constant care is devoted by the *Landeskonservatore* to the upkeep and restoration of historic monuments. Among these latter an essential part of the national architectural patrimony is made up of the medieval brick edifices in the north, the Romanesque churches of the Ottonian era (A.D. 936—1002), the castles that top the hills of south and west, the great cathedrals of the Rhinelands, the Cistercian monasteries, the fifteenth-century late Gothic monuments, the seventeenth-century patrician dwellings in the northern cities and, above all, the unique and highly original collection of abbatial churches and basilicas in eighteenth-century baroque and rococo styles found in Swabia, Franconia and Bavaria. To these must be added the palaces, more or less modelled on Versailles, built in the same golden age in the towns where the princes and bishops resided.

The Germans are much attracted to folklore and there are few towns of any importance where there is not a *Heimatmuseum* or a *Landesmuseum* displaying objects of local interest. Local costumes are no longer worn except in the Lüneburg Heaths, at Bückeburg, in the Hesse Schwalm (on the flanks of

General view of Garmisch-Partenkirchen, summer and winter sports resort of international fame at the foot of a magnificent glacier cirque (left) and the Zugspitze (9,721 feet), the highest peak of Germany, on the border of Bavaria and Austria. P. ALMASY

the Vogelsberg), in the southern part of the Black Forest, and in many villages of Upper Bavaria.

Though Germany is a land of hard work, the traditional local festivals have lost none of their brilliance or their popularity. There are wine-harvest festivals in every village of the Rhine vineyards, a children's festival at Biberach, religious festivals in Catholic southern Germany (the Passion Play at Oberammergau, processions at Weingarten), carnivals at Cologne, Mainz, Munich and Rottweil, and the celebrated music festival at Bayreuth.

An ever-increasing stream of tourists is attracted mainly to the Bavarian lakes and Alps, the Black Forest, and the Rhine Gorge or to those art-towns which survived aerial bombardments — Bamberg, Bayreuth and Rothenburg. In summer German holiday-makers flock to the Frisian Islands beaches, the Holstein lakes, Lake Constance, and the innumerable holiday resorts in the woodlands of the Hercynian zone. Finally, there are no fewer than seventy-six spas which attract great numbers of people to take the waters.

MORE THAN TEN MILLION REFUGEES. The major population problem today is the problem of migration and resettlement. Together, they have increased national expenditure; conversely, they have increased the country's potential. Since 1949, some 320,000 Germans have emigrated (mostly through the port of Bremen) — 105,000 to Canada, 137,000 to the United States, and 27,000 to Australia. Others have joined their families in East Germany. Against this, thirty-five times as many Germans have entered West Germany, either from the former Prussian provinces annexed by Russia and Poland or from various countries in central Europe where they had been settled for centuries, or from the People's Republic of East Germany.

It is estimated that, in all, some 15 million Germans have been obliged to leave the homes where their ancestors lived for centuries. Once almost 10 million of them inhabited lands beyond the Oder, where now only 1,500,000 remain. The intake from Czechoslovakia, Poland, Rumania and Yugoslavia is 6½ million. Of the 15 million Germans who started out

The castle of Hohenzollern in Württemberg, the cradle of the German Imperial family. It was much restored from 1850—57 and stands on an escarpment in the middle of a forest. P. ALMASY

3 million disappeared (deported, exterminated or dead en route), almost 4 million stayed in East Germany, and 8½ million reached their real goal, the Federal Republic, by whatever means they could. The largest contingent (2 million), made up of Silesians, Pomeranians and Prussians, went to Schleswig-Holstein, Lower Saxony and Hesse. Next largest (almost 2 million) were the Sudetes (Sudetenland Germans) from Bohemia who made their way to Bavaria and Hesse. This large-scale exodus of expelled persons (*Vertriebene*) — a high proportion of whom were women and children — took place over the years 1946—49. The number of immigrants has since risen with the arrival of refugees who, despite the establishment in 1952 of a forbidden and strictly guarded strip three miles wide, running along the frontier between West and East Germany, manage to leave the East German zone through Berlin and by air at the rate of 15,000 to 20,000 a month. The total of these immigrants is in the region of 3 million.

The immigrants — most of whom arrived without resources of any kind — now make up 21 per cent of the population of the *Bund*. If the newcomers were not taken in by friends or relatives, they mostly stayed in little towns of the adjacent *Länder* and not near the Rhine. The population of these small towns has thus been considerably increased, and with industrialisation some have doubled their former size.

Measures were taken to receive the immigrants. A special ministry was set up, and it was agreed with the Rhine *Länder* that the financial burden should be evenly spread. A second migration was organised, this time to the Rhine (and especially to the Ruhr, where the demand for labour is never satisfied); it comprised 800,000 persons. Some refugees had managed to preserve their means of existence and the tools of their trade and so were able to set to work and rebuild their fortunes. In all, 9,000 new industrial concerns (making up 11 per cent of the textile factories and 22 per cent of the glass works in Germany) and 63,000 new handicraft enterprises, employing a total of 180,000 workmen were established. Kaufbeuren in Bavaria, for instance, has taken over the Bohemian glass industry.

Little by little, the big businesses have moved all or part of their plant from East to West — Siemens, for example, from Berlin to Essen, Zeiss optical works from Jena to Heidenheim (Württemberg). Other concerns — more numerous — have redeployed their workmen into factories which already existed. However, despite the distribution of 963,000 acres of land in the moors, in the Schleswig Geest and in Lower Saxony, the great mass of the refugees — more or less unemployed — is still stranded in the countryside, where they have received a very cool welcome. Agriculturists (whose farming methods have often brought beneficial changes, as demonstrated by the Silesians in Hanover) arrived in superabundant numbers, especially at first, but only 10 per cent of the 2,300,000 refugees put out on farms could be employed on the land. Later on, came other specialists: technicians, members of the liberal professions and civil servants. In all, only 7 per cent (against 35 per cent at first) have been able to remain independent workers. Seventy-three per cent are labourers (whereas the proportion was 49 per cent in their old homes) and 80 per cent of them live in lodgings or hutments.

Although refugees' societies keep alive regrets for lost homes, assimilation has made much progress. It is estimated that one-third of the refugee intake is already assimilated, and almost one-half in process of becoming so. The independent political parties founded by the refugees are fading away. The excess of births over deaths is 1 per cent among the newcomers, compared with 5 per cent for the country as a whole. School reports on refugee children are, moreover, much better than the average. The refugees provide Germany with a factor for expansion within her own limits.

HOUSING PROBLEMS. A corollary of the refugee problem — and just as urgent — was that of housing in the post-war period. In 1945 400 million cubic metres of rubble and 17,000 million bricks which had been retrieved and utilised in random fashion cluttered up the German towns. Of the housing blocks, 42 per cent were uninhabitable, and about one-half of this number irreparably destroyed. With some exceptions (Flensburg, Lübeck, Wiesbaden, Heidelberg) the large towns had suffered something like 60 per cent destruction (Cologne and Würzburg 75 per cent). Over a recent seven-year period 3 million dwellings (for the most part 'social') have been built by 1,800,000 workmen, with up to 80 per cent of the cost financed by public funds or bank credits. Four-fifths of the urban areas have been reconstructed, and there is not a village which does not boast new streets and buildings. All the same, this considerable achievement has not been sufficient to end overcrowding. Six per cent of the dwellings are still improvised, while 34 per cent of the population live as lodgers. Ownership of more than one place of residence and 'absentee' ownership are uncommon. Even villas and country houses are, for the most part, lived in all the year round.

Agricultural and maritime activity

AGRICULTURE AND FOOD SUPPLY. Agriculture takes second place in Germany, where political and economic priority is given to industry and commerce. Because of the continual exodus to the towns (which attract especially working families) and despite the influx of refugees into certain regions, there is sometimes a lack of farm workers.

The number of country-dwellers continues to decrease (7 million or 27 per cent of persons actively employed in 1939; 23 per cent in 1954). And since agriculture had not made one-fifth as much progress as industry, the proportion of the national income represented by the former has sunk from 13.5 per cent to 10 per cent.

The loss of the provinces beyond the Oder-Neisse line and the separation of West Germany from East Germany have had serious consequences, for although in 1945 West Germany had three-quarters of the population, it contained only 45 per cent of the arable land and livestock, 40 per cent of the potato fields, and 32 per cent of the sugar-beet crop. Moreover, German agriculture has had to face a population pressure of 880 inhabitants to the square mile of arable land and despite

Administrative buildings in the new Bremen, the port of north Germany, on the Weser. Like many German cities, Bremen was largely destroyed during World War II; daring architects have made of it one of the most modern cities of Europe. HED WIESNER, ATLAS-PHOTO

considerable progress over the last few years (since 1938 the total grain and potato crops have increased by one-third) German farmers can satisfy only part of the home demand for foodstuffs. Although the proportion of home-produced foodstuffs is double that in Great Britain, Germany must still import 27 per cent of her grain, 6 per cent of her meat and sugar and 55 per cent of her fats.

The main item of diet is the potato, which is served at every meal (about 372 ℔ per head of the population annually). Flour (consumption is falling) is more often employed in the form of noodles than as bread. More meat is being eaten (14 million pigs slaughtered annually) but less vegetables, butter and sugar (the *Bund* is more or less self-sufficient in the last). The tendency is for the consumption of milk, cheese, eggs, and especially margarine (42 per cent more than in 1939) to rise, together with that of citrus and other fruits (about 147 ℔ per head annually against 92 lb in 1939).

MECHANISATION AND THE PRINCIPAL GRAIN CROPS.

From a technical point of view, German agriculture must be regarded as less advanced than that of Holland, Denmark, Belgium or Switzerland, but a good deal more advanced than that of France. Ninety-two per cent of the German farms have electricity, while two-thirds of them have water laid on. Mechanisation is highly developed. There are 16 tractors per 1,000 acres. About 108 ℔ chemical fertilizer are used per acre. Farmers trained in technical schools (of which there are 530) represent 15 to 20 per cent of the whole, while 23,500 co-operatives of all kinds have a membership of one-half of those engaged on the land. The numbers of members employed in dairy-farming is particularly high.

Rye is still the main grain crop and is grown mostly in the cold-weather lands of the Geest in Lower Saxony and in that part of Franconia centred round Nuremberg. Half the wheat (produced in about the same quantity as rye) is grown in the Baden plain, the Württemberg and Würzburg *Gaue*, and the Straubing plain; the other half comes from Rhenish Hesse and the Cologne-Düren basin. Spelt, grown in the Alb and Upper Swabia, is a declining crop. Barley does best in the Alzey area and is primarily a Franconian crop, with a fair yield in Swabia. Oats, on the other hand, come mostly from the north-west — the Frisian region, Holstein and the Westerwald. Potatoes are cultivated everywhere, particularly in the south of the Great Plain and in the valley of the middle Rhine (Palatinate, Hesse). The area under sugar-beet has doubled since 1938, and two-thirds of the crop is in the region of the lower Rhine and especially in the Hanoverian *Börde*. Market-gardening flourishes near the large towns and in the *Börde* (Brunswick). Asparagus is grown at Mainz and Schwetzingen, *sauerkraut* cabbage to the south of Stuttgart.

GRASSLANDS AND STOCK-BREEDING. FRUITS AND VINES. FISHERIES.

The area under grass amounts to 13,837,000 acres. Hay fields are double the area of the pasture lands and, like the cultivated fields, are rarely enclosed. Hedges are found only in Westphalia and Holstein, wooden fences in the Allgäu, and ditches in the Marschen. Except in these areas and in Hanover, the cattle are stall-fed and, in the south of the Palatinate and of the Main region, are still used to draw long farm-carts. Cattle are very numerous, especially in Bavaria and Upper Swabia and also near the North Sea and the Dutch frontier. These are areas which export milk and produce butter (Upper Swabia) or cheese (Allgäu). Pig-rearing increases, and in Westphalia, particularly near Hanover, is highly intensive. Sheep (Lüneburg Heath, western Schleswig, Alb and Franconia) are decreasing in number and today are hardly more numerous than goats. On the other hand, more and more poultry are being raised. There are about 59 million birds of which 2 million are geese. Bee-keeping is a feature on the Lüneburg Heaths.

The Moselle valley, overlooked by the old castle of Cochem (Rhine-Palatinate). The Moselle winds its solitary and peaceful way through warm slopes covered with vineyards and capped by the undulating forests of the Eifel and the Hunsrück. HANS WAGNER, ATLAS-PHOTO

Potato harvesting in Lower Saxony. Potatoes are the mainstay of the German diet (372 lb. per head per year). P. ALMASY

Orchards of carefully tended, trimmed and inspected fruit-trees dot the slopes of all the Rhineland valleys as far as Cologne, notably in the Bergstrasse from Heidelberg to Darmstadt and in the Ortenau (Baden), whose speciality is cherries. Orchards flourish up to Hamburg and abound round the villages of Lower Swabia and the Main region of Franconia. Here there are 90 million trees in all, one-half of which are apple and one-fifth plum. Apple-juice rather than cider is the national drink, together with beer; consumption of table fruit continues to rise. Tall rows of hops stretch from the Upper Rhine and the Neckar to Lake Constance, but nine-tenths of the crop comes from middle Franconia (Nuremberg) and from the Bavarian Hallertau to the north of Freising. Tobacco is grown on the Baden plain.

The German vineyards, the most northerly of Europe, demand great care because of the danger from frost. They occupy, roughly, parts of the regions that were Romanised in ancient times. The 143,000 acres of vineyards — though the area is shrinking all the time — spread over the slopes of the Rhine banks, on the right bank (Markgräfles Land and Kaiserstuhl in the Breisgau) and then on the left bank from Neustadt to Mainz, over again to the right from Wiesbaden to Rüdesheim and, finally, on terraces through the Rhine Gorge as far as Honnef. Vineyards twist along the winding banks of the Moselle, the Ahr, the Neckar and the Main, too, but are never found on the plains. The yield varies from 260 to 520 gallons an acre and produces only wines of high quality which are classified into a great number of types. Although as prosperity increases more wine is being consumed by the Germans, it remains a luxury drink. Mainz and Trier are the main wine markets.

The 1,900,000 German farms are in the hands of 1,300,000 owners; 87 per cent are owner-run, mostly by single families. There are, in all, only 1,100,000 agricultural labourers. Members of the nobility still own very large estates (reduced to some extent by agrarian reform) but these are mostly made up of forest land. The average holding varies between 12 and 50 acres, though one-third of all the holdings are of less than 5 acres. In the Upper Rhineland and in the Neckar region the land has been subdivided into tiny strips of cultivation, but reconstitution of these small parcels into larger units has already been effected over an area of 6,770 square miles. In the south similar reconstitution is to be applied to two-thirds of the properties, and in Bavaria to a still higher proportion.

The fishing industry is organised on very modern lines. The main fishing-ports are Emden, Norderney, Vegesack, Cuxhaven, Hamburg, Kiel and, especially, Wesermünde. The main fishing areas are the North Sea and the seas off Iceland, for the rocky bed of the Baltic makes it unsuitable for trawling. The annual catch of 730,000 tons of fish (one-half is herring) is enough to furnish every inhabitant of Germany with 26.5 lb of fish. The catch is now the third largest in Europe and is distributed far into Central Europe.

FORESTS EVERYWHERE. Trees and woods occupy an essential place in German art, architecture and civilisation, and are as significant to the German temperament as they are to the German landscape. Even today, woods in some form or other reach right into the suburbs of the largest cities. In West Germany 27 per cent of the land is wooded. Two-thirds of the trees are conifers which have steadily increased during the last two centuries — to the detriment of deciduous trees (beech, oak and birch in the main). As a general rule, conifers are more common on the eastern mountain slopes and deciduous trees on the western slopes. The typical German forest is composed of squares of beech among fir-trees regularly planted and of the same age; 95 per cent of the growth is timber. Except in the Rhineland and Lower Bavaria, brushwood is rarely seen. Despite extensive forests, Germany has to import about 13 million cubic yards of timber each year.

Industrial development

THE ORIGINS. The origins of German industry are found far back in the country's history. Well before the fifteenth century wool, flax and silk were woven in what is now the Ruhr area, as well as in Westphalia, at Ulm, Augsburg, Nuremberg, and in Saxony. By the eighteenth century the peasants of the hill-country in Thuringia, Saxony and Württemberg had managed to eke out a living from their poor soil by the products of their handicraft. The French Huguenots brought with them their manufacturing methods, but it was only from about 1850 that the working of the coalfields allowed Germany to develop her industrial plan on a huge scale and compete, in the front rank of industrial nations, with Great Britain. At the same time, under the leadership of Alfred Krupp, came the first of the 'vertical' combines, the *Konzerne*, which include in one holding company and under a single management a whole group of enterprises needed in the manufacture of a product and in its delivery to the consumer. The *Konzerne*, together with the sales trusts, grew larger and larger at the end of the nineteenth and the beginning of the twentieth centuries until industry dominated and indeed controlled Germany.

Contrary to all forecasts, industry's dominating position in German economy before the Second World War was strengthened during the country's post-war recovery period. Of course, German industry did suffer during the war, but material losses did not amount to more than 15 per cent of the whole. Loss of patents and manufacturing secrets was the most serious blow, for the quickly abandoned scheme for dismantling industrial plant affected only 8 per cent of the installations (25 per cent in the metallurgical industry). Yet this very dismantling brought about a general and complete transformation (carried out with the aid of the Marshall Plan), and the currency reform brought with it a broadminded, liberal policy and, after 1949, an enormous mass of investment. In twenty years (1936—56) industrial output doubled, though the manpower employed did not show a similar increase. There are relatively more craftsmen, who now total 4 million.

COAL, OIL, METALS, ELECTRIC POWER. German industry at the present time depends upon the underground riches of the country — in a word, coal. After the war four of the country's main coalfields fell to the lot of Western Germany. The first, and one of the very highest class, is the great Ruhr basin, with ascertained reserves of 64,000 million tons and probably another 55,000 million tons to be added to that. Lying one above the other are 124 seams of all sorts of coal — ten of anthracite and fifty-seven of soft coal account for 76 per cent of the output, while fifty-seven seams of cannel coal yield 18 per cent. The seams dip without a break in a northerly direction. They are easily worked by shafts which have been used for a long time and have an average depth of 2,450 feet (about 1,300 feet in the south, though these seams are today almost exhausted, with 2,500 feet in the central area, and 3,300 feet in the north, while there is a possible extension at a greater depth in the direction of the Münsterland). The annual output is about 120 million tons.

The Saar basin (part of whose output was for a time earmarked for France) extends under forested land over an area of 467 square miles. The parallel seams of lean coal at Ottweiler in the north-east, and the cannel and soft coal (64 per cent) elsewhere sink down in the west-south-west direction and contain about 10,000 million tons of reserves. Some 60,000 miners working in pits from 650 to 2,950 feet deep bring up 18 million tons of coal annually. The most productive mines are no longer at Ottweiler but in the Warndt Forest near the Lorraine border. Although Saar coal does not coke well, some 4 million tons of coke are produced. Up to now German buyers, mainly from south of the Main, have taken less than one-fifth of the Saar coal because the lack of a modern water transport system makes delivery difficult.

The Aachen coalfield, whose seams are more dislocated, is a continuation of the Franco-Belgian fields; together with the still small Westphalian coalfields it provides an additional output which is as yet only one-twelfth of that of the Ruhr.

The very extensive lignite deposits (6,000 million tons available through open-cast working and 23,000 million tons through deep mining) to the south-west of Cologne are being increasingly worked. There are a few other deposits in Bavaria.

There are oil-wells in production near Celle in Hanover and on the Dutch Frisian frontier (proved reserves are in the region of 51 million tons), and it is proposed to drill another field south of Hamburg. Natural gas and potash are also exploited. The excellent iron deposits of Siegen and the Dill (which provided a starting-point for the Ruhr industry) are now approaching exhaustion and are hardly worth working. The deposits in Hanover, at Ilsede and especially at Salzgitter, are more extensive (2,000 million tons of reserves) but of rather poor quality. The metallurgical industry's needs have to be met by imports (80 per cent of the total) of Scandinavian, Spanish, Canadian, Brazilian and Lorraine ore. German steel

production is now greater than that of Great Britain. Other metals (zinc and lead mines) occur in Germany only in small quantities.

In view of Germany's economic potential, the production and consumption of electric power is comparatively low. Thermal electricity represents 82 per cent of the power total (54 per cent of the whole in Rhineland-Westphalia where output, area for area, is eight times greater than in all other parts of the *Bund*). Only 18 per cent is hydro-electric power, and the Germans buy current from their neighbours. However, large dams have now been constructed. Five of them form lakes, each holding more than 130 million cubic yards of water. A dam is being built at Jochenstein near Passau on the Danube.

THE RUHR. INDUSTRIAL GERMANY'S REAL CAPITAL.

The position of the German coalfields determines the location of today's industry, and during the last hundred years the Ruhr has assumed a position of overwhelming importance. It is the unquestioned industrial capital of continental Europe. For the foreigner, the Ruhr is as much the heart of Germany as Paris is of France, and Rome of Italy.

The growth of this industrial area was favoured by the twin presence of iron and coal. The first blast-furnace (at Mülheim) was set up in 1849, and the first pit-shaft sunk in the north of the Ruhr in 1850. The importance of the Ruhr in German economy may be judged not only by its contribution of 90 per cent of the coal and 80 per cent of the gas piped to all parts of the country, but by the fact that centred there today is about 40 per cent of West German industry's employees and capital, 50 per cent to 60 per cent of its industrial production, 80 per cent of its heavy metallurgy, 40 per cent of the rail freight traffic, and 48 per cent of the tramway lines. Yet this unique area that touches on the Rhineland and Westphalia is, first and foremost, marked by an intense productivity, and by a rational utilisation of manpower, of the soil, of raw materials, and of equipment. Over 6½ million inhabitants live close together within 3,200 square miles. Within the narrower limits of the *Ruhrsiedlungsverband*, 'The Association of Ruhr Settlements', 4½ million people inhabit 1,950 square miles, 445,000 of them miners (out of a total of 600,000 in the whole *Bund*) and about 1½ million industrial workers.

Going from south to north, three zones can be distinguished according to variations in the depth of the seams and differences in operational life to date. The first zone, where the seams were close to the surface and have to all intents and purposes been worked out or relinquished to secondary enterprises, extends to the south of the Ruhr, in the hilly country of the Sauerland and Bergisches Land. It is an area which has remained relatively rural in character, dotted with little groups of houses and small workshops. Nearby are large towns which have long been industrialised (wireworks have existed there since the sixteenth century) and were already of considerable size in 1840. Elberfeld and Barmen then had a combined total of 50,000 inhabitants. Today they are united as Wuppertal, with over 400,000 inhabitants, and stretch along their valley for over eight miles. Grouped round these towns are several other large urban areas. First, where the Ruhr touches on the Rhine stands the splendid city of Düsseldorf (24,000 inhabitants in 1840, over 650,000 today), enjoying an unrivalled position as the administrative, social, financial and commercial capital of the whole Ruhr. Then, on the flatter, left bank of the Rhine are Krefeld and Gladbach-Rheydt.

This southern zone specialises in the manufacture and production of all sorts of finished goods — metallurgy (68 per cent of the engineering of the Ruhr), the various branches of the chemical industry (100 per cent of the dyestuffs, 85 per cent of the pharmaceutical products), plastics, all the Ruhr textiles (cottons and artificial fabrics at Wuppertal and Gladbach, silk at Krefeld), hardware and tools at Solingen, Remscheid and Hagen.

The industrial stretch of the Rhine near Duisburg. Strings of boats or barges, loaded mostly with mineral fuels (coal, lignite and hydrocarbons), ores, sand and gravel, pass or cross each other between the flat banks of the river, the poplars and the rows of factories along the Lower Rhine. LANDESBILDSTELLE NIEDERRHEIN

The slag heaps and coke ovens of Hostenbach, in the Saar.
HELGA STURSBERG, ATLAS-PHOTO

Coke ovens at Kump–Lintfort, one of the most up–to–date coalfields of the Ruhr.

The second zone, in the centre, stretches for thirty-eight miles along a ridge between the rivers Ruhr and Emscher, and with an average breadth of about thirteen miles, from the pit-heads of Mörs and the large port of Duisburg to Dortmund. Here, in the great coalfield, is the real heart of the Ruhr, a hive of human activity since 1860, where vast urban units with huge commercial and administrative buildings stretch in all directions in a fantastic forest of tall factory chimneys, blast-furnaces, coke ovens, gigantic workshops, shunting and marshalling yards, and rows of blackened houses. Still, the country-side is never wholly out of sight and reach. It is present in the form of green, open spaces, bits of woodland that have somehow been preserved, and meadows even among the factories. In 1840 Duisburg-Ruhrort, Essen and Dortmund were old but small towns with 4,000 to 5,000 inhabitants. Today they are cities multiplied a hundred times, powerful centres directing the activities of the Ruhr. Mülheim — once the leading town — has developed less. Between these influential centres extensive workers' settlement have grown up — Oberhausen, Gelsen-kirchen, Bochum, Wanne-Eickel and Herne. This is the realm of raw materials and heavy industry, with four-fifths of the coalmines, an output of 30 million tons of coke, and three-quarters of the output of steel, pig-iron, metallurgical products, sheet-metal, tubing and wagons. To this must be added sheet-glass, basic chemical products (tar, benzol, ammonia, soda, sulphuric acid), synthetic petrol, and so on.

Further north lies the third zone of the coalfield. Yielding cannel coal, it has been worked under the grass and woods between Emscher and Lippe since 1900, and new towns with new steelworks, coke ovens, chemical products and synthetic rubber factories (Marl) have sprung up around the old townships of Recklinghausen, Bottrop, and Gladbeck.

Non-ferrous metal foundries are scattered in every corner of the Ruhr.

The great concentration of workers draws on a very extensive area for its foodstuffs. Northern Westphalia supplies most of the potatoes, pigs, cattle and milk.

The enormous quantities of water needed for so highly industrialised a region present continual problems. 2,882 million cubic yards (1,240 million are needed by the chemical industry alone) are furnished by the Sauerland reservoirs, and the waste waters are drained off by the Emscher into the Rhine.

The tremendous increase in output and in the volume of business since 1860 has been possible only by the continuous development in concentration of such enterprises as the exceptionally powerful 'vertical' *Konzerne* (especially after 1890). Although to some extent broken up after 1952, their methods and ideas survive in subsidiary companies detached from the main block — subsidiary companies which, moreover, are beginning to link up again. Between them fourteen *Konzerne* produced 55 per cent of the coal and turned out 75 per cent of the steel. The most important *Konzern* of all, the *Vereinigte Stahlwerke*, alone contributed 23 per cent of the coal and 44 per cent of the steel. The names of Hibernia, Harpener, Haniel, Hoesch, Kloeckner, Stinnes, Mannesmann, Thyssen and Krupp remain inseparable from the mammoth works of Essen, Hamborn, Oberhausen, the Demag at Duisburg, the *Rheinische Stahlwerke* and so on, each turning out a minimum of 750,000 tons of steel annually. Although first and foremost the *Konzerne* controlled basic products, they also dominated many branches of investment and consumption enterprises both in and outside the Ruhr. Foreign participation in German concerns is considerable and in 1950 amounted to 20 per cent of the total capital invested (mostly American, Swiss and Dutch capital).

SECONDARY INDUSTRIAL AREAS. From the great nerve-centre of the Ruhr there run two main lines of secondary industrial concentrations to which the Ruhr sends power-producing coal, gas and electricity.

The first of these lines stretches out to the north and east, over the plains of Westphalia and Hanover and more or less parallel with the old medieval highway of the Hellweg. In Westphalia, and in contact with the Dutch Twente, there is a preponderance of textile mills (cotton and wool) from Bocholt and Rheine to Münster and Osnabrück. Bielefeld, the largest of these industrial towns, has sewing-machine and bicycle factories in addition to its linen industry. The Detmold area turns out furniture. Equally busy are the industrial centres of Hanover (steel, lorries, trucks, rubber) and Brunswick (canned foods, precision instruments, metallurgy), with the blast-furnaces of Salzgitter-Watenstedt and the Wolfsburg factories (the most modern in Europe) on the Mittellandkanal where 37,000 workmen turn out 3,400 Volkswagens a day.

The second and more important string of factory-cities runs down to the south-east of the great Rhine artery — interrupted by the gorge of the schist massif. Cologne, despite its past history of independence and its commercial importance, is closely subordinated to the neighbouring Ruhr area with which it is linked by the factories of its north-east suburbs (producing machines, cables, chemicals, aluminium, rubber). The Neuwied basin has works for transforming the surrounding tuff into refractory earth or fireclay. Metallurgy and tanning, optical works and camera manufacture flourish in the valley of the Lahn. Near the junction of the Main and the Rhine, the great Frankfurt conurbation, which includes Wiesbaden, Mainz and Darmstadt, contains a population of one million within a triangle measuring 25 miles along each side. It is the seat of many industries, the most important of which are: machines and presses, rubber and wagons (Mainz), dyes and chemical products, motor-cars, jewellery and leather. Then, at the mouth of the Neckar, there is the Mannheim urban area (agricultural implements, mirrors, jute, leather); after that Ludwigshafen (chemical products) and Heidelberg, the old university town, with its huge Anilin und Sodafabrik employing 20,000 skilled chemical workers.

Following the Neckar, fifty miles upstream lies the Bund's second most important industrial area after the Ruhr, although on nothing like the same scale. This is the Baden-Württemberg region, which has a number of very modern factories, especially to the south and east of Stuttgart. The economic structure here is quite different from that farther north and is founded not on the presence of raw materials or fuel but (as in Saxony) solely on the high quality of the labour force. There are not many labourers. The workmen-peasants are usually small landowners and heirs of a centuries-old tradition of handicrafts. These *Pendelarbeiter* travel daily from village to factory. The enterprises, of medium size, are run on patriarchal lines, where the 'boss' is in the workshops and keeps in fairly close touch with his men. There are various industries, each little town having its own speciality and turning out quantities of well-finished products and delicately made objects. The textile works (and especially the knitting-mills) employ 75,000 hands and are scattered in the northern piedmont — the gently sloping plain at the foot of the mountains — and in the short valleys of the Swabian Alb. Metallurgical industries are flourishing: agricultural and industrial machinery, electro-technical products (26,000 employees), motor-cars, locomotives, turbines and toys. Farther west, in the centre of the Alb, is an area that turns out precision tools and surgical and musical instruments; the speciality of the Black Forest is clocks, and of Pforzheim, farther north, jewellery.

The southern plain and edges of the Rhineland are much less industrialised except near Karlsruhe (sewing-machines) and in the Swiss sphere, where there are flourishing textile factories in the Baden (German) suburbs of Basle, in the Wiesental and in Singen.

On the Saar coalfield and at Neunkirchen there is a large-scale iron and steel industry, started in 1759 but developed under the Röchling and Stumm dynasties after 1880. There are thirty blast-furnaces as well as rolling-mills, wireworks, engineering workshops and glass and china factories.

The Aachen-Düren complex (textiles, metals, paper) bears a close resemblance, in the very variety of its activities, to the industries of the neighbouring Walloon parts of Belgium. At the other end of the *Bund*, in Upper Franconia, the textile, china and glass production reflects that of neighbouring Saxony and Bohemia.

There are six large towns where industry is concentrated in the centre itself and in the immediate suburbs: Bremen — motor-cars, shipyards, jute, linoleum; Hamburg — shipyards, electro-technical products, non-ferrous metals, petroleum refineries, oil-works, chemical products, rubber and, to the north, wool at Neumünster; Kassel, more of a residential town in spite of its locomotive works and machine-shops; the twin cities of Nuremberg and Furth — electro-technical products, metal goods, motor-cars and toys; Augsburg — textiles, machinery and motor-cars; and Munich, the most intellectual and least industrialised of German capitals — motor-cars, furniture and beer.

There is also the ball-bearing manufacture of Schweinfurt, the boot and shoe industry of Pirmasens, the little linen-manufacturing centres of the Weser and Baden, the cotton-mills of Upper Swabia, the stringed instrument works of Bavaria, the gem-cutting workshops at Idar-Oberstein, and numerous sawmills, paper-mills and timber yards throughout the region.

Cheese is manufactured in the Allgäu, margarine at Cleves, and chocolate in Cologne and Stuttgart. The breweries are of special importance, producing 660 million gallons of beer annually, and are divided into two rival groups: those of Bavaria (with many breweries at Kulmbach, Munich, Augsburg, Nuremberg and Würzburg); and those of the north, with most breweries at Dortmund, Wuppertal, Bremen and Hamburg.

RELATIVE IMPORTANCE IN INDUSTRY. On the whole, the manufacturing industries have made progress since 1938 and have doubled in size since 1950. Taking account of the number of people employed in them, the machinery and vehicle industries are the most important in Germany, with about 1,300,000 employees. Then come iron and steel, electro-technical products (output has increased five times since 1938), chemical products, paper and books; each of these has between 500,000 and 700,000 workers. China and glass, optical and precision instrument manufacture employ from 120,000 to 150,000. The German output of plastics is the second largest in the world.

Communications and transport

RAILWAYS AND AUTOBAHNEN. The German railways have a total length of about 23,000 miles, of which 19,000 miles belong to the State (*Deutsche Bundesbahn*). Only a few stretches, in Württemberg and Bavaria, have been electrified. The traffic is enormous, and there is no line with less than six to eight trains a day in each direction. Germany runs four times as many trains per mile as France. Along both banks of the Rhine Gorge there are 92 fast trains, 60 slow trains and 230 goods-trains daily. No station handles more international express trains than Cologne, while at Frankfurt, the headquarters of the whole network, two main lines converge — Scandinavia-Hamburg-Basle and Holland- or Dortmund-Cologne-Munich-Austria-Italy. Only six lines are kept open between West and East Germany, with only twenty-four direct trains daily in each direction.

Almost three times as many railway journeys are undertaken in Germany as in France, yet the average length of a journey is only one-half that of France. Two-thirds of the passengers are workmen or children who live in the suburbs, and a mere 17 per cent of the passengers pay full fares. The railways haul 1,260 million tons of freight, one-third of which is coal. The Hamm marshalling yards which control the Ruhr area from the east are among the largest in the world.

Autocars, many of them capable of operating either on road or rail, provide an alternative and comfortable method of travel. The total length of lines is 140,000 miles.

There are 1,375 miles of special motor-roads (*Autobahnen*), running mainly through wooded country and by-passing the

The final assembly lines in the Volkswagen factory at Wolfsburg in Lower Saxony. The factory employs 37,000 people and produces 3,400 passenger cars a day — one every 17 seconds. VOLKSWAGEN

built-up areas. The main artery links Berlin with the Ruhr and Cologne along the track of the old medieval Hellweg. From Cologne the autobahn continues to Frankfurt, Stuttgart, Munich and Salzburg. Branches lead off from Cologne to Aachen, from Frankfurt to Kassel and Thuringia and from Munich to Nuremberg, Hof and Berlin. There is also a strip joining Bremen to Lübeck via Hamburg.

The ordinary roads (about 80,000 miles of them) are often narrow and, in Bavaria, in poor condition, but they carry some of the densest motor traffic in the world. There are 1,800,000 motor-cars, 600,000 lorries and trucks, and more than 3,000,000 motor-cycles and scooters.

THE RHINE, THE MAIN RIVER OF EUROPE.
The system of natural navigable waterways comprises the four rivers flowing from south to north — the Elbe, the Weser, the Ems, and the Rhine with its two affluents, the Main and the Neckar — and the Danube downstream from Regensburg (Ratisbon). The system of fluvial waterways is linked by seven main canals in the northern plain. The total traffic amounts to about 125 million tons.

From Basle to the Dutch frontier, the Rhine (and to a lesser degree, its two tributaries) accounts for more than three-quarters of this traffic. In its course through Germany the Rhine emerges as Europe's main artery, the most majestic and busiest river. Great tugs, long strings of barges (most of them about 1,350 tons but some of them as much as 3,000 tons), motor-boats and elegant passenger steamers maintain a steady flow of traffic. Nearly 100 million tons of freight are handled on the river's banks, more than 60 per cent downstream between Bonn and Cleves. This section of the river despatches much more than it receives, both upstream and downstream. The middle section, from Bonn to Worms, is least busy, while the upper Rhine section unloads over two-and-a-half times as much tonnage as it loads. Duisburg-Ruhrort is the largest river-port in the world, and is the great freight market at the mouth of the Ruhr and the Herne Canal. It despatches coal, stocks wheat, and can berth sea-going ships in its 2,500 acres of docks; it rivals Hamburg in the tonnage of its shipping.

A third of Germany's exports by sea and half her imports (ore, oil) are carried on the Rhine, Rotterdam being her great export terminus. Half the tonnage is carried in German vessels (for the most part the property of the big *Konzerne*); most

of the rest is carried in Dutch (31 per cent, half of which is between the Ruhr and the frontier), French (6 per cent), Belgian (6 per cent) and Swiss (3 per cent) vessels. The main cargoes are coal and lignite, taken on from the Wesseling wharves near Cologne; these are directed principally to the twin ports of Mannheim and Ludwigshafen upstream, the storage centres for southern Germany. The Main is navigable as far as Bamberg (with ports at Frankfurt and Würzburg); shipping on the Neckar can reach Heilbronn, and in the near future will be able to reach Stuttgart. Projects for linking the Neckar or the Main with the Danube are being studied. The Moselle is also being regulated and canalised.

The Herne canal, which now replaces the Ruhr river, can take barges of up to 1,350 tons and is supplemented by the Lippe canal. It is the main economic tributary of the Rhine. The Datteln-Ems canal, which is being deepened, joins the Ruhr to the port of Emden. The network towards the east is completed by the canals from the Ems to the Jade and to Bremen, by the important Mittellandkanal which branches off from the Ems at Rheine and runs through Germany as far as the Oder, and finally by the Hanseatic canal from Lübeck to the Elbe. Upstream from Hamburg, the Elbe has lost a quarter of its traffic. The Weser is not much used, but traffic on the Danube becomes brisk below Regensburg (Ratisbon). There are numerous summer tourist services. Then there is the Nord-Ostseekanal or Kiel Canal, which joins the estuary of the Elbe to Kiel fiord and saves ocean shipping the roundabout route through the straits. The canal has increased its traffic by one-third since 1938.

At the end of the war the German merchant marine no longer existed, but it has now three-quarters of its former tonnage and carries a third of Germany's sea-borne cargoes.

THE RESURRECTION OF THE GREAT PORTS.
Although Germany has had its seaboard reduced to a narrow frontage on the North Sea and to the Baltic shores of Schleswig-Holstein, it has retained its two largest ports. In spite of the invasion of refugees who have doubled its population, Lübeck no longer retains many traces of its opulent past as a Hanseatic town, whilst the ruined and dismantled naval base of Kiel has modestly turned to fishing. There is a scheme to bring new life to Wilhelmshaven by laying down oil pipelines.

Aerial view of an Autobahn *outside Frankfurt. Important* Autobahnen *form a network over all Germany, avoiding the large towns.*

The vast modern shipyards at Hamburg. They are the third largest in the world, employing 31,000 workers, and this in spite of the fact that they were almost totally destroyed in World War II. W. LÜDEN, HAMBURG

The Bayer dyestuffs works at Leverkusen, on a bend of the Rhine below Cologne. This great chemical industry has been reconstructed and has greatly expanded since the war. The works incorporate modern welfare amenities for workers and apprentices. BUNDESBILDSTELLE, BONN

But it is Hamburg, Bremen and Emden (together with the Dutch port of Rotterdam) that share foreign sea-borne trade.

In 1945, the days of Hamburg's prosperity seemed past. Half the city's suburbs had been laid flat; the port and its installations were entirely destroyed. But today Hamburg is again prospering. Since 1953 the port has been entirely reconstructed and restored and now consists of twenty-five huge docks fanning out on to the Elbe. Ships of 205 different lines call at Hamburg and there are 550 sailings a month. Two-thirds of the traffic is represented by imports; British, American and Asian raw materials head the list, consisting mainly of oil, coffee, wheat, wool and jute. Hamburg has also won back its Austrian customers and, despite political barriers, many of those in Berlin, East Germany, Czechoslovakia and Hungary. The feverish activity of the Hamburg shipyards, which were dismantled and then entirely re-equipped, keep 31,000 workmen fully occupied in repairs and in building, and assure Germany of third place among the world's shipbuilding nations. The port of Bremen is also engaged in shipbuilding and with her voluminous cotton and wheat imports enjoys more traffic than before the war; Bremen is the largest cotton market in continental Europe and the main passenger port. But the Weser is not the Elbe, and large ships have to anchor about thirty-five miles below Bremen itself in the outer harbour of Bremerhaven-Wesermünde. Emden, the second maritime outlet of the Ruhr, is on the Ems estuary and has a larger tonnage of imports than Bremen, mainly due to Swedish iron ore and Norwegian timber.

THE RAPID RECOVERY OF COMMERCE. Large trade fairs, each with from 3,000 to 4,000 exhibitors, attract huge crowds of visitors every year to the three principal business towns and railway junctions of inland Germany — Frankfurt, Hanover and Cologne. Foreign trade, which is the primary source of German economic stability, increases annually — especially with the Far East, South America and Africa. This development is directly related to attractive pricing, quick deliveries according to contract, adaptability to customers' tastes and needs — and also to the unobtrusive conduct of Germany's political and military activities. About two-thirds of the foreign trade (especially as far as sales are concerned) is still with Europe (Holland takes first place, then come Belgium, Sweden, Switzerland, Italy and France), and a quarter of all Germany's purchases are made in America. Foodstuffs of animal origin come from Holland and Denmark, cereals from America and France, fruits from Italy. The percentage of finished products (machines, electrical equipment, shipping, motor-cars) is more than half that of the goods exported. The German chemical industry, however, has now fallen back from second to fourth world place.

West Germany is among the principal customers and suppliers of France, Switzerland, Benelux, Italy, Sweden, Austria, Turkey, Denmark, Spain, Iran and Brazil. Except in the case of her relatively undeveloped agriculture, the progress of Germany's economy has been uninterrupted since 1948 and shows a yearly increase of between 10 and 20 per cent.

THE GERMAN DEMOCRATIC REPUBLIC (EAST GERMANY)

The German Democratic Republic, or *Deutsche Demokratische Republik* was founded on 7th October 1949 in the Soviet occupation zone. It is a State which has found difficulty in achieving stability. The D.D.R. has been recognised neither by the Federal Republic (where East Germany is always called the 'Soviet Zone' or 'Central Germany') nor by the Western Allies who use the term 'East Germany'. She is cut off, too, from the former German eastern provinces which used to supply her, separated from Berlin which (officially at any rate) is an 'external enclave', and isolated from the two great sources of industrial power — Silesia and the Ruhr.

THE FOURTEEN DISTRICTS. The D.D.R. — whose capital is the east sector of Berlin, has an area of 41,380 square miles and a population (including that of East Berlin) of 17,300,000 (398 per square mile). The D.D.R. comprises Mecklenburg (until 1918 two separate duchies), part of western Pomerania, Brandenburg as far as the Oder, Saxe-Anhalt (formerly Prussian Saxony and the duchy of Anhalt), Saxony proper (i.e. the former kingdom of Saxony) and Thuringia; the last was formerly a jumble of eight little principalities forming the heart of Old Germany, the cradle of German culture, the land of Luther's Wartburg and Goethe's Weimar, and ceded by the Americans to the Russian zone in July 1945.

These five *Länder* were dissolved in 1952 to effect a greater degree of centralisation, and their place was taken by fourteen districts. Rostock, an ancient Hanseatic city, controls the whole Baltic area; Schwerin and Neubrandenburg, residential towns, divide the agricultural plain of Mecklenburg; Potsdam, 'the Prussian Versailles' on the Havel, and Frankfurt-on-the-Oder, the railway junction leading to Poland and eastern Europe, lie respectively west and east of Berlin. Kottbus is the capital of unproductive Lower Lusatia (Lausitz). Magdeburg, a famous fortified town in the German Middle Ages but now wholly industrialised, dominates both the middle reaches of the Elbe and the Harz. Halle is the centre of the lower basin of the Saale. Gera, with the Upper Saale, Suhl on the Weser slopes

and Erfurt on the central plain, divide Thuringia. Leipzig, on its plain, Karl-Marx-Stadt (formerly Chemnitz) and Dresden, the 'German Florence' which was almost flattened during the war, in the Erzgebirge range and the Sudete hills, divide Saxony. These districts are subdivided into 217 'circles'. The basin of the Elbe is almost more important to East Germany than the Rhine basin to West Germany. Only the Baltic slopes of Mecklenburg, a corner of Brandenburg, and what remains of Pomerania and Silesia lie outside the basin. The East German population is most densely concentrated in the south, on the middle stretches of the Elbe and of its principal tributary, the Saale.

Population and agricultural problems

STABLE POPULATION. Since 1939 the population has increased only very slightly, not amounting to more than 1,200,000 despite the influx of 4,300,000 persons expelled from former German provinces farther east or from Czechoslovakia. Efforts are made to assimilate these 'new citizens', who form 24 per cent of the whole population and 31 per cent in Mecklenburg, where the population has steadily increased. There is now an excess of births over deaths but so far this has failed to compensate for the exodus to the West of tradesmen, industrialists, peasants, doctors and civil servants (72,000 members of the teaching profession) — in all, 1,700,000 people in eight years. Migration in the opposite direction, that is, from West to East, has been much less marked. The years 1948 to 1958 saw a net loss in the population of the D.D.R.

The population includes more workmen (46 per cent) than peasants (21 per cent). The entire labour force amounts to 8 million, with women forming 40 per cent of the total. Protestants make up 81 per cent of the population — as against 92 per cent in 1939. Since the influx of the refugees, the number of Catholics has doubled, and in Mecklenburg almost tripled.

MORE ARABLE LAND THAN PASTURE. Forests cover 27.4 per cent of the land — beech-woods on the Mecklenburg plateaus, immense forests of pines mingled with birches in the Mark of Brandenburg and in Lower Lusatia, and firs on three mountain massifs. The cultivable area is 25,000 square miles; cereals and root-crops cover three-quarters of the total — a much higher proportion than in West Germany. The *Börde*, in the neighbourhood of Magdeburg (80 per cent arable land), the Saale basin (67 per cent), the Saxony 'piedmont' (70 per cent), the marly regions of Mecklenburg, and the Ukermark (65 per cent) are the granaries of wheat, barley and forage crops. Much of Mecklenburg consists of highly productive sugar-beet fields which are numerous in the Magdeburg region too (also rich in vegetables and oil-producing crops); the town of Magdeburg is the sugar capital of continental Europe. Potatoes, especially in the north and in Saxony, are abundant (1,985 ℔ per head annually), but the real national cereal is rye and the crop has increased by 50 per cent since 1938. Hops are grown at Stendal and especially at Naumburg. The apple and plum orchards of Saxony and Thuringia rival each other but towards the north the fruit trees thin out. A scheme for market-garden and fruit production is being carried out in the Havelland (cherries near Potsdam), and in the Oderbruch, round Frankfurt-on-the-Oder. There are extensive nurseries and seed-plots at Erfurt and rose-gardens at Sangerhausen. But the area of pasture (11 per cent of the land) is insufficient and the quantity of livestock bred is inadequate, especially in the north, despite the fact that the number of cattle and pigs has doubled since 1946.

FAR-REACHING AGRARIAN REFORMS. In the industrialised areas of the south (Saxony has only 10 per cent of rural population) very small holdings have always prevailed. In Lusatia and Saxe-Anhalt holdings were of medium size. But Mecklenburg, where the agricultural population exceeds 50 per cent or even 75 per cent, was the traditional land of the Junkers' large estates (*Güter*), which sometimes covered 35,000 or 50,000 acres. Between 1945 and 1947, however, the whole economic and social life of Mecklenburg was revolutionised by the confiscation and breaking up of these estates. Throughout the country all estates of more than 250 acres (100 hectares) have been split up, and most of the land has been made over to farm labourers (53 per cent) or refugees (43 per cent) in the form of small lots of 12 to 50 acres: these are now the commonest type of holding and their numbers have doubled in Saxe-Anhalt and quadrupled in Mecklenburg. What remained of the large estates was made over to the 'State Lands', the 'Common Properties of the People' (similar to the Soviet *sovkhozes*), and to the 6,000 'Agricultural Production Co-operatives', which correspond to the *kolkhozes* and support 220,000 peasants. There is a total of 3,750,000 acres of socialised land against 10,580,000 acres of small farms, whose owners are obliged to make certain deliveries in kind. Since 1950 the 'socialisation' of the property of 'rich peasants' (owners of 110 to 220 acres) has been in full swing. The Production Co-operatives play an important rôle, especially in the 600 centres of agricultural machines and tractors.

Industries and mineral resources

INDUSTRY AND NATIONALISATION. The industries of East Germany (and especially of Saxony and Thuringia where they afford a livelihood to 55 per cent of the population) have totally different foundations and assume a different character from the industries of Rhineland Germany. In East Germany, in an area stretching from the Werra to the Neisse and between the Thuringerwald and the Erzgebirge, there flourished what was probably the oldest established community of craftsmen in Europe. The Erzgebirge silver mines, long

The Thüringer Forest, seen from the castle of Wartburg, near Eisenach. The ancient massif now undulates gently with wooded ridges. The town of Eisenach spreads into the forest. H. SMOTKINE

The town hall at Leipzig. The city has an illustrious history as a cultural centre and, in spite of the Iron Curtain, continues to be a cosmopolitan centre. Every year 700,000 visitors from East and West attend the Leipzig fair. PAUL POPPER

since exhausted, provided the foundations of the mining industry from the Middle Ages onwards. The mines encouraged local crafts and industry and helped to transform the region, which was provided neither with raw materials nor sources of power, into one of remarkable manufacturing productivity. The innumerable family workshops in the valleys of Saxony and Thuringia evolved during the nineteenth century into small and medium-scale factories turning out finished products, but the regional industries never coalesced into the colossal combines and trusts common in West Germany. At present, a million craftsmen are employed by no less than 380,000 enterprises.

Between 1945 and 1958 these East German industries were, on the whole, hard hit by dismantling (about 45 per cent were affected), and this especially affected those producing equipment goods. Then there was the heavy tribute on output levied by the Russian occupation authorities and, after that, the transfer of the main enterprises to Soviet companies. These, however, were handed back in 1954. Since then, industrial output has been restored and, as a result of 'Stakhanovite' methods of premiums on production, has reached a figure 177 per cent above that for 1938. Eighty-five per cent of this output comes from the nationalised factories. The private sector (excluded from basic industries) turns out only 30 per cent of the light industry production — foodstuffs, paper, textiles, etc.

IMPORTANCE OF LIGNITE AND URANIUM. East Germany has little or no iron and coal. The Saxon coalfields of Zwickau and Oelsnitz do not produce more than 3 million tons a year. However, at the end of the nineteenth century lignite deposits were discovered in the Tertiary formations underlying the Great Plain. The deposits extend from the Saale to the Neisse, offering 37,000 million tons of workable reserves, and this lignite today makes East Germany the 'brown coal' country *par excellence*. The deep open-cast workings which transform the face of the countryside are found in two principal areas. The first and most extensive (which furnishes lignite of a higher calorific value) lies to the west of the Elbe and encircles Leipzig and Weissenfels. The second lies to the east, round Senftenberg. Deposits also exist in the east of Brandenburg. It is used for making briquettes for domestic use, and at Lauchhammer (near Spremberg in Lusatia) where the largest specialised coke oven in the world is found, new methods have been evolved to produce coke from lignite among other materials. Lignite, especially when used to produce electric power, has contributed — together with the great dams on the upper Saale — to the intense industrial electrification of the middle Elbe basin (33,000 million Kwh), an electrification which is, proportionately, on a much greater scale than that of the Ruhr. East Germany has copper mines and foundries, but, above all, the largest potash deposits in Europe (stretching from Bleicherode to Stassfurt) and an abundance of salt (three times as much as in West Germany) to the north-west of Magdeburg and between Halle and Dessau. Finally, 250,000 men are employed in the precious uranium mines in the Erzgebirge. Because of these, the heights on the Czech frontier are a forbidden area. Another uranium deposit is also being worked at Wernigerode in the Harz (30,000 workers).

LIGHT ENGINEERING AND HEAVY METALLURGICAL INDUSTRY. There was, in East Germany, a grave shortage of iron and steel production, and of metallurgical and heavy engineering plant. The country indeed depended wholly upon the Ruhr. There were one or two steel works of minor importance in Thuringia, the Harz and on the Saxony plain. Great efforts have now been made to render East Germany self-sufficient; the output of pig-iron has increased fourfold and that of steel threefold. These results have been achieved mainly through the creation of two powerful iron and steel *Kombinats*. One in the west, near Magdeburg (the Calbe Works),

of a more strictly 'national' character, uses lignite coke in special blast-furnaces. The other, in the east, among the Oder pine-forests near Fürstenberg, is the model iron and steel city of Stalinstadt, created from nothing in 1950, whose six blast-furnaces use Russian or Swedish ore and Polish coal. There are other new plants, mainly around Berlin — the Eberswalde hoisting machinery works and the Hennigsdorf steel works, erected in a few months. Except at Magdeburg, where locomotives were produced, only light machinery was made previously, or smaller objects such as ironmongery, hand tools, etc., for which Schmalkalden in the Thuringerwald became famous; or there were works turning out electrical instruments, watches and clocks, printing presses, cameras (Dresden), motor-cars, and tractors, all of which were to a large extent exported eastwards. Flourishing manufacturing activities include musical instruments, toys, glass, china, furniture, paper (two-thirds of the total German production), optical instruments, spectacles, gloves and shoes. Leipzig is the main fur market of continental Europe. The presence of mineral elements in the soil has developed the chemical industry (in contrast with that of the Ruhr where such elements are lacking) principally in the direction of basic products, and this industry too relies upon lignite. The great Leuna works at Merseburg (28,000 workers) turn out ammonia, nitrogen, acids, potash, soda and synthetic motor fuel. Zeitz produces diesel oil; Bitterfeld, aluminium; and the Bunawerke at Schkopau, synthetic rubber (output is six times that of West Germany).

Finally, Saxony, with its many towns, is the great textile centre of Germany (300,000 workers, 80 per cent women). The cotton zone is in the valleys of the central Erzgebirge, touching the plain. It produces embroidered goods, lace and muslins in the west, yarns and fabrics in the centre (Reichenbach) and knitted goods in the east (round Karl-Marx-Stadt). The woollens area (the largest in Germany) is lower in the plain, stretching from the Gera and Greiz dyeworks to the towns of Lusatia. Beyond the Elbe, Kottbus, Bautzen, Görlitz and Zittau also have flax-spinning and linen-weaving mills. Ready-made clothing manufacture gives employment to 187,000 workers in Dresden, Leipzig and Erfurt.

The course of the Elbe through the Saxon 'Switzerland', in winter. This mountainous region stretches to either side of the Elbe above Pirna and into Czechoslovakia. TRUDEL FEHR-BECHTEL

The fourteenth-century Niedzica Castle, which overshadows the Dunajec gorges, in the Beskids. R. S. W. (PRASA)

POLAND

The coke ovens of Lauchhammer in Lusatia. DEUTSCHE FOTOTHEK DRESDEN

The port of Stralsund, Pomerania, on the Baltic.
DEUTSCHE FOTOTHEK DRESDEN

Karl-Marx-Stadt (previously Chemnitz), in Saxony, which specialises in textiles. DEUTSCHE FOTOTHEK DRESDEN

East German industry is becoming increasingly mechanised: Here two workers at the 'Black Pump' Kombinat service coal briquette machinery.
PAUL POPPER

The Stalinallee, the pride of East Berlin. Behind the new buildings are huge sites where the buildings have not yet been completed.
PAUL POPPER, ATLAS–PHOTO

Communications and transport

RAILWAYS, ROADS AND CANALS. There are in East Germany about 10,000 miles of railway lines, of which the Halle to Magdeburg line is electrified for about 43 miles. A new line has been constructed by-passing Berlin. Rolling-stock has been remarkably well restored and renewed (122,000 freight wagons) and is kept moving rapidly. The Leipzig, Halle and Magdeburg areas are the main junctions. As well as rail routes there are 2200 lines of coaches and motor-buses, a large proportion of them concentrated in the vital regions of the Elbe, the south and the south-west. Long-distance road transport accounts for only 2 per cent of the freight hauled, and private cars are very uncommon. Six *Autobahnen* radiate from Berlin for a total distance of 885 miles. Inland water transport on the Elbe and on the axis of the Rhine-Oder canals — the eastern portion of the Mittellandkanal — a total of 1250 miles of navigable waters, is responsible for only 12 per cent of the freight transported. The most important cargoes are lignite, ores and beets.

Since 1950 the docks at Rostock and those of its outer harbour, Warnemünde, have been increased fourfold to take the place of Stettin, which was once the port of Berlin. Traffic is more than two million tons. Shipyards have been rapidly developed at Wismar and Stralsund, Hanseatic cities which otherwise possess only local importance. The main fishing centres are at Sassnitz, the Island of Rügen and Rostock.

Leipzig, which has kept its reputation as a great publishing centre and a headquarters of the printing trades, is also a commercial city and, despite its separation from the West, its annual fair is the most celebrated in Europe and attracts about 9,000 exhibitors and some 700,000 visitors from East and West. Four-fifths of the foreign trade of East Germany is with countries to the east — from Poland to China — and also with the Arab and Scandinavian countries. Eighty-five per cent of the exports are finished products. The U.S.S.R. is the main supplier of raw materials and foodstuffs.

Cultural and social life

Primary and secondary schools have been standardised and secularised. The teaching of Russian as the first foreign language is obligatory. The *Freie Deutsche Jugend*, 'Free German Youth', to which most young people of both sexes belong, supplements the political education given at school. Thirteen special faculties set up in 1949 provide preparatory training for the numerous technical schools, the universities of Berlin, Rostock, Greifswald, Halle, Leipzig and Jena, and schools for advanced studies; there are 31 of these, with 74,000 students (80 per cent scholarship holders, and many the children of workmen and peasants). Scientific research institutions are heavily subsidised. Dresden is becoming a town of technical institutes. Despite this emphasis on scientific and technical education, cultural life, the restoration of damaged buildings and monuments, the reorganisation of museums, and the protection of folklore are not neglected.

Work is obligatory and there are few unemployed. In addition to the recreation and rest centres attached to the big industrial and mining enterprises, there are tourist resorts and spas on the Baltic coast, in the Harz, Thuringia and the 'Saxon Switzerland' which have been nationalised and transformed into low-priced holiday resorts for workers of all kinds.

In spite of the results obtained, and although some foodstuffs are available in greater quantities than in West Germany, rationing of certain foods is still maintained in the East. East Germany's standard of living is lower than that of West Germany and her cost of living a third higher. Even more extensively ravaged by war than West Germany, she has not yet enjoyed the full benefit of reconstruction schemes, whose realisation has been hampered by difficulties in obtaining raw materials.

BERLIN

In the thirteenth century Berlin was an island township of fishermen set amid the forests, swamps and lakes of Brandenburg. In the fifteenth century the Electors of Brandenburg chose Berlin as their capital since it occupied a central position in their dominions — the town is, indeed, halfway between the Elbe and the Oder. The city developed as the capital of Prussia, very largely owing the influx of Huguenot refugees who, by 1700, formed a third of the population. However, in 1871, when it was raised to the position of an imperial capital, Berlin had only 800,000 inhabitants and covered an area of no more than about 22 square miles. But the town spread very rapidly — mostly westwards — and by 1914 its area was about 77 square miles and its population 2 million, composed very largely of immigrants from the eastern provinces. There were 75,000 Slavs. In 1939 the city had 4 million inhabitants (73 per cent Protestant) spread over a huge area of 340 square miles, a district adorned with forest-like parks and delightful lakes. This was the *Gross Berlin* created in 1921, the *Weltstadt*, the 'Metropolis' of the Reich.

The great industries and trade of Berlin were, in 1939, second only to those of the Ruhr and comprised 48 per cent of electrical and telephone equipment output, 23 per cent of optical instrument manufacture, and 39 per cent of the clothing industry. Berlin was, then, the second inland port on the continent of Europe — and today one-quarter of its supplies still reach it by water.

In 1945 Berlin stood in ruins, detached from a dead Prussia and indeed from Germany as a whole, and bore little resemblance to a *Weltstadt*; the city was occupied by the representatives of four world powers, having lost its political importance and its enormous industrial potential. Three-quarters of the plant (85—90 per cent of it in metallurgical and electro-technical industries) was dismantled by the Russians. Some 500,000 of the inhabitants had fled the city. In addition, Berlin —already cut off from all land communications — was divided into two: East Berlin and West Berlin, which were destined to live together in uneasy juxtaposition under two antagonistic administrations and with two currencies.

East Berlin (155 square miles) with 1,090,000 inhabitants is the seat of its government, although not officially a part of the German Democratic Republic. It includes within its boundaries Unter den Linden, the district of government offices, the business sectors, the museums, the Humboldt University and the eastern suburbs. Most of the re-building has been done on the main arteries such as the Stalinallee. However, since 1946, in the Lichtenberg, Schöneweide, and Köpenick districts and along the Spree and its canals, industries including machinery, electrical equipment, cables and the graphic arts have been reorganised, and production has been stepped up to twenty times its former capacity.

West Berlin (185 square miles) is a *Land*, albeit 'in abeyance', of the Federal Republic, participating in its public finances and providing twenty-six representatives (as 'consultants'). West Berlin has a population of about 2,226,000; there is an abnormally high percentage of women and, even more marked, of elderly people (21 per cent over sixty against 15 per cent in the *Bund*), pensioners and persons in receipt of relief.

Along the main axis of this part of Berlin are several open, airy districts which in the nineteenth century were still suburbs. The most important is Charlottenburg, whose Kurfürstendamm is a highway of luxury shops. Only three of these districts, those nearest to the old centres of the city (Kreuzberg, Schöneberg and Wedding) have more than 25,000 inhabitants to the square mile, instead of their pre-war figures of over 60,000. West Berlin also includes the sector of industrial plant in the north (Tegel, Siemenstadt, Spandau and Moabit) and on both sides of the Teltow Canal, as well as the Tempelhof airfield, and the residential suburbs (Dahlem, Zehlendorf) that give on to the Havel lakes and woods and extend towards the south-west as far as Potsdam.

Between 1946 and 1949 many industrial enterprises endeavoured to transfer what remained of their equipment and to move their headquarters to the German Rhineland. But since 1950 the half-city of West Berlin has pulled itself together in determined fashion. The intellectual and artistic activities have recovered much of their old brilliance. The new university attracts an increasing number of undergraduates each year — 35 per cent come from the Democratic Republic; and, above all, industrial activity has revived. Once again the electro-technical precision machinery and clothing industries account for 50 per cent of the total turnover.

Germans abroad

Although Germany possessed an overseas empire only for a short time, her nationals emigrated continuously from the Middle Ages on, and despite enforced repatriations there are still numerous German settlements abroad. In Europe there are the remains of the 'Saxon' colonies in Transylvania (whose origins go back to the thirteenth century) and of the 'Swabian' colonies in the Banat and Batchka, established in the eighteenth century. Outside Europe there are today about 22 million descendants of German families — 18 million of them in the United States, where they have become assimilated though retaining their own traditions in many instances; there are also 1 million in Brazil and 400,000 in Canada.

Between 1820 and 1933 German emigrants to the United States numbered 5½ million, for the exodus was heavy during the crafts crisis in the 1850s and the agricultural crisis of 1880. The most compact groups live in Pennsylvania, where an eighteenth-century Palatinate dialect of German is still occasionally spoken, New York, Ohio, Missouri, the two Dakotas (emigrants from the Ukraine) and especially round Lake Michigan, Illinois and Wisconsin. Thirty-four per cent of the population of Milwaukee is of German origin, 22 per cent in St Louis and Cincinnati, 15 per cent in Chicago. In Canada the proportion is 15 per cent in the prairie provinces (especially Saskatchewan). German colonies of Swabian extraction are found in the southern states of Brazil (Santa Catarina, Rio Grande do Sul), and Argentina (260,000 German immigrants in Buenos Aires, Entre Rios and Misiones) many of whom came from the Volga. In Chile there are 50,000 Germans in Santiago and in the extreme south. Another 16,000 live in Paraguay. There are 60,000 to 70,000 in Australia, mainly in Queensland or round Adelaide, and 12,000 in South-West Africa.

Jean DOLLFUS

The Kurfürstendamm, in the Charlottenburg district, is the liveliest and most elegant street in West Berlin, with luxury shops, theatres and cinemas. It is considerably further west than the commercial centre of pre-war Berlin. BUNDESBILDSTELLE BONN

An extensive winter landscape in the Carpathians.   EMBASSY OF CZECHOSLOVAK REPUBLIC

A general view of the old city of Prague, showing the cathedral of St Vitus (built by Charles IV in the fourteenth century), surrounded by the vast fortified palace of the ancient kings of Bohemia, now used as government offices.   EMBASSY OF CZECHOSLOVAK REPUBLIC

CZECHOSLOVAKIA

IN the middle of Europe, half-way between the North Sea and the Mediterranean and some 220 miles from the nearest seashore, the plateau of Bohemia rises between two great lines of communication, the north German plain and the Danube valley. The history of the peopling of Bohemia — and that of the lands immediately to the east — is such that the natural unit cannot be separated from its eastern annex, Moravia-Silesia, which constitutes a broad belt of north-south communication between the upper valley of the Odra (Oder) and the valley of the Morava. The Oder flows into the Baltic; the Morava into the Black Sea.

Since the ninth century, Bohemia, Moravia and Silesia have been linked politically, although until 1918 these lands came within the sphere of influence of Vienna, and the alien Hapsburg dynasty controlled their development.

Immediately after the First World War, Slovakia, farther east, was joined to the Czech lands; this region is buttressed against the Carpathians and looks southwards on to the Danube. For a thousand years Slovakia (which in the ninth and tenth centuries was part of Moravia) had been separated from the Czech lands and had shared the fortunes of Hungary.

All these regions together make up Czechoslovakia, a state born of the peace treaties concluded after the end of the 1914—18 war. From 1919 Czechoslovakia also comprised (to the east of Slovakia) a region known as Sub-Carpathian Russia or Ruthenia, but this was ceded to the U.S.S.R. in 1945.

The regions of Czechoslovakia

Physically, Czechoslovakia can be divided into two fundamentally different regions. The western zone, comprising the Czech lands (Bohemia, Moravia and Silesia) belongs to the formations the geologists call 'Hercynian'. Here landscapes and ways of life are characteristic of western and central Europe. The eastern zone, consisting of the Moravian-Slovakian confines and of Slovakia itself, belongs to the Carpathian-Danubian complex that is on the threshold of eastern Europe. Between the two zones runs a corridor of great physical and social importance, the valley of the Morava, the link between the Germano-Polish plain and the Danube valley.

The Czech lands

BOHEMIA. Bohemia is, essentially, a peneplain which has the appearance of an asymmetrical basin.

To the north-west, the 'Ore Mountains' (Erz Gebirge, or Krušné Hory) mark the German frontier from the Cheb passage to that of the Elbe (Labe in Czech) known as the 'Gate of Lusatia'. This is a region of moderately high mountains, much influenced by human settlement. Immigrant Germans of the thirteenth century included woodmen, foresters and miners, whilst in the nineteenth and twentieth centuries the industrial revolution completely altered the face of the land. The 'Ore Mountains' extend eastwards as the Středohoří (Mittel Gebirge), a massif of extinct volcanoes cut through by the Labe (Elbe) before it enters Germany. The mountains of Lusatia (Lužické

Hory), the Riesen Gebirge (Krkonoše), the Orlické Hory and the Jeseníky then form a series of continuous ranges between Bohemia and northern Moravia. It is in the Krkonoše on the Czecho-Polish frontier that the Sněžka rises, the highest point in Bohemia (5,260 feet). All these mountains are well populated and in addition to agriculture, forestry and stock-breeding there has been a development of large-scale industry (glass-works and textile mills).

In western Bohemia and all along the Bavarian frontier, the Český Les (Bohemian Forest), a range varying in altitude from 2,250 to 3,300 feet, forms a screen against winds from the Atlantic. The Bohemian Forest is flanked on the south-east by the Šumava, the southern part of the Bohemian plateau. It is in the Šumava that the Vltava (a tributary of the Labe) has its source; it then flows from south to north through a valley so deep that it constitutes a major obstacle to east-west communications. Furthermore, to the north of the Šumava there stretches a region covered with rather infertile Tertiary sediments — that of the Třeboň and České Budějovice meres.

Continuing down the course of the Vltava, we reach a point where the valley widens into a plain on which Prague (Praha) is built. The country around the city is very varied. To the west, beyond the Kladno coalfield, is the Plzeň (Pilsen) basin into which flow four rivers and which has favoured the growth of a large industrial city. To the north-east of Prague, the Labe plain, or Polabí, is an area of Cretaceous sediments covered with loess, 75 miles long by 25 miles wide; this plain is drained by the upper course of the Elbe and is a region of intensive farming and large-scale industry.

Finally, to the east, the Bohemian-Moravian ridges (mostly of low altitude — about 1,650 to 2,000 feet) form a sort of thick fold with rather irregular relief, and constitute a transition area between the plateaus of Bohemia and Moravia.

MORAVIA-SILESIA, AN INTERNATIONAL CORRIDOR: The main axis of Moravia is formed by the course of the river Morava. It is a north-bank tributary of the Danube and flows through the country from north to south, linking Poland with the Danube valley (through the Gate of Moravia, a passage about 6 miles wide between the Jeseníky and the Moravian-Silesian Beskid chain). The plain of Moravia is bounded on the west by the Bohemian-Moravian ridges and on the east by the range of the White Carpathians (Bílé Karpaty), which is easily crossed by the Vlara Pass (935 feet) leading into the valley of the Váh, a tributary of the Danube. Like Bohemia, Moravia has two basins worthy of note: that of Olomouc (or the plain of the Haná) and that of Brno (Brünn). The two regions have a tradition of highly developed agriculture and varied industrial activity. Between the two basins and to the north of Brno, the principal town of Moravia, stretches the region of the Moravian *causses*, whose karst-like grottoes attract numerous tourists. The Znojmo district is renowned for its market-gardens, and the Zlin (now Gottwaldov) area in north-eastern Moravia, formerly neglected and poverty-stricken, was transformed between the two World Wars into an important centre of the shoe industry. Moravia is basically an agricultural land but has become highly industrialised under the influence of Silesia, whose coalfields are among the richest in Europe.

Karlstejn Castle, near Prague. CZECH NEWS AGENCY

SLOVAKIA. THE GATE TO EASTERN EUROPE.
Slovakia is the most mountainous part of Czechoslovakia. The extremity of the Carpathian arc — which reaches as far as the Black Sea — forms Slovakia's backbone. The mountain chains, which enclose fertile and sheltered valleys, are exposed to southern influences.

The core of the Slovakian Carpathians is composed of two ranges, the High and the Low Tatry, between which extends a tectonic depression containing a string of basins. The High Tatry which forms a compact chain of Pyrenean type between Poland and Czechoslovakia is 38 miles long and 16 miles wide, and its summits exceed 6,600 feet in places. The Stalin Peak (formerly the Gerlachovka) is 8,737 feet. The High Tatry were heavily eroded by glacial action, which has left many traces. A number of health resorts lie clustered about the southern slopes. To the south of the High Tatry lie the Low Tatry, much wilder and more thickly wooded but not so lofty. The tallest peak, the Dumbier, is 6,400 feet.

To the south-west, High and Low Tatry join mountain chains which run from south to north-east on either side of the Váh valley. These are the Little Carpathians, the White Carpathians, the Javorníky chain, and the Beskids on the right bank, and on the left bank the Inovec chain and the Great and Small Fatra.

In central Slovakia the Slovenské Rudohorie ('metalliferous mountains' — a significant name) is a mountain mass made up of extinct volcanoes.

The Slovakian plains are, in general, fertile basins, such as that of Liptov at the foot of the High Tatry, or that of Košice. The most extensive of them is formed by the widening of the Váh, Nitra and Hron lower valleys. These rivers empty into the Danube to the east of Bratislava at a point where the great river splits into several branches enclosing the 'Rye Island' (Žitný Ostrov) on the Hungarian frontier.

Such is Slovakia's physical geography. Its economic and agricultural development were for long held up by the vicissitudes of its history.

Climate

Czechoslovakia lies in the centre of Europe, wholly in the northern temperate zone. The country's moderately high mountains present a succession of ridges and hills, of plateaus and of basins surrounded by hills. The climate is varied (due mainly to altitude and orientation) but generally speaking temperate, the result of a balance between oceanic influences (more marked in the Czech lands) and continental influences, which reach Slovakia along the Danube corridor.

The January isotherms are 30° F. for Bohemia, 29° F. for Moravia, 27° F. for eastern Slovakia. The July isotherms of 64° F. and 66° F. follow more or less the line of the Bohemian peripheral mountain ranges, but the interior of the country is warmer (68° F.). Both Moravia and Slovakia have July isotherms of 69.5° F.

Though the rainfall is abundant, especially in the western mountains, the average annual figure drops in most of the basins to about 20 inches, and sometimes less. However, the Polabi, the valleys of the Morava and of the Slovakian rivers have more rain.

There are two main types of climate in Czechoslovakia. The Czecho-Moravian is marked by a clear atmosphere, a rainfall that favours the development of intensive agriculture, rather more severe winters and slightly hotter and drier summers than those of western Europe. The Slovakian climate is characterised by warmer and drier summers than those in the Czech lands and also by harsher winters.

The human factor

Czechoslovakia, which in 1938 had a population of 14,638,000 — or 290 inhabitants to the square mile — had only 13,438,000 inhabitants for an area of 49,354 square miles in 1958. The drop followed the expulsion of the Sudeten Germans, as well as that of many of the Magyars from Slovakia. There was also a loss of population when the U.S.S.R. annexed Subcarpathian Russia in 1945. The number of Germans to have left Czechoslovakia is estimated at 2,674,000, while war losses amounted to more than 100,000 dead.

The most recent demographic researches have shown that during the decade preceding the Second World War the rate of increase in the population was slowing down, for the birthrate had fallen. At the time the war broke out, the population's average age was becoming steadily higher and higher. Whilst in 1921 the 'under twenties' formed 40 per cent of the total, in 1940 they were no more than 25 per cent. During the war and the period of occupation the population rose by 500,000 in seven years. Since the liberation and despite the political, social and economic revolution, the population has again begun to increase, though this tendency is mainly due to a fall in the death rate.

A SLAV POPULATION. The Second World War modified the composition of Czechoslovakia's population considerably. The former German and Magyar minorities have practically disappeared. Czechoslovakia is now a country with a population almost entirely Slav (about 95 per cent).

The Czechs and Slovaks (and also the Poles) belong to the western branch of the Slav ethno-linguistic community. The Czech language (which has affinities with Polish) is written in Roman characters although related to Old Slavonic and Russian. Czech used to be spoken almost only in the country districts and did not become a literary language until the first

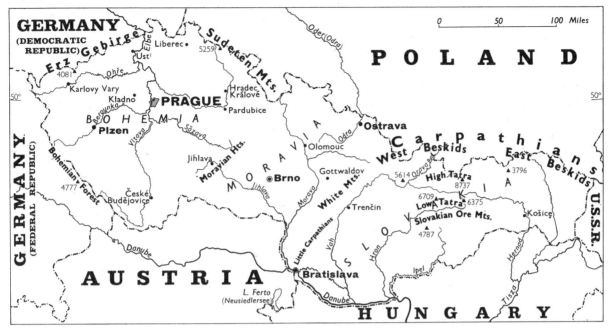

CZECHOSLOVAKIA

half of the nineteenth century. The Slovaks also speak a language (Slovakian) which about the middle of the last century emerged from one of the main dialects current in Slovakia. All Czechs can understand it without having studied it; it contains fewer Germanisms than Czech and is more akin to Polish.

The sense of belonging to the Slav linguistic community helped to awaken Czech and Slovak nationalistic feelings during the years of subjection more than any other factor. Possibly this sentiment has also helped to facilitate the existing arrangements by which Czechoslovakia has been brought into line with U.S.S.R. policy.

WESTERNISED SLAVS. Notwithstanding their Slav origin, the Czechs and Slovaks have also been exposed to non-Slav influences — the Czechs because they lived side by side with Germans for centuries and the Slovaks because of their close connection with Hungarians; both are definitely westernised Slavs. Today it is only in Czech, Moravian and Slovakian rural folklore that traces of the ancestral Slav elements persist.

Bohemian civilisation (which is above all urban) is permeated with western influences, and owes much materially to Austria, Bavaria and Saxony. If he has not been warned in advance, the foreign visitor may well be astonished to find in the Czech towns German-type beer-saloons, or *Weinstuben*, and cafés like those of Vienna or Budapest.

Throughout their history the Czechs have, in times of crisis, found spiritual leaders whose fame has often spread beyond their own frontiers; men like Jan Hus, Comenius, Palacký, Havlíček, Masaryk or Beneš, who were always supported by the Slav majority, responding readily to the rallying cry of liberty and independence. In general the Czechs are phlegmatic and well-disciplined. Long years of subjection taught them the value of solidarity for the eventual attainment of national and cultural independence. During the second half of the nineteenth century the Czechs of Bohemia found in the *Matice* (an association for promoting the development of the language through books) and in the *sokols* (sports associations of a patriotic character) effective instruments for achieving gradual emancipation. The Czech peasant has all the traditional qualities of a tiller of the soil, and the Czech workman has a deep respect for good craftsmanship. Although they are individualists, the Czechs have a tradition of co-operative action and have always been imbued with truly democratic ideals.

The Slovaks, separated for many centuries from the Czechs, are a more spontaneous people. They are in general more impulsive, more artistic and more intuitive than their western relations. They, too, have had leaders fired with ideas of Slav nationalism, men like Kollar and Šafařík, who have even influenced the evolution of Slav culture.

Unfortunately, Czech and Slovak differences of temperament have occasionally given rise to feelings of mutual suspicion — with regrettable consequences. Nor have two different languages made the situation easier. Religious disagreements have also provided fuel for the fire; Catholicism in Bohemia and Moravia is more social than Catholicism in Slovakia, a country still influenced by memories of Hungarian feudalism. Nevertheless union between these two Slav peoples seems natural enough and will certainly strengthen as the respective standards of living tend to become more equalised.

A changing economy

During the second half of the nineteenth century and the beginning of the twentieth, Bohemia, Moravia and Silesia (then part of the Austro-Hungarian monarchy) were provinces whose abundant coal, fertile soils, dense populations, craftsmen and traditional family enterprises put at their disposal an immense home market for their finished products.

Furthermore, the Czech lands had taken full advantage of the nineteenth-century industrial revolution and had raised their country to the level of the industrialised States of western Europe. Slovakia, however, which depended on Budapest and Hungary, was less favoured from the point of view of power potential, and the population was dominated by a foreign, landed aristocracy and was not accustomed to handicrafts in conjunction with large-scale industry. Slovakia remained an agricultural country, under-developed and compelled to exchange its raw materials and foodstuffs for manufactured goods in order to supply its rapidly increasing population — to the detriment of the general standard of living.

When, in October 1918, the Czech lands and Slovakia united to form the first Czechoslovak republic, the new state was immediately faced with the loss of many of its former markets and had to reorganise its commercial and financial policy. Between the two World Wars everything was done to make the country an exporter of manufactured goods and an importer of raw materials. As a consequence, when the world crisis of the early 'thirties hit eastern and east-central Europe, the new state suffered. The agricultural crisis in the Danubian countries was highly damaging to Czechoslovakia. There was a high rate of unemployment among industrial workers and the contrast between the economy of the Czech lands and that of Slovakia was accentuated. The leaders of the Third Reich proceeded to take advantage of the uncertain political situation, the result being the Munich agreement (September 1938), the occupation of Prague (March 1939), and the dismembering of the Czechoslovak State.

The territorial changes after the Second World War could not but bring about a radical transformation of Czechoslovak industry and foreign markets. The new Czechoslovakia became a satellite of the U.S.S.R. and had to reorganise its industry and adopt Soviet-type planning.

The first economic plan, called the Two Year Plan (1947–48), established by the first post-war government, paved the way for total assimilation within the Soviet economy. Its main object was to restore an economy that had been ruined by war and occupation. The essential features of the scheme were the nationalisation of industry, banks and foreign trade, an economic change-over in the frontier zones evacuated by Germans and Hungarians, and an agrarian reform based on confiscation of German 'collaborator' and Hungarian traitor property. The primary aim was to restore agricultural and industrial production as nearly as possible to pre-war levels.

The Two Year Plan (which was quite successful, probably because of aid furnished by U.N.R.R.A., an organisation initiated by the United States) was followed by the first Five Year Plan (1949–53). This, although completed in four years, did not yield the expected results. Its main aim was to eliminate the differences between Czech and Slovakian economies. Industries supplying capital goods were to be encouraged, the numbers of skilled workmen and technicians (reduced by the departure of Sudeten Germans) were to be increased by an appropriate direction of labour, and industrial and agricultural output was to be rationalised. Stress was laid on the development of power supply, and the supply of machinery for the consumer goods industries and collectivised agricultural enterprises.

DEVELOPMENT OF POWER SUPPLY. Czechoslovakia has been especially favoured by nature with sources of power. The country has huge reserves of solid fuel, to some extent compensating for the lack of petroleum. Power is produced from thermal sources and from hydro-electric stations, particularly in Slovakia.

Most of the coalfields and lignite deposits are in Bohemia and Silesia, while Moravia and Slovakia are deficient in this sort of fuel. The most important coalfield is the Moravská Ostrava-Karvina in Silesia. Its unworked reserves are estimated at more than 20,000 million tons of high calorific value and are suitable for coking. Even before the war this field's output was about 12 million tons, and during the years of post-war planning, production was raised to about 20 million tons, allowing the manufacture of 7—8 million tons of furnace-coke. The Moravská Ostrava deposits belong to the most extensive coalfield in eastern Europe, the Silesian basin, which is as important to the East as the Ruhr is to the West.

The largest coalfields in Bohemia are those of Kladno-Rakovnik and Plzeň-Radnice; the former, being nearer to Prague, supplies the capital's great industrial plants. The Plzeň-Radnice collieries contributed greatly to the growth of the engineering plant at Plzeň (formerly the Škoda Works). In Moravia, the Rosice-Oslavany basin supplies the fuel for the factories of Brno.

In the Ohře (Eger) valley of Bohemia, at the foot of the Erz Gebirge, there are exceptionally extensive lignite deposits which are easily worked by open-cast methods. It is a basin of Tertiary coal (Falknov-Loket and the lignite basin of northern Bohemia) situated both in the Ohře valley and in that of the Bilina. The fuel, which is not of very high heating power, is partly used by a thermo-electric station supplying Prague with current, and also by the synthetic fuel plant at Most constructed by the Germans during the Occupation. Lignite is also exchanged for imported coal. There are deposits of brown coal at Dubňany, not far from Brno in Moravia, and there is a deposit of lignite at Handlová in the Nitra valley (Slovakia). Neither of these fields furnishes much more than 2 per cent of the country's lignite extraction. The total amount produced is estimated at 33 million tons, against 12 million tons in pre-war years.

MINERAL RESOURCES AND CHIEF INDUSTRIES IN CZECHOSLOVAKIA

The famous pitchblende (uranium ore) deposit at Jáchymov in northern Bohemia could also contribute significantly towards Czechoslovakia's resources in power if the U.S.S.R. had not obtained a monopoly of the output. If used for the development of Czechoslovakia, the whole economic outlook of the country would be changed. As it is, the Czechoslovaks cannot increase their power resources except by adding to their already numerous thermo-electric stations (fed by coal, lignite, or gas from the Silesian blast-furnaces) or by constructing more hydro-electric stations. In 1937 the total electric current produced was 4,100 million kWh (3.6 per cent of world production). By the end of the first Five Year Plan the figure was 11,200 million kWh. In addition, agreements have been concluded with Poland, East Germany, Hungary and Austria for exchange of current. The largest thermo-electric stations are those of Most and Trutnov in Bohemia, Ostrava in Silesia, and Krompachy in Slovakia. The hydro-electric stations (whose numbers must, of course, depend upon the construction of dams) already supply 15 per cent of the current used; among the largest are those of Slapy on the Vltava and Orava in Silesia. However, prospects seem brightest in Slovakia, where eleven dams have been or are being built in the Váh valley alone. Plans are being drawn up for the electrification of the Hron and Hornad valleys, and at the present time it would seem that Slovakia alone supplies about 4,000 million kWh, which is something like the whole production of Czechoslovakia before the war.

THE LEADING INDUSTRIAL COUNTRY IN CENTRAL EUROPE.

The Czech lands and Slovakia have long been considered particularly rich in metallic ores. During the Middle Ages the Kutná Hora mines of argentiferous lead allowed the Bohemians to mint money and put the thaler (ancestor of the dollar) on the international market. During the time of the First Republic a mint was established at Kremnica in Slovakia, using the gold and silver extracted from the nearby mines of Kremnica and Banská Štiavnica. More important to modern Czechoslovak economy are the iron ore deposits. There are iron mines in the region between Kladno and Plzeň (Bohemia), which facilitated the development of the Plzeň metallurgical industry, specialising in the construction of machinery. The second area of iron ore production is in the Slovakian 'Ore Mountains'. The existence of manganese deposits and their relative proximity to the Silesian power-producing area lend these central Slovakian mines considerable importance. The quantity of ore mined at Šternberk, in Moravia, is also increasing, though the total amount of ore extracted is still far from enough to satisfy the demands of Czechoslovak heavy industry. Before the war imported iron ore came mostly from Sweden, but nowadays the greater part comes up the Danube from the U.S.S.R.

At present Silesia is still the principal centre of the heavy metallurgical industry, and the region contains many blast-furnaces, foundries and steel works. In addition to the old plant at Vitkovice and Třinec, a new group of iron and steel works was recently put up at Kunčice. The works at Kladno near Prague (Bohemia) are less important than those in Silesia, although the town of Kladno is the centre of an iron and steel industry comprising two steel plants and employing 15,000 men.

Under the Five Year Plan a huge iron, steel and multi-metal *kombinat* was erected at Huko, to the south of Košice in Slovakia, to treat both ferrous and non-ferrous ores from the Ore Mountains.

Before the war, machinery manufacture utilising materials furnished by the heavy metal industry was established at Plzeň (Škoda Works) and turned out large quantities of armaments, locomotives, factory equipment and machine-tools. This large industrial centre has not only survived but has grown since nationalisation. Similarly, Prague, Brno and the surrounding country (Blansko), and Prostějov still have works turning

A foundry in Czechoslovakia. The development of heavy industry is more and more shaping the landscape and economy of the country.
EMBASSY OF CZECHOSLOVAK REPUBLIC

out specialised machinery, and branches of industry have now been extended to almost all parts of the country and particularly to Slovakia. Lastly, Czechoslovakia still has a high reputation for its precision instruments, which are exported to other Eastern European countries. This industry, which has to rely on imported metals, is concentrated mostly in the valley of the Labe.

The chemical industry is also expanding. There are home-produced raw materials — pyrites and magnesite from the Ore Mountains, by-products from Silesian coal, lignite and graphite from near Budějovice; but certain raw materials are imported. Among the more important chemical plants are the synthetic petrol works at Most, which treats lignite, and the works in the Labe valley where the manufacture of fertilizers, acids, pharmaceutical and photographic products is concentrated near Ústi. In Moravia the former Bata factories at Gottwaldov treat rubber, and at Bratislava there are synthetic fibre factories. Finally, the graphite of southern Bohemia provides raw material for two pencil factories of international repute.

A SLOWING-DOWN IN LIGHT INDUSTRY.

Among the different branches of so-called 'light' industry — that is, manufacturing consumer goods — those depending on agriculture are of special importance. The industries dealing with wood occupy an outstanding position. Before the Second World War, forest covered about one-third of the country, but the woodlands were much ravaged during the war. Whereas in 1930 the consumption of wood was 18 million cubic metres,

A glass factory at Karlovy Vary, in Bohemia. The presence of fine sand and of skilled craftsmen has for long favoured the glassware industry of Bohemia, which is famed throughout the world.

ERICH LESSING, MAGNUM-PHOTO

Blast furnaces at Kladno, in Bohemia. The coalfield of Kladno-Rakovnik is very near Prague and serves its heavy industries.

CZECHOSLOVAK CHAMBER OF COMMERCE

very strict control has reduced this figure to 10 million cubic metres. Moreover, the industrial utilisation of wood has been rationalised, and two *kombinats* (at Svolen and Banská Bystrica in Slovakia) have recently been established for the treatment of ligneous by-products. Between the two World Wars Czechoslovakia was already exporting paper. It is manufactured mostly in mills situated in north-western Slovakia and in northern Moravia, where Zábřeh boasts one of the largest papermills of central Europe. Though the amount of sawn timber has decreased, cabinet-making has developed immensely in connection with the State's housing policy. Bent-wood furniture (a speciality of the Vsetín region in northern Moravia) is still in much demand, particularly abroad.

The manufacture of glass and artificial jewellery has long been encouraged by the abundance of fine sand in the Labe valley as well as by the existence of large numbers of skilled glass workers on the southern slopes of the Erz Gebirge and the Riesen Gebirge. These products were exported all over the world as 'Jablonec ware'. The departure of the Sudeten Germans dealt a hard blow to this industry, which has now been largely reconverted owing to the lack of skilled workmen and technicians, and also to the dwindling foreign markets for artificial and costume jewellery. There is, however, no noticeable falling-off in the output of window-glass, glass vessels, laboratory glassware, and bottles. Slovakia — chiefly the Váh valley — has inherited part of the Czech glass industry which has been considerably decentralised since 1945.

The ceramics industry has had to face similar problems. It has for long been located near the north-western Bohemian kaolin deposits — in the neighbourhood of Karlovy Vary (Karlsbad). Changed circumstances have modified the nature of ceramic production. Although luxury ware is still the speciality of Karlovy Vary, there has been a great development in the production of china for technical uses (at Plzeň and at Ostrava) and of household crockery (at České Budějovice). The southern Moravian factories (Znojmo and Břeclav) and

those in the southern section of central Slovakia are expanding rapidly.

The cement industry has benefited from the reconversion of the economy. Total annual production is now one-half that of France.

The old-established textile industry, together with its numerous associated activities — spinning, twisting, weaving, dressing, bleaching, dyeing, printing and preparing ready-made clothing — was the most prosperous of all before the war, providing employment for more than half a million people. But this industry has suffered more than any other from the new economic policies.

Before 1939, the textile industry was concentrated in four main areas: northern Bohemia (the main centres, Liberec and Cheb, treating cotton and wool); central Moravia (Brno, specialising in woollen goods) and Prostějov (ready-made clothing); Silesia (cotton goods and rather coarse cloths); and Slovakia (wool at Trenčín and cotton at Ružomberok).

Since 1945 many changes have occurred. The U.S.S.R. has partially replaced non-European sources of raw materials. The mills in northern Bohemia, which no longer had the necessary technicians, have been shut down or transferred elsewhere. Gottwaldov (in Moravia) and a number of places in southern Bohemia, on the other hand, have been developed as textile centres, and the industry is showing signs of rapid growth in Slovakia. Mills and factories have been set up at Dolní Kubin, Liptovský Mikuláš and Púchov. Bratislava specialises in man-made fibres.

Boot and shoe manufacture is linked with the textile and chemical industries. The works of Bata, the great industrialist, at Zlin (now Gottwaldov) are nationalised; they continue to supply the home market but exports are now mostly to the U.S.S.R. and the 'Democratic Republics'. The Plan called for a total national production of over 76 million pairs of boots and shoes during the year 1960.

Gloves, famous for their high quality before the Second World War, were manufactured in the Sudeten mountain regions and in Prague. Production still continues but luxury-type gloves are now made in smaller quantities.

Those food-products whose raw materials are home-grown (for example, sugar, beer, spirits, flour and canned goods) have not entirely maintained their former reputation. Production of refined sugar and beer are both running above pre-war levels. Of course, the future of the foodstuffs industries depends upon the development of agriculture, which is now

A farm at Cesky Brod, in Bohemia. ERICH LESSING, MAGNUM-PHOTO

being completely transformed by the revolutionary new methods introduced by the present regime.

THE NEW AGRICULTURAL ECONOMY. Broadly speaking, Czech agriculture, being closely connected with industry, is intensive; Slovak agriculture is in many regions extensive. Agricultural planning since 1945 has attempted to remove this disparity. After the 1914—18 war a first measure of reform reduced the size of the great landed estates considerably, aiming to create a body of middle-class peasantry with smallholdings. Nevertheless, a rural proletariat made up of a great number of landless country-dwellers remained. In Slovakia the great landed properties were to some extent reconstituted. After the Second World War confiscated estates led to a redistribution of land. By a decree published in June 1945 the confiscated lands were distributed in this order of priority: to wage-earning agricultural labourers (at the rate of nearly 20 acres of arable land per family); to small landowners (who received about 30 acres each); to large peasant families (from 25 to 38 acres); to workmen, civil servants and craftsmen (about an acre and a quarter); and finally to communes and public associations. This decree also encouraged the resettlement of the frontier regions. The redistributed land amounted to 3,103,500 acres. After the 1948 coup d'état, a second, less comprehensive redistribution swept away all that remained of large estates in the Czech lands and in Slovakia, and reduced the largest farms to a standard holding of about 125 acres of arable land. After the 1949 reform, the new allocations were as follows: out of 1,500,000 holdings less than a third were farms of 12½ acres or over, and among these were 35,000 properties of rich peasants owning from 50 to 125 acres; there were 351,000 holdings of 5 to 12 acres; finally, there were 750,000 peasants who owned less than 5 acres per family. To prevent too great a drop in output by this extreme subdivision of land, agricultural machinery stations, agricultural production co-operatives and State-owned model farms were set up. There are now four different types of agricultural production co-operative. In the first, the system of individual farming is preserved and the farmer applies to the co-operative or the agricultural machinery station for help only with very heavy work. In the second, the farmer owns only his livestock. In the third, the peasant receives from the co-operative a ground-rent and a pro rata payment for his working days. In the fourth, there is a real *kolkhoz* organisation fashioned on the Soviet model.

As early as 1953 — at the end of the Five Year Plan — there were 6,679 agricultural co-operatives of the third and fourth types, and 671 of the second type. The so-called 'socialist'

Fields of sugar-beet on a collective farm in Bohemia.
ERICH LESSING, MAGNUM-PHOTO

area amounted to 44 per cent of the arable land. On the other hand, State farms had 1,235,000 acres under cultivation, and there were 255 agricultural machine and tractor stations with nearly 20,000 tractors, 20,000 combine-harvesters, and 819 other types of agricultural machine.

According to the most recent statistics, the yield from cultivated land rose in Slovakia from a pre-war average of 9.7 cwt. per acre to 13.5 cwt. The proportion of each crop in the total yield has not varied to any great extent.

The largest crop is wheat, the main cereal grown in the plains and valleys, and covering a third of all the cultivated land. Then comes rye (covering a quarter) which grows on poorer soil and especially on the Czech-Moravian hills. After rye comes barley, a crop of high quality used in malting and brewing, and formerly grown almost exclusively in Bohemia and Moravia but now spreading to Slovakia. Cultivation of leguminous vegetables is encouraged. There is a large potato crop. Hops are grown with much care in Bohemia and are exported, but the development of this crop is also linked with the fortunes of the brewing industry. Beet for sugar or for distilling is now up to roughly the figures of the immediate pre-war years, whereas the cultivation of oil-producing plants, though encouraged by the government, is developing only slowly.

Flocks and herds are not increasing rapidly, though the total numbers of livestock were up to the pre-war level by 1949 — again thanks to U.N.R.R.A. assistance. In this year there were 3,660,000 cattle, 3,240,000 pigs, 460,000 sheep and 980,000 goats. Ten years later the number of cattle had increased to only 4,350,000, but the number of pigs had risen to 6,150,000 and the number of sheep to 900,000.

RURAL DWELLINGS. The profound transformation wrought in the agricultural economy of the country has not as yet had any very decisive effect on the traditional appearance of rural dwellings and villages. Despite the progressive change from private to collective ownership, most of the Bohemian and Moravian villages (built to a rather haphazard plan) are still made up of enclosed farms. In the German-type mountain villages of the frontier wooden houses are common; in the villages on the plains and plateaus and in the valleys, the dwellings are of plaster-covered brick. In the Slovakian mountains the commonest type is the small house with rough-cast walls and a wooden framework at the base. In the Tatry, however, the houses are made entirely of wood, while in eastern Slovakia *pisé* dwellings are the most usual. Street-villages are common on the plains and in the valleys; unlike those in the Czech regions, they have a broad gutter down the middle of the main street; on each side are rows of farm buildings, their houses gaudily painted and giving on to the street. Other buildings are set at right angles to the street, and there are separate out-houses such as the bakery and the barn.

In many parts, however, and especially in Slovakia, one can see the beginning of a slow transformation in building technique. Two-storeyed houses and 'community' buildings are under construction, designed to serve in implementing the cultural and social programme adopted by the regime.

THE MAIN URBAN CENTRES. The most obvious visible results of planning are in the towns. Czechoslovakia has five towns of more than 100,000 inhabitants — Prague (Praha) with nearly a million, Brno, Ostrava, Bratislava, and Plzeň. These towns have for long been regional capitals and all are administrative and industrial centres. About twenty other towns have populations ranging from 20,000 to 64,000. Most of these places are large market towns or small industrial towns which are also local 'capitals'.

The most obvious results of town-planning are to be seen in Prague, where the greatest efforts have been made. But Prague is essentially an historic city whose plan and general appearance reveal different stages of development throughout the centuries. It is undoubtedly one of the most beautiful towns in Central Europe and rich in historical monuments and relics of the past. The capital of Czechoslovakia, it is situated on the Vltava, a tributary of the Labe, at a point where the valley widens out. The city is surrounded by hills that afford good defensive positions. The Vltava is not deep and was once easily forded. Prague grew slowly through the centuries, having been originally a mere fortified settlement (*hrad*) on the Vyšehrad and Hradčany hills, to which was added the Malá Strana, a district of aristocratic mansions and servants' dwellings.

The old medieval city, where the Town Hall is situated, has remained the principal business district. The new city (Nové Město), with streets at right angles and two immense squares, was laid out under the Luxemburg dynasty of Bohemian kings in the fourteenth century. There are magnificent specimens of seventeenth century Italo-Spanish baroque art in certain parts of the town. Like most Western European towns, Prague expanded in the nineteenth and twentieth centuries, adding industrial districts (Smíchov, Žižkov) and residential areas (Dejvice, Bubeneč). Yet between the two World Wars, Greater Prague grew rather haphazardly because of the difficulties involved in absorbing the built-up areas annexed immediately after 1918. The new regime seems to have established more systematic plans, which are also being applied to all the other large towns.

Easy communications with foreign countries and with other 'lands' of the republic have made Prague the political, administrative, economic and cultural metropolis of Czechoslovakia.

A CROSSROADS OF INTERNATIONAL COMMUNICATIONS. Czechoslovakia is a country of international transit. The Calais-Paris-Nuremberg-Plzeň-Prague line links Czechoslovakia with Western Europe. The line to Děčín and Dresden leads to East Germany. The Prague-Ostrava-Warsaw railway (a very important line with a branch at Ostrava leading to the Soviet border) communicates with Poland. The line from Brno through Budapest to Bucharest links Czechoslovakia with Hungary and Rumania. In addition to these lines there are important ones linking her to Austria and, through Upper Austria, to Italy. A good deal of work has been done in recent years to extend the railway system in Slovakia. The railways known as the 'Youth Line' (Hrónska Dúbrava-Banská Štiavnica) and the 'First of May Line' (from Velke Stracin to Nógrádszakál in Hungary) have been constructed and, together with the cross-country line from Bratislava to Košice, are helping the industrial development of Slovakia. As well as the railway

AGRICULTURAL MAP OF CZECHOSLOVAKIA

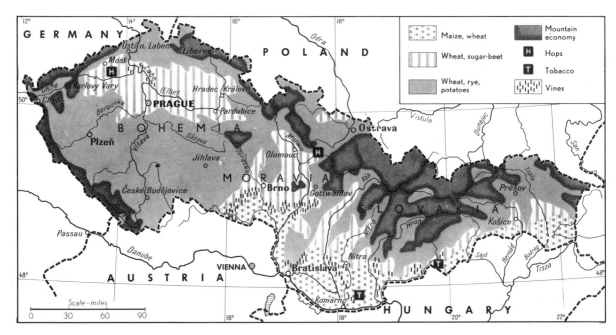

network (7,800 miles) there is a road system (about 44,000 miles) which is much more extensive in the Czech lands than in Slovakia, where there are only about 9,370 miles of highways. Czechoslovak roads (often with macadamised or concrete surfaces) are excellent.

Water communications are much less satisfactory. The navigable mileage of the Vltava-Labe system is very short. It is only below Mělnik that the Labe can be used for river traffic, being navigable from that point to Hamburg. The main river ports are Ústí nad Labem and Děčín. In the east the Danube is of increasing importance for Czechoslovakia, especially since the ports of Bratislava and Komárno now handle from the U.S.S.R. heavy freight comprising materials necessary for large-scale industry.

Much can be expected of an impressive project worked out before the war but only recently begun — the construction of a navigable canal between the Odra (Oder) and the Danube. When completed, this engineering feat will allow the Morava to be regulated. Both Poland and Silesia would stand to gain much by the facilities they would enjoy in transporting heavy freight directly down to the Danube, and Czechoslovakia would be able to make more use of the Polish port of Szczecin (Stettin) at the mouth of the Odra, where she has been ceded an extra-territorial area

Sugar-beet being fed mechanically into the processing plant of a modern sugar refinery near Bratislava, in Slovakia. The industry is highly developed in Czechoslovakia. CZECHOSLOVAK NEWS AGENCY

Opposite: *The mountains of Czechoslovakia are an important international tourist attraction.* EMBASSY OF CZECHOSLOVAK REPUBLIC

Above: *Karlovy Vary (formerly Karlsbad) a well known spa in Bohemia.*
EMBASSY OF CZECHOSLOVAK REPUBLIC

Opposite: *Telč, in south-west Moravia. The square of this historic town has recently been restored.* EMBASSY OF CZECHOSLOVAK REPUBLIC

New trends in trade

The reconversion of the Czechoslovak economy and the establishment of a new map of central Europe necessarily modified the trends of foreign trade. Before the war, the principal supplier and customer of Czechoslovakia was Germany (24 per cent by volume of all the foreign trade), then — far behind — came Great Britain (4.5 per cent) and France (4 per cent). Thirty per cent of Czechoslovak foreign trade was with countries outside Europe, with the U.S.A. heading the list (12 per cent), and India (5 per cent) next. Austria occupied first place among the Danubian lands, while commercial relations between the U.S.S.R. and Czechoslovakia were almost non-existent. Now, and more especially since 1948, the U.S.S.R. is Czechoslovakia's principal customer and main supplier. The Soviet Union buys machines, textiles, shoes, rubber goods, glass and paper, and sells to Czechoslovakia iron and manganese ore, pyrites, agricultural implements and cereals.

Poland, too, has become one of the biggest customers and suppliers, buying machinery, chemical products, hops, livestock and seed, and selling coal, electric current, newsprint, pig's bristles, poultry and fish. Rumania takes sheet-metal, china, coke, machinery and chemical products in exchange for petroleum, meat and maize. Bulgaria buys machinery, automobiles, textiles, paper — and sells vegetables, fruit and tobacco. There is also an increasing trade with East Germany, and trade with China is developing (exchange of Chinese metallic ores, vegetable oils and fodder against machinery, rolling-stock and chemical products).

Czechoslovakia is also supplying finished products and industrial equipment to the under-developed countries of the Near and Middle East as well as to South America. These new trends are determined very largely by politics and may not last, for Czechoslovakia's rôle in view of its geographical position tends to be that of a turntable between West and East, and between central Europe to the north and the Mediterranean countries to the south.

Alfred FICHELLE

Traditional folk dancing. EMBASSY OF CZECHOSLOVAK REPUBLIC

Esztergom, ancient capital of Hungary, situated on the Danube above Budapest and facing Czechoslovakia across the river. Esztergom is the seat of the Primate of Hungary and the town is dominated by the cathedral (seen in the foreground), a basilica built in the nineteenth century on the lines of St Peter's, Rome. The town was the birthplace of St Stephen, first apostolic King of Hungary.

HUNGARIAN NEWS AND INFORMATION SERVICE

HUNGARY

IN contrast to Poland, a resuscitated state, and to Czechoslovakia and Yugoslavia, both recently created states, Hungary is the rump of a former and much larger country. In 1914 — as part of the Austro-Hungarian Empire — Hungary had an area of 125,500 square miles and a population of 21 million, of whom only 54 per cent spoke the Magyar language. By the Treaty of Trianon the country was reduced to about 35,900 square miles and a population of 8 million. The Second World War occasioned fleeting territorial readjustments in Hungary's favour — southern Slovakia fell to her under the Munich agreements, Subcarpathian Russia (Ruthenia) when the independent State of Slovakia was constituted in 1939, and northern Transylvania and the Banat of Temesvar (Timişoara) were regained in 1940 and 1941. However, since Hungary's fortunes were bound up with those of the Axis powers, the country was in 1945 once more reduced to its 1919 boundaries — with the exception of a few frontier rectifications. The present boundaries enclose a population which is ethnically fairly uniform, since about 90 per cent of the inhabitants are of Hungarian origin and speak the Magyar language. Germans form the largest alien group (about 200,000). There is a scattering of Yugoslavs in the south-east, and a Slovak minority (about 10,000) is found mainly in the north. The Rumanian minority also numbers about 10,000.

Hungarians settled abroad are fairly numerous (most of them left before the First World War) and may total more than three million. There are Hungarian colonies in Austria (Vienna and the Burgenland), in Subcarpathian Russia (where they live in the townships), in Slovakia (691,000 according to the official figures), in Rumania (from 1½ to 2 million in Transylvania and the Banat), and about 500,000 in Yugoslavia. More than 1,500,000 Hungarians live in the United States; Cleveland has the second largest Hungarian population of any city in the world.

Hungary is a small country, full of life and, in contrast to Yugoslavia and Rumania, geographically homogeneous, composed of the plains and valleys of the Pannonian basin's northern region. From the end of the ninth century, the region was occupied by a people of Finno-Ugrian origin.

HUNGARY'S TWO AXES. The Danube (Duna) and the mountain ridges stretching from Lake Balaton to the Carpathians form the two axes of the Hungarian State. Hungarian economy gravitates toward the Danube, on whose banks are sited large towns, including the capital itself. It is by this great river that Hungary, now without ports or coasts, maintains contact with its northern and southern neighbours. During the nineteenth century Hungarian capital developed navigation

HUNGARY

on the Danube and the Sava rivers, and also built the railway from Budapest to Fiume (Rijeka). The waters of the Danube, slowed down in the Pannonian plain, flood and fertilize a valley several miles wide and feed the canals and irrigation channels on the plain.

The Danube is a natural frontier between western and eastern Hungary. To the west extend regions of higher altitude and more varied relief, where the population is more dense and where life in the countryside is in many respects like that in Austria or southern Germany. To the east, however, stretch monotonous plains with a drier climate and a sparser population — a foretaste of eastern Europe, the world of the steppes.

The Danube has not always been the main artery of the Magyar lands. In the sixteenth century Hungary was occupied by the Turks sweeping on towards Vienna. During the ages of invasion, the real frontier was not the Danube but the mountain backbone cut through by the river swirling through picturesque gorges. These mountains — or rather hills, for they do not exceed about 3,300 feet in height — present a most varied relief: rounded summits covered with oak and beech forests, arid limestone plateaus on which flocks of sheep graze, hills cut out of the mass of clay and sand deposits laid down by the Pannonian Sea, and volcanic hills to the east of the Danube, where the fertile soil is most favourable for market-gardens and vineyards. Deep valleys cut into the mountains and isolate both massifs and ridges, which lie in a general south-west to north-east direction. There is the asymmetrical Bakony (2,200 feet) which dominates the Balaton trough, the Vértes (2,070 feet), and the Pilis (2,480 feet) whose southern section is cut through by the Danube. There are also precursors of the more lofty Carpathians, such as Mounts Hegyalja, Bükk (3,150 feet) and Mátra (3,400 feet). The heights are mantled with fir forests, and thermal springs follow the fault-lines. In the basins there are extensive deposits of lignite, bauxite and various ores. This was the region where the first Hungarian industries were established, and it is still one of the areas which holds out most promise for modern Hungary.

THE NORTH-WEST: RÁBA AND KISALFÖLD. In
the north-west, where it borders on Czechoslovakia and Austria,

Hungary has a very mixed population. There are groups of Slovaks, Germans and Croats, and the high density of the population can be ascribed to the excellent soil and to the fact that this region, protected by the Bakony, served as a refuge area when the Pannonian plain was occupied by the Turks. All the soil is tilled, and the climate favours cereal crops. Extremes of temperature are less marked and rainfall is heavier than in the southern plains. The covering of deciduous forest was cleared in Roman times, so that there is a landscape of varied crops, of *bocage*, and of open fields — very much like the countryside in Moravia or Lower Austria. There is still marshy ground at the bottom of the Danube and Rába valleys, but the dry terraces and hills of the Kisalföld (the 'Little Plain') have lent themselves to the establishment of large villages. The yield of wheat and oats is decidedly higher than in other parts of Hungary, and a prosperous agriculture (run on modern lines with a rotation of cereals, sugar-beet, hops and forage plants) is combined with the breeding of livestock.

FIELDS AND STEPPES. ALFÖLD AND PUSZTA.
The landscape changes to the south and east of the mountain backbone. The climate becomes drier, trees are scarcer, the villages more widely spaced, and population density lower. These are areas which have frequently been devastated and depopulated, a no-man's-land during the sixteenth and seventeenth centuries, a bone of contention between Hapsburg and Turk. The region was resettled as the wave of Islam rolled back at the beginning of the eighteenth century — after the conclusion of the Treaty of Karlowitz in 1699. The development of the Pannonian South was encouraged by a number of factors: proximity to Vienna, the rise of a middle-class trading community at Budapest, and the dense population to the north of Bakony and in the German lands. But until quite recently both settlement and economic progress were directed by men from the north. The feudal magnates and the Hungarian and Austrian landed proprietors attracted Serbians, Hungarians and Germans, who built villages, repopulated the valleys, drained the marshes and tilled the steppe. Consequently, there are two types of country characteristic of the Danubian plains — Alföld, or 'field' (i.e. cultivated plain) and the Puszta, the wild steppes,

land still discouraging to permanent settlement, where the earth is too dry or too wet, and where huge flocks of sheep find pasture. This is the region of the old, traditional, picturesque Hungary, the Hungary of shepherds, poets and artists, 'the country of gypsies, fine horses, good wines, colourful costumes and beautiful women'. It is hard to distinguish any clearly defined natural regions in this vast expanse of plains. To the west of the Danube the ground is still fairly rolling. The Mecsek hills rise, isolated, out of the plain to more than 2,000 feet. Round the town of Pécs there are mines and industries. In the region of low hills and broad, marshy valleys stretching between the Mecsek hills and Lake Balaton on one side, and the Drava River on the other, there is considerable variety in the systems of cultivation. However, because of the great heat of summer, maize is the principal cereal crop. The shores of Lake Balaton have always attracted settlers and the average population there is more than 350 to the square mile. The steep northern slopes are covered with vineyards, while market-gardens are more common on the south side where the lakeside homes of the fishermen, spas and holiday resorts are dotted along the shore.

To the east of the Danube, three features stand out in the landscape. The rivers have very meandering courses, spreading sheets of alluvial soil and eating into the edges of the plateaus. The villages, surrounded by natural or man-made dykes, are perched on the little hills rising above the marshes, are set on the steep banks, or take on the semicircular form of the abandoned meanders of the river. Despite efforts made by the co-operative associations, most of the region is still given over to hunting and fishing and is often subject to floods. The Tisza valley is narrower and less humid than the Danube valley.

The loess plateaus form the most attractive region. They make up most of the Nagyalföld, or 'Great Plain', where, owing to the dryness of the climate (a very irregular rainfall with an average of a bare 16 inches a year), there are no woods, and where irrigation is often necessary for the cultivation of the more delicate plants. Maize and wheat in a two-year rotation are the sole crops on the tilled land and their yield is rather low.

The Puszta also has deserts of sand-dunes stretching in parallel rows, pin-pointed with stagnant pools and, as in the Kiskun between the Danube and the Tisza and in the Nyírség to the north of Debrecen, relieved only by clumps of grass and groves of acacias. Expanses of salt cover the valley floors to the east of the Tisza. In winter they lie under water, and in summer evaporation leaves a white crust which makes the soil quite useless for cultivation. Such are the conditions in the Hortobágy Puszta, once the domain of virtually wild horses, cattle and pigs.

The age-old contrast between Alföld and Puszta is now less clear-cut than once it was. Cultivation is spreading at the expense of the steppe, and ambitious agricultural development schemes are being carried out. The transformation is slow but the development of the country's resources is indicated by the appearance of some curious types of rural settlement.

A SINGULAR TYPE OF VILLAGE. When the lands devastated by the Turks were resettled, large villages grew up, surrounded by huge expanses of land. These settlements were the *varos* or *vasar* which later became trading centres. Details concerning their origin are not very clear. It is not known whether the *varos* became the traditional form of settlement for the Magyars when they adopted a sedentary life, or whether they were a form of habitation chosen by the shepherds at the time of the invasions. The villages which existed before the Turkish invasions may have been of this type, but most of the *varos* date from the large-scale settlement directed by German civil engineers in the eighteenth century. All these villages are alike. Round a spacious, open central area, square or rectangular, are the administrative buildings, the inns, and the shops. The ground plan of the village resembles a chessboard;

The Bükk Mountains (3,150 feet) are deeply dissected by rivers and covered with beautiful forests. HUNGARIAN PRESS OFFICE

A market in a village near Budapest. ERICH LESSING, MAGNUM-PHOTO

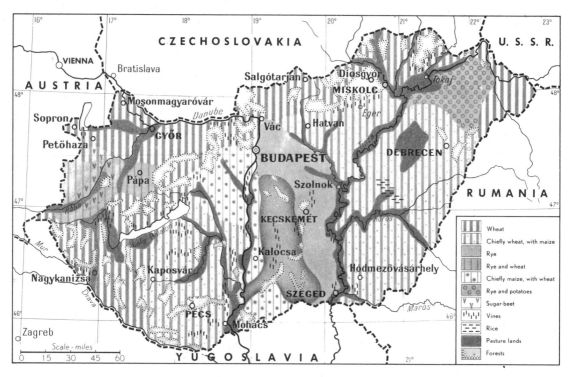

AGRICULTURAL MAP OF HUNGARY

	Wheat
	Chiefly wheat, with maize
	Rye
	Rye and wheat
	Chiefly maize, with wheat
	Rye and potatoes
	Sugar-beet
	Vines
	Rice
	Pasture lands
	Forests

the houses are at right angles to the streets, which intersect at right angles. Roads radiate from the central nucleus like the spokes of a wheel and are bordered for mile after mile by straggling farms. These villages have grown steadily with the influx of immigrants, and their population may amount to several tens of thousands; almost the whole community is peasant, so that the way of life remains entirely rural.

At some distance from these villages the landed proprietors built isolated dwellings, haylofts or granaries (*salas*), which were occupied seasonally by agricultural labourers. The *salas* have now become small hamlets around which stretch the subdivided lands of the former large estates (*tanyaks*). Thus, when they were emptied of part of their rural population, certain centres such as Szeged and Debrecen — which also enjoyed an active political and economic life — acquired an urban appearance.

This pattern of social structure and these types of settlement are also being changed. After the last agrarian reform, several thousand people were resettled in modern communities which will doubtless develop as agriculture becomes increasingly mechanised. The success or failure of the collectivisation movement will determine their future.

Hungarian economy

AGRARIAN REFORM. Hungarian agrarian economy was in pre-war days marked, more than that of any other part of central Europe, by the overwhelming preponderance of great estates worked by thousands of peasant-servants. The Esterhazy family, for instance, owned more than 320,000 acres, which included 164 villages. Estates of more than 1,200 acres covered a third of the cultivated land surface. Properties of 285 to 1,200 acres occupied 13 per cent, while small owners farmed barely one-fifth of the cultivable land. More than a quarter of the peasant families owned no land at all.

The huge estates, half of whose acreage was composed of forests and pasture and was preserved for hunting and shooting,

remained intact. Of all the states in the Danubian area Hungary was the least affected by the agrarian reforms which followed on the First World War. In the period between the two wars only a few of the large estates were broken up.

However, in March 1945 the law prescribing the expropriation and division of all properties over 144 acres was strictly enforced; the changes effected by this second agrarian reform appear more far-reaching in Hungary than in any other country of central or eastern Europe. More than a third of the country's area (about 7½ million acres) has been redistributed. A million agricultural labourers have received tiny holdings of about 5 to 7½ acres. The estates of German and Hungarian magnates

Cultivation of potatoes on the immense Alföld plain.
H. HOLMES, CAMERA PRESS

HUNGARY, SHOWING MINERAL RESOURCES AND THE PRINCIPAL INDUSTRIES

have been divided up for peasant families from Slovakia and other poor areas. Yet some of the *latifundia*, or large estates, have been spared. Forests and model farms (more than 16 per cent of the total area) are directly administered by the State. The disadvantages of running a vast number of tiny holdings have been to some extent offset by the formation of various types of production and labour co-operatives. Their numbers have increased greatly since 1952, and more than 5,000 co-operatives with 400,000 members cultivate one-quarter of the agricultural land.

AGRICULTURAL PROBLEMS. The trend towards State-run and collectivised agriculture stopped after 1953.

Shepherds in their traditional cloaks on the Puszta, an immense steppe that stretches between the foothills of the Transylvanian mountains in the east, the Carpathians in the north, and the Danube in the west. Extensive stock-rearing is carried on. J. ALLAN CASH

The marked drop in agricultural output can be explained by the division of the arable land into far too many tiny units; by the opposition of the middle-class group of peasants; by the considerable losses sustained by Hungarian agriculture in the war (half the livestock, a third of the machines, and a tenth of the buildings); by the preference accorded to heavy industry during the first Three Year Plan; by the succession of droughts after the war; and by political difficulties. A sixth of the arable land is untilled. The acreage under grain crops is smaller than before the war: the wheat and maize harvest is still insufficient. Unprofitable co-operatives have been disbanded, and lower taxes are now imposed on private property. Small landowners have received a good deal of State aid in the form of seed, fertilizers, livestock, and machines. The quantity of compulsory levies in kind by the government has been reduced. It is hard to say whether the new agrarian legislation has had immediate and favourable effects. More than 60 per cent of the cultivated land is still under grain crops. Only in the north-west is there more wheat than maize, but rye is still the main crop on the sandy soil of Nyírség or Kiskun. In large-scale farming, whether by the State or the collectives, 'white cereals' are substituted for the traditional maize. The yield reaches 12 cwt. per acre for wheat, and 19 cwt. for maize. Recent changes have aimed at developing industrial crops. The sugar-beet area is increasing. There was an ambitious plan to plant about 320,000 acres with sub-tropical crops: cotton and rice on the irrigated lands of the Tisza valley and on those of its tributaries as well as in the Hortobágy; citrus fruits in sheltered trenches; groundnuts; *koksaghiz*, a rubber-plant; and *kenaf*, a plant yielding a fibre used as a substitute for jute. But these plans, adopted on the advice of Soviet specialists, do not seem to have come to much.

However, such crops could change the traditional face of the Puszta, where the problems presented by poor soil, dry climate and human negligence are comparable to those encountered on the Russian steppes. Good results have already been obtained by planting screens of trees, by reforestation, by combating soil erosion, and by tilling some of the migration lands hitherto reserved for flocks and herds. Such measures

Raw materials arriving at the Danube Steelworks in Sztálinváros.
HUNGARIAN NEWS AND INFORMATION SERVICE

A view of Sztálinváros from the water tower. One of several new towns built since 1950. HUNGARIAN NEWS AND INFORMATION SERVICE

A chemicals factory at Kozincbarcika, in north-east Hungary.
HUNGARIAN PRESS OFFICE

were to have been rapidly undertaken by a concentration of the old *tanyaks* and by the establishment of huge, modern, rural population units and highly mechanised collective centres. But these plans have encountered resistance also.

CONDITIONS OF INDUSTRIAL DEVELOPMENT.

Hungarian industry is hampered by economic and technical backwardness, a consequence of age-long economic and political subordination, and by the loss of much of its former territory. Before 1914 the government in Vienna did everything to hamper development in all branches of Hungarian industry (especially metallurgy and textiles) which might compete with those of Austria. The leading Hungarian port, Rijeka, had poor connections with Budapest, and navigation on the Danube was mostly under Austrian control. After the First World War Hungary had close connections with Germany, which invested capital, delivered manufactured goods in exchange for agricultural produce, and controlled Hungarian commerce and industry. It is true that in 1938 a fifth of the population was employed in industry, bur nearly two-thirds of this labour force was concentrated in Budapest and its suburbs. German pillage and war damage still further weakened the industrial potential. By 1945 the Hungarian population was starving and its currency worthless.

However, the prospects for a restoration of Hungarian industry and for its future development are very far from unfavourable. The coal and lignite are of poor quality (except the Mecsek coal), the deposits are scattered, and communication between them is not good. Vértesalja-Esztergom, Dorog, Tatabánya, Tokód, Salgótarján, Borsod and Ajka are the principal mining centres and are all in the mountains. Nevertheless output, which was not more than 10 million tons before the war, reached 12 million tons in 1950 and has since risen to over 20 million tons; most of this, however, consists of lignite.

Hungary is one of the richest European countries in petroleum. The Lipse field, to the north of the Drava, is in production, and a pipeline links Lipse and Szöny to Budapest. Extensive reserves of natural gas have been prospected to the east of the Tisza.

As there are no high mountains, Hungary cannot count on hydro-electric power, and lignite is used to supply the thermo-electric stations in the north-west. The recently constructed dams on the Tisza (Tiszalök, 55 million kWh) and the Danube have increased the current production, though it is still insufficient.

Metallic ores are not abundant, with the sole exception of bauxite. The extraction of this important ore was intensified by the Germans during the war (north and north-west of Balaton and south of Pécs) and has put Hungary second only to France among European bauxite producers (excluding the U.S.S.R.).

The nationalisation policy has been carried out more slowly in Hungary than in other eastern European countries. In 1945 the coal mines were expropriated, then, in 1946, the electric plants. Heavy industry and enterprises employing more than 100 persons were not taken over until 1948. Businesses with more than 10 employees were nationalised in December 1949. Two Plans have been adopted since the war: the Three Year Plan (from 1947—49) which was to effect the reconstruction of the country, and the Five Year Plan (1950—54), whose object was to increase output by modernising equipment. The rapid application of these Plans (according to official figures, production has more than doubled since 1938) has greatly changed the location of the industrial zones. Towns that have hitherto always been agricultural have become industrialised. *Kombinats* spring up near sources of power or lines of communication.

However, the first years of the Five Year Plan were marked by too sudden a spurt in the development of heavy industry.

In July 1953 a revised Plan was put into operation — very largely because a serious food shortage afflicted the towns during 1951 and 1952. The new measures were aimed at reducing investments in the large industrial centres and in engineering and at developing manufactures and the output of consumer goods. Attempts have been made to check the spread of the towns and at the same time to encourage the production of high-quality goods, even luxury goods.

NEW INDUSTRIAL GEOGRAPHY. The heavy industry *kombinats* are located on the lignite deposits stretching from Lake Balaton to the Slovakian frontier. These plants use the iron ore from the north-east basin divided between Hungary and Slovakia, Czech and Polish coke brought in through Bratislava, current from the thermo-electric stations, and bauxite from north and north-east of Lake Balaton. Although the 'vertical' structure of State enterprises is fairly far advanced, each industrial centre of any size tends to specialise: thus Borsod and Miskolc are mining towns with foundries and chemical works; rolling-mills are concentrated at Tatabánya; Ajka and Almásfüzitö treat bauxite, and Urkut processes manganese. Two isolated groups of iron and steel plants are fast developing: at Pécs (near the Mecsek coalfield and bauxite deposits) and at Dunapentele (on the Danube upstream from Budapest) where there is a new steelworks. The Dunapentele plant has been established at a point where advantage· can be taken of river transport. The first works there were opened in 1951 and the town — which in 1955 already had 50,000 inhabitants out of an expected total of 100,000 — is destined to become the main centre of Hungarian heavy industry.

The main manufacturing industries (especially for agriculture) are grouped on the north-western plains (chiefly spinning and weaving) and in the Alföld (principally flour-mills, tobacco, canning, starch factories and refineries). But the industries of these 'peasant towns' can develop only when the output of agricultural machinery is sufficient to supply the needs of State or collective farms; only the mechanisation of agriculture will free the rural labour force that is still scattered among the traditional-style villages.

Budapest

The oldest town in Hungary remains the most important. Budapest, like Vienna, is the large capital of a small state, and its population (about 1,850,000) is more than a sixth of that of the whole country. The town has, of course, owed its good fortune to its geographical position. The old districts, perched on Buda hill, overlook the alluvial plain of the Danube, a river that is navigable and easy to cross. Budapest is a river town, a town commanding many lines of communication. Its historical rôle as the focal point of a large and unified state

has been considerable. Buda citadel was first a Turkish stronghold and then a headquarters of Hapsburg domination. It was also the seat of the government, the place of residence of the Magyar aristocracy and the foreign bourgeoisie.

The town's growth was closely conditioned by the reconquest, settlement and cultivation of the south-eastern territories and by the development of traffic between Vienna and Budapest. From the end of the eighteenth century the population of Budapest grew rapidly; there were 35,000 inhabitants in 1780, 178,000 by 1850, 850,000 in 1900, and 1,585,000 in 1940.

The present-day pattern of the different sections of the city still shows their traditional character. Buda remains a historical town of palaces, churches, mansions, parks and thermal establishments. Across the Danube (about 440 yards wide) lie the streets of Pest, regularly laid out, strung along the banks of the river and spreading into the plain beyond. Surrounding the whole is a belt of workers' districts which bear witness to the industrialisation of the latter part of the nineteenth century, encouraged — more than in any other part of the country — by the investment of Austrian, German and Czech capital.

Buda was bombed during the Second World War. The bridges and river port were destroyed and much reconstruction and rebuilding had to be done. The town-planning programme aims at transforming Buda into an area of parks and museums; at improving communications between Pest and the outskirts (especially by the construction of a five-mile-long underground railway); at laying out a 'Greater Budapest' reaching 15 miles from north to south and 19 miles from west to east; at setting up new factories to be supplied with coal and bauxite from the north-west; and finally at enlarging the port at Csepel island.

Hungary's future

Hungary's future depends, without doubt, on the industrialisation of the south-west, on the transformation of the steppe-lands, and on increased output. Since the tragic events of October 1956, Hungary has been linked more closely than ever with the policy of the Soviet Union and with that of the Warsaw Pact signatories. Most of her foreign trade is with the eastern States, which take her raw materials and agricultural produce. Navigation on the Danube is controlled by the U.S.S.R. and Rumania. Joint Soviet and Hungarian concerns direct the oil and bauxite production.

Hungary's resumption of commercial relations with Western countries and Yugoslavia, her participation in the big trade fairs of France and Germany, and the conclusion of commercial agreements with Switzerland and Great Britain seemed, before 1956, to be promising signs — especially as Hungary, like Czechoslovakia and Poland, is well placed for playing the rôle of intermediary with the West.

André BLANC

General view of Budapest. Though it is the capital of a relatively small state, Budapest is a huge city. In the foreground is the historic city of Buda with its citadel, while on the other side of the river is the modern city and business centre of Pest. At more than 1,800,000, the population of Budapest is more than one-sixth of the total population of Hungary. HUNGARIAN NEWS AND INFORMATION SERVICE

Warsaw, capital of Poland. This view across the city and the River Vistula, on which it stands, shows the juxtaposition of new construction and the few old buildings that survived the war. In the foreground is the Church of the Holy Cross. POLISH CULTURAL INSTITUTE

The Market Square in Cracow, former capital of Poland, on the left bank of the Vistula. PAUL POPPER

POLAND

No country in the world suffered more profound changes from the results of the Second World War than Poland. Not only did that war inflict upon her incalculable damage and great loss of life, not only did it bring far-reaching social and political transformations, but it completely revolutionised the country by a 185-miles translation from east to west — a phenomenon almost unique in the recent history of the world.

Two agreements, that of Potsdam signed by U.S.S.R., the United States and Great Britain on the 2nd August, 1945, and then the Treaty of Moscow signed on 17th August, 1945 by the U.S.S.R. and Poland, laid down the ways and means of effecting these very considerable territorial changes.

The landscape of Poland

THE NEW FRONTIERS. The Treaty of Moscow settled the controversy about Poland's eastern boundaries. With the exception of two small concessions to Poland, the new frontier follows approximately the Curzon Line (suggested by Lord Curzon at the Paris Peace Conference of 1920, as a frontier between Poland and the new Russian Soviet Socialist Republic). The first concession is in the region of Krilow, between the Bug and the Volokia; the second comprises the Białowieza, Niemirov, and Białystok area. These amount to frontier rectifications of about 19 miles in the south and north.

The amount of Polish territory lost to the east of the new frontiers is about 66,200 square miles, which in 1938 held a population of 11,750,000. According to the Potsdam Agreement, the new Polish-German frontier was to run from the north-eastern corner of the Bohemian quadrilateral, following the line of the western Nysa (Neisse), then that of the Odra (Oder) as far as Görlitz, and then in a straight line to the Zalew Szczecinski (the Haff, or Pool, of Stettin) and Świnoujscie (Swinemünde). This agreement has not yet been officially recognised *de jure* but is recognised *de facto* by the U.S.A., Great Britain and France, pending final delimitation in the signing of a peace treaty with Germany. It was agreed that the territories in question should be handed over to Polish administration, and the section of the Potsdam Agreement laying down that the German population of the Western Territories still resident there were to be evacuated to Germany was recognised both *de facto* and *de jure*. Thus Poland's pre-war frontiers were extended westwards by the addition of Dolny Slask (Lower Silesia) and part of Górny Slask (Upper Silesia), Ziemia Lubuska (East Brandenburg), and the greater part of Pomorze. The Polish Government at once proceeded to organise these territories in a Polish voivodship (county) system, under the name of 'regained territories of the West'. In 1948, a decree was issued declaring these territories to be an integral part of Poland. Most of the German inhabitants who had not already left these regions of their own free will were transferred to Germany. Polish place names have been restored. Thus Swinemünde has become Świnoujscie; Stettin has become Szczecin; Breslau is now Wrocław and so on. Poland has thus regained in the west an area of about 40,000 square miles which had a population of 8,463,000 inhabitants in 1938.

AN IMMENSE PLAIN. Poland today consists mostly of an immense plain whose surface and soil are largely a legacy of the great Quaternary glaciers which left behind large accumulations of detritus as they retreated. In the south the surface presents a more varied character, for it includes an area of hills and high plains stretching from the San to the Nysa, together with a mountainous fringe which is of a very different character on each side of the low hills at the Gate of Moravia. To the east are the Carpathians, the Tatra massif, and to the west the Sudeten mountains.

The Polish plain, with a maximum width of some 315 miles from north to south, is broader than the north German plain, though they resemble each other in the glaciated surface and the nature of the shore-line.

The Scandinavian glaciers were able to spread easily over this plain for the pre-glacial relief presented no obstacle to their southward advance. They had a threefold effect on the plain: they gave it its present-day relief, its soil, and its river system.

From Pomorze to Mazury (formerly East Prussia) and from Ziemia Lubuska as far as the Bug the surface relief is entirely formed by glacial deposits. Here, as far as the eye can see, stretches the vast plain left by ground moraines and subglacial drift. Elsewhere, and especially in the north of the plain, the old terminal moraines form isolated hills, often in parallel lines and generally preceded by a glacial slope caused by the action of streams in spreading the moraine sands. In other areas there are great numbers of hills, all in a line and pointing in the same direction. These are the drumlins, long, branching ridges of irregular pattern. The predominance of terminal moraines in the centre and south, and of drumlins and eskers in the north gives the Polish plain a relief that is more uniform in the south and more complex in the north.

The soil consists of glacial accumulations which almost everywhere mask the bedrock. The clay soils of the ground-moraine or subglacial drift are the most numerous. They are not infertile, but impermeable and rather mixed. The terminal moraines and their dispersal zones, on the other hand, are much poorer, with a predominance of sands, heaped up as dunes in some places and spreading out as extensive moorland in others.

The long coastline of this plain, from Zalew Wisłany (formerly Frisches Haff) to Świnoujscie, is made up of light glacial material which tends to silt up. Since the Baltic has only weak tides, the old river estuaries become blocked and closed in by spits of sand. In consequence the shore is low and not very inviting. Gdynia is an artificial port and at Szczecin an outport has had to be constructed — Świnoujscie.

The most distinctive feature of the Polish plain is the very wide corridor formed by the middle and lower course of the Vistula; this corridor seems to follow a line of depression in the bedrock. The river flows at no great depth below the ground-moraine plain and the slow stream here describes innumerable meanders, bordered by very broad terraces.

Northwards, in the moraine ridges near the Baltic, the Vistula plain is narrower and more deeply embanked, but in the Warsaw (Warszawa in Polish) region it spreads out to a width of 19 to 25 miles and forms the heartland of Poland. Here the glacial terrains have been covered by the alluvial soil brought down by the river, to which the plain owes its great agricultural wealth.

HILLS AND MOUNTAINS IN THE SOUTH. The hills and high plains of the south form a belt 150 miles long, separating the great plain from the mountainous region which forms the southern frontier of Poland. The main feature of the relief in Silesia and in Little Poland is a number of rather high plateaus, often dry and covered with glacial deposits and particularly with loess, which makes them very fertile. These plateaus are not uniform and local uplift of the old bedrock has raised them here and there, as in the neighbourhood of Ziębice (Münsterberg) and in the Lyso Góry.

This belt of high land is not, however, continuous. The Upper Silesian depression separates the Silesian plains from the plateaus of Little Poland. Farther east, the broad valley of the Upper Vistula has a rich soil of glacial muds and silts. It forms a depression between Little Poland and the Góry Swietokrzyskie to the west and the Lublin plateau to the east.

The southern and mountainous frontiers of Poland are divided into two groups of unequal size, one on each side of the Moravian depression — to the south-east part of the Carpathians, and to the south-west the Sudeten mountains.

Consequent upon the changes in the Soviet-Polish frontiers the Beskid massif, a geologically recent range extending from the Carpathians, now lies outside Poland. One part of this chain — the northern face of the Tatras — is a small portion of the Carpathian 'central massif'. This has been left to Poland by a bend in the Polono-Slovak frontier to the south of Nowy Targ. It is an Alpine region with steep, high mountains (the Rysy peak is 8,200 feet high), deep-cut, glaciated valleys, and huge forests, in marked contrast to the Zakopane trough.

Farther north, the most important feature is that of the much lower Beskid ridges running from west to east. Altitudes vary from about 3,900 to 4,260 feet, and drop to below 3,300 feet in the east where crests of 2,300 to 2,600 feet are crossed by broad, low passes (Dukla and Lupków). The heights, moreover, are often of soft rocks and take the form of rounded eminences separated by wide valleys containing lazily meandering rivers.

To the west of the Moravian Gate the new frontier with Bohemia is of a different character. It is an ancient massif whose summits (between 3,000 and 5,000 feet) are formed by tabular plateaus. There are, however, dislocations running in a north-west to south-east direction, including a number of sunk basins more or less well linked together by valleys with deep gorges. Thus there stretch from the Nysa to the source of the Odra the plateaus of the Karkonosze (the Riesen Gebirge), the Góry Sowie (Eulen Gebirge) and the Góry Orlickie (Adler Gebirge).

SOILS AND CLIMATES. The glaciation which extended over the Polish plain as far as the southern plateaus and the northern part of the Sandomierz basin resulted in a great part of the area being of rather indifferent quality as agricultural land. Its soil is better for rye than for wheat, and often better for forests and peat-bogs than for any sort of cultivation. It is a region of grey, powdery soil more or less podzolised, of sandy or stony soil, or of spongy soil: land on which good crops cannot be expected without extensive drainage and improvements. Still, there are in Poland some regions of excellent soil: for instance, on the alluvial plains, such as those of the Vistula (especially in the Warsaw basin), on the beds of former lakes, and on drained marshes. Then there are the southern Silesian plains and their extension east as far as the Lublin plateau. Indeed, there is a long belt of loess and chernozem (black earth) running along the foot of the Carpathians and reaching its greatest width north of Cracow (Kraków). In this area lies more than half the agricultural potential of Poland.

Plainly the climate restricts crops to those of temperate lands with a continental climate. Although the winters are cold (in January at Warsaw about 27° F; at Cracow about 30° F.), the summers are warm (in July at Warsaw about 65° F; at Cracow about 66° F.) and allow of good harvests, especially as summer rains are abundant in a continental climate (8 inches for June-

August at Warsaw and 12 inches at Cracow). The fertile soils of Poland are suitable for sugar-beet and wheat, while the north and centre of the Polish plain, which are less warm in summer (about 63° F. at Gdańsk in July), are better suited for certain poorer grain crops, for stock-breeding, and for forests.

So although it is not a particularly rich agricultural country, Poland can rely on a varied output from farming and stock-breeding — and to these products must be added those derived from working the forests.

Profit and loss account

POPULATION. The Second World War was immensely destructive, the amount of damage having been estimated at 51,600,000 U.S. dollars (38 per cent of the entire national wealth). Many towns were utterly destroyed. The old town of Warsaw on the left bank of the Vistula was razed to the ground.

More than six million Poles were killed: 123,000 soldiers in combat, 521,000 civilians, and 5,384,000 in concentration camps. Thus Poland lost almost 22 per cent of her population which, by 1946, was down to 23,929,000. To the losses must be added some 1,600,000 persons wholly or partially disabled.

Furthermore, immediately after the war profound modifications were made in the distribution of the population. In the 'regained territories of the West', there remained 3½ million Germans, yet the Poles there numbered not more than 1 million. For security reasons, the Polish government, in accordance with the provisions of the Potsdam Agreement, proceeded to carry out measures of wholesale expulsion during the first months of their occupation. This went on until October 1945. The majority of the 1½ million Germans who still remained at that date were expelled later; by October 1946 some 1,285,000 had been obliged to seek refuge in Germany.

These measures had two consequences. First, Poland suffered a serious drop in population; density fell from 35 to 30 per square mile and the new Poland lacked labour at a time when it was urgently needed for the reconstruction of the country. Second, population was distributed unevenly. After the expulsion of the German population, the 'regained territories of the West' had no more than 4½ million inhabitants in 1946, including 2½ million recent Polish immigrants; in other words, these regions had less than half their 1938 population. On the other hand, many country districts of 'old' Poland were over-populated, especially in the southern voivodships (the areas of Rzeszow, Cracow and Katowice). It was by no means uncommon to find holdings of about 2½ to 3½ acres of tilled land to each peasant. It was estimated that eight million people were 'redundant'.

The new Polish government thus inherited a double demographic problem: on the one hand was lack of population, and on the other bad distribution of population.

The normal population increase could, in time, solve the first problem. Though the birth rate has gone down since 1955, the death rate has also gone down — especially the infant mortality rate. The natural increase in the Polish population is in the order of half a million a year. But in 1945-6 there was an immediate demand for manpower.

To meet this need the government took a number of measures to increase the population. Two million Poles were brought in from eastern territories ceded to the U.S.S.R. and efforts were made — with varying degrees of success — to attract back to their homeland Poles living abroad, in France, in Germany, in Danubian Europe, and in the Balkans. On 20th February 1946, a repatriation agreement was signed with France. By the end of 1946 almost 2½ million Poles had returned home. The results were on the whole satisfactory for, counting the repatriations and the rapid population increase, the total population was about 30 million in 1960 and is still increasing.

POLAND

MATERIAL LOSSES. NEW RESOURCES. In the east, Poland lost the greater part of the north Carpathian oilfield (the Borislav area) which yielded 500,000 tons of crude oil in 1938. Poland lost too all its former deposits of potash. From the agricultural standpoint, the new situation is not so unfavourable. Still, Poland is now deprived of excellent lands in Podolia and Volhynia (annexed to the Ukraine) and of the flax-growing districts of Brest (Brest-Litovsk) and Vilnius (Vilna). Furthermore, the areas ceded to the U.S.S.R. comprised 17 per cent of the Polish forests, and a drop in wood exports was to be feared, since before 1939 timber represented one-quarter in value of the country's exports. However, the losses in the agricultural domain are in no way dramatic, for production is down only 20 per cent on 1937 figures.

Losses of territory have also been abundantly compensated for by four kinds of gain. Poland was formerly squeezed in between Pomerania and East Prussia and had but one port at her disposal — Gdynia. Now the Polish seaboard extends for over 300 miles along the Baltic shores and there are two new Polish ports, Gdańsk (Danzig) and Szeczecin — Świnoujście. Moreover, in addition to the Vistula, the Poles now have a second great navigable river, the Odra (Oder), linked by canal with the Upper Silesian coalfield.

The second gain is in new agricultural resources far superior to those lost in the east — pasture lands and potato-fields in Pomerania and Brandenburg and, above all, the rich loess soils of Silesia, two-thirds of which are arable and one-tenth grasslands. In 1937 Silesia produced the third largest potato crop in the German provinces; it also held the second place for wheat and sugar-beet, and third for barley. Though less livestock is bred here than in the north, quality is very good.

The third gain — and the most valuable — is that of the Silesian coalfield which with the lignite deposits to the east of the Nysa provides the bulk of the new Poland's solid fuel.

Finally, the fourth gain: Germany, in order to relieve congested and vulnerable areas in the West, established in Silesia a great number of new factories and installed much industrial equipment. In so far as these were not destroyed by the military operations of 1944—45 and not ceded in war reparations to Russia, they constitute a very important industrial Polish asset and include, notably, the four synthetic petrol plants at Police (Pölitz) near Szczecin, and at Dwory near Oświęcim (Auschwitz). The great natural resources of Silesia and its industries are now much more highly developed.

It is, then, possible to define the natural conditions of the new Poland's economy.

POLAND BECOMES A GREAT COAL POWER.

The essential fact is that Poland now enjoys two features indispensable in a great modern economy — coal and conditions favourable for agriculture.

Coal, and abundant deposits of lignite, have moved Poland to sixth position as a world solid fuel power (after the United States, the U.S.S.R., Great Britain, Germany and China). The bulk of the supply is in the Upper Silesian basin, now entirely within the Polish frontier, with the exception of the Czech Moravska-Ostrava area. The basin is held entirely by Poland, whereas after the First World War it was divided between Germany, Poland and Czechoslovakia, and then from 1939 to 1945 annexed by Germany. It must, of course, be borne in mind that the relative backwardness of Poland's economy is explained by the fact that through the whole of the nineteenth century, a period of industrial revolution and the greatest technical and economic progress and expansion in the rest of Europe, Poland was not independent but divided by occupying powers interested not in developing her resources but only in exploiting her. Poland's backwardness was not inherent but historically induced.

The advantages offered by the Upper Silesian basin are considerable. First, the reserves are larger even than those of the Ruhr (67,000 million tons as against 45,000 million tons). Secondly, the seams are thick, and according to their depths, constitute three deposits. To the west, a total of 127 seams have a workable thickness of about 560 feet. To the east 30 seams lie in tiers to a thickness of some 200 feet. The third advantage is that working is facilitated by the average depths of the deposit; the seams, indeed, comprise a sort of flattened basin surrounded by faults. The depth is almost everywhere less than 1,300 feet, and it is only in a few places that it reaches a maximum of over 3,000 feet. Finally, and this is a particularly important advantage, the Upper Silesia field yields all types of industrial coal: coking coal in the lower seams, and coking coal and cannel coal in the upper seams. Generally speaking, gas-coal, containing 40 to 50 per cent volatile matter and 10 per cent ash is commonest (71 per cent of the whole), but processes whereby different coals are mixed allow the production of oven-coke in apparently sufficient quantities. As long ago as 1943 Upper Silesia's coke output was nearly 7 million tons; today the field furnishes about nine-tenths of the country's entire coal production.

Poland has other coalfields, too: the annexation of Lower Silesia secured the collieries in the Walbrzych area of the Sudeten mountains. Mining there is carried on in less favourable conditions than in Upper Silesia (seams are very deep, tilted,

shallow and heavily faulted) but good coking coal is extracted. In 1943 Germany drew 5 million tons of coal and 1½ million tons of coke from this basin. The Walbrzych field yields today about a tenth of the total coal mined in Poland.

In addition to coal there is Tertiary lignite in the western part of the Polish plain. These deposits are easily worked by open-cast mining and yield a lignite with a calorific value only 50 per cent less than that of coal. The reserves are in the region of 10,000 million tons, and output suffices not only for local domestic needs but also for some industrial needs: for instance, those of the new thermo-electric stations at Konin from which current is sent to the recently erected industrial plants at Kujawy. Even peat is used in eastern Poland and is employed at electric power stations such as those of the Białystok area.

SHORTAGE OF SUBSOIL RESOURCES.

To begin with, Poland lost most of her oil and has kept only a small field of crude oil in the Jaslo, Krosno, Ustrzyki Dolne area. Natural gas, too, is tapped in the Jaslo and Krosno districts as well as in the south of the Silesian basin, and a pipeline takes the gas to Warsaw. But the loss in liquid fuel has been a severe one, for the richest fields, those of Borislav, have been ceded to the U.S.S.R.

There is iron ore in Poland but it is low grade with 30 per cent iron content and sometimes less, except in the small deposits in the Sudetes, where it reaches 45 to 50 per cent. Most of the ore comes from the Częstochowa region, but new deposits have been found at Łęczyca in central Poland, where the reserves are estimated at 300 million tons.

Only one non-ferrous metal occurs in any quantity — zinc, which is mined at Bytom in Upper Silesia, and in small workings at Olkusz and Chrzanów. Other non-ferrous metals are found only in insignificant amounts — lead in Silesia from mines near Bytom which formerly allowed the Poles to export very large quantities; and copper in Silesia, near Bolesławiec, as well as in the neighbourhood of Kielce and in the Sudeten mountains. There is nickel at Klodzko, chromium at Swidnica, arsenic at Klodzko and at Jelenia Góra, and uranium at Jelenia Góra. The amounts extracted are small, though the output (largely localised in or near Silesia) explains the existence of a non-ferrous metal industry on the coalfields.

There is only one saline resource of any importance: the salt extracted from the rock-salt mines at the foot of the Carpathians (near Wieliczka and Bochnia, where the deposits are almost exhausted) and also in the Kujawy and Bydgoszcz area, south of the Lower Vistula. The Poles are endeavouring

One of the new housing estates being erected at Gdynia and Gdánsk.

Gdańsk (Danzig), a Baltic port at the mouth of the River Vistula, which recently has gained fresh importance as one of the centres of the rapidly developing Polish chemicals industry.
POLISH CULTURAL INSTITUTE

The grain harvest on a State farm in the province of Olsztyn, in the Masurian lakes region. Young people come from the towns to help with the harvest. POLISH CULTURAL INSTITUTE

Poland has a large Catholic majority, whose fervour is shown by this photograph of the huge crowd at the consecration of the new cathedral of Katowice (Upper Silesia). PAUL POPPER, ATLAS-PHOTO

Kazimierz, a pleasant holiday resort in the country on the right bank of the Vistula, above Warsaw. POLISH INFORMATION BUREAU

Poznań, in western Poland: façade of the Town Hall (1550—1560). This town hall and the Wawel of Cracow are the best examples of Renaissance architecture in Poland. POLISH INFORMATION BUREAU

to make up their loss of potash by working a deposit of potash salt in the Kujawy area. In the Tarnobrzeg region, to the south of Little Poland, sulphur has been discovered and production has increased greatly of late. Phosphate deposits, too, have been discovered recently in the voivodships of Lublin and Kielce, in the neighbourhood of Kraśnik, Radom and Sieradz. The reserves would seem to amount to several hundred thousand tons, but the low phosphorus content (12 per cent) and the shallowness of the beds (roughly 12 to 16 inches) seems to be holding up output. With the exception of zinc, sulphur, salt and lime, which are produced in quantities exceeding the home demand, other Polish mineral resources are such that, although the country presents a fairly complete range, it must depend largely on imports of such raw materials as iron and entirely on foreign supplies of bauxite.

New trends in Polish economy

Very soon after the war, from 1945 onwards in fact, first the Polish National Liberation Committee and then the Warsaw government were controlled by the Polish Workers' Party. From 1948 onwards the government was entirely in the hands of the Polish United Workers' Party. It is, then, not surprising that the government revolutionised the economic and social structure of the country and followed Soviet example in nationalising industry and commerce and effecting agrarian reform.

AGRARIAN REFORMS. The main reason for these reforms was economic and social. The landlord class (of big and small holdings) had to make way for small farms which would flourish. According to the 1921 census, very small farms (less than 14 acres) made up 65 per cent of the holdings but occupied only 15 per cent of the total area of arable land. On the other hand, large landowners (more than about 130 acres) possessed only a tenth of the total number of estates but these covered nearly one half of the land.

The social structure of the country created a very numerous peasant class, poor and in debt, and a handful of big landowners with huge fortunes in estates. Agrarian reform was therefore undertaken in two phases: first came the creation of an agrarian democracy and then evolution toward co-operative farming.

The reform began with the decree of 6th September 1944 and was later supplemented by the decree of 6th September 1946 covering the 'regained territories of the West'. German properties were at this point expropriated without compensation. Large Polish-owned estates were partially expropriated, this time with compensation. In the old Polish lands, except in the Poznań and Bydgoszcz voivodships, where the upper limit

A model pig-rearing establishment on a collective farm in Poland.
POLISH CULTURAL INSTITUTE

was 250 acres, all properties of more than 130 acres and in the 'regained territories' all over about 260 acres were nationalised, although Church lands were excluded from this reform. The State proceeded to a redistribution of the land thus acquired (without making any lot larger than about 25 acres) to the owners of 'dwarf' holdings, to landless peasants, and to farm labourers. Owners of less than 14 acres thus received more than 30 per cent of the redistributed lands, landless peasants got 18 per cent, and farm labourers 47 per cent. The purchase terms were very liberal, with low prices and long repayment periods. The sums thus received by the State were made over to a 'Rural Fund' whose object was to provide agricultural equipment.

The reform was, then, far-reaching. Between 1944 and 1949 about fifteen million acres were distributed to the peasants. Over a million families benefited by the reform. Large estates disappeared and 87.5 per cent of the land in the country belonged to farmers owning about 52 acres as a maximum, but an area of 6,175,000 acres was still divided among medium-sized properties of 60 to 250 acres.

However, the view of the Polish government was that an agrarian democracy was but a step on the road to the collectivisation and nationalisation of the land. A trend in this direction was already perceptible when the great State agricultural enterprises were started, whose evolution recalls that of the *sovkhozes* in the U.S.S.R. These State enterprises (set up on lands that were in part fallow and in part confiscated from the big landlords) were divided into three groups. First were those specialising in cereals and industrial crops; then those producing seeds for sowing; and thirdly those devoted to stock-breeding. These establishments were to be models of rationalised agriculture and stock-farming. It was logical, then, that in these conditions the State farms should be scattered up and down the country — and especially in the 'regained territories of the West' because these latter comprised a higher percentage of land acquired by the State and, above all, because the large-scale transfer of new farmers to this region made training a necessity. These farms have not yet given the hoped for results.

The same tendency toward collectivisation and nationalisation has been strengthened since 1949 by setting-up 'State machine centres', the Polish version of the U.S.S.R. machine and tractor centres. But the most important event was the introduction of production co-operatives in 1949. It is true that the co-operative movement was not previously unknown in the Polish countryside since, before 1949, half the peasants were members of the 'Peasant's Mutual Aid'. The production co-operatives, however, constitute an attempt at collectivisation of the *kolkhoz* type, for to all intents and purposes members abandon the free disposal of their lands. However, the production co-operatives have made very slow headway. By the end of 1949 there were only 200 (with 6,100 members) farming about 102,500 acres. By the end of 1953 numbers had risen to 8,000 (with about 200,000 members) farming about 3,700,000 acres. However, it is mostly in the 'regained territories of the West', where redistribution of land has been very thorough, that the movement has developed fairly rapidly; production co-operatives have given only moderate results in the central part of the country.

AGRICULTURAL PROGRESS AND DIFFICULTIES. Natural conditions explain the development of farming of the continental temperate type, of forestry and of stock-breeding. The last is still only moderately important, though improving despite war losses.

Crops come first and fall into three classes: cereals, potatoes and sugar-beet. The two main crops that provide the basis of the nation's food are potatoes and rye. Wheat and oats fall a long way behind, followed by barley. Maize is a very unimportant crop. In addition to the main crops there is a recent small-scale development of industrial crops, flax and hemp, hops and some oil-producing crops (colza and linseed). Poland is rich in forests, which cover almost one quarter of the country's area. Most of the trees are conifers.

Stock-breeding is practised on a comparatively small scale, except for pigs, which numbered 11 million in 1959; flocks and herds are not yet up to their pre-war numbers. There is also the fishing industry: sea fishing in the Baltic, the North Sea and subpolar areas; lake fishing in northern Poland.

The relatively small amounts of certain products compel Poland to depend upon imports. There is not enough home-grown wheat to satisfy demand and rye-bread is still commoner than white. The number of cattle is also insufficient — partly the effect of war and partly the effect of the lack of foodstuffs. Industrial crops (except sugar-beet) are too recent in date to meet the demands of the processing industries. Generally, agricultural output has increased on pre-war figures by only one-third — that is, by a percentage much less than that of mounting industrial production.

Another weak point — and it concerns quality — seems widespread. The agricultural yield, despite its slight improvement over pre-war conditions, is still very low. Technically, Polish agriculture is very backward indeed. The amount of fertilizers employed per acre has, it is true, increased enormously since the war but quantities are still too small. Mechanisation, too, although five times what it was in 1949, is still poorly developed. The reason for the general situation is to be sought, probably, in the subdivision of Polish farms under agrarian reforms.

In view of these weaknesses the State has endeavoured to apply a number of remedies to agriculture. Attempts have been made to step up production of the four main cereal crops and of potatoes, to increase the number of cattle by developing forage-plant culture and, thirdly, to establish advice centres for the stock-breeders.

With a view to testing out the possibilities of certain new crops, agronomical research has been pushed forward vigorously. For instance *kenaf* (gumbo hemp) and *kanatnik* (flax dodder) are being developed to yield superior quality fibres. Virginia tobacco is in the initial stages of development in the west of Poland. Castor-oil plants (whose seed has been imported from China) are being grown experimentally. Attempts to acclimatise cotton are being made in the south. Still more out-of-the-way plants, such as *koksaghiz* and the Abyssinian cabbage (both yielding edible and industrial oil), are being tried out, and even rice has been grown. These last three crops, however, are still in the experimental stage.

Efforts are also being made to improve the technical side of agriculture which is largely out-of-date. Progress is being made in training agricultural technicians. Against 30 agricultural schools (with an average of 2,000 students) before the war, there are now 175 with 20,000 students. Special newspapers designed to convey information to the peasants are also distributed.

The Polish State has adopted a system for encouraging the peasants to grow new crops: one of contracts whereby the State agrees to take a fixed quantity of a given crop at prices favourable to the farmers. Such contracts are concluded with private farmers and with the production co-operatives. The agreements relate mostly to industrial crops such as sugar-beet, chicory, flax, hemp, and oil-producing plants.

We see, then, that the critical condition of Polish agriculture, which has been still more adversely affected during some recent years by irregularities of climate and especially by insufficient summer rainfall, claims much of the attention of the Polish leaders. They are attempting to improve a situation which contrasts strongly with the country's flourishing industry. An additional difficulty arises from the fact that urban industries every year attract large numbers of the more enterprising young people from the rural areas.

The port of Gdynia, which was created artificially on the Baltic. It is principally a port for long-distance traffic and contains the head offices of passenger lines as well as being a busy commercial port.
POLISH INFORMATION BUREAU

But the new policy of the government, less exacting and more sympathetic to the peasants, has already resulted in better yields and an agricultural output that is increasing.

NATIONALISATION. Before the Second World War, Polish industry was to a very large extent monopolised by foreign capitalists who had invested heavily in mines, steel works and textile mills. The proportion of Polish capital invested in the collieries did not amount to 25 per cent of the whole, while the German share was as much as 37 per cent (since most of the mines in Polish Silesia remained under German control or fell under it once more), and French capital made up 19 per cent of the investments and controlled, for instance, Dąbrowa. The amount of British and American capital was 11 per cent of the whole.

Nationalisation was not only a politico-social reaction against industrial capitalism in general, but a nationalist reaction against foreign capitalism. There were two other reasons for nationalisation. Firstly, the State had to take over a number of works whose owners had disappeared during the war. It was also authorised to confiscate German enterprises, and did so in 1945. The Polish State had become inevitably the largest employer of industrial labour in the country.

Secondly, in the new Poland, industry was unevenly distributed. Is was too concentrated in a few places, while the over-populated country districts of the centre and south were far away from the industrial development areas. To avoid over-crowding in industrial areas and unemployment in the country-side, a better distribution of industrial plant was necessary.

Add to this political pressure, and we have the explanation for the nationalisation law of 1946, relating to commerce and industry. All enterprises employing more than fifty workmen were declared nationalised without further ado. However, it was decreed that new enterprises might be set up and might employ more than fifty workers without such concerns being automatically nationalised. Within a year, 70 per cent of Polish industry and commerce was entirely controlled by the State. This percentage has risen a good deal since and the pattern of industry and commerce is modelled on that of the U.S.S.R., comprising only a small, nominally free handicraft sector, existing side by side with large and medium-sized industries that are completely State-controlled.

PLANNING AND THE SIX YEAR PLAN. Poland's state of disorganisation at the end of the war was such that a number of extremely urgent measures had to be taken for the country's reconstruction. Therefore two successive plans were adopted. First there was the Three Year Plan (covering the period from 1947—49). This was first and foremost a programme of economic reconstruction. Then came the Six Year Plan (for the period 1950—55), which was much more like the Soviet plans — especially in the place accorded to industrial development. The economic policy represented in the Six Year Plan was a much more far-reaching one than that of the Three Year Plan, which was entirely devoted to the immediately urgent task of reconstruction. By 1950 the task was not one of reconstruction but of ending the chronic pre-war inferiority of Polish industry, and the main aim of the Polish Six Year Plan was the large-scale industrialisation of the country. The rôle of agriculture was to ensure the necessary food supply.

This rapid industrial development presents two main features: the marked growth of basic industries (power, iron and steel) and a new and better-balanced distribution of industrial enterprises within the present-day territory of Poland. As part of this reorganisation two new groups of equipment industries have been introduced into Poland — engineering (machine tools and motor-cars) and chemical industries (especially those producing nitrogenous fertilizers and superphosphates). Both are centred mainly in two great new production units, the first in Silesia and the second near Poznań. It must be admitted that the extent of this industrial effort is astonishing, for 350 plants have been built and an additional 300,000 workmen employed.

As the Plan called for a more balanced distribution of industry, it sought to industrialise the north and east of the country. As a result, Warsaw is becoming a great metallurgical and textile centre, and the eastern districts, Białystok and Lublin, which had no industry at all in 1949, have numerous new factories.

For implementing the agricultural programme, four lines of approach have been adopted: first, mechanisation (facilitated by the development of the new tractor works); second, electrification of many rural centres; third, large-scale use of fertilizers (made possible by the growth of the chemical industries); and, lastly, the development of production co-operatives 'on the basis of free participation', which according to the Plan 'represent superior types of farming'.

From the year 1953 a new tendency was noticeable which aimed at modifying or at least at redirecting economic policy. The weak points in the policy hitherto pursued were denounced. Agriculture had remained too backward and the disparity between its development and that of industry had become so serious that it was hampering progress of the national economy as a whole. The increased output of consumer goods, considerable as it was, did not satisfy the increasing needs of the working population, whose standard of living is still lower than that of most European countries.

The general improvement of Polish agriculture (increases in harvest yields and in stock-breeding produce) constituted the most immediate aim and the most urgent problem from 1953 onwards. To effect such improvement much was done to increase the number of production co-operatives and to secure a higher yield on the State farms. At the same time — and here we have a feature that is symptomatic — an appeal was made to the peasants' self-interest. The obligatory deliveries in kind made to the State were maintained at their former level or decreased; some were abolished altogether. In the production co-operatives the principle was solemnly laid down that 'the peasants must have a material interest in increasing the productivity of the co-operatives'.

A similar trend can be noted in industry. Of course, there could be no question of neglecting heavy industry, but two innovations in the 1954 and 1955 industrial planning programmes are particularly interesting. While, in 1950, agriculture occupied a minor place in planning and was encouraged mainly as a source of raw materials for industry, a policy almost diametrically opposite was henceforth to be noted. Industry had to be organised in order to improve agricultural output and, to this end, production first of farm machinery and then of chemical fertilizers had to be stepped up. And there was another innovation. A very real improvement was effected in the domain of consumer goods (textiles, wireless sets, bicycles, etc.) which up to then had been badly neglected. The disparity between the output of capital goods and that of consumer goods is great. Increased output of the latter in the post-war years lags far behind that of capital goods.

These, then, are the factors that profoundly transformed the Polish economic structure which, broadly speaking, has switched from an agricultural to an industrial one.

The rural population has decreased and is calculated at a maximum 1,200,000 (probably a low estimate) compared with 5 to 8 million before the war; the former over-population of the country districts is therefore no longer so marked.

Taking into account the present tendencies of the Polish economy — now weighted in favour of industry — we see that Poland's part in world industry is a considerable one. She stands sixth among coal-producing countries and, in view of her large output of steel, electricity and cement, must be accounted a great industrial Power.

INDUSTRIALISATION. To what extent have the main economic aims of the Plan been carried out? The two sources of power for industry have been considerably developed. Polish economy, by the immense extent of its resources in coal, recalls the economies of Britain or Germany, and it is logical that Poland should become a highly industrialised land. This fact indicates that an important stage has been reached in the evolution of central Europe. However, Poland today is faced with technical difficulties caused by disparity between the output of coal (which is nevertheless great) and the rapid progress of industry. From 1949 to 1954 industrial production increased by 61 per cent but coal output rose only 24 per cent. While this situation prevails, Poland is confronted with two alternatives — reducing coal exports (resulting in the reduction of various imports covered by the coal exports) or increasing coal output. The problem inherent in the second alternative is to recruit new miners. The latest figures show an increase in coal production.

Production of electricity increases rapidly but hydro-electricity still awaits large-scale development. A few stations exist in the Sudeten mountains and in the lakes region. Some plants destroyed during the war have been reconstructed, such as the Dychów dam on the Bobr. The Czchow barrage plant was completed after the war, and others have been built on the Upper Vistula and on the Pilica. Other projects are under way. But the main stand-by is still coal. The greatest quantities of electricity have been generated from Silesian coal, but both lignite and peat are also used. In Upper Silesia, for instance, (and it is there that most of the electrical developments under the Six Year Plan have been made) there are Jaworzno I, Jaworzno II and Miechowice, the last-named consuming the waste-products of the collieries. Following the German example, the Poles are making more and more use of lignite for thermo-electricity. Stations have been built or are under construction on the lignite basin of the river Nysa as well as in the new industrial region of Kujawy.

Iron and steel manufacture is an old Polish industry which before the war was concentrated mostly in the Silesian basin (output of steel 1½ million tons in 1938). The increase in production in only a few years has been due to three different kinds of enterprise. First, existing plants have been rebuilt, enlarged or modernised, and their output much increased. Thus, many plants in Upper Silesia (such as the Kosciuszko at Chorzów) have been enlarged. Secondly, a number of

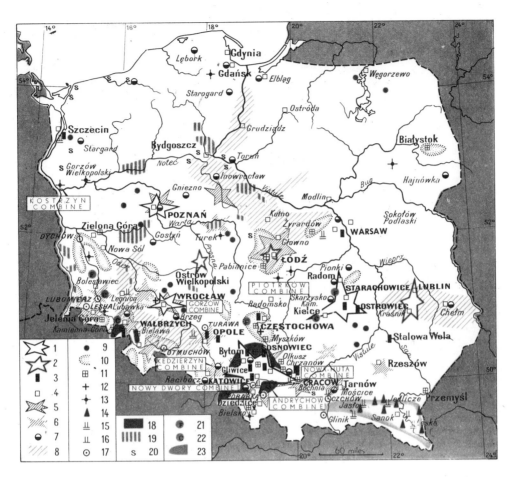

MAP OF POLAND, SHOWING MINERAL RESOURCES AND THE PRINCIPAL INDUSTRIES. *1. Metallurgical centres in existence or being developed; 2. New projects (metallurgy); 3. Blast furnaces; 4. Mechanical construction; 5. Centres for the chemical industry in existence or being developed; 6. New projects (chemical industry); 7. Chemical industry; 8. Region of scattered sugar refineries; 9. Sugar refining; 10. Region of scattered textile industry; 11. Centre for textile industry; 12. Man-made textile industry; 13. New projects (textiles); 14. Oil well; 15. Oil refinery; 16. Oil refinery planned or being built; 17. Hydro-electric stations; 18. Coalfields; 19. Lignite deposits; 20. Salt extraction; 21. Iron mines; 22. Copper; 23. Oil-bearing areas.*

new plants have been erected. At Częstochowa, the old Rakow works have been replaced by the Bierut iron and steel group. Thirdly, the large V.I. Lenin works began production in 1951 and have been working to capacity since 1954 (at Nowa-Huta near Cracow). A third works, more important because it produces high-grade steels, has also been set up at Bielany-Młociny near Warsaw. It consists of a steelworks, a forge, a foundry and rolling-mills — and an industrial suburb of 120,000 inhabitants.

We have already noted the aim to increase production of such consumer goods as textiles, which in fact occupy a high place among traditional Polish manufactures. Łódź was already a notable cotton-spinning town in the nineteenth century. Wool, flax and hemp were treated in smaller industrial centres at Częstochowa, Poznań, Warsaw, Lublin and Białystok. Marked progress has been made, notably in the textile *kombinat* at Piotrków Trybunalski and in that at Andrychów — the former employs several thousand workers. Compared with the situation before the war, progress has been striking. In only fifteen years cottons have shown an increase of 173 per cent, woollens 177 per cent, and silks 290 per cent.

The production of cotton goods is still necessarily concentrated round Łódź (three-quarters of the output), while a secondary group of cotton-mills exists in the Sudetes (Bielawa, Kamienna Góra) and at Wrocław. The woollen factories are more dispersed — at Łódź, Bielsko-Biała, Zielona Góra and Białystok. Poland also produces millions of yards of silk goods, while hemp and flax manufactures are still important, especially at Wrocław and at new factories in the north-east of the country, where the raw materials are grown. In addition to these traditional manufactures, Poland now has works for spinning and weaving synthetic fibres — at Gorzów, Jelenia Góra, Tomaszów Mazowiecki, Chodaków, Wrocław and Żydowce.

Another old-established industry is food production — mostly sugar-refineries, breweries, and canneries. Poland has become the world's fifth producer of beet-sugar. The refineries are naturally sited in the fertile regions of the west where the beets are grown — Lower Silesia, the Poznań district, and the middle Vistula plain, especially the Kujawy area.

Cement, glass and china works existed long before the war and have continued to prosper. The cement industry is particularly flourishing, and in addition to the old works (often enlarged) situated in Silesia and Little Poland, new plants have been set up, such as those in the Kielce region (at Wierzbica), the Rejowiec II in the Lublin voivodship and the Odra works.

NEW INDUSTRIES. The development of metallurgical manufactures has been particularly marked if we compare their very slight importance before the war (1938) with the results now obtained. In 1938 the output of machines was just

The Lenin steel foundry at Nowa-Huta, a large metallurgical centre near Cracow. POLISH INFORMATION BUREAU

beginning and only 1,715 tons of machine-tools were made; Poland manufactured no tractors and no electrically driven machines; automobiles were only assembled from component parts supplied by Fiat and Chevrolet.

The creation of machine and machine-tool industries was considered essential for the new Poland. She must produce her own machines for the industrialisation and agricultural mechanisation programme, and must endeavour to export to under-developed countries such as the Danubian lands and China. So almost from scratch a machine-tool industry developed whose 1953 output was eleven-and-a-half times greater than that of 1938. Equipment of high quality has since maintained this upward trend. The 1959 figure for output of metal-working machine-tools is 36,250 tons. Two examples: in the Racibórz works, a shop has been set up that turns out heavy machine-tools of a kind not made at all in Poland before the war; at Pruszków, near Warsaw, a large machine-tool plant has been erected.

The motor-car and tractor industry is also a new one. The output figures are: 1937, nil; 1949, nil; 1955, 4,015; 1958, 11,507; 1959, 14,201. Manufacture of trucks and lorries has also increased — in 1938 there were only 6,843 such vehicles in all the country. The old Starachowice works have been modernised and enlarged for the manufacture of trucks. The largest automobile plant in Poland — at Lublin — even has furnaces and a foundry. The two Starachowice works are equipped to turn out 25,000 lorries a year. The agricultural machinery industry has also made great strides, mainly owing to the Staroleka works near Poznań, which turns out mostly harvester-threshers and reaper-binders, and the two tractor factories, the Ursus near Warsaw and the Nowy Ursus. The output of tractors had risen from 1,000 in 1938 to 6,900 by 1953. The figures are significant.

Existing shipyards were enlarged and modernised. Not only is their output much greater than before the war, but they can now build ships of considerable tonnage. The reconstruction of the Wrocław railway-carriage works brought considerable progress in the manufacture of rolling-stock. Total output of various kinds of rolling-stock is some thirty times as great as it was before the war.

Pre-1937, the electro-technical industry was represented by an output of some objects of common use (lamps, telephone material, cables). Heavy electro-technical material (turbines, generators, transformers) was imported. Now turbines and all sorts of material for electrical equipment are manufactured in Poland. Worthy of mention are the Elblag, Poznań, Wrocław works, those of the Katowice region, and those at Tarnów and Toruń which produce large generators.

Another striking new feature is the appearance and development of a chemical industry which looks like becoming, after metallurgy, the most important of Polish industries. The creation of a special Ministry of Chemical Industry in December 1950 was proof of official determination to fill a gap in the national economy. Compared with the figures for 1938, the total output of chemical products had risen by 400 per cent fifteen years later. Indeed, in 1938 what little chemical industry there was turned out only nitrogenous compounds (at Chorzów and Tarnów) and treated gas from the coke-ovens. Now, Poland's coal, lignite, sulphur, rock salt, gypsum and anhydrite are chemical raw materials of first-rate importance. She also benefited from Germany's involuntary contribution in the shape of some synthetic rubber and petrol plant in Silesia, and therefore decided to set up a heavy chemical industry turning out important basic products, and a light chemical industry. The latter is still in its early stages but the results obtained are by no means negligible. The output of artificial fibres and plastics is rising steadily.

Among the basic chemical industries those producing sulphuric acid, soda and fertilizers have made marked progress. Sulphuric acid manufacture is something fairly new for Poland and is carried on in recently constructed works such as those of Wizów in Lower Silesia (utilising anhydrite) and those of Busk, Gdańsk and Szczecin. Soda is produced at three large works: Matwy, near Inowrocław, Janikowo on the Kujawy salt deposits, and Boreck Falecki near Cracow. Both nitrogenous and phosphatic fertilizers are produced. Much of the fertilizer comes from the Nowy Dwory works near Oswięcim and those of Kędzierzyn as well as from the recently enlarged works at Tarnów and Chorzów.

The light chemical industries also show a similar tendency to make progress, notably in the output of dyestuffs (at Brzeg Dolny), plastic materials and various synthetic products. The output of plastics increased twentyfold from 1949 to 1953, that of synthetic rubber fourfold, and that of varnish sixfold in the same four years. This shows once more that important results have been obtained in the space of a few years. Poland now turns out a synthetic fabric comparable with nylon — steelon. An entirely new photographic products industry has been created, and another for pharmaceutical products (including antibiotics) at Tarchomin near Warsaw. Synthetic petrol is prepared at plants in Koźle and Oswięcim. Nothing indicates more clearly the growing importance of the chemical industry in Poland than the creation of several great chemical combines such as that of Nowy Dwory, near Oswięcim, which specialises in numerous synthetic chemical products: synthetic petrol, plastics, methanol, acetic acid, and their derivatives. There is also a new chemical combine in Kujawy.

There are two other new industries. First, that of non-ferrous metals. Before the war the territories making up present-day Poland produced only zinc and lead, but now a copper metallurgy (including the production of electrolytic copper) has been created with works at Bolesław near Olkusz, at Chrzanów and Skawina. Similarly, an aluminium industry has been created out of nothing and is supplied with imported Hungarian bauxite.

The second new industry is that of wood and wood products. Before the war there were sawmills but no wood-processing plant. Now there are factories turning out plywood, furniture and veneers. The output of paper has doubled. Poland now has a viscose plant too (at Jelenia Góra), and cellulose works (especially at Gorzów, Kostrzyn and Włocławek).

REDISTRIBUTION OF INDUSTRIAL AREAS. The old distribution of industry in Poland presented two features: the first was its concentration into four regions — Upper Silesia, the Lódź district, the Warsaw area and the 'central industrial region' (Rzeszów-Sandomierz) which was being organised in 1939. It must be emphasised that Silesia had 36 per cent of the total industrial labour-force, whereas the voivodship of Warsaw-City and that of Białystok had only 2 per cent each. The second feature was the specialisation of industrial centres in one given type of industry, for example Lódź in textiles, Upper Silesia in metallurgy.

This geographical lack of balance had grave consequences for the country's economy. Many regions, without industry and subsisting only on a poor agriculture, had too large a rural population with a low standard of living. On the other hand, it was desirable that industries should be transferred to the source of raw material supply or to the main centres of consumption.

Therefore new industrial areas were created. The Wrocław region and those bordering on the Sudeten mountains (which were formerly but indifferently industrialised) became areas of large-scale and diversified production, both at Wrocław itself and at Brzeg Gorny and Brzeg Dolny. Industrialisation (cement works at Opole and chemical industry at Kędzierzyn) is spreading to Opole in the south-east and, in the west, Wałbrzych, Dzierźoniów, Jelenia Góra and Bielawa in the Sudeten mountains. In the centre and east of Poland new industrial areas have appeared on the rural plains. Thus, west-north-west of Warsaw there is the area of Kujawy near the lignite, potash and salt workings; to the south of Warsaw the Kielce area — in the Swietokrzyskie mountains which are rich in metals. The industrial region of Lublin is also expanding, not only with new plant treating agricultural products for the foodstuffs industry, but also with the large-scale automobile and other machine industries. Industrialisation has pushed as far as Krasnik to the south of Lublin. In north-east Poland, Białystok has become the centre of a small industrial zone. Again, two industrial areas are growing up near the Baltic, Gdańsk-Gdynia and Szczecin — with shipyards and even iron and steel works. Between these two areas in the Noteć basin, new industrial enterprises founded on wood processing (cellulose, paper, man-made fibres) are growing up.

COMMUNICATIONS AND TRANSPORT. Distribution of goods within the country and foreign trade depend almost entirely on the railways, but these are most unsatisfactorily planned. The western areas (the former German territories) are best served and contain half the total mileage although they cover only one-third of the total area. Even new lines laid in the central and eastern districts of the country in accordance with the Six Year Plan (notably, the new Warsaw-Silesia railway) make the mileage only one-third of that in the west. The length of electrified line is wholly inadequate.

Again, the waterways play much too small a part in transport — they take only about 1.5 per cent of the freight that goes by rail. Indeed, out of the 3,000 miles of rivers and canals which could be utilised, only 1,280 miles are used for navigation, and of these only 656 miles can be regarded as economically important: the Odra, linked to the Silesian basin by the Gliwice canal, and the lower Vistula for about 125 miles — and even these two waterways are often accessible only to barges of 200 tons and less. The lower reaches of the Odra, the Gliwice canal, part of the Noteć and the Bydkoski canal are indeed the only

A shepherd and his flock in the Polish Tatry.

waterways that can take vessels of more than 400 tons. This situation hampers the development of the country, and a programme of improvement has been drawn up that will require large-scale engineering works for its completion. According to the plan, a whole circuit of navigable waterways would be constructed, consisting of the Odra-Warta-Noteć Canal, the Gliwice-Vistula Canal and the Odra-Vistula network, to link up the most important of the industrial centres all over the country. This circuit would have two outlets to the sea, through the lower reaches of the Odra and Vistula. The close and frequent communications with the U.S.S.R. no doubt constitute a reason for the decision to undertake first the regulation of the Bug between Modlin and Brzesc so that it can take barges of up to 250 tons.

CHANGES IN FOREIGN TRADE. Poland's foreign trade, too, has been subjected to profound modification. Before the war it had almost a 'colonial' character: Poland exported the raw materials of industry (coal, wood, textiles) and raw or semi-processed agricultural products; the current of trade flowed mostly towards the Western countries. Two factors have contributed to the increase in the volume of Polish trade. First, the recent economic changes have released large exportable surpluses of coal and industrial products; on the other hand, they have created new demands for imported foodstuffs because of the crisis in agriculture, and for ores, industrial raw materials and equipment needed in the expansion of Polish industries.

Secondly, Poland today enjoys commercial facilities far better than those before the war, since in addition to the port of Gdynia (created between the two World Wars) there are now the two ports of Szczecin and Gdańsk. Szczecin, on the Odra, has a huge harbour which quite simple engineering operations could deepen to about 30 feet and so provide useful communication with the industrial region of Upper Silesia. The port, in fact, handles about three million tons of shipping a year. Gdańsk, on a mouth of the Vistula, is a well-equipped port but needs dredging — the present depth is under 20 feet. The port consists of old docks round the island of Holm (and near the old town of Gdańsk) and of a new port near the river mouth, on the gulf of Gdańsk. Gdynia-Gdańsk-Sopot are now run by a single port authority that distributes shipping between the three; between them, they handle a high proportion of trade. Gdynia is especially a port for ocean shipping and passenger lines, but also handles various sorts of freight. Gdańsk is more a port for European coastal shipping and specialises in cargoes of coal and in bulk goods.

Other considerations have directed Polish trade towards the U.S.S.R. The 'Battle Act' and the refusal by the Import-Export Bank to extend credits to Poland led the Poles to turn to the U.S.S.R. for the industrial equipment material necessary for the reconstruction plan and then for the industrialisation plan.

Polish trade has assumed the proportions of that of a great modern State. Available statistics are often no more than percentages, but it is clear that while Poland still remains a great European coal exporter — the leading one in fact, taking precedence over Western Germany — she also exports electrical products, zinc, glass, china, wood and wooden articles. The significant new feature is the appearance of Polish goods in the great import markets for metallurgical products, machines and machine-tools, wagons and locomotives. Such metallurgical equipment amounted to no more than 3 per cent of total Polish sales in 1949; four years later it had risen to 12 per cent.

Imports, too, have changed their character. Poland still buys foodstuffs and certain industrial equipment (such as the plant for the Nowa Huta and the Silesian Boleslaw, Bierut and Kosciuszko iron and steel works, and for the automobile factories at Warsaw and Lublin), but the two essential changes are the rapid increase in the import of raw materials (related to industrial development) and an increase in the purchase of consumer goods. The simultaneous increase in imports and exports explains, then, the growth in volume and in value of Poland's trade.

Another new feature, and one that is easy to understand, is the now prevailing direction of Polish foreign trade. The U.S.S.R. has become Poland's chief commercial partner. The succession of agreements concluded between the two States shows well enough the continued increase in importance of the U.S.S.R. in the Polish market.

Still, Polish foreign trade is too active to be confined solely within the limits of bilateral Polono-Soviet relations. Commercial relations have been developed with Czechoslovakia, Rumania, Hungary, Bulgaria and East Germany. Trade with People's China began in 1950 and was developed by an agreement in January 1951 and by later trade treaties. Poland is trying also to increase her commerce with other countries, Great Britain, France, the Scandinavian countries, Argentina, India, Pakistan and Egypt among them.

In becoming industrialised, Poland has become more dependent than before on foreign trade, by which she may export the surplus of her industrial output and import the indispensable raw materials in increasing quantities. What Poland needs is foreign commercial relations on an ever-larger scale and without any political restrictions.

Jean CHARDONNET

A cattle market in Săleine in the Tara Motilor, a district of gentle hills and wide, flat valleys. RUMANIAN LEGATION

RUMANIA

THE word 'Rumania' did not appear on the political map of Europe until the end of the nineteenth century. However, Rumania constitutes a geographical entity that is remarkably original and attractive, though its destiny was for long an adverse one. To appreciate this we have only to consider Rumania's position on what are, really, the confines of Europe. The country adjoins the vast and monotonous Russian steppes, and the winding, wooded mountain ranges of the over-partitioned Balkan peninsula. In Rumania two famous highways meet: that of the Danube valley and that of the Polono-Moldavian corridor running from the Baltic to the Black Sea. Rumania is a small Latin state surrounded by Slavs and set on the shifting frontiers of Orthodoxy, Catholicism, Protestantism and even Islam. The country was, in fact, in former times torn between the Russian, Turkish and Austro-Hungarian empires. Rumania is a crossroad of rival routes and influences, a fruitful and attractive land, an open glacis of wide plains surrounding a mountain fastness. For centuries, the country was prey to foreign cupidity and to innumerable invasions.

THE MAIN FACTS IN RUMANIAN HISTORY. Dacia, a turbulent land of proud people, was conquered by the Emperor Trajan in two hard-fought campaigns (A.D. 101 and 105). This was the core of what was later to become Rumania. The heartland of Dacia was Transylvania, but it spread out beyond the mountains (like modern Rumania) and was well protected on the east by a succession of *valla*. During a hundred and fifty years of Roman occupation, Dacia adopted the Latin language and civilisation while its people exploited the land's considerable natural resources (gold, salt, wood).

In A.D. 270 the Emperor Aurelian withdrew his legions to the south of the Danube, but it is unlikely that the whole Dacian population followed them. For seven centuries Dacia was the victim of innumerable invaders and rival foreign princes. It was the Magyars (who arrived in Pannonia in the ninth century and then penetrated into Transylvania) and the German settlers (whom the Hungarians invited in) who fixed a political frontier on the Carpathians — one that was in no way justified. Old Dacia, henceforth cut into two, developed under the dual influence of the West and of the Byzantine East, the latter being superseded later by the Moslem East. The effect was sometimes beneficial, sometimes disastrous. However, the almost legendary memory of Dacian-Rumanian unity survived, and under Michael the Brave (1593—1601) it was almost reconstituted. Then came another setback: the Danubian and Carpathian lands fell into the hands of the Turks and were subjected to the most ruinous oppression, while the princes' courts maintained a brilliant Neo-Greek culture. The weakness of the Ottoman Empire encouraged the greed of Austria and Russia, and there followed annexations (Oltenia in 1712 and Bessarabia in 1812), new colonisations, and policies of assimilation. Only the principalities of Moldavia and Wallachia remained under Turkish suzerainty.

However, among the other Rumanians, who were reduced to a condition of near slavery, there appeared symptoms of a national awakening as early as the seventeenth century. On several occasions the Hungarians, the Russians and the Poles sought to turn these symptoms to their advantage, but the mutual hostility of their peoples was the best guarantee for Rumanian survival. It was not until 1856, however, that the independence of Wallachia and Moldavia was recognised.

Then, quickly, the two provinces chose a single ruler (Alexander Cuza) and then a king (Charles of Hohenzollern). In 1878 the Rumanians, with some reluctance, exchanged the Dobrogea for the southern part of Bessarabia. However, after their costly participation in the First World War, they recovered almost all the Dacian heartland; the population was 15 to 16 million (67 per cent Rumanian) in a country with an area of 113,850 square miles.

With twenty years of zealous effort, the Rumanians endeavoured to make up — not without some failures — for the time lost under the foreign yoke. The difficult task was by no means completed when the country was involved in the Second World War — first against the U.S.S.R. and then against Nazi Germany. The result was invasions, Russian occupation, widespread ruin, thousands of dead and, lastly, a harsh peace treaty in which the country was reduced to 91,671 square miles with some 16 million inhabitants. When Rumania became a People's Republic, the Constitution was modelled on that of the U.S.S.R.

RELICS OF THE PAST. It is perhaps surprising that the Rumanian people has survived so many trials and tribulations. The strong old traditions among a mainly peasant population deeply attached to the soil of their ancestors have been the major factor in ensuring survival.

Rumania has kept many vestiges of her past. The language remains very close to Latin despite a number of foreign elements. There are customs which undoubtedly pre-date the Romanisation of Dacia. Then there is the national folk art, remarkable for a harmony and delicacy of colouring, and decorative motifs

The Suharcelul (6,401 feet) in the Bistrita mountains. Its chalky block stands out like ruins in this heavily forested region, Vatra Dornei, well known as a pass through the Carpathians of Moldavia.
RUMANIAN INFORMATION BUREAU

that are mainly geometric and floral. The poetry, songs and popular dances reflect the alternation of suffering and mourning with joy and hope.

Archaeological remains attract the visitor's attention less than the Transylvanian castles perched on rocky spurs, and the Carpathian churches and monasteries whose Byzantine and Oriental art is touched with Western influences. Yet there is no servile imitation, for all is merged into something specifically Rumanian.

FROM MOUNTAIN TO PLAIN. These words seem to sum up the history of the peopling of the Rumanian lands. During the nineteenth century the peasants were still 'going down' into the Wallachian or Pannonian steppes. By then most of the best areas were already occupied — the forest ridges of the *codru* from Oltenia to Deliorman (Bulgaria), of Vlasia and Motistea in Muntenia, of the Moldavian *codru*, trade routes and tracks for migrating flocks and herds, damp valleys that cut into the bare expanses of the steppe.

The marked ethnical and religious unity of the Rumanians appears to be closely related to the mountain refuge where the purest and oldest of their peoples are found. From the eleventh to the nineteenth centuries a number of foreign settlers were planted officially and with economic, fiscal, military or political aims on this Rumanian foundation. These settlements, however, did not modify the numerical predominance of the compactly established Rumanian people. In 1960, 86 per cent of the country's 18 million inhabitants were Rumanian. With the exception of the Magyar-Szekeler and German colonies in the heart of Transylvania, it would seem to be only on the edges of the Rumanian bloc (both within and beyond the political frontiers) that non-Rumanians live side by side with Rumanians. After 1919, among the non-Rumanians only the Hungarians, the Germans and the Jews presented problems for the new and enlarged Rumanian State. In the frontier areas experiments in colonisation and settlement were carried out by the government to increase the number of Rumanians in these regions and to relieve some of the over-populated areas with poor soil.

WHO OWNS THE LAND? Until 1919 survival of ancient customs made Rumania one of those European countries where large estates predominated. These were formed between the sixteenth and the eighteenth centuries, and the land-owners jealously maintained their privileges — and some abuses. It was not until 1864 that serfdom was abolished, and then a very modest measure of agrarian reform showed that some of the more liberal-minded boyars (privileged classes) were concerned with improving the peasants' lot. But the laws enacted between 1866 and 1908 (after the peasant uprisings in 1907) did not give very satisfactory results. Five per cent of the land-owners held 60 per cent of the properties over 25 acres, while 78 per cent had less than 12½ acres each. In 1914 it was proposed to modify the Constitution to effect another agrarian reform; this was, in fact, made inevitable by the First World War. Expropriations were prescribed by Orders in Council in an attempt to deal with the various land-owning systems prevailing in the different regions of the newly united State. By 1921 large estates had been reduced from 47 to 8 per cent of the arable land. Despite great practical and legal difficulties, abuses and errors, 14½ million acres were distributed among nearly 1½ million families. Rumania by this time had taken its place among the European countries where smallholdings predominated. Seventy-five per cent of the owners had less than 12½ acres and 17 per cent had from 12½ to 25 acres. In 1927 these figures were respectively 84 per cent and 11 per cent.

These were the first results, but by 1935 612,000 men with justified claims were still clamouring for land; in twenty years new families had grown up whose demands had to be satisfied.

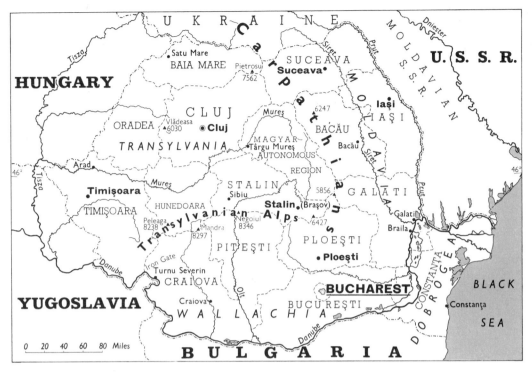

RUMANIA

Also, the peasants' holdings (too small in any case to support large families) had been further diminished by subdivision among several heirs. There was, in addition, the serious problem of rural debts to add to the tension. Even radical measures (reduction of debts by as much as 75 per cent) were ineffective, and a new agrarian reform had to be envisaged. A law was enacted authorising the sale of land up to a maximum of about 125 acres with the result that a period of excessive subdivision was followed by a certain amount of reconstitution into larger units, though this did not always favour the old boyars. At the same time other measures were adopted to increase industrialisation and so absorb surplus rural manpower.

Since 1945 the agrarian problem has taken on a different look. In March 1945, almost 3 million acres and their livestock were taken without compensation from 143,219 owners. Two-fifths of this land was to be distributed to the State, the rest to 796,129 peasants. In 1948 the number of farms belonging to 'free peasants' was still estimated at just over 3 million, of which 72 per cent were of less than 12½ acres and split into 23 million different 'parcels'. However, the campaign against the *chiaburi*, the Rumanian *kulaks*, had begun: they were accused of being too rich and of having too much power. Through the exercise of persuasion — or force — a new development was promoted. On the one hand, 360 State model-farms were granted about 3 million acres, over half of which consisted of arable land. In addition, 220 centres for the loan of agricultural equipment and tractors were established. Collective farms of the Soviet *kolkhoz* type increased from 56 to 2,045 during the five-year period from 1949—54. However, in view of the peasants' reluctance to join these *kolkhozes*, there were intensive propaganda campaigns during 1951 and 1952 in favour of 'permanent agricultural associations', in which the work was to be performed in common, though the peasants would still retain absolute ownership of their land, livestock and equipment. In 1951 such associations numbered 351 and covered 617,750 acres. Three years later the number had risen to 2,344 but the total area farmed was no more than 667,170 acres, since some of the land had gone to the *kolkhozes* or had been taken back into private ownership.

It is often difficult to interpret the official figures; from them it might be inferred that the socialised sector of Rumanian agriculture had shrunk. In point of fact, collectivisation of the land met with so much resistance that the process had to be slowed down — no doubt only for a time. The new agrarian policy could not be carried out among peasants traditionally and by temperament individualists — unless they were prepared to co-operate. A fairly long period of experiment and of adaptation was required, and a number of favourable climatic and economic factors essential. The obstacles have not been all overcome; in 1954 only 22 per cent of the arable land had been socialised and in 1955 only 26.5 per cent. The fact is that small individual farms still predominate in Rumania and provide three-quarters of the country's cereal output.

GROWING PAINS. The treaties of 1919 left Rumania with particularly difficult problems to solve. The country was suddenly doubled in size and population. It was still suffering from the effects of the war against Germany, from the Russian defection, and from the harsh Treaty of Bucharest. Among these problems some of the most pressing were those relating to the assimilation (in a newly formed unity) of provinces which differed from each other in geographical, ethnical, social, economic, administrative, religious and cultural conditions. What was needed was a period of slow, patient and prudent development, but this was hardly possible at home or abroad during the years between the two World Wars. However, much progress was made in many directions, and it is hardly fair to minimise the progress of this period in order to magnify the achievements of recent years. Before 1939 Rumania still seemed a land of contrasts, where East and West were superposed rather than amalgamated and where many traces of the past existed side by side with feverish 'modern' activity. Modernism, it is true, was more marked in institutions than in ways of life. Still, from year to year progress was made in reconciling the two. When the Second World War broke out Rumania was suffering from many growing pains. Isolated on the edge of a seething Europe, she had to try to preserve a balance between two Powers each intent upon reducing her to the status of a satellite. Then, after 1945, the country had to adapt herself to the new political, social, cultural and economic conditions imposed upon her. So it is easy to realise the difficulties Rumania has to face. Although Rumanian recovery is still a controversial subject, there can be no doubt about her rapid economic progress. Admittedly she is a weak power dragged along by the U.S.S.R., but she still retains her identity as a State and nation, for nature provided her with a perfect geographical setting, and a compact population within it.

Rumania, a Carpathian land

Rumania might equally well be called Carpathia, since the country owes its origin to the Carpathians and has been able to survive only because of them. The Carpathians are a mountain mass stretching 250 miles north to south and 380 miles east to west. This curved range, pushed towards the east, the north-east and the south-east during the ultimate phases of the Alpine uplift, includes the Eastern Carpathians (Transylvanian Alps to the south and Moldavian Carpathians to the north) and the Western Carpathians.

The almost circular shape of the mass has long been noted. The Carpathians have been aptly described as a citadel, and Transylvania as a geographical and historical keep. The Carpathians are ramparts, cut through by the rivers or traversed by easily negotiable passes. At the foot, the Subcarpathian counterscarp conceals a maze of small basins and corridors. Beyond this stretches the glacis, sometimes flat, sometimes rolling, wooded in part and elsewhere bare; there are huge plains bounded by moats — three in the north (Siret, Prut and formerly the Dniester) and two in the south (the Danube and the Black Sea).

THE TRANSYLVANIAN KEEP. This is a sunken basin in the heart of the Carpathians and was once occupied by seas and lakes; it is today a plateau of about 1,300 to 2,600 feet, divided into winding ridges. Two transversal cuts and a ring of wide valleys determine the site of the string of towns — the 'Seven Fortified Towns'. The mineral wealth of Transylvania attracted settlers in very ancient times. Except in the south-east, where the German and Magyar settlements can at once be recognised from the appearance of the villages, the Rumanian inhabitants predominate, and more and more are making their way into the towns that were so long the administrative and cultural preserves of the foreign conquerors. The considerable reserves of methane gas will soon accentuate still more sharply the present industrial pre-eminence of Transylvania in the national economy.

THE CARPATHIAN RAMPARTS. On the whole, the transition from the hills of the keep to the Carpathian ramparts is abrupt. Throughout their length the latter present a number of similar features. For instance, the mountains all rise over 3,000 feet. The highest peaks are Rodna (7,560 feet) in the north, Retezat (8,076 feet) in the south, and Vladeasa (5,922 feet) in the west. Even at these altitudes formations due to glacial action (more Pyrenean than Alpine in appearance) cover only a small area. Needles and sharp peaks are uncommon. Above the deep valleys and the forest-line (5,000 to 6,000 feet up according to the district), the long, grass-grown ridges are dotted with dwarf juniper bushes. In the crystalline rock regions, even at heights over 6,000 feet the flattened summits are remarkable. In places where the nature of the rocks is more varied (especially where flysch of argillaceous schists and soft sandstones predominates), the relief is more cut up and the crests more rounded. The only exceptions are the steep-walled limestone outcrops, the causses (limestone plateaus) of Mehedinti, Padurea Craiului and Moma in the Banat mountains, and the wooded cones of ancient volcanoes.

The Carpathians have never presented a barrier to communications. The movements of woodsmen and migrating shepherds are unhampered. The existence of the little basins within the range also facilitates travel in and over the mountains.

In so great a massif there are, of course, many local peculiarities and differences. From north-west to south-east, the Moldavian Carpathians form a range of stumpy, wooded massifs, seventy-five miles broad, their narrow crests dominated by escarpments. They comprise:

1) To the west, and on one of the most marked seismic rifts in Rumania, an almost uninterrupted succession of volcanic massifs, covered with forests but little inhabited (population density is 10 to the square mile) except in the areas of the spas;

2) In the middle, a string of little basins linked by high passes, natural clearings and crossroads, where native Rumanians live together with Slav, Magyar and German aliens. Those of the north (Maramureș, Dornele) are engaged in forestry and pastoral activities, while those of the south (Trei Scaune, Tara Bârsei) farm rich agricultural land;

3) In the east, little ridges covering the flysch zone of a well-watered region. Valleys with swift rivers lead to passes in use for centuries, some of which are crossed by rail routes today. The Moldavian Carpathians with their extensive forests, their famous pastures, and their hydro-electric potentialities (Bicaz) may constitute a core of industrial development.

From east to west, from the Bucegi to the Danube cutting, the southern Carpathians are loftier, more massive, more enclosed, despite the deep troughs of the Olt, the Jiu and the Danube. Uplift movements partitioned these mountains into massifs that differ in height, appearance and relief. There is the indented crest of the Făgăras, the sloping tables of the Lotru or the Sebeş mountains, the karst-like undulations of the Bucegi and the plateau of Mehedinti. The whole makes up a vast domain of woodlands and pastures, but one where through communications are difficult, and except in the Petroşani coal-field the population — which is purely Rumanian — is concentrated on the fringe.

Different again are the Pannonian Carpathians. These are composed of isolated massifs (Banat, Poiana Rusca, Bihor, Lapus) separated by great gulfs of plains (Caransebeş, Beius) and containing interior basins (Oraviţa, Zlatna). These mountains are easily penetrated. The wooded or grassy causses are more extensive here than elsewhere, especially in the Bihor, and intense volcanic action has left impressive traces in the topography and in the mineral deposits (auriferous quadrilateral near Zlatna; iron in the Banat and Poiana Rusca). The mineral resources have given rise to small industrial centres, isolated in a rustic countryside where archaic modes of life have subsisted. It is the basins and valleys which attract the population. The Beius basin, set in a framework of near-deserted mountains, looks like a galaxy of tiny villages scattered in typical Rumanian style, where compact foreign settlements seem like recent intruders.

THE SUBCARPATHIAN PODGORIA. In the Carpathians as in the Vosges the external foothills between the wooded mountains and the fertile plains have offered the most attractive living conditions. In a region of more varied soils there has grown up a denser Rumanian population. The first political units (knezats) developed here, and the earliest princely capitals (Suceava, Curtea de Argeş). The depressions that stretch between mountain and hill enjoy an exceptionally good climate. These lowlands, cleared long ago, are now covered with tilled fields, vineyards, orchards, chestnut and walnut groves. This is the Podgoria, whose influence extends over the steppes and on to the valley-terraces leading to the Danube. A string of market-towns runs across the basins, while another marks the line of junction between hill and plain. The plain's prosperity is closely linked with the roads, the railway, the salt-mines, the oil-wells and cultivation. Only a narrow fringe in Bukovina, the Podgoria widens out from the Moldova river to the Prahova, ends at the curve of the Carpathians, and then reappears in the west, from Cîmpulung to Tîrgu-Jiu.

In the nature of its relief the piedmont of the Pannonian Carpathians is different. Sometimes the mountains cease abruptly above the plain (Siria), sometimes they sweep out into great amphitheatres (Taut) with wooded or cultivated terraces. Here rocky islands project upwards at some distance from the mountains; there tongues of flat country worm their way right into the heart of the massifs, often cut by picturesque little gorges. Elsewhere, wide slopes, cool and wooded, drop down to the old, badly drained region of the plains. The ancient roads followed Podgoria closely whereas the market-towns which are linked by rail have developed along the rivers farther west. Here, the ethnical frontier is rather difficult to trace. But there is a striking contrast between the Rumanian villages of twisting, narrow streets, the geometric plan of the 'colonies', and the innumerable isolated farms, or salase, in the mists of the Pannonian 'lake'.

THE GLACIS OF PERIPHERAL PLAINS.
In the west, Rumania has only a narrow strip of rich and densely populated plain. To the east of the Carpathians, the glacis is more extensive and of more varied appearance. Oltenia is deeply rolling country that flattens out as it approaches the Danube. Farther north-west the plain reaches a width of about 95 miles but is infinitely monotonous. The valleys, boasting little water in summer, partition off the cultivated areas, whether they have been cleared recently, like Vlasia, or whether they have become bare and steppe-like, like Bărăgan.

These are fertile lands, with extremes of climate, seasonally burning hot or freezing cold under the lash of the east wind. There are few villages. From the Carpathians to the Prut there extends a low plateau cut up into strips by a series of rivers flowing into the Danube. In the north the soil is a rich loess with côtes or vine-covered slopes and orchards; in the south there are steppe-like plains. It was over the codru (wooded region) of the centre that the Rumanian population spread beyond the Dniester until Rumanians constituted more than half the population of Bessarabia. The Moldavian reigning princes fixed their eastern frontier on the Dniester and their imposing fortresses can still be seen along its banks. But the plateau strips of Moldavia and Bessarabia are such excellent trade-routes that they are still objects of envy, explaining the mosaic of peoples inhabiting the Rumanian borderlands. The U.S.S.R. seems to have substituted wholesale transfer of Moldavian peasants (from Bessarabia) for the old type of colonisation.

A BELT OF RIVERS.
All the eastern plains lead to wide river corridors — those of the Prut, the Siret and the Danube. For about 940 miles from Suceava to Bazias a continuous line of navigable waterways forms the frontier. The valleys are broad and uniformly wide, with flat bottoms and slight gradients. The contrast between the slopes (steep to the east) is made more striking by differences in vegetation and population.

The Danube offers all these characteristics on a larger scale. At the Iron Gates the waters foam over rocky ledges, and a canal with locks enables vessels to pass the rapids. At Turnu-Severin (some 565 miles from the sea) the Danube is only 112 feet above sea level, and its valley so wide that it is spanned by only two bridges (Giurgiu and Cernavodă). The water brought in by the Wallachian rivers alters the flow only slightly but increases the already considerable amount of alluvial matter. When the waters are low, huge areas of meadow, reed-brake and willow are exposed. Near Galaţi, the Siret, the Prut and the Danube meet in an area of progressive subsidence once penetrated by an arm of the sea. By damming the estuaries of the tributary valleys an accumulation of alluvial material has formed an immense and curious delta of lagoons of fresh water or, where it faces the sea, of salt water.

The Danube delta consists of two sections: the interior delta, covering 1,062,100 acres, and the external delta stretching out its lagoons behind curved littoral cordons formed by the north-south coastal current. Small secondary deltas are continually pushing out into the sea (it is estimated that the Chilia arm gained from 130 to 390 feet between 1906 and 1922). The oldest cordons of the delta are covered with oak forests (that of Letea covers about 34,000 acres), pastures and even tilled fields, with a few scattered villages.

A rich fauna of birds and fishes is found in this terrain, and the Rumanian People's Republic (R.P.R.) is proposing to engage in a more rational utilisation of the waters, fauna and flora (reeds).

THE MARITIME FRONTAGE OF THE DOBROGEA.
The advantages of the peninsula between the sea and the Danube are those of a bridge leading from the Moldavian steppes to the Balkans and those of a seaport that is almost always open. This is a redoubt quite different from the Carpathian structure, for it is a fragment of a Hercynian massif (maximum height 1,495 feet). It is joined to the south by a low plateau dropping to a minimum of about 390 feet, sometimes flat, sometimes

The Danube above the Iron Gates, at the Kazan defile, where high walls of chalky rock drop into a short stretch of calm water. On the left, a road has been cut into the rock face, the completion of work begun by the legions of Trajan. The Danube here forms the frontier with Yugoslavia. RUMANIAN INFORMATION BUREAU

undulating, but always bare and monotonous. On its edge are sunk valleys ending in rather shallow lagoons. That of the Carasu is marshy and unhealthy but was selected as the line for the Danube-Black Sea canal, an old scheme begun by the British, then taken up by the R.P.R. but now abandoned. The rich 'Silver Coast' has once more become Bulgarian territory, for the southern marches of the Dobrogea have formed a bone of contention between the two countries since 1878. Recent settlements have been made in this region of mixed and scattered population where traces of the Turk have remained very obvious. The coast has few natural harbours and consists of crumbling cliffs and salt lagoons. The port of Constanţa is largely an artificial one and serves for the export of Rumanian oil and wheat rather than for passenger traffic to Istanbul, the Levant and Egypt.

Rumanian economy

Not so long ago a visitor to Rumania would not have suspected a rich country. Yet Rumania has an appreciable number of economic potentialities. The problem is to develop them. Unfortunately, statistics are not yet as complete and precise as would be desirable.

AN UNEVENLY DISTRIBUTED POPULATION. The 1930 census gave a population figure of just over 18 million; that of 1948, nearly 16 million; by 1954 the figure had risen to 16½ million, by 1959 to 18 million, and it is steadily increasing. The density has risen from 158 to 199 per square mile, a relatively high figure for a country that is mainly rural and remains so in spite of the recent growth of the towns and industrial centres (nearly 6 million inhabitants in 1953). This can be explained by the upward movement of the birth rate between 1920 and 1939. Only a very high infant mortality rate (now falling) prevented the natural increase from being one of the highest in Europe. There is now a fall in the birth rate, offset in part by a drop in the mortality rate.

Rumania suffers less from over-population than from unevenly distributed population. There is a marked contrast between the thickly settled hill country and the sparsely populated plains and mountains. Between the two wars attempts were made to relieve the congestion by forming settlements in the more sparsely peopled areas, but this did not give the hoped for results. Rumanian peasants have their roots deep in the soil, and will not leave their native homes unless forced to do so; in 1930 nearly four-fifths of the working population was engaged in agriculture.

Young students (whose numbers had increased rather too rapidly) chose civil service careers or the liberal professions, leaving a great number of key posts in industry to foreign technicians (the present-day technical assistance furnished by the U.S.S.R. helps to fill a gap that has long existed); trade and banking was largely in the hands of Jewish concerns. The R.P.R. is speeding up the training of its own skilled workmen, while co-operatives and State shops are changing the pattern of the nation's trade. In agriculture, progress has been slower. Shepherds and farmers lacked the experience and capital needed to derive much profit from their land and labour. There has been a tendency to compare the results obtained by the Rumanian peasantry with those of the Bulgarian horticulturists, the German settlers, the former great estates, and those of the State farms. The truth is that the Rumanian peasants, prolific and robust, need only time and peace to adapt themselves to progress. The great problem is to lead them into new paths without violently upsetting their way of life and, above all, without interfering with traditions and the ownership of their land, for they cling tenaciously to their property. It is certain that the rising generation, trained in new methods and new ways, will speed up the process of agricultural education.

VILLAGES, HOUSES AND TOWNS. The strength of the old traditions is strikingly shown in the various types of dwellings, particularly in differences between the old villages and those built to a more precise plan, the products of a more highly evolved social organisation or a directing authority.

To the first type belong the villages or hamlets in the Padureni of Poiana Rusca or in the Motzi of the Bihor, with brown wooden houses covered with high thatched or shingled roofs. These are rustically picturesque but uncomfortable. Then, there is the most characteristic Rumanian settlement, the 'dissociated' village, half-hidden in an oasis of greenery. The houses are scattered in gardens and orchards; the dwellings are separated from each other and strung haphazardly along winding alleys or river banks that serve as highway, laundry and duck-pond. Regional differences are seen only in the architecture of the houses themselves; wood is used in the forest regions, *pisé* (rammed clay or earth) on the plains. The dwellings are built on a foundation of trampled earth or of stone, or they may be set above a ground floor of storerooms. They almost always have a balcony that affords shelter against rain, snow or sun, and extra sleeping accommodation on summer nights. There is a little kitchen with an open hearth, and a common living-room-cum-bedroom at the back of the house. It is cool, with narrow windows; benches, a table and two beds covered with cushions make up the furniture. Sometimes there is a spare bedroom that is more attractively furnished and decorated. It is a type of dwelling that seems all too small for a large family.

The second type of rural settlement is more like that of western Europe: a village without any definite plan spreading outwards from a small central square, or taking the form of a large encampment with a geometric ground plan and broad streets intersecting at right angles. These are the settlements of the Swabian, Saxon, Magyar or Rumanian rural or military colonies, which have a more prosperous air than the recent settlements in the Dobrogea, the Bărăgan or the Pannonian Plain.

The urban districts offer contrasts just as interesting. Officially, Rumania has 176 towns but, with the exception of Bucharest, only seven have populations exceeding 100,000. Seven have between 50,000 and 100,000 inhabitants, and 85 have less than 10,000. As elsewhere, most of these towns are market centres (in contact with the regions supplying complementary products) or they are situated on highways. Generally, Rumanian towns offer little interest to the tourist, but the green open spaces of the residential districts are pleasant enough, and the densely populated *mahallas*, which are more rural than urban, are picturesque and not always sordid. Indeed clean streets, magnificent parks and modern apartment houses are reported of today's *mahallas*. Bucharest itself was such a town before it was subjected to a town-planning scheme.

The old fortified towns of Transylvania, Orasul Stalin (Brasov), Sibiu and Sighişoara have kept their ancient German traits. At Cluj, Arad, Orâdea and Tirgu-Mureş the houses extend along endless streets, and the central squares are lined with huge buildings in rather poor taste. Timişoara has a character of its own, for it consists of three towns joined together, while the ground-plan of Brăila is that of a fan giving on to the Danube. Iaşi, Galaţi, Turnu-Severin and Craiova present a contrast between their old commercial core and their fine residential districts. Constanţa suggests the East rather than the West. There is still a Turkish minaret and formerly there was a bazaar. None of these towns resembles the industrial cities of western Europe, for rural influence is felt everywhere, even in the scattered mining, oil, and steel towns. Sometimes, especially in Transylvania, the towns are remarkable for their high percentage of non-Rumanian inhabitants, though the immediate countryside is entirely Rumanian.

CLIMATE AND SOIL FERTILITY. Rumania's brown soils of forest origin bordered by a broad belt of chernozem (black earth) make a superb agricultural domain. For many years it escaped intensive cultivation, and little was done to enrich it with fertilizers. However, extensive farming methods were considerably changed and improvements were made as far back as 1921.

Even so, Rumanian agriculture has always had to contend with a fickle climate. The country is more exposed to harsh weather from the east than to soft Atlantic rain-clouds. In fact, Rumania has a continental type of climate described as 'Danubian'. The winters are freezing cold and the summers are scorching hot. A mean annual range of temperature of about 43° F., with a maximum range of about 106° F., prevailing dry north-east winds, and drought on the plains are the main features. Since it lies on a climate crossroads, the

Turda, a town in Transylvania renowned for its Daco-Roman salt mines and, today, for its chemical industries and cement works. In the background, beyond a slope dotted with vineyards and orchards, is the chalky ridge of Kövesleercz, which is cut through by a picturesque gorge (Cheia Turzii). To the left are the last foothills of the Trascau Mountains. The River Aries forms a narrow stream through the middle of its wide valley after emerging from the Bihor Mountains. RUMANIAN INFORMATION BUREAU

Young musicians. WERNER BISCHOF, MAGNUM-PHOTO

Grape harvest in the Ploesti region. This grape picker wears a blouse with traditional embroidery.
RUMANIAN LEGATION

A new workers' housing estate at Floreasca, outside Bucharest. Its fine setting makes a strong contrast with the severely functional character of the building. CAMERA PRESS

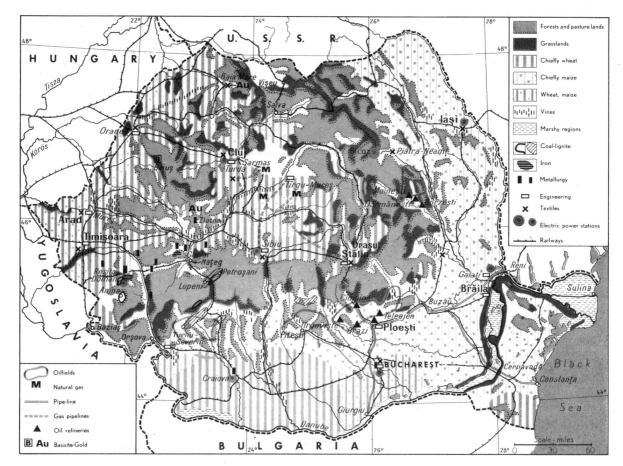

ECONOMIC MAP. *Forests, pasture land and prairies are grouped inside the mountainous framework of the eastern and western Carpathians; the extension of the maize-growing steppe region from the east predominates. Industry is so dispersed that it is impossible to show its distribution; this map shows only petrol and coal-bearing areas, thus emphasising the present and future importance of the outer edge of the Carpathians and the localisation of metallurgy in the south-west, and of natural gas in Transylvania. Regions of non-specialised cultivation are shown in white. (After information supplied by Robert Ficheux.)*

country shows marked regional differences in landscape and agricultural products. But, however stimulating, the climate is still a drawback. The snow lies long, the rivers freeze — including the Danube and sometimes the inshore waters of the Black Sea — and, above all, there is drought. The graphs of the harvest show extraordinary spurts of abundant crops (bringing low prices) and years of scarcity (followed by high prices); both are damaging to the country's economy. In 1950 it was estimated that almost seven million acres were hit by drought. Irrigation is indispensable for production of cereals, forage plants, sugar-beet, and even rice and cotton. The R.P.R., following Russian example, has planned to modify local climatic conditions by planting belts of trees (7,400 acres of forest screens to protect 123,000 acres of arable land); just as urgent are measures for soil conservation, especially in view of the ravages of summer rains in regions that have been recklessly deforested.

A LAND OF FARMERS. Despite the capricious climate, Rumanian agriculture (on a soil that is especially suited to grain crops, fruits, vines and pasture lands) is still the foundation of the country's economy. In 1945, after the losses of territory, almost one-half of Rumania consisted of arable land — against 12 per cent pastures and natural grasslands, 2 per cent vineyards, 28 per cent forest and only 7 per cent not utilisable. The R.P.R. is now aiming at two long-envisaged objectives:

an increase in cultivated land (by drainage and irrigation) and, above all, higher yields, for current figures seem low compared with those of Western agriculture.

Maize is still the cereal best suited to most of the farming regions, and it forms the basis of the peasants' diet. During recent years wheat production has sometimes exceeded that of maize; rye, oats and barley are grown on a much smaller scale than either. Including rye (a crop which has doubled in twenty years), there was 554 lb of breadstuffs per head of population in 1945 and 598 lb in 1950, against 614 lb in 1939. Buckwheat, sorghum and industrial crops occupy the acreage lost by oats and barley. Despite progress made from 1921 to 1939 (and much more marked today), sugar (about 13¼ lb per head yearly) and vegetable oils are particularly lacking. Wine (about 10½ gallons per head yearly) and fruits are exported but could find a better market at home.

Agrarian reforms and an appreciable rise in the peasants' standard of living induced a sacrifice of forest land in favour of areas devoted to stock-breeding (nearly 12,350,000 acres in 1939), but territorial losses reduced this figure by almost one-half. Before the war the cattle (including many buffaloes), sheep and goats showed a tendency to decrease in number while horses and pigs increased. But mechanisation (much advocated today) and the ravages of war have combined to reduce the numbers of all livestock. To increase the herds and improve the rather poor quality of the livestock, the area under forage crops must be increased and the pastures improved in a country where transhumance — the age-old migratory movement of flocks and herds — is rapidly coming to an end.

It is certain that Rumanian agricultural output can be increased in quantity and improved in quality. For years special government organisations have been taking measures to effect such changes — by the introduction of new crops, selected seeds and a more mixed farming, and by offering farmers the example of the co-operatives. It must be admitted that progress has been slow, that enthusiasm for first one crop and then another has induced alternation of hope and disappointment. An added retarding factor is the peasants' reluctance to take advantage of the benefits of co-operation. It may well be asked whether State planning and official pressure have been able to rationalise and improve Rumanian agricultural production.

At least, the country has at her disposal sufficient foodstuffs resources, even though they are not very varied. The frugality of the peasants might surprise foreigners but, except in one or two very isolated mountain regions, real scarcity is unusual. However, dearth of foodstuffs became more and more tragically marked during and after the Second World War, a situation that is all the more surprising when we reflect that Europe's 'wheat granary' was no longer exporting the large grain surplus that it sent pre-war to the industrial lands of the West. The starting-point for the famine was the drought of 1945—46, aggravated by reduced acreage under maize, resistance of the peasants to the new agrarian system, and reparations in kind made as part of the war indemnity. The bad times lasted until 1954, when two abundant grain harvests meant that rationing could be abolished. The lesson of the lean years has been learned; although the R.P.R. can do nothing to change the climate, it is endeavouring to increase the acreage of cultivated land and to step up the yields.

Rumania possesses, too, splendid and immense forest regions which are almost virgin in places. More than a quarter of the country is covered with conifers, beech, oak, ash and lime. The forests provide an additional source of income for the peasants, and furnish almost all the domestic fuel, building material, and wood for carpentry. Timber is also an important export item. But the forests have been mistakenly sacrificed to extend the area of pasture lands and ravaged (especially in the north) to satisfy the U.S.S.R.'s demands for war indemnity. The R.P.R. is wisely planning to conduct large-scale reforestation and to exploit rationally those forest areas which have so far been neglected because of the lack of transport.

LACK OF INDUSTRIAL RAW MATERIALS. Except for its power resources, Rumania has no appreciable quantities of basic industrial materials. A map showing the usual economic resources may give a wrong impression. Gold and salt, for instance, once so eagerly sought, now occupy minor places in the country's economy, although the salt is used in the chemical works. The ores needed in modern heavy industry are widely distributed in deposits of small extent, difficult and expensive to reach, of complex composition, and of such doubtful value that in many cases mines have been worked, abandoned, then worked again.

OIL AND NATURAL GAS. The very name Rumania traditionally suggests abundance of oil. Natural gas resources, though less often mentioned, are even greater than those of oil and may well take its place one day.

Although deposits had been known from the fifteenth century, petroleum did not become a source of national wealth until 1857. The oilfields were in Rumanian hands up to 1907. After the First World War (when the wells were seized by Germany and capital was needed to repair the damage) foreign participation in the oil industry increased. In 1927 the State was still the largest producer, but by 1938 foreign companies predominated and were producing 3,630,556 tons against a State output of 2,865,908 tons. Thereafter, measures taken to limit and even eliminate non-Rumanian capital explain, at least in part, the drop in output from 1936 to 1939 — from 8,575,000 to 6,153,000 tons. By employing technical methods now used by oil specialists everywhere, the Rumano-Soviet 'Sovrompetrol' has been able to increase output considerably beyond pre-war totals. All in all, about 200 million tons of petroleum have been extracted from Rumanian soil during the last century. This figure indicates how eagerly its high

The extensive oilfield at Moreni. It stretches along the valley floor and up to the foot of the hills. PAUL POPPER

quality oil has been sought and how great the drain on the country's oil resources has been. Although it is difficult to estimate the amount of the reserves, there is little doubt that they are sizeable. An annual production of 10 to 20 million tons is nevertheless a heavy drain. As long ago as 1936, it was advised that extraction should be limited so that the reserves might last longer and oil might continue to play its predominant rôle in the Rumanian trade balance. To date oil has been found only in the curved belt of the Eastern Carpathians, and although output of the various wells has varied, the general area of operation has not changed much and is still confined to three zones in Muntenia (Prahova, Buzău and Dâmbovița) and to the Moldavian group (Bacău). Most of the prospecting is now taking place in the second group, but the Muntenia wells are still the most productive.

Natural gas reserves are even more difficult to estimate. Deposits are found in Transylvania, in the form of methane, cheap and almost pure, and in the oil regions of the 'Old Kingdom'.

These sources of power supplement the meagre coal and hydro-electric production. The only coalfields (in the Banat and in Transylvania) give fuel of poor quality: reserves have been estimated at 3,000 million tons, but output was not more than about 1¾ million tons until 1938. Since then great efforts have been made and over 4 million tons were mined in 1953, an increased yield, though quality and quantity still remain inadequate.

There is in the R.P.R. much talk about harnessing the rivers to produce hydro-electric current. However, for geographical and financial reasons, the ambitious projects conceived between the two World Wars have not been executed. Production is limited to numerous small stations utilising the power of low waterfalls and supplying local current, either urban or industrial. The production in 1938 was little more than 1,000 million kWh. The R.P.R. has hopes of raising the production fivefold by treating as a single project the schemes for irrigation and for the Danube-Black Sea canal on the one hand, and those for producing hydro-electric power on the other. Part of the current was to go to the electrification of two thousand villages. It was estimated that by 1954–55 a figure of 4,500,000 kWh had been reached. Output had then been quadrupled. The work done has concentrated largely on reconditioning the Bicaz station.

In 1950 only 8 per cent of the total power consumption was produced by hydro-electric sources, against 40 per cent from natural gas, 30 per cent from oil, 20 per cent from coal and lignite, and 2 per cent from other fuels. Since that date the amount of hydro-electric current has increased.

IS RUMANIAN HEAVY INDUSTRY POSSIBLE?
Rumania today has increased need of sources of power since, following the example of the U.S.S.R., the R.P.R. is today recommending and advocating industrialisation and especially the development of heavy industry. Industrial equipment of pre-war Rumania did not even satisfy its then moderate needs. Producing only for the home market, the factories developed slowly: there were not enough customers — since local craftsmen supplied the bulk of the peasants' requirements; neither could Rumanian products compete in quality or price with foreign goods with a long-established reputation (those from Germany and France, for example). Moreover, lack of capital, raw materials and skilled labour hindered any great development. Rumanian industry was centred round the sources of hydro-electric current and lines of communication, so that it was sited in isolated clusters (especially round the towns), and never — not even at Resitza — attained a concentrated grouping of the Western type. In organisation and manpower, many of the industrial plants retained a rural and rustic character. The provinces richest in factories — and richest in mining resources — were and still are the Banat and Transylvania.

Although the country had considerable assets, she could not take a place among Europe's industrial states. Before 1914 her needs were met by foreign imports. From 1919 to 1939 measures were undertaken (often too hastily) which did increase the number of manufactures. Textiles and clothing gave employment to the biggest group of workers, followed by foodstuffs, wood products, building materials, metallurgy and chemical products and — well behind — paper, leather and hides, glass, china, and electro-technical equipment. Side by side with progress in industrial equipment, there was a marked tendency towards concentration to meet foreign competition more efficiently.

Today the R.P.R. is concentrating on heavy industry, to the extent of sacrificing temporarily its output of consumer goods. The statistics for 1938 show how small Rumanian heavy industry was. In those days, although iron ore, pyrites, ferromanganese, copper and bauxite were mined, ferrous products had to be imported. There were works turning out steel (276,000 tons), cast iron (132,000 tons), lead, zinc, copper and sulphur. In the 1950s, the output of cast iron had quadrupled and that of steel had tripled.

The marked progress is due in part to imports of Russian iron and coke which reach Orşova up the Danube. But Rumanian heavy industry is more fitted to meet the country's immediate needs (rural, industrial and railway equipment) than to engage in a large-scale export of manufactured goods.

However, the fact remains that Rumania now has a fairly large industry. The supply of power has greatly increased, and with a bigger steel output it has been possible to develop machine manufacture, the electro-technical industry, chemical and pharmaceutical products, and the wood and textile industries. The craftsmen's output has not yet been supplemented by the concentration and modernisation of new factories, and consumer goods do not yet meet demand.

To sum up: the efforts made over the last few years have not brought any significant changes in the siting of the industrial centres; they are still tied to the towns, that is, to the lines of communication or the sources of raw materials. Recent industrialisation has, above all, given a very vigorous stimulus to centres which had previously been out-dated.

INADEQUATE COMMUNICATIONS.
According to statistics, Rumania has a considerable mileage of lines of communication, but in 1939 — and today too — their poor condition brought many complaints. The only two metalled roads were those crossing the country from side to side. Out of some 7,370 miles of track, only one stretch was double — the 135 miles from Bucharest to Bazău. Of the five lines crossing the Carpathians, only those of Prahova and the Iron Gates carried frequent or fast trains. The northern line (Salva-Vişeu) has become increasingly important as a link (through Maramureş) between Hungary and the U.S.S.R. The Petroşani-Hațeg line will be of more use to Transylvania (Poiana Rusca) than to Oltenia. A second bridge (at Giurgiu) now crosses the Danube south of that of Cernavodă. Rumania, which was only a short time ago badly connected with the Balkan countries and shut off from Russia, is now much more accessible from the east. The main lines follow the relief of the land closely and describe two concentric rings, one around Transylvania and the other on the outside of the Carpathians. The subsidiary lines are in urgent need of improvement and of many additional miles of rail to link them with other lines. The war wrought havoc on tracks and rolling-stock alike. Much will have to be done before Rumania possesses an adequate network of road and rail communications.

Waterways are confined to the Danube, the Prut (now a frontier) and the Siret. There are only a few barges on the Bega and the Mureş, and timber-rafts on the Olt, Bistrița, Tisza and Siret. Everywhere frost and silt hamper navigation. River traffic on the 668 miles of the Danube's course through

Rumanian territory is mostly downstream, despite the slow passage through the Iron Gates and despite the heavy cost of preventing the silting up of the delta. The Danube-Black Sea canal has been abandoned. Rumanian shipping is of little importance. Sea traffic is confined to three ports, Constanţa, Galaţi and Brăila (with more exports than imports). Giurgiu is merely the terminus of the oil pipelines.

LACK OF CAPITAL AND FOREIGN INVESTMENTS.

Until 1945 attempts to develop the resources of the country and to equip it industrially repeatedly came up against the problem of investments. The weakness of Rumanian finances was that the savings of a population with modest resources and a low standard of living were insufficient to provide loans to the government, and foreign capital had to be called on. Two ruinous wars militated against a balanced budget for many years. The Second World War brought heavy loss of life, equipment and stocks of all sorts, and a tremendous burden of war debt to the U.S.S.R. Inflation and its effect on prices raised the face value of the banknotes in circulation from 35,000 million *lei* in 1938 to 211,000 million in June 1944, and to 25,000,000 million in June 1947. Inflation was followed by two very harsh devaluations (1947 and 1952) and the linking of the Rumanian *lei* with the Soviet *rouble*.

Just as foreign capital had in former days allowed the recovery of the country, the U.S.S.R. provided economic support on a large scale after 1945. Joint Russo-Rumanian companies (Sovrompetrol, Sovromwood, Sovrommetal, Sovromcoal, Sovromtransport, Sovromair (now Tarom), Sovrombank, Sovromtractors, etc.) are reminiscent of the holding-companies in capitalist societies. Each party holds 50 per cent of the shares and the profits are divided equally. Rumania

has supplied resources and labour, the U.S.S.R. part of the property annexed from former enemies (Germany, France, Belgium, Holland, Switzerland) and the gear and equipment. The real management is in the hands of Russian technicians; so, too, is a part of the teaching directed at the technical and ideological education of the managerial class. For ten years the *sovroms* enjoyed exceptional privileges. Since 1954 twelve of them have been dissolved, following the 'purchase' of the Russian 'shares' by the R.P.R., but the remaining *sovroms* still dominate the main branches of Rumanian economy.

It is, however, in Rumanian trade that Russian control is most clearly visible. Before 1939 Rumania exported great quantities of a small range of raw materials (oils, cereals, wood) to thirty different countries (six of them taking 60 per cent of the total) and imported manufactured articles, equipment and consumer goods, mostly from neighbouring countries (seven of them supplied 70 per cent of the imports). Trade with the U.S.S.R. was virtually non-existent. Today the U.S.S.R. and the 'Popular Democracies' supply 80 per cent of Rumania's imports. Agreements concluded in 1954—55 with ten countries related only to small quantities of goods (mostly wood and oil), but could serve as a starting-point for further developments.

So, as we have seen, Rumania does not lack resources, and their utilisation, long hampered and delayed, seems to be speeding up. But it is still difficult to pass general judgment, although it is clear that we are witnessing a complete break with the past. In the melting-pot where the social and economic life of Rumania is being revolutionised, a new spirit is being created, although some of those features are being retained which for centuries have been so attractive and have gained so many friends for the Rumanian people.

Robert FICHEUX

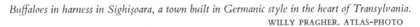

Buffaloes in harness in Sighişoara, a town built in Germanic style in the heart of Transylvania.
WILLY PRAGHER. ATLAS-PHOTO

Sofia, capital of Bulgaria, in a fertile basin at the foot of the Vitoša (6,857 feet), has about 725,000 inhabitants. The mosque in the foreground was built when Sofia was part of the Ottoman Empire; it is surrounded by modern buildings. To the right is George Dimitrov Street, the animated centre of the city. H. HOLMES, CAMERA PRESS

Herds in Bulgaria. Cattle-breeding, though less important than sheep-breeding, is gaining a foothold in Bulgaria. But it will be necessary to grow more fodder, as some mountainous districts, with their thin and infertile soil, are unable to provide enough grass. PAUL POPPER, ATLAS-PHOTO

BULGARIA

Bulgaria lies in the east of the Balkan peninsula, bounded to the north by the lower reaches of the Danube and to the east by the Black Sea. The country borders on Rumania in the north, Turkey to the south-east, Greece to the south and Yugoslavia to the west. Bulgaria's area is 42,796 square miles.

During the ninth, tenth and eleventh centuries, and especially during the reigns of Kings Boris (852—888) and Simeon (893—927), Bulgaria was the most flourishing state in the Balkans, but later on, because of rivalry with Byzantium, the country suffered many afflictions. Although Bulgaria recovered a precarious independence under the Asen dynasty in the thirteenth century, it was finally conquered by the Turks at the end of the fourteenth, and remained under their rule until 1878, when it regained partial independence. Since then the country has undergone a number of territorial changes — some of loss and some of gain. In 1886, Eastern Rumelia (which remained a Turkish province after 1878) was united with northern Bulgaria, while further territorial modifications occurred after the Balkan wars of 1913 and the First and Second World Wars.

Bulgaria lies on one of the main crossroads of eastern Europe and her strategic position makes her very vulnerable. In ancient times the country was crossed by the Silk Route and until 1961 was traversed by the railway known as the 'Simplon-Orient-Express', linking western Europe with the Near East.

Bulgaria's landscape

A CENTRAL RANGE SURROUNDED BY PLAINS. The main physical feature of Bulgaria is the ancient Stara Planina (Balkan) range which cuts through the middle of the country from west to east for about 375 miles. Over part of this distance the Stara Planina is accompanied by a parallel range, the Sredna Gora (Anti-Balkan). Between the two chains lies a depression formed by a line of basins. In the south-west corner of the country rises the imposing Rhodope massif, divided between Bulgaria, Yugoslavia and Greece, and forming a mountain mass whose highest point rises to 9,600 feet.

Two-thirds of Bulgaria is occupied by the Stara Planina chain and the Rhodope massif; the remaining third consists of plains, the largest of which lies between the northern slopes of the Stara Planina and the Danube. This plain, 250 miles long and ranging from 20 to 75 miles wide is part of the Danubian plain linked directly with central Europe. To the south of the Stara Planina, the rivers on the Aegean slope — the Maritsa, the Mesta and the Struma — flow through very wide valleys which, eastwards, broaden out into the huge coastal plain of the Black Sea. In addition, a number of basins, the most characteristic of which is that of Sofia, are scattered between the Stara Planina and the Rhodope.

Bulgaria is cut off from the influence of Atlantic winds but in the north is exposed to that of north and north-east winds, icy in winter, hot and dry in summer. However, south of the Stara Planina (which forms a protecting screen), at least on the plains, under the influence of the Aegean and Black Seas, the climate is more variable. In the rest of the country temperature and rainfall are determined by altitude and exposure.

A SLAVISED TURCO-TATAR POPULATION. In the sixth century a horde of warriors of Turco-Tatar stock subjugated the Slav population which had been established around the mouths of the Danube in what is today Bulgaria. The invaders had first settled in the Volga valley, and then migrated to a region in the north of the Caucasus. The newcomers were soon assimilated by the native Balkan population, and the present-day Bulgarians seem to be a Slavised people speaking a language that is akin to Russian but still more closely related to Old Slavonic. It is written in Cyrillic characters.

Bulgaria's population developed in a very irregular manner throughout the centuries, particularly since territorial changes have taken place. In 1956 there were 7,630,000 inhabitants; estimates show that 85 per cent are 'Slavs' and Orthodox by religion. There is still a Turkish minority. The Tziganes, or gypsies, once more numerous, make up only 1.2 per cent of the population. Some Rumanians, mostly migratory shepherds, are still found in parts of the north-east. The Jewish population (which settled in Bulgaria from Spain in the sixteenth century) is no more than 6,000 strong, for heavy emigration to Israel has reduced the numbers from a fairly recent total of 50,000.

The population density is approximately 182 to the square mile, but the figure varies from 200 to 250 on the Danube and Maritsa plains; it is about 130 in the Dobrudža (Dobrogea) and 100 in the Stara Planina. New economic trends tend to increase the urban population (18.8 per cent of the whole in 1887 and 33.5 per cent by 1956). The birth rate is falling; 40 per thousand in 1887 but now no more than 20 per thousand. About 550,000 Bulgarians are settled abroad.

RURAL DWELLINGS AND TOWNS. Bulgaria is a country where living conditions in the rural areas have long remained primitive. In the mountains the typical peasant dwelling is a single-roomed wooden hut — the equivalent of the Russian *isba*. On the plains houses are a little more comfortable and, generally, strung out along a road that cuts through the village. The thatched cottages tend to prevail in the outskirts, their places being taken in the urban centres by two-storeyed houses with a shop on the ground-floor, or by the administrative or 'cultural' buildings prescribed by the new regime.

There are few large towns in Bulgaria although there are many big market-villages. Sofia, the capital, which in 1956 had a population of 725,800, dates from Roman times. The city lies in a fertile basin, about 1,800 feet above sea level and at the foot of the Vitoša (7,500 feet), part of the Rhodope massif. The nodal point of the country's communication lines, Sofia is also the most important political, administrative, economic and cultural centre. Plovdiv (formerly Philippopolis) on the Maritsa river and, like Sofia, on the Calais-Istanbul railway route, has 162,500 inhabitants. It is a tobacco town and is linked by rail with Burgas, a military and commercial port on the Black Sea. Varna (formerly Stalin), with a population of about 120,000, is also a maritime base. Tŭrnovo (a previous capital), situated on the Danubian plain, on a deeply embanked

BULGARIA

meander of the River Jantra, is one of the most picturesque towns in the Balkans. Ruse, formerly Ruschuk (83,500 inhabitants), on the Danube, is at the end of the recently constructed bridge linking Bulgaria and Rumania. Pleven (formerly Plevna), famous for the battles fought between Russians and Turks in 1877, is little more than an overgrown village. At the foot of the Stara Planina's southern slopes the little towns of Kalofer, Karlovo and Stara Zagora are associated with the exploits of Bulgarian patriots during the war of liberation. Mention must also be made of two urban centres which are being rapidly transformed; they are the so-called 'socialist' towns of Dimitrovo (formerly Pernik), a mining centre, and Dimitrovgrad on the Maritsa, the headquarters of the chemical industry.

The new Bulgarian economy

Since the end of the Second World War Bulgaria has been a 'People's Democracy' whose political and economic systems closely resemble those of the U.S.S.R. The Bulgarian leaders have adopted an industrial and agricultural planning policy in which stress is laid upon the importance of developing industry and increasing the output of goods for the country's equipment. The first phase of transformation, following closely on the nationalisation of industry, was marked by progress in heavy industry and by the beginning of agricultural collectivisation, which is now being carried right through following the Soviet model and methods. However, although a certain amount of progress has been made in industrialisation, Bulgaria remains first and foremost an agricultural country.

A LAND OF GRAIN FIELDS AND ORCHARDS. Bulgaria's plains and basins are favourable for agriculture. In the mountains an extensive type of stock-breeding is practised.

Cereals are grown in the inland basins and on the plains, especially those of the Danube and the Dobrudža, and also in the basins at the foot of the Stara Planina and in that of the Maritsa. Fifty per cent of the land under grain crops is devoted to wheat (about 1,235,000 acres). Rye is grown on the hillier ground, especially in the lower areas of the Rhodope. Maize does well in the western part of the Danubian plain, in the Dobrudža, and at the foot of the Stara Planina's southern slopes. Rice (the Bulgarian crop is Europe's third largest after those

of Italy and Spain) is cultivated mostly in the Maritsa basin. However, it is the acreage of industrial crops that shows the greatest tendency to increase. The tobacco of the Rhodope and the Maritsa and Mesta basins is of high quality, and its cultivation and processing afford a livelihood to more than 150,000 families. Tobacco products represent one-third in value of Bulgarian exports. However, the most characteristically Bulgarian culture is that of rose-bushes in the celebrated Vale of Roses, at the foot of the Stara Planina. The roses, which covered an area of 15,300 acres in 1939 now cover some 16,000 acres. Although their cultivation is encouraged by the State, it has not increased very rapidly, since on the international market synthetic perfumes are ousting the Bulgarian attar of roses, which is costly and an export of great value.

In the sheltered basins, orchards abound. Kjustendil apples and Bulgarian prunes are celebrated all over eastern Europe. Vines grow mostly in the south, but the grapes, for the table rather than the wine-press, are exported in large quantities.

Bulgarian livestock has not yet recovered from the losses incurred during the two World Wars (717 head of cattle per thousand inhabitants in 1900, 165 head in 1959). Cattle, with the exception of those in the Iskar valley, are mostly second-rate and productivity is low. The number of sheep, however, is considerable. Mulberry trees grown on the southern plains encourage silkworm breeding and set Bulgaria fourth among European producers of raw silk (after Italy, Greece and Spain).

It would seem that the 1947 agrarian reform, by which 370,000 acres of arable land was distributed among 130,000 families, has brought a fall in output. It was hoped that this condition would be improved by the creation of agricultural production co-operatives, machine and tractor stations, and *sovkhozes* or model farms. But although collectivisation is now almost completed, the results to date are not particularly encouraging, largely owing to the priority given to industry.

THE ADVANCE TOWARDS INDUSTRIALISATION. After the Two Year Plan of 1947—49, the primary aim of which was to restore the war-weakened economy, a Five Year Plan (executed in four years, 1949—53) was established to increase the country's power resources and create an industry producing essential equipment without the aid of foreign capital.

Bulgaria is not rich in good quality coal, but there is abundant lignite. The Dimitrovo field, not far from Sofia, and that of the Black Sea coast are the most important. Even so, the mining

The Stalin Dam near Sofia. The development of hydro-electricity is helping to stabilise the Bulgarian economy, which has suffered from the necessity of importing fuel. BULGARIAN LEGATION

Forestry in the Rhodope Mountains. The timber is still generally transported on four-wheeled carts drawn by yoked oxen, which are typical of central Europe and the Balkans. PAUL POPPER, ATLAS-PHOTO

The town of Bansko, in south-west Bulgaria, overshadowed by the Pirin massif (9,564 feet). H. HOLMES, CAMERA PRESS

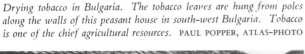

Drying tobacco in Bulgaria. The tobacco leaves are hung from poles along the walls of this peasant house in south-west Bulgaria. Tobacco is one of the chief agricultural resources. PAUL POPPER, ATLAS-PHOTO

The monastery of Rila, built in the fourteenth century round a quad-rangle, and set in the wooded valley of the Rilska. Only the crenellated keep of the original building remains, the other parts having been reconstructed after a fire in 1833. Every year in August thousands of pilgrims flock here from all parts of Bulgaria for the feast of the Assumption. BULGARIAN INFORMATION BUREAU

The cement plant near the village of Bely Izvor, Vratza district, opened in November 1960. S. NENOV, CAMERA PRESS

of solid fuel is on a relatively small scale. There are no oilfields but the outlook for increasing the production of electric current seems good. In addition to the old thermo-electric stations, some hydro-electric stations have been built, mostly in the Rhodope. The Danube plain has to rely on Rumanian current.

Dimitrovo, on the lignite deposits, has become quite a large producer of heavy metallurgical goods; machine-shops have been set up all over the country, and the small pre-war output of machines has increased tenfold. A chemical industry is being developed, and its future is linked with that of agriculture. The Dimitrovgrad chemical *kombinat* was turning out 70,000 tons of fertilizer a year within a short time of opening; the latest figures show 93,000 tons. At Sofia, Pazardžik and Pleven manufacture of synthetic rubber has been started.

However; the output of consumer goods — which before the war represented three-quarters of the large manufactures — has been somewhat checked. Nevertheless, the consumer goods industries should find in agricultural produce a sure means of developing certain lines — the most prosperous of which is tobacco. The textile industry had to be set on its feet again since it was formerly backed by German finance and machines. New works have been erected, such as the Gabrovo cotton-mills (in production since 1953) and the Maritsa textile *kombinat* at Plovdiv, which treats the Bulgarian cotton that is being grown in increasing quantities. The principal woollen centres are Gabrovo, Sofia and Sliven.

New trade relations

Before the war there were few railways in Bulgaria. Since 1945 existing lines have been improved and new ones laid.

The total length of line is now about 2,700 miles, the main route being that of the old Simplon-Orient-Express, part of the famous route from Calais to Istanbul and running through Sofia and Plovdiv. In 1952 work was completed on a line that runs along the southern slopes of the Stara Planina and links Sofia directly with the shores of the Black Sea. This new railway is more or less parallel with the Sofia-Varna line that crosses the Danube plain. Among other main lines is the north-south one linking Ruse in the north with Podkova in the extreme south, via Tǔrnovo and Stara Zagora.

Of the 53,000 miles of highways needed, under one-third exists. Still, 1,250 miles of new roads have been constructed since 1945. A start has been made.

Bulgaria has, moreover, a good network of navigable waterways. First there is the Danube, providing communication with Austria, Czechoslovakia, Hungary, Rumania and the U.S.S.R. Sea traffic is now considerable, especially since Bulgarian foreign trade is more and more with the U.S.S.R. There are various airlines linking the principal Bulgarian towns with the capitals of the other 'People's Republics' and with Moscow.

Between the two World Wars Bulgaria imported from the Western countries, and Germany in particular, both finished products and machines in exchange for raw materials and foodstuffs. Today Bulgarian foreign trade has taken an entirely different direction. The U.S.S.R., which once had very little trade or contact with Bulgaria, has now become the main customer and supplier. After the U.S.S.R. come the other 'People's Republics', with Czechoslovakia in first place. Trade relations with the West are restricted. If these conditions continue, they will necessarily influence the mode of life of the Bulgarian people and the nature of their activities, determining the destiny of Bulgaria, the crossroads of eastern Europe.

Alfred FICHELLE

MAP OF BULGARIA, *showing the different forms of soil utilisation and the chief agricultural products, mineral resources, industries, towns and the main rail routes.*

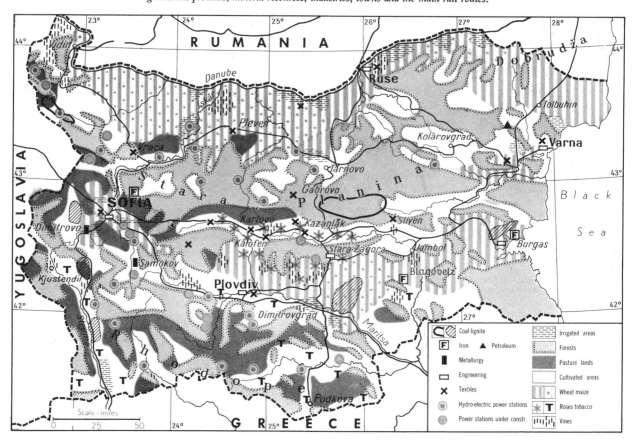

Cetara, a fishing port lying between Amalfi and Salerno and dominated by a fine Saracen tower. J. ALLAN CASH

Kamniško Sedlo, near Ljubljana in the Alps of Slovenia.
YUGOSLAV NATIONAL TOURIST OFFICE

YUGOSLAVIA

YUGOSLAVIA, together with Bulgaria, forms the 'Land of the Southern Slavs'. The State has no linguistic unity. Several closely related languages are spoken — Serbo-Croat, Slovenian and Macedonian — but each differs from the other and each is subdivided into a number of dialects. Nor is there any religious unity. In Slovenia and Croatia there are some groups of Protestants; Roman Catholics form the majority in Croatia and in Dalmatia; and most of the inhabitants of Serbia and Macedonia are Orthodox. Certain districts of Bosnia, Herzegovina and Macedonia have a Moslem majority. In addition, the various parts of Yugoslavia have no common history, for before 1914 they were divided between Austria-Hungary, Turkey, Italy and Serbia. Islamic, Byzantine, Germanic and Roman civilisations have all left a deep imprint on this part of the Balkans. Finally, there is no geographical unity. From the Danube to the Adriatic, from the Alps to the Rhodope, there is a succession of very varied landscapes. The lands to the north of the Sava belong to central Europe; to the south the Balkan world begins, a meeting-place of peoples of different races, and an age-old battlefield.

Nevertheless, the present Yugoslav State is both stable and assured of a continued existence. The country survived the Second World War and under the Agreement of February 1947 increased its territory by annexing from Italy about 2,850 square miles with a population of some 500,000 Slavs. The strength of Yugoslavia springs from its ethnical unity. The creation of a Slav state in the south of Austria-Hungary and the liberation of oppressed peoples was the aim of the Illyrian movement in the nineteenth century. Called the 'Kingdom of the Serbs, Croats and Slovenes' immediately after the First World War, it became the 'Kingdom of Yugoslavia' in 1929. After the 1939—45 war and the Constitution of January 1946, it became a 'People's Federal Republic' composed of six republics: Serbia (that is, Serbia proper plus the territories of Kosovo-Metohija and the Vojvodina), Croatia, Slovenia, Bosnia-Herzegovina, Macedonia and Montenegro (Crna Gora). Each of these units enjoys a large measure of administrative and financial autonomy (especially since the decentralisation policy of 1950), has its own legislative assembly, and is governed by its own council of ministers. The language in use in the army is Serbo-Croat, but official documents and enrolments are drawn up in two languages in districts where there are ethnical minorities, and these (750,000 Albanians, 500,000 Hungarians, 250,000 Turks, 117,000 Czechs and Slovaks, 62,000 Rumanians, 57,000 Bulgarians and 33,000 Italians) enjoy the benefit of special statutes. Most of the German population was expelled by 1945; some 60,000 remain.

Its very diversity makes the Yugoslav state a harmonious geographical unit. The country comprises two regions of complementary cultures and economies, between which a constant exchange of products, ideas and men has been maintained. The two regions are the mountain nucleus and the surrounding plains. The contrast between the central redoubt and its glacis is emphasised on relief maps, and is marked by the nature of agricultural and industrial activities, by communications and by the distribution of population. In the centre are high plateaus and mountain ranges with a harsh climate (even near the Adriatic), regions of forests and grasslands penetrated by the Pannonian valleys, so that access to the coast is not easy. These are regions hostile to occupation,

peopled by Aromani or Wallachs (speaking a Latin language and formerly shepherds), or by Serbs from Old Serbia who took refuge in the mountains during the Turkish invasions. The periphery is made up of plains or valleys threaded with the great, ancient highways of commerce. These are conveniently linked by the passages afforded by the Postojna gap, the corridor of the Morava, and that of the Vardar. It is here that rich agricultural land abounds and here that towns and industries flourish. The population is mixed; Slavs intermingle with peoples of central or Mediterranean Europe. Montenegro, Raška and Stari Vlah have been regions with distinctive cultures based on pastoral occupations and on the family communal unit. In our times the surplus of the mountain population has spilled over on to the plains. Albanians, Serbs and Bosnians have flooded the peripheral areas, especially the Vojvodina and Slavonia, where the Austrians established military Marches, a strategic cordon surrounding the central redoubt on the west and north to contain the forward thrust of Islam.

The contrast between the 'hive-lands' and the 'colonisation lands' is marked. Now that the resources of the mountains are being developed and there is increased activity in the mining areas, labour from the plains has been attracted once more towards the central areas. It is just this demographic and ethnical osmosis, this life of economic symbiosis, that strengthens the unity of Yugoslav civilisation today. Whatever the regional differences, there is no longer fundamental opposition between the various population groups. But only geographical description can bring out the great natural contrasts. When we have examined the nature of the central mountainous zone (and it is one most unfriendly to man), we shall deal at some length with the economic rôle of the peripheral regions — the corridors of the Morava and Vardar, the Danubian plains, Slovenia and the Adriatic coast.

The central redoubt

The traditional epithet for this redoubt is 'Dinaric', although the term is usually reserved for the ranges overhanging the Adriatic coast. From Trieste to Albania there stretches a huge mountain mass which covers more than half of Yugoslavia. Some edges of this mass are steep — for the great subsidence of the Adriatic caused a rift in the Dinaric structure and induced the uplift of a coastal barrier. Others are indistinct: the line of contact between the Alpine and Dinaric ranges in the Postojna area, the gently sloping terraces that join the last crystalline massif of the north to the Tertiary hills of Pannonia, and the eastern border, where recent tectonic disturbances have interrupted the continuity of the ranges, offering a foretaste of the architectonic style characteristic of Greece and Macedonia.

Yugoslavia's relief is jumbled and broken. On the whole the formations are folded in a north-west to south-east direction, widening and rising towards the south-east. But it is difficult to distinguish, classify and compare the different formations with the naked eye. The terraced high plateaus, the *planina*, are curiously horizontal and stretch as far as eye can see, with only a few stumps of hard rock that have resisted the slow process of peneplanation jutting up here and there. In some places the plateaus have been rejuvenated by Tertiary movements which provoked — as in the Durmitor — a rapid sinking of canyons (the Piva and Tara are the most beautiful in Europe) or the subsidence of extensive basins.

Penetration of the massif is not easy: the valleys, narrow and very deep, rarely run longitudinally; they isolate rather than link the mountain blocks and basins.

The harshness of the mountain climate accentuates the impression of isolation, and the asymmetry of the whole complex, the rarity of through corridors, and altitude have all combined to restrict the zone of Mediterranean vegetation. Above about 1,600 feet it freezes for three months of the year. The slopes are covered with grass and trees. Wheat grows only below 3,500 feet, and maize below 3,000 feet. Resinous trees have disappeared from the heavily eroded coastal slopes — a consequence of the disastrous deforestation practised by Venice and the Dalmatian cities, or of the strain imposed on Montenegro's pastoral resources at times of danger from the Turk. 'Many flocks, little forest' runs an old proverb. It is reflected in the small centres of pastoral life that have grown up in clearings conveniently situated for the migrating flocks of sheep and herds of cattle. The high valleys were for long isolated and constituted *župe*, autonomous units in which ancient legal institutions and customs were maintained. It is only within quite recent years that pastoral farming has seen a rapid decline. The mountains are now deserted or are becoming industrialised, though there may still be seen a number of old features. The relief of the land, the historical and social evolution, and the degree of economic backwardness have induced perceptible differences between one region and another.

THE DINARIC KARST. The karst lands are something apart, turning Yugoslavia into a museum of strange limestone formations. Over a wide area geological conditions conspire to add to the dryness that results from water seepage: the strata are more than 4,900 feet thick, the limestone is particularly pure and hard, and there are no interposed strata. It is only through faults that the clays or sandstones outcrop to produce extremely strange landscapes. There are tall, jagged crests, asymmetrical peaks, and isolated domes gashed by dry ravines; wide areas are deeply scored and perforated with *dolinas*, or closed hollows; *lapies* as sharp as a knife's edge are everywhere. The two greatest obstacles to settlement are lack of water and discontinuity of the soil. The smallest spring attracts a house or a village. During the summer the cisterns are mostly dry, and in high mountain regions huge masses of ice are covered with straw and kept to provide water for this period. In Montenegro, for instance, the traveller will more often be offered milk to drink than water. The arable land is leached red earth or softer and fairly impermeable dolomitic sands, which occur in very small sheets. Dwellings, then, are isolated. Each farm lies near cultivable land. But in a country without valleys, communications are difficult — tracks over the rugged rock are the links between villages. The oases, the inhabited spots more than 5,500 feet up, are covered with moraines, depressions hollowed out in the mass of impermeable rock, and *poljes* (closed-in depressions traversed by a short stream which tumbles into a bottomless pit, or *ponor*, at the foot of the slope). These basins all offer the same advantage to the peasant: deep soil, easy communications, abundance of water — even too much water, for most of these areas are partially flooded or marshy for several months of the year. Nevertheless, the alluvial soil of the bottoms is cultivated, and round them are big market-villages on the roads linking the Adriatic with Pannonia.

This classical karst landscape is moderated or accentuated according to the nature of the limestone, the altitude, the historical development of each region, and the present-day economic transformation.

GREEN BOSNIA, GOLDEN BOSNIA. North of a line running from Bihać to Foča, the relief changes in character.

Outcrops of impermeable rocks are indicated by a countryside of verdant plateaus and isolated hillocks or ridges crisscrossed with an extraordinary network of tiny valleys. Despite a progressive drop in altitude in the direction of the Sava, the climate is still harsh (—4° F in January at about 1,600 feet) and typically continental, although rainfall is abundant. This is also a region of forests and pasture lands, but little grain is grown. The main source of prosperity will probably long remain stock-breeding, though in this part of Bosnia there are other resources. A treasury of mineral wealth lies in the ancient geological formations. The region has been variously described as damp Bosnia, green Bosnia, and golden Bosnia.

It was the Turks who developed the mines, so it is not surprising that the imprint of Islam is much more marked here than in the karst. It is in 'impermeable' Bosnia that the *komsiluk* (patronymic hamlets) are scattered along the valley terraces, overlooking the streams — these are the typical dwelling-places of the Islamised Slav shepherds. The houses of the ancient *begs* are no longer distinguishable from the huts of the Christian population, the *rayah*. However, the architecture is still oriental and white minarets rise from the villages. In the valleys, at the crossroads, in the middle of the basins, are large villages whose streets wind between the shops of the *čarsija*, the domain of the leather-workers, potters and coppersmiths. These towns have developed as markets, commercial centres, fairs. The influence of the East is today diminishing. The harems are closed. Veils are forbidden. The big estates have been carved up. And with the collapse of the middle-classes, handicrafts have declined. New districts have been built on to the towns. The cemeteries and the mosques, a few of the old traditions, and a curious outlook on life all bear witness to the once flourishing and colourful Eastern civilisation.

Contrasting with the spacious valleys are the backward mountain areas. To the west, the Krajina (the Turkish counterpart of the Austrian Marches) is an advance post of Islam; the people, still shy and retiring, are 95 per cent Moslem. The Una, the Sana and the Vrbas attract all the economic activities of the region. The upper basins are the domain of extensive stock-breeding, while agriculture of the Pannonian type is spreading upstream. Where the rivers reach the plain, large urban centres, such as Banja Luka, are found. The vital area of Bosnia is, however, the valley of the Bosna and the Sarajevo basin, containing a string of towns and factories which are religious (Sarajevo is Moslem, and Visoko is Catholic) and economic headquarters. The only great highways to cross the Dinaric mass meet at Sarajevo, originally a Turkish capital and a military base, and now prospering from the industrial development of the Bosna valley.

PASTORAL MOUNTAINS: STARI VLAH AND RAŠKA. To the east of the Drina appear signs of another type of geological formation. Between the Upper Drina, Kosovo and the western Morava, there rises a massif with few valleys and covered with oak and beech forests, where the cores of ancient volcanic rocks project. This was once the domain of shepherds (Wallachs and Serbs), and then a Turkish stronghold commanding the roads from the Adriatic to Serbia, Bosnia and Macedonia. The armies of the sultans used the valleys and passes of what, at the end of the nineteenth century, was to be the famous *sanjak* of Novi Pazar (or Novi Bazar), a buffer-state between Serbia and Montenegro administered by Austria-Hungary.

The south-west is in complete contrast to the north-east; the basins of the Drina and its tributaries have Moslem populations; a few karst-like *poljes* recall those of Montenegro, while the upper valleys incised in the schist formations are Alpine in appearance. On the other hand, the massifs overlooking the Ibar and the western Morava are made up of crystalline cores; there are fewer rivers and streams, the valleys are shallower,

YUGOSLAVIA

the general appearance is wilder, and the mountains still serve as refuge areas.

The early Serbian population cleared very small areas of pasture land, which were centres of a high culture, reflected in the great Orthodox monasteries. Today these mountains are deserted. The exhaustion of the Ibar mines, the losses of livestock and the dissolution of the religious communities have combined to induce an exodus of the population. The shepherds have bought land in the valleys of the periphery; the highest villages are inhabited only for short periods at a time; flocks and herds are becoming rare, and during the past half-century the cultivation of maize in the valley bottoms has brought about an agrarian and social revolution. The mountain people have emigrated to the basins and hills of the Morava and the Vardar; Stari Vlah and Raška are transition areas.

The Morava-Vardar trough

Because of their mountainous character, the relatively backward state of their economy, and Moslem influence, these regions are those most like the Dinaric redoubt. But they are primarily areas of communications important to Europe as a whole, linking the Mediterranean and central Europe, and West and East. The Niš fair used to attract merchants from Vienna, Leipzig, Trieste and Constantinople. From Belgrade to Sofia or to Salonica roads and railways cross the fairly low ridges, linking basins and valleys. The Crusaders took advantage of the Morava-Vardar corridor, which was a route for invasion as well as for the Serbian State's southward expansion. The region is still a meeting place of nations — Greeks, Turks, Bulgarians, Rumanians, Albanians, Serbs — a country of contacts between north and south where different climatic influences and civilisations mingle. The resultant opposed elements are to be seen in the agrarian system,

in the kind of crops grown, in the layout of the villages and in the style of the houses.

PLAINS AND MOUNTAINS IN MACEDONIA. South of the Morava, climate and landscape afford a foretaste of the Aegean world; even so, it freezes for twenty days a year at Skopje, the peaks are more than 6,500 feet high, and the Vardar has to flow through very narrow gorges before reaching the coast. Westwards transhumance is still practised, from the valleys of the Tetovo, Debar and Bitola (Monastir) to the heights of the Šar Planina and the Prokletije, the domain of the Aromani and Tzintzars. After the Serbs left these regions in the eighteenth and nineteenth centuries, they were settled by Albanians who practised a rural economy of a very primitive type. The settlers in the cleared or drained areas of the Kosovo or in the Polog and Bitola basin spread the cultivation of maize and vines, but on the whole time stands still and the countryside has changed little for hundreds of years. However, the region's rôle as a highway is affirmed by the former prosperity of lake-side towns such as Ohrid, by the traditional *pečalba* (itinerant hawking), and by the constant intermingling of populations neither very numerous nor really permanent.

The economy is of a more varied character to the east of the Vardar, and here recent development has been more rapid. Mediterranean features can be distinguished in the farming. There are rice fields on the irrigated lands of the Strumica and the Bregalnica. When the rice is harvested in September millet is sown on the same ground. Sheep graze the sides of the basins. Speculative crops, such as mulberries, poppies and tobacco have brought some slight prosperity to the Vardar peasants despite the irregularity in yield. Population is, then, very dense on the Greek and Bulgarian frontiers. The mountain framework is, however, being gradually deserted. Skopje owes its prosperity to the well-known Salonica railway and to the roads that link it to the Morava.

The Plitvice Falls in the karst of western Croatia. ROGER PERRIN

The Danubian granary

To the north of the Sava and the Danube lies Pannonia. Roman settlers cultivating the loess plains, and legionaries keeping guard on the imperial frontier were more numerous here than in any other part of present-day Yugoslavia except Dalmatia. Pannonia, long famous for its cereals, supplies 60 per cent of Yugoslavia's agricultural output, and population density is in some areas more than 260 to the square mile. The large, prosperous villages stand amid fields of wheat and maize. The people of Syrmia and the Banat are cheerful and hospitable. In spite of wars and droughts, the peasants are still rich and, though quite modern in their outlook (and inclined to take risks), they have not forsaken their ancestral traditions. It was not so long ago, for example, that marriageable girls wore their dowries as breastplates of gold coins and medals.

This prosperity is due to soil and climate. The loess and Quaternary alluvium are impermeable, fertile and continuous, and lie several yards thick over the rocky substratum. Stone is so scarce that the houses are built of *pisé* or brick. Clouds of penetrating dust rise from the ground in summer; in winter the earth changes to thick mud which, by December, is overlain with snow. However, the harsh, typically continental climate — like that of the Hungarian *puszta* — is everywhere favourable to grain crops. Torrid though rainy summers and brilliant autumnal skies are excellent for maize and even for such subtropical crops as mulberries, rice and cotton. Pannonia has been rich since Roman times, though the long period of prosperity was broken by the Turkish invasions, which ravaged the plains to such an extent that resettlement did not take place until rather late. After the Treaty of Karlovci (Karlowitz) in 1699, Pannonia was peopled mostly by Serbs, though there were some Germans (Swabians), Hungarians and even some French (three villages in the Vojvodina, Saint-Hubert, Charleville and Seultour, were founded in 1771 by families from Lorraine). Instead of scattered farms large villages sprang up — strung out along one street or forming a compact cluster. These villages were re-sited by the Austrian army in the Marches zone — street-villages along the highways, fortified *palanke* on the Danube's banks. The Austrian administration insisted, too, on triennial rotation of crops, forest rights and common pasture — in fact, an agrarian regime modelled on that of the West. But this regime lasted only a few decades. In the regions not under military control, real-estate capitalism developed round the towns, which are more like overgrown villages. From the eighteenth century on, Hungarian magnates, Austrian nobles, Croatian bishops and Serbian horse-dealers grew speculative crops, annexed the common lands, improved the soil, drained the marshes, cleared the forests and invested their profits in rural industry. Here, then, is the explanation of a type of agriculture relatively rich for central Europe and marked by a regular increase in yield and a preponderance of cereals, industrial or market-garden crops. Such are the elements of unity.

THE VOJVODINA. To the east of the Danube, in the Vojvodina, wheat is king. The region is flat and monotonous and has certain steppe-like features of climate. There are no trees, and wood for fuel is very expensive in a land where there is no coal. Wheat covers more than 60 per cent of the area under grain crops on the loess soils of the Baranja, the Banat, the Bačka and the Titel; only acacias grow in the dune belt of Pešćara. Valleys like that of the Tisa (Tisza) were the first areas to be occupied during resettlement in the eighteenth century. The large villages are laid out chess-board fashion. Grain trade on the Danube led to the growth of large towns. After the 1919 agrarian reform hamlets were established on the sites of places destroyed long before. Water is scarce, and wells have to be dug to a depth of several dozen yards. On the

NORTHERN SERBIA: ŠUMADIJA, MORAVA, TIMOK.

North of the Morava-Vardar corridor, the basins are deeper and wider, the surrounding massifs are pierced by broad, high-walled valleys, and the summers are wetter. Pannonian farming systems have moved on up the Morava, the Timok and the Nišava. Wheat and maize cover the hill-terraces while the alluvial fans and gentler slopes bear vineyards, orchards and market-gardens. The thick, deciduous forests on the upper slopes were cleared only at the end of the nineteenth century. The Šumadija, to the west, recalls only by its name (*šuma* means 'forest') the oak and beech woods that once covered the crystalline bedrock and the lake terraces as far as the gates of Belgrade. Southern Serbs, living in innumerable scattered hamlets, have given new life to a definite type of economy based on maize, pig-breeding and the sale of plums for making spirits. This is a region of a rather well-to-do though rather rough rural middle-class, whose land was the centre and arsenal of the Serbian revolt against the Turks.

The steppe-like climate and the working of the mines have played a bigger part than systematic deforestation in stripping the Carpathian extension south of the Iron Gates. In the Timok valley (an area that yields good crops only if the land is irrigated) large villages huddle at the bottom of the slopes, half-hidden in oases of greenery. The development of this area of rich soil has been hampered by the old organisation of the *Krajina* (the frontier region) and, despite the rise in the output of the Bor mines, by its belated peopling.

big State farms as well as on the small properties, crop rotation of the modern type is practised, and sugar-beet is increasingly grown. Hops, forage plants, oil-producing plants and maize are the main crops on the small farms. The towns have a character that is all their own: just over half of Subotica's 100,000 inhabitants are agricultural workers, and the proportion is even higher in Senta. The town centres are essentially agricultural, occupied by farms, while shops and factories string out along the roads that radiate from it. Only Novi Sad has taken on a conventional look.

SLAVONIA AND CROATIA. To the west of the Danube, the land surface and the type of agriculture are more varied. Slavonia's characteristic feature is a number of curious forest patches that cover the remains of collapsed crystalline massifs enclosed in the deposits of the Pannonian sea, which is dissected by a network of small streams. These are the Prigorje (that is, lands at the foot of and around the mountains), whose economy recalls that of the French vine-growing hillsides. Strips of vineyard or orchard owned by the bourgeois of the plain fan out along the slopes. At the upper end of each holding is a shed containing a wine-press and a storehouse for wine (kle). But here, as everywhere else, the vineyards producing high-quality wine have suffered crises, and maize fields have partly replaced them, although in recent years increasingly large quantities of table grapes have been produced. The hollows of the plains and the bottoms of the Sava and Drava valleys present two different landscapes.

Bordering the rivers is the *lug*, an amphibious zone of meandering streams, inhabited by frogs, beavers and storks, a game and fishing preserve, a No-man's Land in the nineteenth century, the inviolate fringe of the Austrian Marches. Some of the plains have now been drained by the State or by the co-operatives, and experimental rice crops are being tried. The large villages, which in former times benefited from the traffic on the Sava, stand on abandoned meanders or the steep banks of the stream. In the drier areas are magnificent oak forests whose wood has been exported throughout Europe since the eighteenth century. Still the haunts of herds of wild pigs, the forest was ruined between the two World Wars by ill-advised deforestation by Yugoslav and French firms.

The second landscape: remarkably well-defined continuous terraces with dry, well-cleared terrains. Contrasting with conditions in the Vojvodina, maize is the main crop here. Only a few areas specialise in speculative crops — hops grown by Czechs round Daruvar, sugar-beet in the Podravina (Drava plain), forage plants and chicory near Bjelovar, market-gardening around Zagreb. Croatian Zagorje (the land 'behind the mountains') is over-populated and remains faithful to the old type of mixed farming. The towns resemble villages strung along the highways or the valley terraces. Each farm, at right angles to the road, has a long strip of field that stretches as far as the woodlands. Such towns were command-posts in the Marches (e.g. Varaždin), bridge towns or frontier towns on the Drava (such as Djurdjevac), contact towns between the Prigorje and the plain (Križevci), twin towns on the Sava (the two Brods), or navigation termini (Sisak).

The Slovenian Alps

Yugoslav territory includes only the most southerly spurs of the southern Pre-Alps — the Karawanken and Julian Alps — whose peaks are little higher than the Dinaric mountains.

Lake Ohrid, the Lychnidos of ancient times. It occupies a large basin 18 miles long and 9 miles wide at an altitude of 2,280 feet. A third of the lake belongs to Albania. Its waters are very rich in fish. YUGOSLAV NATIONAL TOURIST OFFICE

The abundance of mineral ores attracted settlers to this region even in Roman times. Pastoral life (developed during the Slav occupation) still predominates in the upper valley of the Soča (Isonzo) and in the Triglav massif, but the valleys are shallow and do not offer room for a true mountain life. Only a few inhabitants follow the flocks and herds, and for some years past the high pastures and summer chalets have been given over to tourists, while the cattle, fed with forage from the artificial pastures, are kept in stalls in the hamlets perched on the moraines and fluvio-glacial terraces. More milk and

The dramatic valley of the Jelenko massif in the Prokletije, Macedonia. In this region of high mountains cleft by deep, narrow valleys, farming has remained primitive. Here, sheep are seen in their summer pastures. YUGOSLAV INFORMATION SERVICE

butter (supplied to Gorica and Ljubljana) is now produced than cheese. The Slovenian mountain people, like the Tyroleans and the Swiss, have adapted themselves to changing economic conditions, and have taken advantage of developments in industry and tourism, and work to cater for the towns and plains.

The vital artery is the Sava trough. The villages — of German pattern — are strung round the edge of the Ljubljana basin. The marshy and wooded bottoms were drained and cleared in the Middle Ages, and it is possible that the numerous peasant population then practised some system of crop rotation; now hayfields are taking over at the expense of cereals, flax and hops. The men travel daily to the textile factories of Kranj and the metallurgical works of Jesenice. There is a distinct migration towards Ljubljana that is becoming more marked. Ljubljana is a former provincial capital, Austrian in appearance, with numerous baroque buildings. It was once the capital of the Illyrian provinces of Napoleon's empire. The approaches to Maribor and Celje are marked by prosperous villages with tall white churches, dotting attractive hollows or lining the river courses. Rye and maize, hops and apple trees cover the fields, while planned forestry and wool-weaving form the basis of a very varied economy.

The Adriatic coast

Yugoslavia is also a maritime state with a Mediterranean coastline of well over 400 miles. The Croats are traditionally

the nation's seamen, and Croatian songs tell of fishermen's adventures and of the exploits of the *Uscocchi*, who were doughty pirates. The Adriatic ports have had most of the emigration traffic; most of the foreign trade goes through Rijeka (Fiume). For the southern Slav world, then, this seaboard is of special importance. Here, in the Primorje, contrasting with inland regions of cold, mist and mud, are lands of stone and sun, of wine and fruits, of salt and fish. This coast has also a place apart in the Mediterranean world, for it is indeed one of the strangest in Europe. Postglacial encroachment raised the sea level by over 300 feet and partly drowned a relief of limestone anticlines and synclines packed with softer, impermeable deposits. The anticlines constitute the island heights whose narrow ridges rise like marine monsters from the waves. The depressions deepened into channels (*kanali*). This invasion by the sea is so recent that erosion has hardly had time to modify the shape of the shore, whose outlines are moulded on the forms of the ancient relief. Communications are easy and constantly maintained. When Dalmatia was swept by invasions, the inhabitants sought refuge on the islands, which enjoy a milder climate than the mainland. The coast facing the open sea is sheltered from the *bora* (a cold wind heavy with salt blowing from the continent), and offers areas very suitable for settlement. However, while some of the islands are over-populated (Prvić has 500 inhabitants to the square mile), others, such as Kornat, have been inhabited only for a few decades. In times of drought, flocks and herds are shipped across from the mainland to feed on the short grass of the uninhabited islands. The *kanali* facilitate coastal shipping and fishing. All communication is by sea, since there is no good road along the coast from Rijeka to Dubrovnik (Ragusa). Reefs, however, present a danger to navigation, and legend has it that the boat says to the fisherman, 'Save me from the land and I'll save you from the sea'.

The climate is distinctive. It can be as cold as in the interior, and the port of Senj, for instance, presents a strange winter spectacle of boats covered with ice, unable to put to sea because of the *bora*. The winter months are cold and dry; the summer is burning hot under the prevailing *jugo*, sirocco or south wind. Except in autumn, drought — the curse of the limestone islands — is always a danger, and often water has to be distributed by tanker.

The agriculture of the islands cannot, then, be considered typically Mediterranean. Grain crops are not important, and less wheat is grown than maize. It is only south of Split that olive trees are numerous, and then they yield fruit only every other year. The decrease in acreage under vines is the result of phylloxera and a slump in the market. Irrigation is possible only in the hollows. Forestry was again the main pursuit of the inhabitants, but the Venetians ravaged the coasts, and attempts made to reforest the Karst have not been very successful. The sheep were decimated during the war. Though the Adriatic is not rich in fauna, individual fishing, practised at night and by the light of acetylene lamps, is still moderately rewarding and offers a supplementary means of livelihood to some of the people. As a consequence the population congregates more and more in the large ports — Roman towns that were once constantly menaced by waves of Slav invaders, towns that have now become industrial or commercial centres, such as Rijeka, Zadar (Zara), Šibenik and Split.

There are distinct variations in coastline. To the north, Istria, whose sparsely populated continental areas ('White' Istria) are cold, has plains and a coast ('Grey and Red Istria') where a different climate prevails. Here population is more numerous, originally settled by Slavs living on *stancia* (large estates) whose Italian owners resided in the towns. The Kvarner — with large islands and indented coastline — is an industrial area that also attracts tourists. Rijeka is its capital. In the central section of the coast, the fall in coastal relief has caused a widening of the plains in the Ravni and Kotari. But the coast is dotted with silted-up ports, such as Nin, and the people abandon

The Bays of Kotor, a gulf on the Adriatic coast in Dalmatia, seen from the road to Cetinje. A number of bays separated by high mountains are linked by channels of varying width.   D. STANIMIROVITCH, GIRAUDON

The Lake of Perast, with the town of Perast on the left and the Island of St George on the right.   PAUL POPPER

The map's legend reads:

Percentage of the area sown with wheat
in relation to the total cultivated area

30%   25%   15%   10%   5%

Percentage of the area sown with maize
in relation to the total cultivated area

30%   20%   10%   5%

Percentage of pasture lands in relation
to the total area of cultivated and
pasture lands

50%   20%

Moorlands   Vines
Forests   Tobacco

SOIL UTILISATION IN YUGOSLAVIA

little used harbours such as Zadar and Šibenik and migrate to the islands or south to the mainland. The extent of the Split hinterland (and that in western Bosnia, the *poljes* of Knin, Senj or Imotski), the abundance of livestock and wine in the large islands (for example Brač, Hvar and Korčula), combined with the mild climate are all favourable factors for human settlement. Split is no longer a town confined within the ruins of Diocletian's palace; houses have spread beyond the walls and the tentacles of a great industrial port reach round the shores of the Kastel bay.

Farther south, the sea deepens and the eroded coast, no longer protected by islands, is buffeted by the high waves. The mountain crests overlooking the shores rise up into a brilliant sky. The *bora* no longer blows so fiercely. Fig and olive flourish in the warm basins of the Konavlje and the Župa of Dubrovnik. Oranges and lemons ripen on the shores of the Kotor Bay (the Bocche di Cattaro), and many of the features recall the shores of Greece. At Cavtat (Civitas) the temple of Aesculapius has been restored. On all sides are relics of Ragusa's ancient splendour. This former republic, now Dubrovnik, attracts tourists from all over the world. Not only has the town preserved intact many vestiges of its glorious past, but present-day economy has benefited much by the drainage of the delta of the Neretva, the coastal plains and

Lake Shkodër (Scutari). With the development of Montenegrin mines and industries, traffic in the southern ports is increasing — the region is, in fact, one of the provinces of the Yugoslav Federation with a very rosy future.

Yugoslav Economy

CLIMATE AND AGRICULTURE. More than 68 per cent of the Yugoslav population live in the country. In addition, some large 'towns' are peopled by peasants. And, if we exclude Slovenia (which is more urbanised) the peasant population constitutes more than 75 per cent of the whole, and reaches 85 per cent in the Kosovo-Metohija region. The problems, then, which must preoccupy government and people are rural problems, for they determine the economy of the country. They relate, first of all, to the inadequacy and irregularity of the grain harvest. One factor, a climatic one — drought — seems insurmountable; the other difficulties have been inherited from former regimes or from the application of earlier agrarian reforms.

The great disadvantage of the continental or Mediterranean climate is the irregular rainfall. Summer droughts have occurred annually since 1945. The example of 1952 is illuminating and characteristic. After an excessively mild autumn and winter, March frosts caused considerable damage, while drought, together with very high temperatures (maximum 111° F.), prevailed over the whole region from Slavonia to Macedonia. In Serbia the rainfall was only 30 per cent of what was needed, and a hot dry wind burned up what remained of the harvest. Compared with the yields of an average year, the figures were 55 per cent for wheat, 32 per cent for maize, and 23 per cent for sugar-beet. On the whole harvests were only half those of normal years. Lack of forage forced the peasants to kill off their livestock, and the mountain areas had to supply food-stuffs to the plains, for it is in the richest regions that spring and summer droughts have their most disastrous consequences. In Yugoslavia, moreover, these misfortunes have even more serious results than would normally be found in other countries, for such a combination of unfavourable natural factors revealed the defects of an agrarian system based entirely on small family farms which were quite unable to cope with such crises.

VICISSITUDES OF THE AGRARIAN SYSTEM.

Yugo-slavia is one of the European countries where the legal and economic results of a feudal-type regime were longest maintained. In the Austrian dominions the peasants were freed in 1848, but not until 1919 in the regions controlled by the Turks. The peasants were never owners of their land, their livestock or even their harvests. Under Turkish rule there prevailed a system of re-forming large farming estates by which the *rayah* (non-Moslem subjects) were reduced to the condition of serfs. In the areas colonised by the Venetians, the Slav peasantry near the towns was bound by share-cropping contracts to the urban nobility, and as commerce declined so did agriculture. In the military Marches, the soldier-peasant was in fact provided with tiny holdings, but he had neither the time nor the means to farm them. Where feudalism of the German or Magyar type prevailed, either very small concessions were made out of the big estates or the peasants had to work as serfs on the *latifundia*. In Serbia the laws promulgated during Miloš's reign resulted in the multiplication of smallholdings between 1804 and 1890. Either because the peasants, under the burden of financial obligations, desired it or because the governing classes wanted it for military reasons, the ancient patriarchal communities were maintained, often under tutelage, with elders, or *starješine*, appointed by the government or by the land owners. There was no place for development of that class of small owner-farmers which in other countries constituted a factor of stability and even prosperity.

Thus it was that sudden liberation, without any guarantees, coming at different dates, provoked a widespread crisis in the nation's agricultural life. Large properties were retained by the nobility, and the partition of estates in Slovenia and Croatia met with insurmountable difficulties. The dissolution of the patriarchal communities (a consequence of the abolition of feudal obligations) resulted in an exodus of population, the end of joint land ownership, rapid diminution in the size of properties recently acquired, unwarranted subdivision of land, the decay of pastoral activities and heavy debts on the farms.

The subdivision of the land was accentuated by the effects of the two agrarian reforms. The first — from 1920 to 1939 — was not completely carried out, though the *latifundia* in Slavonia were broken up; the new owners were not sufficiently backed by a government that was miserly with credits, and they received only land in poor condition, which they were unable to farm properly without capital and equipment.

The second agrarian reform, promulgated by the law of August 1945, decreed the expropriation of 740,000 acres in the Vojvodina alone — and 3,700,000 acres throughout Yugo-slavia. Some 316,000 families received parcels of land, but the disadvantages of tiny holdings became only the more evident. By 1950, 95 per cent of the rural population lived on farms that were too small. The aim of recent reform has

Drying tobacco at Skopje, in Macedonia.
YUGOSLAV NATIONAL TOURIST OFFICE

Ploughing in Yugoslavia. In the Dinaric lands single-furrow ploughs drawn by yoked oxen are still common. VAGN HANSEN, RAPHO

Horse breeding in the Vojvodina. ROBERT DOISNEAU

been to reconstitute large farms in the form of co-operatives of various types, ranging from simple buying and selling associations to fully-fledged *kolkhozes*. A proportion of the expropriated lands is managed by the State, and their part in the country's economy is already an important one, although only a very small proportion (5 per cent) of the peasant population is employed on them. The co-operatives and the State farms comprise respectively 13 per cent and 29 per cent of the cultivated land, and produce more than a quarter of the total yield of 'white' cereals, artificial forage and industrial crops, whereas maize growing is principally confined to private farms, most of which are very small. Properties of more than about 75 acres are uncommon. Sixty per cent of the tilled land is in the hands of peasants with holdings of less than 12½ acres each. The State sector is by far the best provided with agricultural machinery — on average one reaper per 385 acres of arable land against one per 395 acres of co-operative land,

The hinterland of Zadar, in Dalmatia. In the background is the Velebit mountain range. In the foreground is an alluvial plain, broken up into thousands of small fields bearing a variety of crops, but mostly maize. PAUL ALMASY

and one per 740 acres of privately owned land. The figures for tractors are one per 1,420 acres, one per 1,265 acres and one per 11,300 acres respectively. The disparity is spectacular.

IMPROVEMENTS. Many obstacles of a material or psychological nature have hampered the application of the new policy. Some co-operatives were dissolved in 1953 and, at the same time, a new agrarian law limited the size of rural properties to a maximum of about 25 acres. The State domains do not as yet have the necessary personnel, material or credits. The average agricultural output is no higher than before the war, and flocks and herds have been brought up to their pre-war figures only with great difficulty. However, the crop switch-over (begun after the partition of the family communities) has been continued. Maize, which gives a high yield and is most cultivated where the population is densest, has taken the place of the old traditional crops, buckwheat, rye and millet. Stock-breeding is improving, even in the south, thanks to wise stock selection and progress in hygienic conditions.

Market-gardens have taken the place of the uprooted vineyards. In the Vojvodina more and more sugar-beet is being grown. Potatoes are not as yet very common but are being increasingly favoured in Slovenia and Croatia. Increased acreage of oil-producing and fibre plants has given good results.

Attempts to increase the cultivated areas and to increase the yields are being made by large-scale improvement measures. The Yugoslav forests are rich in fine timber trees and are therefore too precious to be sacrificed to extensive clearing. But the marshy lands in the Lika and Herzegovina *poljes* have been drained. *Podzol* and *vriština* soils, a sort of leached red earth, have been dressed with lime. The marshes of Macedonia, the Sava (Jelas and Lonja), the Vojvodina, the Istrian plains, and the lands around Lake Shkodër (where malaria is still rampant) are becoming progressively healthier, while new crops are being grown on the fertile soils: rice, cotton (40,000 acres), vegetables and fruits that are sent to the large canning factories. The irrigation of the Banat, undertaken in conjunction with the construction of the Danube-Tisa-Danube canal, will offset some of the dangers from drought and provide 1,235,000 acres of arable land. The Popovo Polje and the Macedonian basins could become the Tennessees of Yugoslavia.

Open-cast coal mining at the 'Tito' mines, Banovići. YUGOSLAV INFORMATION SERVICE

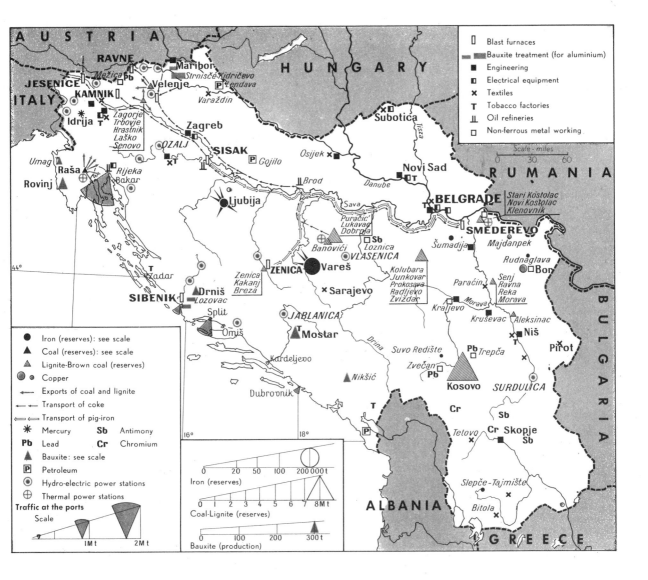

Legend (map key):

- ☐ Blast furnaces
- ▨ Bauxite treatment (for aluminium)
- ■ Engineering
- ◨ Electrical equipment
- ✕ Textiles
- T Tobacco factories
- ⨜ Oil refineries
- ▢ Non-ferrous metal working

- ● Iron (reserves): see scale
- ▲ Coal (reserves): see scale
- △ Lignite-Brown coal (reserves)
- ◉ ◦ Copper
- ⊷ Exports of coal and lignite
- ← Transport of coke
- ⇒ Transport of pig-iron
- ✳ Mercury   **Sb** Antimony
- **Pb** Lead   **Cr** Chromium
- ▲ Bauxite: see scale
- ℗ Petroleum
- ◉ Hydro-electric power stations
- ⊕ Thermal power stations

Traffic at the ports
Scale

Iron (reserves)   0   20   50   100   200 000 t
Coal-Lignite (reserves)   0 1 2 3 4 5 6 7 8 M t
Bauxite (production)   0   100   200   300 t

MINING AND INDUSTRY IN YUGOSLAVIA

Finally, developments of the last few years have led more and more to centralising production and to the formation of huge highly specialised farms, furnished with modern farming equipment. In 1949, there were 1,227 State domains (half of them in the Vojvodina) covering 871,000 acres, with an average of about 660 acres per farm. In 1952, the number had dropped to 737 (with three-quarters of them in the Vojvodina), but the total area had risen to about 1,507,000 acres, an average of 2,046 acres per farm. Smallholdings have received large subsidies, but many problems still remain: reconstitution of larger farming units, supplies of seed and fertilizers, electrification of rural areas. Now, more than ever, Yugoslav agriculture has need of support from industry.

Progress in industry and urbanisation

ECONOMIC BACKWARDNESS. Yugoslav industry is in its early stages, and the general situation is still not favourable. This can be ascribed, in the main, to the economic and technical backwardness of the Balkan countries. The heritage of former regimes lies heavy on economic life. The Turks encouraged nothing but handicrafts. The Austro-Hungarian government showed an interest in the food industries. The output of the mines, worked with the help of foreign capital before 1939, was exported, and equipment industries and manufactures were sited in the north and north-west, that is, near the Austrian and Hungarian frontiers. Yugoslav industry is handicapped by old-fashioned equipment, and output is at once too small and too expensive. Almost everywhere the craftsman's tradition has been preserved. High-quality metallurgical and textile products have to be imported.

The general economic backwardness is shown, too, by the unsatisfactory state of communications. The rail system is inadequate and the average speed (including stops) is low (about 18 m.p.h. on the best runs). The mining areas and the Adriatic ports are badly served. Freight charges are high and the volume of main-line traffic is not great. It is only in the north that there are good roads, but the number of vehicles in use is still much too small. The Belgrade-Zagreb motorway, which is to be extended to Ljubljana, was finished in 1950, but construction of the Dalmatian 'Tourist Highway' is proceeding very slowly. However, attention must be drawn to the economic importance of the railways built since 1945 in Bosnia (Šamac-Sarajevo and Bihać-Split) and Montenegro (Nikšić-Titograd).

Population statistics present a more satisfactory picture. Despite war losses (estimated at 1,700,000 dead), the total population (with an average density of more than 185 to the square mile) continues to increase. In only five years, from 1948 to 1953, the total rose from 15,772,000 to 17 million and today is well over 18 million. The birth rate exceeds 23 per thousand. The death rate has continued to fall and is now below 9 per thousand; the infant mortality rate on the other hand is one of the highest in the world. The distribution of population is rapidly changing, and the number of town-dwellers continues to rise. Indeed, after the war, the peasants flocked to the towns. The young people take jobs in the factories, which thus absorb part of the surplus population in the poorer parts of the land. But this sudden social transformation raises problems that are not easy to solve. How, for instance, can skilled workmen and competent technicians be trained in a very short space of time?

The distribution of sources of power does not seem to favour the development of large industrial centres. Coal furnishes four-fifths of the energy used, but the coalfields are scattered (the largest of them yields 400,000 tons annually), so that difficulties of communication are increased and exploitation is less concentrated than it might be. The Raša coal from Istria is of fine quality, but nine-tenths of Yugoslav solid fuel production consists of lignite and brown coal which cannot be used for coking, and coal has to be imported. Great hopes are set on oil but output does not meet one-quarter of the demand. No doubt hydro-electric power, which already furnishes 42 per cent of the total current produced, will be the great resource of the future. Large modern stations like that of Jablanica, on the Neretva, have recently begun operation. Dam-building in Slovenia, Croatia and Macedonia is progressing rather slowly.

Yugoslavia is rich in ores, whose working has always been profitable, and export or local processing provide an important source of State revenue. Iron is found mostly in Bosnia, copper in eastern Serbia, bauxite in Istria, Dalmatia and Montenegro. Lead, antimony, chromium, molybdenum and wolfram deposits are of considerable size. The Idrija mercury mine — which before the war belonged to Italy — is among the largest in Europe. In non-ferrous metal production Yugoslavia occupies an enviable place in the world.

The electro-chemical works at Jajce, in Bosnia. The factory uses power from one of the dams on the Pliva, and produces calcium carbide, soda, ferrosilicon. ROGER PERRIN

THE INDUSTRIALISATION TREND. Positive results have been obtained from the application of a drastic industrialisation programme. Nationalisation has been extended to include small enterprises. The targets of the first Five Year Plan turned out to be too ambitious, and external difficulties have prevented the full accomplishment of the programme laid down. The aims of the second Plan, although of the same kind (that is, concentrating on development of heavy industry and economic expansion in the more backward areas) were more modest and, despite some failures, it is certain that the traditional geography of Yugoslavia has been transformed rapidly.

The essential features of recent developments have been a general increase in output and expansion of the metallurgical industry. Yugoslavia now has at its disposal a greater quantity of coal, steel and cast-iron than before the war. The Jesenice, Sisak and Zenica blast-furnaces have been re-equipped. The problem of coke supply has been solved, in part, by the erection of the Lukavac works in Bosnia, where experiments are being made with new processes. Non-ferrous ores are being treated near the mines (as in the case of Bor) or near the hydro-electric dams by 'colour' metallurgy. Aluminium works are confined to Slovenia and Dalmatia. Efforts have been made to increase the output of machinery and agricultural, electrical and railway equipment. Some oriental countries are already buying machines and vehicles in Yugoslavia. On the other hand, the lack of skilled workmen and high-quality raw materials leaves the textile and chemical industries in a precarious condition. The spinning and weaving mills are hampered by old-fashioned equipment and suffer from irregular and indifferent supplies. Half the country's leather, 60 per cent of the woollens, and 90 per cent of the cottons are imported.

Yugoslav industry is changing and concentrating fairly rapidly. The old, traditional centres are expanding — in Slovenia, the Dalmatian ports, the Serbian and Bosnian mining towns, the headquarters of agricultural industry on the Pannonian plain, and the capitals of the federal republics. New achievements and really successful economic ventures have in some cases increased the importance of these places: for example, the 'Litostroj' works turning out electrical equipment in the suburbs of Ljubljana, and the 'Jugovinil' enterprise producing plastic goods near Split. What strikes the traveller from western Europe most forcibly is the immense progress made in the backward regions of Macedonia and, still more, in those of Bosnia and Montenegro. The population of northern Bosnia clings to the coalfields and the valley bottoms, where some factories employ more than 2,000 workmen. Almost half the rural population has migrated to big industrial centres like Banja Luka, Doboj, Zenica and Tuzla, and round the edge of the Pannonian basin a new economic area is growing up.

A comparable development has taken place in Montenegro. Shepherds and peasants are leaving the mountains for the coast in large numbers (in the Zeta valley at Nikšić and at Titograd). Despite heavy losses in the war, the population in the five main towns of Yugoslavia's smallest republic has continued to increase, and between 1948 and 1953 rose by 40 per cent.

RAPID GROWTH OF THE TOWNS. It is in the capitals that the rapid growth of population is most marked. The towns show clearly, in architecture, layout, social structure and activities, the influence of those civilisations that have dominated them. The old Moslem townships are those which have changed least, but they too have lost some of their craftsmen. The Dalmatian and Istrian cities, which lay half-asleep within their walls, have been partially awakened by tourists and increasing traffic in the ports. Pula and Zadar are slowly recovering from the exodus of the Italians; not so Rijeka and Split. The towns making the most remarkable progress are those on the plains or in the valleys, former fortresses or places

Above: *Albanian national dress.* ALLIBALL, ATLAS
PHOTO. Opposite: *Market outside a mosque at
Sarajevo.* ROGER PERRIN

The old harbour and ramparts of Dubrovnik.
CHARBONNIER, BRIZEMUR

Galičnik, a typical village of Macedonia. The scattered houses are perched on slopes above defiles. D. STANIMIROVITCH, GIRAUDON

of residence of the Austrian, Serbian or Magyar middle-classes (with the exception of the Banat towns); the populations of Maribor, Novi Sad, Niš, Subotica, Osijek and Ljubljana are mostly made up of workmen. Everywhere, the expansion of State commerce and the nationalised industries has attracted inhabitants from the surrounding countryside into the towns. Mushroom towns — temporary or permanent — are constantly springing up near the dams, the mines and the big metallurgical plants.

Zagreb and Belgrade are far and away the largest towns and have all the appearance of metropolitan cities. Zagreb has grown along the banks of the Sava and at the foot of the Medvednica (a massif over 3,000 feet high); it lies on the cross-roads between the Adriatic, Hungary and Austria, and is linked with Slovenia and Croatia. The geographical position and the site of Belgrade are much more favourable for the development of a great city, for it lies on one of the great European cross-roads. Highways from the south (Salonica, Sofia, Istanbul) along the Morava, the Vardar and the Strumica, roads from the east (Iron Gates, Bucharest and Black Sea), roads from the west (Slavonia and Slovenia) and roads from the north cross at the meeting point of the Sava and Drava rivers, where the

waters are dominated by the terraces of the 330 feet high Kalamegdan, the site of a fortress since Celtic times. Yet fortune tended to favour Zagreb, at least until the end of the nineteenth century. It has always been an important market for Venetian, Austrian and Hungarian goods, with an active and prosperous population which has directed the town's expansion along hills overlooking the river (and thus out of the way of floods) and, later, along a highway parallel to the Sava, the Ilica. Zagreb has nonetheless preserved the calm, rather baroque appearance of an Austrian provincial town, for it was never occupied by the Turks, nor even seriously threatened by them.

In contrast, it was the varied fortunes of Austro-Turkish warfare that hindered the growth of Belgrade, whose cobbled streets, balconied houses, and picturesque craftsmen's shops still give an oriental impression. The fortress, today surrounded by a park, was several times the stake in bloody battles, and the old wooden town itself was often attacked by fire. It was only after 1804, particularly after 1919, that the unique situation of the town influenced its development and it became first the capital of Serbia and then of Yugoslavia. In 1830 Belgrade had only 30,000 inhabitants. Today, with its suburbs, it has well over 500,000 inhabitants — against Zagreb's 400,000.

Mostar, the former capital of Herzegovina. Its Old Bridge, with many minarets, was built in the sixteenth century by a Turkish architect, on the site of a Roman bridge spanning the River Neretva with a single 90-foot arch. In the distance are great chalk plateaus, harsh and bare. YUGOSLAV NATIONAL TOURIST OFFICE

One of the principal streets of Belgrade. In 1830 the city had only 30,000 inhabitants; today, with its suburbs, it has more than 500,000. YUGOSLAV NATIONAL TOURIST OFFICE

The old part of Zagreb, showing the fifteenth-century cathedral surrounded by the towers of the eleventh-century fortress. Zagreb is the capital of Croatia and the second largest city of Yugoslavia, and is still growing. YUGOSLAV NATIONAL TOURIST OFFICE

Macedonian peasants. VAGN HANSEN, RAPHO

Opposite: *Once a year all the Moslems of Bosnia-Herzegovina come together at Vrnograč for the 'great invocation of Allah'.* ANDRÉ ZUCCA

Below: *Macedonian folk-dancing.* YUGOSLAV NATIONAL TOURIST OFFICE

New factories have sprung up to the south-west, at Rakovica and Zelezniki. On the other side of the Sava and the Danube, the satellite towns of Zemun and Pančevo have always been large markets for Pannonian produce; now they are becoming important industrial and commercial centres. The development of the Belgrade conurbation has been somewhat held up since the Second World War by the rather unsuccessful attempt made to create the town of Novi Beograd on the alluvial plain nearby.

The expansion of Zagreb and Belgrade is proof of the new Yugoslavia's economic and political renaissance. However, rapid urbanisation presents new problems. Increased agricultural output is necessary and the almost insoluble problem of housing is especially acute. Industrialisation thus has very grave limitations. If increased demands are to be met, agriculture must be modernised; but it cannot be modernised unless industry can supply machines and fertilizers. As Yugoslav industrial output is too low to bring this balance, recourse must be had to foreign sources of supply. Since, too, foreign exchange can be obtained only by exports of agricultural produce (the traditional pre-war exports), care must be taken that over-industrialisation does not compromise the future of agriculture. This is one of the vicious circles of Yugoslav economy. And the problem becomes still more complicated in years of poor grain harvests. In 1952, 900,000 tons of wheat had to be imported, 200,000 tons in 1954, and an average of over 1,000,000 tons annually from 1955 to 1958. The problem of economic independence is far from solved; everything depends upon Yugoslavia's political relations with her neighbours — and with the Great Powers.

Yugoslavia and the world

A BALKAN, MEDITERRANEAN AND DANUBIAN STATE. During the last hundred years, increased population has sparked off a movement of emigration. From 1870 to 1940 hundreds of thousands of peasants (probably more than half a million) were driven abroad by destitution and the slump in agricultural prices. There were Serbs from the Šumadija, Slovenes from the coast, Croats from the Lika and the Zagorje, Montenegrins and Dalmatians from the islands. Until 1914 all headed for America, then, after the First World War, for Germany, Belgium and France. Yugoslavs can be found in fairly compact groups in the Great Lakes region, in the northeast United States, in the Mississippi delta and in the Canadian woodlands. Some have established themselves and founded families in Brazil and Australia. Others have returned to Yugoslavia after making their fortunes abroad — these are the 'Americans' who have built villas on the coast, constructed roads and modernised villages. Many, again, have remained permanently overseas and have been assimilated in the New World. Their children no longer learn their mother-tongue, though the emigrants still remember relatives who have stayed at home; postal-orders and packets from all over the world pour into Yugoslavia, and some islands, like Vis or Krk, live at least in part on supplies sent through Rijeka. Abroad, the Yugoslavs retain their old customs and found folklore clubs (as at Pittsburgh and Cleveland). The economic and political influence of these groups of emigrants is considerable.

Yugoslav foreign trade is expanding, although on the whole the balance is unfavourable. Half the traffic of the Danube is in the hands of Yugoslav companies. The merchant fleet, wiped out during the war, has been rebuilt. Ocean-going freighters and coastal vessels carry most of the exports, which are transported by sea rather than rail or road. There are five shipyards and they are working to capacity. Even the fighting fleet has been considerably increased. Rijeka, well situated at the head of a sheltered roadstead, is linked with Susak, and is in closer touch with an industrial and forested hinterland than are the other Adriatic ports. Since 1946 Rijeka has been reconstructed and industrialised and is in the process of becoming a great Mediterranean port — the successful rival of Trieste. Traffic is now much greater than that of the other Yugoslav ports, Split, Sibenik, Dubrovnik-Gruz, and commercial aviation too is expanding; international lines are already in operation.

The pattern of Yugoslav foreign trade is subject to all the sudden fluctuations which may be produced by political situation, and changes in currents of trade have been as many as four times in fifteen years (1940—55). Yugoslavia imports cereals, coal, cotton and machinery from the West; she exports wood, maize, fruit, tobacco and ores to Great Britain and France. But new trends are already visible: there is exchange of maize and ores for Austrian and Swiss textiles, electrical and optical appliances; of agricultural produce for West German coke and machinery. Textiles, cement and even some equipment are exported to countries still more backward than Yugoslavia itself — to the Near and Middle East (mainly to Turkey), Egypt, India, Pakistan, Ethiopia and Burma.

Then the tourist industry must not be overlooked, for there are few European countries as rich in varied natural beauty — high Alpine or Dinaric mountains, Adriatic beaches, Montenegrin canyons, and grottoes in the Karst. The mineral and hot springs of Serbia and Slovenia have been famous since Roman times. Yugoslav art treasures and folk-lore are rich and rare — the Macedonian and Bosnian mosques, the Orthodox monasteries of Metohija and Serbia, the Romanesque churches and Renaissance palaces of Dalmatia. In 1939 720,000 tourists visited the country; in 1957 the figure had risen to nearly two million. There are still relatively few foreign residents, but their numbers are increasing. Swiss, Germans and Austrians are gradually taking possession of the coast again and are replacing the Czechs and Hungarians. The French run short-stay cruises, while Americans of Yugoslav origin flock to the coast.

Since relations between Italy and Yugoslavia have improved, Italian tourists are now found in Istria and Dalmatia. But internal communications and roads and standards of comfort are in need of considerable improvement. And, from this point of view, there is much still to be done. However, new winter-sports resorts have been set up in Slovenia and Montenegro. The coast road is under construction. Dubrovnik and the southern islands are organising themselves to receive winter visitors, while camping is popular with the younger people.

This then is the place of Yugoslavia in international politics: she is a Danubian Power, the most important of the Balkan lands, with a strong position in the Mediterranean. Despite traditional economic difficulties (related to geographical and historical factors), and because of the vitality and patriotism of her people, Yugoslavia may come to play a part in world politics. When she found no support for her territorial claims to Greek and Bulgarian Macedonia, Slovenian Carinthia, Trieste and Gorica — regions or towns peopled only in part by Yugoslavs — she wisely renounced them, and may be reconciled with Italy. Still, the country is set between two blocs. The internal regime is inspired by Marxist principles, and foreign policy tends towards a prudent neutralism.

Steering her way between threats and promises, Yugoslavia seeks to follow a middle course — no doubt that which is most advantageous for her. Adversity has strengthened national unity, but this question remains: will Yugoslavia be able to effect and secure at one and the same time the revival and independence of her economy?

André BLANC

General view of Tirana, capital of Albania. The mosque is surrounded by houses with low roofs of curved tiles. Orchards encircle the town. The Mediterranean climate enables tropical plants to be grown. JACQUES KANAPA, ATLAS–PHOTO

ALBANIA

ALBANIA is one of the wildest and most mountainous countries in Europe, a little bigger than Sicily and a little smaller than Belgium, with a sea coast of something over 150 miles. The average density of population is only about 148 per square mile. Up to 1947 Albania was the only European country with no railway at all. Thirty years ago the capital, Tirana (Tiranë), had only about 20,000 inhabitants. Agriculture is primitive and industry is hardly developed at all. Both conditions stem from the nature of the country and from its history.

WILD MOUNTAINS. Two-thirds of Albania's area lies at a height of over 3,000 feet, and the country is closed in on the land side by a barrier of tall massifs over 6,000 feet, and reaching in places over 8,000 feet. Geological structure and morphology are complex and varied. To the north, the limestones of the Prokletia (Prokletije), or 'Accursed Mountains', are tilted as in Montenegro (Crna Gora). The sharp crests, the glacial cirques, the deep valleys littered with moraines, give them an Alpine look. Above the Yugoslav plains of the Kosovo and the Metohija rise tall massifs, cut by the middle course of the Drin. Karst-like platforms alternate with more jagged ridges in the ancient formations of the Korab, the Dejes, the Lopes, and the Merdita. To the south-east and south, as well as in the centre, the Dinaric folds, full of crystalline nuclei, are lower. Some basins have subsided; others, as in Macedonia, are still occupied by lakes. The intensely folded coastal ranges overlook a rocky shore running from north-west to south-east beyond the Gulf of Vlonë (Valona). The network of rivers is of little help in penetrating this mass of mountains. The Black Drin, flowing from Lake Ohrit (Ohrid), runs through impressive gorges spanned by flimsy wooden bridges and joins up a number of marshy basins. The rivers of the Mediterranean basin do not reach as far as the Yugoslav frontier, and the upper valleys are simply narrow gashes in the rocks. Only the Korçë and Ohrit basins, the valley of the White Drin coming from the Metohija, present a few gaps. Through them the *Via Egnatia* ran in ancient times, taking the trading caravans from Italy into Macedonia. Caravanserais, or *han*, are still dotted along the line of these ancient roads.

The mountains, then, have remained wild. Patriarchal families, grouped together in clans (*stirpes* or *fis*) preserve their old traditions there. Ancient customs (fidelity to the sworn word and the vendetta, for example) flourished until recently,

Gjinokastër (formerly Argyrocastro) near the Greek frontier.
JACQUES KANAPA, ATLAS-PHOTO

and even the present Albanian government has had to recognise the tribal regime. Moreover, the massifs and the high valleys are divided into a number of units with closed economies. Activity is confined to handicrafts and stock-breeding. The heights are covered with grass and are favoured by a wet climate (rainfall about 160 inches a year) and cool summers (average for July about 63° F.). Since the Second World War there have been fewer migrating flocks and herds, but pastoral life generally has altered little. The mountains, too, offer an asylum. In addition to the shepherd's hut, the commonest type of dwelling is the stone *kula*, a sort of square tower with thick, high walls and very few windows: in fact, a fortress within which chiefs, women and outlaws can gather together. In the south, on the other hand, a feudal regime has replaced the clan system and here, as in Macedonia, the *cifliks* or large farming units can be seen.

UNHEALTHY PLAINS. Plains make up only one-seventh of the total area of the country. They stretch along the sides of the rivers and form a belt about 6 to 18 miles wide along the seashore. Landwards, Albania is protected by its mountain barrier but opens on to the Adriatic. Here more than in any other region round the Mediterranean shores, the lowlands are marshy. The torrents dashing from the heights scatter a rather coarse alluvial soil, winding about on the alluvial fans, capturing each other's waters and silting up the coastal bays already half shut in by headlands of Miocene sands and clays. The climate, which is mild in winter, becomes very hot in summer and unhealthily humid. The coast is infested with malaria and, before the war, more than half the local population was infected. Drainage of the marshes is not very effective

and a plain like that of the Myzegeja is flooded during the winter months. Crops do well only in the driest areas — in the Arzen valley, for instance — or after drainage has been undertaken. There is no site on the coast where a large port could develop. Only the Vlonë Gulf, protected by the Island of Sazan, offers fair anchorage, but the hinterland is poor.

A HILLY AND POPULATED FRINGE. Where mountain and plain meet population is thickest. This is a region of drier hillside terraces, of fertile alluvial fans, and hills cut out of the Tertiary deposits. In this area there are more than 150 inhabitants to the square mile. At the entrances to the narrow valleys are the large market-towns — Shkodër (Scutari), Tirana, Elbasan and Berat. Here, as far as temperature is concerned, the climate is still Mediterranean. Rain is heavier in the autumn than in the spring. It is only in the south that the summer is really dry, and here more rain falls in March and April than elsewhere. On the slopes, bush and scrub mingle with forests of oak, pine and chestnut. In the valleys and hollows cereals are grown (more maize than wheat). These areas are dotted with fruit-trees: apricots, peaches and figs in the centre, citrus fruits in the south. The olive is the most widely cultivated fruit-tree, though they are fewer in the south and on the coast than in the north and the interior. The shores of Lake Shkodër form a region apart; the fishermen, like those of Ohrit, use flat-bottomed boats known as *lundras*. The fields of the peasants are well irrigated and their life is a relatively easy one. This hilly country still forms the economic centre of the Albanian state, for in it is concentrated most of the agriculture and industry.

POLITICAL AND ECONOMIC STRUCTURE. Albania is, according to its Constitution of March 1946 (the republic was proclaimed in January 1944), a 'People's Democracy'. It is, in fact, the only one giving on to the Mediterranean, and the 'advance post of the Soviet Bloc'. Linguistically and ethnically Albania is a united country. A language of Asiatic origin, Albanian has annexed a number of Slav, Greek, Turkish and Latin elements and is divided into two dialects, Tosk in the south and Gheg in the north. Non-Albanian minorities are not numerous — only 4 per cent are Slavs and Greeks, and nearly 70 per cent of the population is Moslem. The Bektashis form independent communities. Albanians are scattered all over the world. According to a recent Yugoslav census, there are 750,000 in Macedonia, Kosovo, Metohija and Montenegro. Hundreds of thousands live in Greece, Italy, Sicily, and, above all, the United States.

This state of things can be explained by Albania's history. It is a country whose people have always opposed the Turks with a fierce resistance, yet it is a modern state that achieved independence only by the Treaty of London in 1913. The reign of the German Prince William of Wied — imposed upon the country by the Great Powers — did not last long. Between the two World Wars, Albania, whose southern regions were coveted by the Greeks, became an Italian colony. Capitalists from Milan, Rome and Naples invested in a number of industrial and agricultural enterprises on the Albanian plains. 300,000 Italians occupied the country and the famous 'Good Friday attack' in 1939 was the death-knell of Albanian independence. After the Italo-Greek war, the German occupation of Albania cost the country about 2.5 per cent of its population, 37 per cent of its buildings, and 50 per cent of its livestock. Since the end of the Second World War, quarrels between Yugoslavia and Albania — quarrels in which ideological, ethnical and economic considerations are curiously mixed — have hindered the application of economic development plans, the Two Year Plans (1947—48 and 1949—50) as well as the Five Year Plan (1951—55). The result is that Albania has remained isolated, with nothing but her own resources. At the present time the country has to ask for help from the U.S.S.R.

and far distant sister republics with which she has no common frontier. The present condition of the Albanian economy presents many problems, all very far from being solved.

AGRARIAN REFORM.

The law of 20th August, 1945, prescribed the expropriation of large estates which, before the war, comprised rather more than 52 per cent of the arable land. Some 500,000 to 640,000 acres were divided among the poor families in the mountains or landless peasants at the rate of about 12 acres to each family of six members. Contrary to the pattern in other 'People's Democracies', co-operatives have not developed much and comprise only a relatively small area (6 per cent) of the land under grain crops. On the other hand, flocks and herds of more than 400 beasts have been taken over by the State, which now possesses 100,000 head of cattle, sheep and other animals. Because of the important place held by stock-breeding and by Mediterranean or small shrub crops, the agrarian reform has not yet had any effect on agricultural output. Furthermore, only 11 per cent of the land is productive. Large-scale engineering works have been undertaken to drain the marshes round Lakes Maliq and Shkodër (Scutari) and on the plain between the rivers Semeni and Shkumbeni. Maize is the commonest cereal and covers twice the acreage devoted to wheat. The yields do not, however, satisfy home demands, and wheat has to be imported from the Ukraine. The Italians extended the area of sugar-beet cultivation, and production should increase tenfold. A modern sugar refinery has been set up at Korçë. But the real hope for agriculture lies in the improvement and development of industrial crops. Cotton and rice should do well in the marshy plains. More potatoes are being grown. Tobacco — a traditional crop — may become, as in Turkey, a large-scale export item. Several million olive trees are being planted, while presses and refineries are being set up for processing the oil. Stock-breeding (the principal product of which is the *kackaval* cheese) suffers from the lack of hygiene and routine, and from prejudice. Pig-breeding cannot, of course, be of much importance in a Moslem community. Cattle are far less numerous than sheep and goats; horses are few.

INDUSTRIALISATION BEGINS.

In addition to the food industries, Albanian mines may bring future prosperity to the country. Though lignites of the Tirana and Tepelenë basins are poor, the bitumen mine at Selenica — already exploited by the Italians — is one of the best in the world. The Pukë hematite and copper, and the Kukës, Krumë and Pogradec chromium (several hundred thousand tons of ore) are exported. The petroleum deposits were formerly worked by British, French and Italian companies. During the war output was a million tons, but production seems now to be sagging.

Exploitation of subsoil riches and the construction of plant come up against a number of difficulties: lack of skilled labour, lack of technicians (now supplied by the U.S.S.R.), poor quality material and, above all, lack of communications. The first railway line (about 27 miles long) from Durrës (Durazzo) to Pequin (the first section of the Durrës-Elbasan line) was opened in November 1947. The second section (20 miles) was opened to traffic in December 1950, while the Durrës-Tirana line (24 miles) started working in March 1948. The mining centres are to be linked by rail with the capital.

It is still too early to judge what has been achieved in Albania. The development of this backward country has certainly been speeded up by the legal measures taken to emancipate Albanian women, who were formerly little better than slaves; by improving public health and medical services; by the spread of education (made obligatory for all in 1952) and by the foundation of agronomical and technical schools. The future of Albania, a country surrounded and isolated by states rather hostile to her, is not only bound up with that of the other 'People's Democracies' with which Albania does most of her trade — East Germany, Rumania, Hungary and Poland, which supply her with the coke, machines, mining equipment and the textiles she needs — but depends also upon neighbours more powerful than herself — on Yugoslavia and Greece.

André BLANC

A market at Shkodër (formerly Scutari). JACQUES KANAPA, ATLAS-PHOTO

The Acropolis looks like the fortress it once was. In the centre of the rock are the ruins of the Parthenon, in the foreground the Propylaea, and to the left the Erechtheum. To the right of the rock, in the foreground, is an amphitheatre where the Greek tragedies are performed today; beyond is the Amphitheatre of Dionysus where they were performed in ancient times. IKONES, CAMERA PRESS

GREECE

IT is only since 1830 that Greece has existed as an independent state. Before that date 'Greece' was a rather vague geographical expression since it did not suggest any very definite limits nor did it convey the extent of what may be called 'Hellenism' or the 'Greek World', broader entities whose frontiers were susceptible to change from age to age. Since 1830 Greece has added territory which has changed the nature of the country, although it does not yet include all Greeks. For us, Greece means as much the 'Hellenism' of the past as the formal territorial limits of the country today.

The landscape and regions of Greece

THE INFLUENCE OF PHYSICAL CHARACTER. The physical character of the Greek lands has played an all-important rôle in the life of the Greeks and has imposed upon them conditions of existence which are reflected in the present-day economy. Greece's physical features are by no means uniform, and within its 51,168 square miles there are many differences and many striking contrasts.

The country consists mainly of regions of indented coastlines and island-dotted seas. It is, nevertheless, firmly riveted to the continental mass of south-eastern Europe where it borders on Albania, Yugoslavia, Bulgaria and Turkey. Northern Greece is linked with the Balkan world and, of necessity, bears the mark of Balkan influence. From a historical point of view, the north is the only part of present-day Greece that was on the borders of the ancient Greek world or, indeed, beyond its limits. Farther south is a domain that is really Mediterranean. Another though minor contrast is presented by the difference between the western slopes (generally rather abrupt) and the eastern slopes which are more gentle and open toward the sea. The complex nature of the physical relief and the extraordinary division of the country into small natural units have fostered numerous local differences.

Northern Greece has a more spacious landscape, more massive mountains and more extensive plains than the rest of the country. Northwards from the Aegean Sea, Thrace and Macedonia contain the prolongation of the Rhodope massif (itself situated farther north), a powerful, resistant mass that is comparable with the Hercynian massifs of western Europe. Between the plateaus and residual buttes (rising almost to 6,500 feet) there are subsidence basins occupied by plains, such as those of Serrai, Drama or ancient Philippi. Here the rivers slow down and during the rainy season waters are stagnant or form lakes. The coast is flat and little indented. There is, however, the Khalkidike peninsula which thrusts its three 'prongs' seaward; at the end of the most northerly prong stands Mount Athos, which for centuries has sheltered a monastic community that still forms a sort of autonomous republic. Two islands, Thasos and Samothrace (Samothraki), occupy the Sea of Thrace. Safe anchorages and natural harbours are rare. Kavalla, a town which owes its importance to the tobacco trade, has grown up round an isolated rock where moorings are good. The Vardar valley (ancient Axios), cutting through a broad belt of sediments, opens a highway into the interior — toward Yugoslavia — and ends at the head of the Gulf of Salonica (Thermai) in a huge alluvial plain. This is a cross-roads where the ancient *Via Egnatia* ran from the Adriatic to the Sea of Thrace. A large town, Thessaloniki (Salonica), with a busy port has grown up in this area.

Thessaly is a land of plains surrounded by mountains (Ossa and Pelion lie to the east and separate Thessaly from the sea; 9,573-foot Olympus, the highest point in Greece, to the north; Pindus and Thymphrestus to the west; Othrys to the south) and by hills encircling the Gulf of Volos. In Thessaly, as in northern Greece, the wet seasons alternate with periods so dry that the earth takes on the appearance of a desiccated, dusty steppe. The waters, drained by the Pinios, make their way through a narrow corridor cut in the limestones of Olympus, where great trees intermingle with shrubs, bushes and climbing and twining plants, offering a strong contrast in summer with the burning plains. This is the Vale of Tempe extolled by the poets.

The climate of these regions is, generally speaking, harsh. The winters are cold. At the end of autumn rainfall is much more abundant than is typical in Mediterranean lands. The summers are usually dry and, in spite of the storms, the heat is stifling in the inland basins. The inhabitants avoid the unhealthy plains and move up the hills or the mountain slopes. Pelion's flanks leading down to the Gulf of Volos enjoy the mildness of the Mediterranean climate, and the port and busy town of Volos is a pleasant place of residence.

The western regions, western Macedonia and the Epirus, owe their characteristics to a series of mountain ranges parallel to the coast which drop precipitously to the sea; the highest is the Pindus (8,445 feet). These ranges have a plentiful rainfall (coming mostly from the west) and are covered, especially in the north, by splendid forests. Their topographical features, however, do not favour penetration by Mediterranean influences. There are valleys or small basins, often occupied by picturesque lakes, such as those of Kastoria and Ioannina (Jannina). In the south, Acarnania and Aetolia have the same mountainous aspect as north-western Greece, but the Gulf of Amvrakia (or Gulf of Arta), the valley of the Achelous (Akheloos) and the Agrinion basin are more open to the sea breezes.

Offshore, the Ionian Islands, which resemble the mainland opposite in relief, were never occupied by the Turks and have, in contrast to the mainland, fruitful and well-tended fields as well as a very dense population.

Central Greece and the Peloponnese (Morea) make up the heartland of the classical Greek scene. Here sea and land meet and mingle, and the traveller's impression is of an ever-changing landscape. Mountain masses seem to spread in all directions. There is a great variety of rocks, though limestones and marble predominate. Small plains dot coastal areas and, less often, the mountains. To the south of the valley of the Sperchius, the tallest mountains (Oeta, Parnassus) rise well above 6,500 feet with patches of pine and fir forests. At their feet stretch the Locris, Phocis and Boeotia basins, exposed to cold winds in winter but very hot in summer. To the south-east the more markedly Mediterranean promontory of Attica thrusts out into the sea.

'The Isle of Pelops' or Peloponnese, joined to the mainland by the narrow isthmus of Corinth, has a complicated topographical pattern. On the northern shores mountains rise abruptly in the region of Achaia to surround the basins of Arcadia — always an area of refuge — and then spread out to form the peninsula of Messene, the long, rocky ridge of the

GREECE

Taygetus (7,700 feet), which stretches as far as Cape Matapan (Tainaron), and the mass of the Parnon. A smaller branch breaks off towards the east in Argolis. Here and there plains managed to form: in the north and east there are those of Corinth and Argos, to the south the valley of the Eurotas, the Messene (warm enough for bananas to ripen), and in the west, the far-reaching landscape of Elis.

In these historic areas climate varies according to exposure, distance from the sea, and altitude. The regions giving on to the west are dampest and greenest. The inland basins, with more extreme temperatures, are less suited to Mediterranean crops. Arcadia, whose basins lie at altitudes of 2,000 to 2,600 feet, has few vines and no olives, but there are patches of oak forest and some of the valleys are very verdant. The eastern areas are drier. During the heat of summer the long hours of sunshine on the limestone landscape give everything an air of desiccation that is accentuated by the irregularity of the rainfall (Athens had only about 4.3 inches in 1898, against about 34 inches in 1883) and the permeable nature of the soil. The run-off waters accumulate in the hollows from which they issue, not through valleys but through chasms in the permeable rocks — the *katavothrai* — and if the subterranean passages become blocked a lake may form, like Stymphalus. Lake Pheneus is now dry. In Boeotia extensive construction work has secured the drainage of Lake Copais and its vast area is now cultivated land.

THE GREEK ISLANDS. Geologically the islands are closely related to the mainland: they are, in fact, the peaks of mountain ridges that once united the Balkan peninsula to Asia Minor and were partially submerged by the subsidence of the Aegean Sea. The Sporades, in the north, are an extension

of the Othrys range and reach Mitilini (Lesbos) and Chios. Euboea and Attica seem to crumble away in the Cyclades that lead to Ikaria and Samos. Strung along the wide arc of a circle, Kithira, the great island of Crete, Karpathos and Rhodes are stepping-stones to the indented peninsulas of south-western Asia Minor. Between the submarine platforms supporting these groups of islands run deep troughs — more than 9,500 feet deep — to the north of Crete.

Among these islands, the influence of the sea is, of course, all-powerful. Still, they present a number of different faces. The largest islands — Mitilini, Chios, Rhodes and especially Crete — have fertile, well-cultivated plains, still fresh-looking in, say, Mitilini but almost African in Crete. The most typical island aspect is that of the Cyclades, where trees are scarce and the inhabitants are forced to build terraces to retain the soil. Regular northerly winds keep the summer temperatures lower than on the mainland, but rain is not so abundant and from June onwards the whole countryside is baked tawny by the sun. White villages and green vineyards and a few orchards sheltered from the wind stand out in a predominantly yellowish-brown landscape.

However great the contrasts between the sunlit isles and the wooded or snowy peaks of Pindus, between the orchards of Messene or Crete and the dusty steppes of Macedonia, there are certain common features: the extent of the mountains — covering 80 per cent of the country's area; an impression of dryness in the long hours of intense summer sunlight; the irregularity of the rainfall; the rarity of running waters. Such conditions do not favour abundant vegetation, and there is reason to wonder whether climate and natural vegetation have changed since classical times. Some regions have lost their trees, it is true, but such deforestation can have had only local and limited effects. The few detailed accounts left by classical writers suggest that the Greek climate has not been modified to any marked degree. We may recall also that the last episodes in the country's geological history are quite recent, and from these the earth in the Aegean region has retained a marked instability, proved by frequent earthquakes and the existence of volcanoes, one of which (Santorin — ancient Thira) is still active.

From past to present

THE PAST. A very long time ago peoples of different origins settled in this part of the Mediterranean. From the beginning of the third millenium B.C. brilliant civilisations flourished around the shores, civilisations created by Mediterranean peoples whose focal point was the island of Crete. The Hellenes came down in several waves from the north — the Achaeans about the twentieth century B.C. and the Dorians about the twelfth century B.C. By an amalgamation of these diverse elements the Greek people was formed. By the eighth century B.C. Greeks were settled in the whole Aegean region, in the south of the Balkan peninsula, on the coasts of Asia Minor, and as far away as Cyprus. They were grouped into numerous separate communities, some of which established famous classical cities. Then, during the eighth, seventh and sixth centuries B.C. came a vigorous movement of expansion and colonisation. New Greek communities were founded on the shores of the Black Sea, in North Africa (Cyrenaica), in southern Italy, in Sicily, and as far afield as Gaul and Spain. At its peak, Greek civilisation flourished over a considerable area, though the centre of Hellenism was still the narrow belt that stretches from Thermopylae to Sparta and the political horizon was limited by the neighbouring mountains. Yet the cities within this restricted area succeeded in creating a civilisation at once highly original and profoundly human.

In the fourth century B.C. Hellenism — as a consequence of Alexander's conquests — spread over the East. Later, after the Roman annexation of Greece, Hellenic influence was felt in Italy and the provinces of the Caesars' Empire. When that Empire crumbled under barbarian blows, it was Hellenism that took the place of Rome in the Mediterranean. Byzantium, or Constantinople (now Istanbul), became the New Rome and guardian of classical tradition. However, in that Greek Empire, whose capital was on the Bosporus, Greece itself was but an obscure province which was overwhelmed by Slav invaders in the seventh and eighth centuries A.D., attacked by Moslems and Normans, and then annexed by the Crusaders in 1204.

After the fall of Constantinople in 1453 and the Turkish conquest, Greece entered upon the most sombre phase of her history. For more than three centuries the country was to all intents and purposes cut off from the rest of the world and reduced to one of the most miserable lands in Europe. The condition of Greece during that period was related to certain physical factors and underlines the problems that the Greeks have had to face. The cities of ancient Greece prospered because they developed industrial and commercial activities as well as agriculture. Decadence set in when the great trade routes ceased to make use of Greek ports. The small units (with some rare exceptions, such as that of Corinth) dropped back into a wretched, circumscribed, rural way of life. The population began to decrease. Wallachian shepherds with their flocks moved along the mountains in the west, while the Turks endeavoured to colonise Greece with Albanians.

THE REBIRTH OF THE GREEK PEOPLE. Trial and tribulation did not destroy the Greek people, but many fled from their native land. Rich and busy Greek communities grew up elsewhere: in south Russia, in Rumania, at Constantinople. In Greece itself a feeling of nationalism was retained despite their Turkish masters, and the people did their best to defend their traditions, language and religion. Of all who fell beneath the Turkish yoke, the Greeks were the first to gain their independence. By the Treaty of Adrianople and the London Protocol of 1829—30, an independent kingdom was created, consisting of the Peloponnese, central Greece and the Cyclades. Thereafter, the main phases of Greece's territorial history were as follows: 1864 the annexation of the Ionian Islands (ceded by Great Britain); in 1881 the Arta and Thessaly regions were received from Turkey; in 1897 Crete was separated from Turkey and, in 1908, annexed to Greece. The southern Epirus, Macedonia and Thrace as far as the Mesta were added after the 1912—13 Balkan Wars.

Although she entered the First World War late, Greece received, by the Sèvres and Neuilly Treaties (1919—20), eastern Thrace and the administration of the Smyrna region. For a few short months she dreamed of capturing Constantinople and of conquering Asia Minor, but Mustafa Kemal and his Turkish armies shattered this illusion. At the Trianon Treaty of 1923 the Greeks had to renounce Asia Minor, eastern Thrace, and the islands of Imroz and Tenedos. However, if the Anatolian catastrophe ruined many hopes, it served to strengthen Hellenism in Greece itself. Exchanges of minority populations resulted in the return of 1,222,000 Greeks from Turkey, while 450,000 Turks and 93,000 Bulgars left Greece. The Anatolian coast where Greek civilisation had flourished for so long was lost, and the influx of refugees produced in Greece a very painful situation from the point of view of public health and that of the national economy. On the other hand, the refugees provided a valuable, hard-working and active population that has done much towards the modernisation of Greece.

The events of the Second World War, the Italo-German occupation and then the civil war between Communists and non-Communists (which went on until 1949) caused immense damage. But hard work backed by generous help, first from Great Britain and then from the United States, allowed Greece (now embracing the Dodecanese) to heal her wounds and enter a new phase of national progress.

THE GREEKS AND THEIR VITALITY. History bears witness to the extraordinary vitality of the Greek people. Whatever the vicissitudes endured in the past, the people today are remarkably homogeneous. Foreign elements, even when numerous, have been assimilated. In regions annexed in recent years, Turkish and Bulgarian minorities have been eliminated. The differences between the Greeks of these regions, those of 'Old Greece', and the refugees from Turkey are fading. The last descendants of the Albanian settlers are slowly giving up their language. The only minority groups are non-Orthodox Greeks (Catholics who owe their religion to Venetian domination), Jews (descended from refugees who left Spain in the Middle Ages), Moslems, and small ethnical groups of Slavo-Macedonians, Armenians or Kutzo-Vlachs. Together these make up less than six per cent of the population.

Language and religion are, then, the essential characteristics of the Greek people. The religion is that of the Orthodox Church, the autocephalous Greek Church governed by a synod of diocesan bishops presided over by the Metropolitan of Athens. The modern Greek language, directly descended from ancient Greek, has been much transformed by a long evolution and is a living language.

Since 1830 the population has increased rapidly with annexations of new territory, the influx of refugees from Turkey, and a marked excess of births over deaths. The birth rate between 1929 and 1939 ranged from 24.5 to 31.4 per thousand. Despite war losses and the high death rate (directly related to the deplorable conditions in which refugees had to live on their arrival in Greece and the famine that followed the Italo-German occupation), the population has continued to increase. Sanitary conditions have been improved. The draining of

The theatre at Epidauros, the best preserved and most perfect of its kind. It was hewn out of the north-west slope of Mount Chynortium. The 55 tiers seat 14,000 spectators. It was the work of Polycletus the Younger, a sculptor and architect of the fourth century B.C.   J. ALLAN CASH

A donkey in a village on the island of Poros, off the east coast of Morea. On many mountain roads in Greece the only method of transporting goods is on the back of a donkey or mule. J. ALLAN CASH

A flock of sheep being driven along a road between the olive groves near Sparta. Note the enormous burdens carried by the donkeys in the background. J. ALLAN CASH

Mount Olympus (9,573 feet), the highest point of Greece, and the home of the classical gods. The imposing mass of Olympus, which keeps its snows till late in the year, overshadows the plain of Thessaly.
GREEK TOPOGRAPHICAL SERVICE

The fishing port of Tourkolimano, near Athens.
IKONES, CAMERA PRESS

marshy areas and the destruction of mosquitoes by American teams have abolished the malaria scourge, once the cause of much of the tuberculosis. The density of the population has risen steadily from 41 per square mile in 1828 to 161 per square mile in 1959. Today the total population of Greece exceeds eight million.

But this figure does not, of course, give any estimate of the number of Greeks throughout the world. Account must be taken of emigration. Between 1820 and 1934, 520,000 Greeks left their country, and rather less than a third of these ultimately returned. Although the current of emigration is not as strong as it was at the beginning of the century, it is still flowing. In Turkey — except at Istanbul — large Greek communities have disappeared, and the largest colonies are now to be found in the United States, in France, around the Rio de la Plata (Argentina), in Egypt, in Ethiopia, along the Red Sea and in Madagascar. On the whole the Greeks are slow to give up their own customs and become assimilated. In two regions they have defended their ethnical character and demanded annexation to Greece; one is northern Epirus (joined to Albania), the other Cyprus, until recently a British colony, where Greeks form 80 per cent of the population.

The Greeks have a tradition of sobriety and very simple tastes. In the seaboard regions where they engage in trade they may show themselves more resourceful and clever, but in the mountain areas they display to the full those qualities of endurance, economy, perseverance, and independently proud spirit that have enabled them to maintain their ethnical character and to find the strength necessary for recovery

COUNTRY AND TOWN. For a long time the population was mainly rural, and indeed a considerable number of the inhabitants still live in towns of less than 2,000. There are few isolated dwellings because of the scarcity of springs and because the country was for very long unsafe. The villages are of various types. On the islands the whitewashed houses are covered with flat or domed roofs and huddle together. The furniture consists of very low tables and chairs, and sometimes there are fine collections of brass and copper utensils, embroidered linen and ancient pottery. On the mainland the stone dwellings with four-slope roofs are not built as close together as those of the islands. The traditional dress is the *fustanella*, a short, white, very closely pleated skirt, high woollen gaiters and shoes with upturned points decorated with a pompom. In northern Greece there are houses with outside woodwork and sash-windows as in the Turkish lands. The local costumes of the women are very much more varied than those of the men, and with their embroidery and stamped silver jewellery they are particularly striking in appearance.

The urban population has risen considerably with the influx of refugees and the trends after the Second World War. The areas showing the biggest increases are those around Athens, the capital itself (a few thousand inhabitants in 1828, now more than 500,000), the Piraeus, and their suburbs which, together, now have a population of about 1,400,000. Salonica has about 220,000. The other large towns are Patras, Volos, Kavalla, Iraklion (formerly Candia, in Crete); all are seaports and have at least a few factories. It is due in part to the rise in urban population that the increase in density per square mile is most marked in central Greece and in Macedonia.

Those who have studied ancient history tend to think of Greek political instability as a traditional characteristic. Political strife is lively, and it is individuals rather than ideas that conflict. Political struggles can also be explained by the economic difficulties of everyday life and by the play of foreign interference or influence. The monarchical regime has, however, lasted since 1832, except for the period from 1924 to 1940 during which the dominant influence was that exercised by the powerful personality of the great democratic leader Venizelos. Taking it all in all, it is the regions of 'Old Greece' that are the most firmly attached to the monarchical tradition. Republican tendencies with social demands and claims are more marked in the large towns and in the northern area.

Greek economy

MONETARY INSTABILITY. Greece is a country at once very old and very young, a land where there is striking contrast between traditional forms of life unchanged since classical times and quite up-to-date resources. There are, for instance, regions served neither by road nor by railway but with radio and air services. Greek economy, medieval until 1830, has since developed continuously — despite unfavourable conditions, meagre resources, great scarcity of capital, frequent wars, and political instability. However, alternation between disastrous crises (such as those of 1912—22 and 1939—49) and periods of recovery make it impossible to present a clear, simple picture of Greek economic development — or even one of the present economy, for it is in the throes of a complete transformation. Because of the instability of the currency, it is difficult even to compare the money-value of the figures for output and trade. Proof of economic troubles lies in the many fluctuations suffered by the drachma.

AGRICULTURE THEN AND NOW. For several centuries Greek economy was based on foundations which were paradoxical. The people's only means of support was the produce of a poor, dry soil, relatively small in area. At best it was unhealthy or cut up into large estates unsuitable for intensive farming.

In these primitive economic conditions the peasant tilled with an archaic hoe-like plough a soil he could never manure. On his plot of land he planted wheat, barley and a little maize, and every other year he left his land fallow. Other traditional crops were vines — mostly on the plains — and olives, which grow fairly high up the mountain slopes. Sheep and goats were kept on fallow land, stubblefields and wide stretches of heath and woodless hills where the beasts prevented any growth of brushwood or forest. As season followed season great flocks migrated from place to place. Only in northern Greece, however, did cattle form real herds. All transport was by donkey or muleback. This archaic agricultural life still survives in the mountains and on the smaller islands. Only mule-tracks give access to fields whose soil is so shallow that only wooden ploughs can be used. Grain threshing and grape pressing is done on the spot, and windmills grind the flour. The products of his land provide the peasant with enough food for himself. Clothes are made from his sheep's wool, spun and woven or knitted at home. In some areas families manage to eke out an existence thus, much as their ancestors did.

But wherever possible efforts have been made to improve agricultural productivity in systematic fashion. Cultivated land, which in 1920 formed not more than 20 per cent of the country's total area, is now estimated at 30 per cent, and this is being further increased by tilling plains and valleys that were once marshy or exposed to flooding, and by irrigating areas that were too dry. Operations for draining Lake Copais were begun in 1886. Since 1922 other engineering operations have been carried out, especially along the course of the Strymon, the Axios and the Aliakmon. This has transformed large plains and valleys in northern and western Greece. Already 247,000 acres have been drained, and 292,000 acres protected from flooding while operations now in progress cover 863,000 acres. To the 642,200 acres already irrigated, another 120,000 to 180,000 acres are to be added.

Refugees from Asia Minor provided most of the labour needed to cultivate these areas. Other arable land has been gained by clearing the belts that served as tracks for migrating flocks and herds, and by adopting crop rotation and fertilizers

Above: *Factories at Eleusis, on the shore of the Bay of Salamis. The town, which was re-inhabited in the nineteenth century, has become an industrial centre.* PAUL POPPER

Left: *A hydro-electric dam under construction, at Megdova. The plant will give 250 million Kw yearly, and 114,000 square yards of land will be irrigated.* GREEK EMBASSY

Above: *Gathering apricots at Corinth. The Greek government encourages fruit-growing in order to make the best use of the country's soil and climate.*   Right: *A fair in the western Peloponnesos. In Greece the tradition has been maintained of big spring and autumn fairs, or 'panegyris'. This cattle market is held in the smiling, fertile valley of the lower Alphens, and the peasants come to it from far away, sometimes travelling four or five days on foot.*   GEORGES VIOLLON and DAVID SEYMOUR, MAGNUM-PHOTO

instead of allowing fields to lie fallow. In southern Greece fruit trees can be grown on uncultivated slopes up to a height of about 3,500 feet, and vines up to nearly 2,800 feet. Farming has been helped by the disappearance of large estates, mostly between 1917 and 1923. Irrigation and the use of agricultural machinery, fertilizers and selected seed have increased yields, while the farmer's lot has been further improved by the establishment of co-operatives, insurance schemes and credit facilities.

Moreover, crops are being sown which take full advantage of physical conditions. Side by side with traditional cereals, crops with a high yield have been developed (leguminous plants, potatoes, maize, rice); the output of fresh and dried fruits (which can be exported) and of industrial crops such as cotton has risen, and sugar-beet cultivation has been introduced. Efforts have been made to improve quality rather than increase quantity of the main export crops (grapes and tobacco), for greater output might well bring a slump in the market.

In sum, Greek agricultural production is today more varied than it was thirty-five years ago, as well as having a higher output and higher quality.

Progress in stock-breeding is not so marked. However, the flocks and herds that suffered heavy losses between 1940 and 1945 are being slowly restored. The increased acreage of arable land has reduced that available for grazing and hampers transhumance in the northern plains. However, the compensation lies in an increase in the area under forage plants. The number of domestic animals (with the exception of milch cows) is just about what it was in 1938, and the amount of fresh meat available barely meets increasing demand.

Woods and forests, though a secondary factor in Greek economy, are by no means a negligible one. In 1938 less than a fifth of the country's surface was tree-covered. There are no woods on the islands, except on Cephalonia, Rhodes and those in the north. Woodland is rare in the Peloponnese and

it is abundant only in central Greece, Euboea, Thessaly and the mountains of the west and north. The forests suffered heavily during the war. Today, efforts are being made to safeguard the trees and to increase their coverage as well as to improve forestry methods. Even so, Greece produces barely half the wood she needs.

The fisheries, too, satisfy only a part of the home demand, and the coastal population lives less from the sea than might be imagined. On many of the islands the inhabitants are farmers first and foremost The fishingfleet was almost entirely destroyed during the war, but a new one, with motor vessels and modern equipment, has now been built, and attempts have been made to increase the amount of sea-food eaten.

Taken as a whole, agricultural output is now 37 per cent greater than in 1938 and it still represents more than a third of the national income. Although this production is insufficient for home needs, it does furnish a considerable proportion of the exports and thus allows Greece to reduce the deficit in her trading balance in some measure.

CAN GREECE BE INDUSTRIALISED? Ancient Greece owed its prosperity to industry and commerce. However, for a long time, modern Greece produced only articles for common use, manufactured mostly from local raw material by craftsmen or in home industries. Indeed, it was held that there could be no modern industry in Greece. This question of industry is vital in view of the limited possibilities of agricultural output and the rise in population. Greece has neither coal nor oil. Her only sources of power are lignite deposits and the water of mountain streams and rivers. Nevertheless, careful prospecting of the subsoil has revealed the existence of mineral wealth that is greater and more varied than had been suspected: bauxite, barytes, chromium, copper, emery, iron, magnesite, manganese, nickel (produced in only one other

An isolated valley about 20 miles south of Ioannina, in northern Epirus. J. ALLAN CASH

An ancient method of ploughing. In certain regions the peasants use a wooden single-furrow plough which can reach every corner of the field and can be carried easily along the paths leading to the small fields tucked away in the mountains. ANTOINE BON

European country — Finland), lead and zinc. But any industrial development presupposes costly installations and equipment as well as imports of certain basic products such as coal, oil and iron.

Between 1923 and 1938 some industries expanded considerably, and some of the labour was furnished by refugees. But war reduced productivity by more than 50 per cent, while in 1945 the output of the mines fell to 8 per cent of the 1939 figures. The whole programme of industrial restoration depends on the production of electric current. Some dams and hydro-electric stations have been constructed and others are planned. The utilisation of the Mekdova, an affluent of the Achelous, has been a notable achievement. The thermo-electric stations use Greek lignite, and a very large station is situated at Ptolemais, near the Yugoslav frontier. Total production has increased eightfold since 1933.

There are industries processing Greek products: foodstuff factories (flour, noodles, canned goods, edible oil, alcohol and its derivatives, beer); cigarette factories; textile mills using Greek cotton, wool (mostly imported), silk (introduced by the 1923 refugees) and, quite recently, man-made fibres. Carpets are made and building materials are produced. Other plant under construction will treat ores (so far exported as raw material) and turn out aluminium, magnesium and ferronickel. In addition to the old oil and soap works, new chemical works have been built for the production of nitrogen (fertilizers) and soda. Petroleum refineries are being erected. The industrial output index shows a very marked upward trend since 1938.

TRANSPORT DIFFICULTIES. The size and the number of the mountains and the isolation of some regions restrict transport in many areas to donkey- or mule-back. On many of the islands there are no wheeled vehicles. There are, of course, modern transport facilities in Greece, but the Second World War destroyed almost all the roads, railways and bridges as well as most of the rolling-stock, automobiles, merchant marine (three-quarters) and port and harbour installations.

The railway network has been rebuilt, but the mountainous nature of the country forbids extensive mileage. The only long lines of normal gauge run from Athens to Salonica and from there to the Yugoslav and Turkish frontiers. In recent years more attention has been paid to roads than to railways. All parts of the Greek mainland can now be reached by highways carrying regular motorbus services. Sea transport has always been very active in Greece, for the country has more than a hundred islands and a very long coastline. Regular services of coastal vessels run between the islands and most of the ports and the Piraeus, which at some hours of the day is more like a crowded and lively railway terminus than a commercial port. The most modern means of communication — air transport — is already fairly well developed. Athens is linked by regular airlines with Salonica, Kavalla, Alexandroupolis, Mitilini, Rhodes, Crete, Agrinion, Ioannina, Phlorina and the principal capitals of Europe and the Near East.

In volume and weight goods transported by sea occupy first place. The Greeks, in fact, tend to invest their money in commercial enterprises and shipping rather than in industry. Ports have been built or improved. At Kavalla, Alexandroupolis and Iraklion piers and moles now protect roadsteads which were exposed to all the winds for many years. The Piraeus, which was transformed about 1930, is again to be enlarged and modernised. Though the merchant marine has been reconstituted, only some of the vessels chartered by Greek shippers fly the Greek flag.

IMPORT AND EXPORT BALANCE. The structure of Greek economy explains clearly enough the nature of Greek foreign trade. The country has to buy extensively abroad, and every attempt to increase home produce — and thus reduce imports — results at once in initial increases in basic materials.

A bread oven on the Greek mainland. It is small, made of plaster and rough earth bricks, and stands out of doors. A. COSTA, RAPHO

Shearing sheep in a field at Corfu. The land available for grazing is decreasing as agriculture develops, and Greece produces scarcely enough meat for her requirements. PAUL POPPER

Agricultural produce occupies an important place in Greece's foreign trade — before 1939 about 20 per cent of the total value of imports and from 80 per cent to 90 per cent of the exports. Even today agricultural produce accounts for more than 60 per cent of the exports. Imports include cereals, flour, leguminous plants, sugar and meat. As we have seen, there is increased cultivation of those crops which will make the country more self-supporting or will provide useful exports. Tobacco is still the main export and represents, on average, 50 per cent of the total exports value; then, in order, come raisins, currants, olives and other fruits.

Among raw materials imported are coal and petroleum (which come first in volume), then metals, basic products for the chemical industry, wool and hides and building materials. Products not manufactured at home must be bought too: fertilizers and chemical products, machines, motor-cars, electrical

A street in Kerkira, the principal town of Corfu.
J. ALLAN CASH

equipment and paper. Almost all the ores mined were exported at one time — in 1950 four-fifths of the production went out of the country, but from 1951 an increase in output and a decrease in exports were to be noted — the difference was being processed locally.

As a result, the foreign trade balance must show a deficit. Exports that constituted 70 per cent (in value) of imports before the war now amount only to 50 per cent. Balancing exports against imports is all the more difficult since most of the exports consist of agricultural luxury products that are not easy to sell and depend upon the uncertainties of seasons and harvests. On the other hand, Greece cannot possibly do without the goods already imported. Commercial treaties aim at obtaining what the country needs in exchange for what it can give, and in conclusion of such agreements political considerations may be a determining factor. This explains why before 1939, Germany held first place in Greek foreign trade, whereas from 1948 to 1950 it was the United States. Normally the greatest volume of foreign trade is with countries of eastern and central Europe, Turkey, and Yugoslavia, Austria and Germany, then with Great Britain and finally the United States.

How can the Greeks wipe out the deficit in their trade balance? When the war ended, the country could export nothing and needed everything — and had, moreover, to meet a very heavy military budget. Foreign aid had to be sought. From 1946 to 1954 Greece received, on one account or another, more than 2,000 million dollars. But this sum constituted, of course, a quite exceptional sort of income.

The imbalance between exports and imports is to some extent made up by remittances from Greeks abroad, by the earnings of the merchant navy and by money brought into the country by tourists for Greece is, of course, the ideal land for the tourist. There is every attraction — beauty and variety of landscape, mildness of climate, famous monuments dating from classical times, Byzantine buildings, splendid museums, and thermal and mineral spas. Nevertheless constant improvements must be made to hotels, roads and other means of transport.

What the Greeks have achieved

The Greeks have had to face very grave problems. To provide a normal livelihood for the population and to bring the foreign trade into balance, all resources must be exploited and these are neither very extensive nor very accessible. However, work is zealously going on to carry out a plan whose first results seem encouraging. But progress demands more and more capital expenditure on equipment, and financing improvement schemes is a crucial problem, for investment of this kind depends on the confidence felt in the enterprises and on political stability. As a nation the Greeks are torn between the need to take advantage of foreign aid and capital and the desire to do without it.

Greece today is quite unlike Greece 125 years ago. Moreover, even if the results attained are not yet entirely secure, admiration for the successes of ancient Greece should not prevent us from recognising the efforts and progress made by its descendant.

Antoine BON

The Tholos of Marmaria at Delphi. The magnificent landscape on the side of Mount Parnassus is a wonderful setting for the famous temple of Apollo whose oracle was of considerable importance in the ancient Greek world. The French School at Athens discovered The Tholos in the Temple of Athene, next to that of Apollo, and undertook its restoration. J. ALLAN CASH

Famagusta, the former capital of the island of Cyprus, seen from the south-east. The town, which is now relatively small, is dominated by the gothic Cathedral of St Nicholas, built in the early fourteenth century; it was here that the Lusignans, the kings of Cyprus and Jerusalem, were crowned. In the distance are the sea and the Karpas Mountains at the north-east extremity of the island. ROGER VIOLLET

CYPRUS

O
F the Mediterranean islands, Cyprus is the most easterly and the third largest. By geological structure Cyprus belongs to Asia Minor. Two mountain ranges cross the island from west to east, parallel with the Taurus. The range to the north is a narrow limestone ridge 3,135 feet high; the other, to the south, is more massive (highest point, Mount Troödos, 6,403 feet) and is composed of diabase and serpentine rocks. Between the two ranges lies a plain, the Messaria, about 10 to 20 miles wide. The capital, Nicosia, has developed in an oasis on the very dry central plain. The island as a whole enjoys a warm Mediterranean climate, while forests cover nearly one-fifth of the surface. In ancient times the island was rich in metals — especially in copper, and indeed the island's name suggests this link. However, copper-mining has long since been abandoned, and the island's resources are almost wholly agricultural — cereals, vetches, a little cotton and tobacco, and large quantities of carobs, olives, citrus fruits and wine. Trade is not on an extensive scale, and the ports — Limassol, Larnaka and Famagusta — are neither populous nor busy, but they are picturesque and at Famagusta there are the remains of a celebrated Gothic cathedral.

Cyprus is more interesting for its history than for its landscapes. Set at the intersection of sea routes between Egypt and Asia Minor, between Syria and the world of the Aegean, the island was subjected to the influence of widely varied civilisations which, intermingled, gave an impetus to arts which are here represented by objects in composite styles and shapes that are often curious. Rich in copper, Cyprus lived through a brilliant Bronze Age. In the first millenium B.C. it was divided between Greek and Phoenician cities. Later, the island was held at one stage or another by all the great oriental empires of antiquity and the Middle Ages. First conquered by Richard Coeur de Lion, Cyprus came under the rule of Guy de Lusignan in 1192 and then, in 1485, was annexed by the Venetians before falling into the hands of the Turks in 1571. In 1878 the Sultan ceded administration of the island to Great Britain who annexed it in 1914, and made it a Crown Colony in 1925.

The population (about 550,000) is fairly homogeneous, for nearly 80 per cent of them are Greek-speaking. The British government did much to develop the island's resources. A Ten Year Plan (1946-56) produced some important results, and pumping stations have improved inland water-supplies.

Some of the mineral deposits have been worked and there is a network of roads over the island, which has also become an airline junction. However, despite attempts to introduce liberal institutions, Great Britain was assailed by the claims of the Turkish minority and exposed to the hostility of the Greek population which, under the leadership of the Metropolitan of Nicosia, head of the Orthodox Church and Ethnarch of the island, demanded union with Greece. Recent agreements (those of London and Zürich) have recognised the island's independence and Cyprus has become a republic.

Antoine Bon

A general view of Valletta, capital of Malta and former British naval base. BROWN, FOX PHOTOS

MALTA

MALTA is not a single island but a little archipelago (63 miles from Sicily) made up of three isles: Malta, the main one, with the port and roadstead of Valletta, and two smaller islands, Gozo and Comino. The combined area is 122 square miles and the population is about 325,000; this gives a high density — 2,663 inhabitants to the square mile.

Malta's resources are economic — and military. However, the former are slight; the ground is stony and the surface soil thin. Rainfall is sufficient but is not well captured, and the islands lack both springs and trees. The land is subdivided among a great number of owners; crops are just a few vegetables (including potatoes), citrus fruits, some cereals, and vines.

A few manufacturing and processing industries have been set up — breweries, textile-mills, workshops turning out pipes and stockings, and a few small-scale handicrafts. There are few exports. Indeed, Malta must import most of its inhabitants' needs as well as raw materials for the various activities of the islands, and imports represent 90 per cent of the total trade. Of this, three-quarters come from Great Britain (with a pre-ferential tariff) and the rest from Sicily. Labour is over-plentiful and was only partially absorbed by the British dockyard,

although a great number of hands were employed there. In 1959 the dockyard was transferred to a Welsh ship-repairing firm. Malta's most pressing problem is that of emigration which, ideally, should be roughly double the actual figures (i.e. 20,000 a year instead to the 10,000 who now leave, mostly for Canada and Australia), for only by emigration can the standard of living be raised in such overpopulated islands.

A TRAFFIC JUNCTION AND A MEETING POINT.
The Maltese islands are the remains of subsided Mediterranean mountains. Their habitation in very remote times is proved by the discovery of human fossils, ancient temples and many rock-paintings. Malta was a regular halting-place on the way from the Tripolitanian desert to Sicily.

The archipelago was inhabited successively by Phoenicians, Carthaginians, Romans and Moslems, and from the eleventh century onwards, under the rule of Angevin and Aragonese dynasties, the population was increased by Norman, Sicilian and Spanish settlers, not counting a few Greeks and Jews. In 1530 when the Knights of the Order of St John of Jerusalem arrived, the Maltese 'type' was more or less fixed. Physically, the Maltese rather resemble Arabs, but it is a resemblance due more to Sicilian and Spanish influx from the twelfth to the seventeenth century than to the Moslem domination from A.D. 870 to A.D. 1090. The Maltese language is of Phoenician origin but is now composed of roots that are Arabic by etymology and by intonation. Italian and English, too, have influenced the language. The educated Maltese speaks three languages (Maltese, English and Italian) while some speak French too. There is a university and numerous primary and secondary schools. The Maltese are a courteous and affable people, in no way embittered by the vicissitudes of existence and able to face life (which is by no means always easy for all) with a simple, innate cheerfulness.

Malta was converted to Christianity by early missionaries (St Paul was shipwrecked on the island and stayed there three months) and soon adopted Roman Catholicism which, under the Angevin and Aragonese dynasties and under the rule of the Knights, gained an even stronger hold. The influence of the clergy is still decisive and the parishes are also administrative units, even electoral ones.

THE KNIGHTS OF MALTA.

From 1530 to 1798 Malta was governed by the Knights of the Order of St John of Jerusalem, who continued their rôle as paladins of Christendom which they had played for five centuries on land and sea against the infidel. The Order of the Brethren of St John of Jerusalem was founded by a Frenchman in Palestine at the time of the First Crusade. Many Crusaders joined the order, which at first was an order of hospitalers but rapidly became military too, first in Palestine and then in Rhodes. The Turks drove the knights from Rhodes in 1523 and it was then that they received Malta as their apanage from the Emperor Charles V, who prescribed for them the mission of containing the Turkish forces and of clearing the southern Mediterranean of pirates. When the Turks laid siege to Malta, the Grand Master de La Valette, with the aid of the whole population, put up a vigorous defence and obliged the Turks to withdraw in September 1565. This victory saved Christendom and marked the beginning of the Ottoman Empire's decline. The victory is still commemorated annually in Malta. In 1798 the Order withdrew to Rome.

The island prospered under the rule of the Knights since, after 1565, most of the Western sovereigns made a number of presents to the Order, and the Grand Masters used these offerings to the island's benefit. The knights were great builders, and the hospital at Vittoriosa was the most famous in Europe. Despite a number of demolitions, there are many monuments of their munificence remaining. The Knights were divided by 'languages'; each 'language' had its own monastery, or auberge, charged with the duty of protecting a section of the fortifications. Most of the buildings still exist.

PRESENT-DAY MALTA.

Bonaparte seized Malta in 1798 but had to relinquish it after his defeat at the Battle of the Nile. The British then occupied the island and have been there continuously since 1801. Malta is a Crown Colony which has enjoyed self-government since 1947, that is, autonomy in all home affairs, though the British are responsible for defence and diplomatic representation. Of late there has been a movement for the political union of Malta and Great Britain with common citizenship for British and Maltese. Only a section of the Maltese has so far been in favour of this solution to the island's problems.

For centuries Malta's strategic importance was considerable; set in the middle of the Mediterranean, its many deep-water inlets could accommodate two or three fleets, and its chalky, soft rock (Maltese building stone can be cut with a hatchet or even with a knife) provides great underground storehouses, caverns and cellars.

The value of the British naval base is no longer what it was, for it is a particularly easy target for air attack, and the narrowness of the inlets which in former days offered maximum protection is now a fatal trap and turns the ships into sitting ducks for bombers. Again, despite the enormous subterranean storage space (which could be utilised to better advantage) Malta would prove a heavy liability for the Power that used it in time of war, since the over-populated island must first be fed before effective use could be made of it for the transit of armed forces. During the years 1941 and 1942 there was famine in Malta.

Nevertheless, Malta with its great port installations at Valletta is still, in peacetime, a naval base of the first rank.

André PAULY

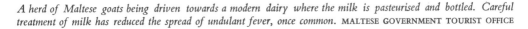

A herd of Maltese goats being driven towards a modern dairy where the milk is pasteurised and bottled. Careful treatment of milk has reduced the spread of undulant fever, once common. MALTESE GOVERNMENT TOURIST OFFICE

The Appian Way, near Rome. This route from Rome to Brindisi was built in 312 B.C. by Appius Claudius, and was part of the vast network of Roman roads that linked all parts of the Empire. PIERRE BELZEAU, RAPHO

ITALY

ITALY is probably the European country we think we know most about, and the one which we really know least well . . . Italy, the land of eternal spring, the land of gondolas, mandolins... the country of *far niente* and spaghetti... 'See Naples and die . . .' Of course, but the admirable Apulian cathedrals, the Cornigliano steelworks, the Calabrian forests and the model factories in the Valdagno are just as much the Italian heritage as the panorama of Naples Bay.

Any map of Europe shows that Italy has all the appearance of a Mediterranean peninsula; it has a contorted surface relief, its climate is one of extremes, and its inhabitants are brown-skinned and dark-haired. Still, in many ways, Italy is sharply distinguished from the other two Mediterranean peninsulas — first by its narrowness, which allows the sea air to influence it and makes it damper and greener, and then by its geographical position. Italy is a kind of bridge between Europe and Africa and a midriff, as it were, between West and East. Italy has been a meeting-place throughout the ages, where oriental gold mosaics adorned Gothic arches, and the energy of the North came into contact with Alexandrine subtlety. Again, Italy's abundant population and high degree of technical skill had a much greater influence on the country's politics and economy than the populations of Spain or the Balkans had on theirs. Italy is, indeed, the least Mediterranean of the Mediterranean peninsulas.

Two Italies

It is perhaps unnecessary to point out that, physically, there are two Italies: northern or continental Italy, and southern or peninsular Italy. At every turn the fact is confirmed and emphasised.

THE RAMPART OF THE ALPS. From whatever direction the land traveller approaches Italy he cannot avoid the Alps, whose immense 600-mile rampart determines the geography of northern Italy.

We know that the Alps are a 'recent' range, that is, one whose rocks were folded in the second half of the Tertiary Period. This explains the sharpness of the eroded Alpine outlines and the bold character of the peaks. The classical division of the range gives three almost equal sections: to the west the Piedmont Alps, in the middle the Lombard Alps, and in the east the Venetian Alps.

The Piedmont Alps extend from the Cadibone Pass to the Simplon. Like the French side of the Pyrenees, the Piedmonts resemble cliff edges rather than mountain slopes. In some places as little as 15 miles separate the plain from 9,000-foot peaks; it follows that the gradients are steep.

This narrow slope makes up a single geological zone of lustrous schists. However, it is not a monotonous landscape, since the vast expanses of black schist are often pierced by crystalline massifs 13,000 feet high; such are the Grand Paradis, the Monte Rosa, and the terrifying barrier of Mont Blanc. The general impression is of a very high range with no marked gaps, since even the lowest passes lie at 3,500 feet or over (Tenda and Mont-Genèvre). Towards the north, planing by ancient glaciers has widened the valleys a good deal more, especially in the Val di Susa's windy trough and Val d'Aosta's majestic valley. The Piedmont Alps form a rampart but it is not one that is unscalable.

Beyond the Simplon, and stretching as far as the Passo di Resia, come the Lombard Alps. They differ from the Piedmonts in that they are wider, more varied in aspect, and easier of access. They owe their special character to the harmonious development of three geological zones: in the north a continuation of the Piedmont lustrous schists; then a crystalline axial zone; and finally, in the south, the limestone Pre-Alps or Bergamasques. In each of these zones and at heights between 11,500 and 13,500 feet, there are classical types of high mountains: the Adamello, the Ortler, the Bernina. Moreover, there is another feature, one of the utmost importance for communications: because of the position of the structural layers of rock the massifs are generally separated by longitudinal furrows, such as the Toce basin or the Valtellina-Valdisole trough.

Naturally enough, since the range is greater in mass than the Piedmont Alps, precipitation too is greater and glaciers larger. During the Quaternary Era, conditions were similar, and it was ice that reduced Sondrio, in the Valtellina, to less than 1,000 feet, and widened such passes as the Splügen, the Stelvio and the Tonale. Again, if the valleys are suited for hydro-electric stations, that too is because of ice action in the past. Glaciers produced the magnificent lakes of the Alpine foothills — Maggiore, Lugano, Como, Iseo, Garda — fashioned from above by tongues of ice and dammed below by terminal moraines. The five lakes of the Lombard plain are justly celebrated.

Formerly Italy possessed all the southern slope of the Alpine chain, but peace treaties after the 1939-45 war confirmed the cession of the Julian Alps to Yugoslavia, and the Italian portion of the Venetian Alps now ends at the Tarvis Pass. The Venetian Alps show some resemblance to the Lombard Alps — they have, for instance, similar longitudinal furrows in the Val Venosta and the Val Sugana. In addition, they display many original features. First they are on the whole lower: the Tyrolean massifs — the tallest — barely exceed 11,000 feet, and the Carnic Alps, 8,000 feet. The same can be said of the passes: the Tarvis and the Predil are below 4,900 feet, while the celebrated Brenner reaches only 4,693 feet. In consequence, although precipitation is very heavy, there are few glaciers. Another distinctive feature is the more open character of the Venetian Alps, where intersecting transverse fractures produce an extraordinary maze of valleys. The curious corridor of the Adige was also caused by a fracture. The accessible character of the mountains is all the more useful since due north of Verona the Alps are twice as broad as the plain of the Po itself.

Excessive widening of the calcareous zone explains the characteristic 'bulge' of the Venetian Alps and has a number of consequences. First, it has influenced the formation of a curious surface relief, known as 'Karst' and characteristic of the Carso plateau behind Trieste. The plateaus are dry and pitted with funnels, and the rivers are often subterranean; the Preta chasm (2,100 feet) was for long the deepest known. Then, in the Dolomites, the properties of magnesian, a particular sort of limestone, have produced walls remarkably like those of ruined buildings, and panoramas of striking and unusual colours.

THE PO PLAIN. The Po plain is a deep geological trough which before the end of the Tertiary Era was a huge gulf of the Adriatic. Gradually the gulf was filled in with debris brought down from the mountains, and the sea finally retreated to its present position. Here, as in every plain of the piedmont type, the debris nearest the mountain barrier is the coarsest, while the middle of the plain is made up of fine, alluvial, clayey soil. One phase in this formation occurred during the Quaternary Era, when the tongues of glaciers from the Alps pushed forward their load of stones to the plain's edge. The Apennine slopes, which are lower and have been less extensively covered with ice in the past, have no such moraines.

Geological history, then, explains why the topography of the Po valley is an arrangement of parallel strips. This is the position in the northern half of the plain: right up against the Alps lies a belt of moraines forming high hills, generally arranged arc-wise, which play their part in damming up the sub-alpine lakes. The semi-circle around Lake Garda is the most perfectly formed of these accumulations. In many cases the waters have managed to break through the barrage, so that the moraine is gashed open and takes the shape of a broken horseshoe. This can be seen most clearly in the imposing semi-circle at Ivrea.

The zone of high terraces composed of broken stone (between 500 and 1,000 feet high) is a little like the Lannemezan plateau in France. The ground surface is covered with a hard crust, called *ferreto*, but this is so coarse that water percolates all the same. This area of rather unproductive heaths widens in Friuli.

Then comes the zone of low terraces (the Lomellina, for instance) composed of finer materials and furrowed with streams rising in the *fontanili*, springs along the line of contact between the high and the low terrace, where the difference in permeability forces the subterranean sheets of water to well up to the surface. This row of springs, of the greatest utility, pours out from 90 to 270 gallons of water per second per mile of its length.

Lastly, there is the flood-plain of the Po. On the whole narrow, this subaquatic area broadens out in the Polesine downstream. The Po and its affluents carry a considerable amount of alluvium; the Tanaro, for instance, carries more than seven tons of mud a minute. When the water is exceptionally high in the streams, the dykes and banks burst, and the countryside is flooded far and wide — as happened in November 1951 and in June 1957.

On the right bank of the Po is the same succession of topographical strips, except that the line of *fontanili* is narrower and the morainic hills are lacking.

Luckily, the monotony of this landscape — which, it must be confessed, is very flat indeed — is broken by a few hills from 1,250 to 1,900 feet high which, in remote ages, were islands in the sea gulf that formerly occupied the Po plain. There are the Montferrat Hills above Turin, the Berici Mountains, and the extinct Euganean volcanoes in Venetia.

To sum up: it is a huge plain and a splendid one — 'the most fertile plain in the world' said Napoleon. True, but only engineering skill and prolonged effort has allowed man to get the most out of a soil that is sometimes too dry and sometimes too wet.

The sea-frontage of the plain is low and marshy, as might be expected. The mud and sand deposited in the Adriatic by the rivers are pushed south by the inshore current and extend as long coastal strips (or *lidos*) enclosing lagoons, some of which still communicate with the sea and are 'alive' — such is the lagoon of Venice and its celebrated Lido. Other lagoons, to the south of the Po, are closed and are silting up (e.g. Commachio). These phenomena are marked in the Po delta, where the increase in area of alluvial land has been noted since the Middle Ages. The Adriatic tides are so slight (maximum 3.25 feet) that silting goes on almost unchecked.

ERRATIC ACTION OF CLIMATE AND WATERS.

The climate of northern Italy is temperate, continental and sub-Mediterranean — that is, it is comparable in many respects with the climate of Hungary. The temperate nature of the north Italian climate is not surprising if we reflect that Milan and Venice are at the same latitude as Saint-Étienne in France. Again, northern Italy is, like central Europe, exposed to polar air in winter, and in summer is swept by warm air from the Atlantic. At the same time it is deeply embedded in the European mass, separated from the ocean by more than 350 miles of land, screened by the Alps, isolated from the Mediterranean by another mountain barrier, and washed by the Adriatic which has only slight moderating influence. Northern Italy therefore presents a number of distinctly continental features: surprising differences between summer and winter temperatures, lowest rainfall in winter, and regular seasons. Even so, the climate is sub-Mediterranean, since the heaviest rainfall is in spring and autumn, and not in summer as at Strasbourg or Warsaw. In the Po valley the succession of seasons generally follows this pattern: little rain in winter, which is misty and very cold with frequent frosts (Piacenza has a mean January temperature of 31° F. and is thus colder than Copenhagen, while Venice has about the same temperature as Paris); the spring is warm but very wet; the summer heat is stifling, the thermometer rising as high as in Naples, but the atmosphere is sultry and there are frequent storms; in October the heavy rains fall. Taking it all in all, this is a trying climate but it is excellent for maize and rice, as well as for mulberries and sugar-beet.

As soon as the Po's icy mists are left behind, the climate becomes a great deal more agreeable, and vines and sometimes olive trees make their appearance. The best-known example of this climate (Insubrian) is that of the great lakes, where Mediterranean plants flourish, and in the Borromean Islands. The climate on the Adriatic is less equable and the shores are often swept by gusts of the *bora* (a cold north-east wind).

The Alpine mountains have, of course, the usual characteristics of Alpine climate: the higher the altitude, the greater the precipitation and the lower the temperature. This produces different levels of vegetation, and the eastern Alps, which are exposed to humidity from the Adriatic and so have a heavy rainfall, show lower height limits than the western Alps: woods, for instance, which reach 7,550 feet in the Piedmont, stop at 5,250 feet in the Carnic Alps.

The varied character of northern Italy is reflected in the complex regime of the Po. We know that rivers are sensitive to climatic variations. The Po is the largest river in Italy, yet it is hardly navigable at all and has been always more of a barrier than a link. Its seasonal variations are interesting to note. In January comes the first low water, for the rainfall is slight; then in May comes the first spate from the Alpine tributaries swollen by melting snows. In July-August there is a second period of low water (caused by evaporation), but this is moderate since the river is fed by glacial waters from the Alps. Lastly, in November, comes the full flood produced by abundant autumn rains. The Po regime is, then, dependent upon snow and rain, and this imparts to northern Italy a central European physiognomy.

THE APENNINE JIGSAW. The Apennines are as important to Italy as the Alps, perhaps more important since they constitute the backbone of the peninsula.

Occupying what is now the Tyrrhenian Sea there was formerly a land mass of crystalline rocks, called Tyrrhenis. During the Tertiary Era, folded mountain ranges were grouped round the mass. Then Tyrrhenis sank beneath the waves, and portions of the mountain framework were left above the surface. In this way the Apennines and the large islands took on a distinct individuality; they were the only survivors of a great geological drama.

The first thing to be noted is the geologically recent date of these earth movements. Although, like the Alps, they contain some ancient rocks, the Apennines as a whole are a

The Italian side of the 15,217-foot Monte Rosa in the Piedmont Alps, on the Italian-Swiss border. CICCIONE, RAPHO

The three peaks of Lavaredo (9,850 feet) in the Dolomites. The craggy structure of the Dolomites is due to the special composition of its limestone rocks. E.N.I.T.

The River Sele, near Eboli in the Campania. J. ALLAN CASH

very young chain, and as erosion has not yet weathered the old surfaces, their landscape presents plenty of plateaus and gorges but few peaks and few sharp needles. Furthermore, the frequency of earthquakes (the Abruzzi and Calabria have more earth tremors than any other part of Europe) proves that folding is not yet finished.

But the word 'folding' is misleading in this context, for the rocks here have been broken more often than folded. One direct consequence of the tendency to fracture is the formation of numerous hollows or basins which, a few millenia ago, were still lakes. The most curious is without doubt that of Fucino — in the Abruzzi — which dried up completely only in the nineteenth century.

With the prevalence of fractures is linked another special feature of the Apennines — the presence, on the Tyrrhenian slopes, of a 'Pre-Apennine' chain that is often volcanic; there are the extinct volcanoes of Tuscany and Latium and the active ones such as Vesuvius, Stromboli and Etna.

Again, the abundance of argillo-schistose rocks and violent storms produce *frane* (dangerous landslides which may efface roads and shift villages) and *calanchi*, which split the ground into widening gullies, swallowing fields and pastures.

The Apennines also present an astonishing variety of landscapes, so that it is apt that the range should be styled — plurally — the Apennines.

In the north is the very narrow screen of the Ligurian Apennines, dropping sharply down into the Gulf of Genoa and forming a precipitous face which the road cannot always follow. The Apennines of Tuscany and Emilia, although not very high (from 3,000 to 5,000 feet) are of a much more complicated structure, though this would hardle be suspected from the monotonous character of the sandstone-schist ridges. The white marble walls of the Apuan Alps are the only formations that are different. The subterranean extension of these Apennines — hidden under the Po valley alluviums — contains the Cortemaggiore oilfield.

In the central Apennines, the presence of limestone rocks produces a sequence of various forms. First come the Apennines of Umbria and the Marches with karst plateaus and the first of the sunk basins (Gubbio, for instance). Then, in the Abruzzi, they broaden into a massive fortress-like feature. Progressively, as the green hollows of Aquila, Sulmona and Avezzano spread out, the arid high plateaus expand, the limestone blocks grow higher, and in the complex of the Gran Sasso d'Italia (9,560 feet and the loftiest point in the peninsula) the scenery takes on an Alpine character; there is even a small glacier to complete the illusion.

Beyond the Sangro, in the southern Apennines, limestone still occupies an outstanding place in the landscape, but in the Neapolitan Apennines and in those of Lucania, the limestone is split into great squarish slabs (little more than 6,500 feet high) between which run argillo-schistose corridors. This is very poor country where *frane* and *calanchi* have always disheartened the peasant population.

Finally, in the far south, lie the Calabrian Apennines, a granite 'big toe' unexpectedly sticking out of a limestone 'boot'. Their soft outlines and the deep forests recall those found in the Vosges or the Morvan of France.

A FEW GOOD PLAINS. There are also useful low-lying areas, but they are flattened against the flanks of the Apennines, and are more often hills and little plateaus than real plains. These good lands are all situated (with the exception of those in Apulia) on the Tyrrhenian side of the Apennine arc. Thus all are overshadowed by the volcanic heights of the Pre-Apennines and filled with fertile alluvial soil. It is not difficult to see why these regions are much more densely populated than the Apennines themselves.

In Tuscany the volcanic influence is not very marked. The typical Tuscan landscape — illustrated in the paintings of the Florentine and Sienese Primitives — is made up, principally, of argillo-schistose hills whose outlines are soft and gentle. Farther south, extinct volcanoes follow one another in quick succession. Forests, crater-lakes and ravines of the old firemountains contribute to the picturesqueness of the Latium countryside, and their ashes consolidated into tuffs contribute much to the region's fertility. Since it has been drained, the Roman Campagna yields wonderful harvests, while the gardens on the Alban Hills have been famed since classical times. Still more fruitful are the Neapolitan plains, padded and cushioned by material thrown from Vesuvius or from the Phlegrean Fields.

Unfortunately, the picture is not complete without mention of the disadvantages of the coast. A rise in sea level during prehistoric times has made the shores alluvial, malarial, uninviting, and if the Pontine Plain (formerly marshes) and the delta of the Tiber have been improved, the Tuscan Maremma and the mouths of the Volturno and the Sele are still marshland where wild boar and buffalo roam freely.

Marshes are less common on the Adriatic slope of the peninsula, but the lowlands are far from being as hospitable to man. The coastal regions of the Marches and the Abruzzi are composed of argillo-schistose hills subject to *frane*. Aquila is an extraordinarily flat table-land but its limestone structure is fertile only when irrigated.

Etna (10,741 feet) in north-east Sicily. Eruptions from this volcano have many times laid waste to the countryside of Catania, but the earth is so fertile that settlers have always been attracted to the area. E.N.I.T.

The village of Aggius, in Sardinia, set against the rocky landscape, its small fields interspersed with trees. E.N.I.T.

Amalfi, a small fishing port in the Gulf of Salerno and perhaps the most popular resort on the Sorrento peninsula. J. ALLAN CASH

THE MEDITERRANEAN ISLANDS. Italy possesses the two largest Mediterranean islands — Sicily and Sardinia. The richer and more famous is Sicily. The ancients called it *Trinacria*, that is, the 'Island of the Three Points'. In general lines, its mountain-skeleton is a simple one. In the north there are the Sicilian Apennines, a mountain chain less than 7,000 feet high, and an extension of the Calabrian heights. On the Tyrrhenian side this range drops down steeply into the sea and forms a rocky coast almost as difficult to negotiate as that of Liguria. A few small irrigable recesses such as the famous Palermitan Conca d'Oro break up the arid stretch of mountains. On the southern side, however, the land slopes gently towards Africa in a slanting plane from which erosion has cut hills, whitish ravines and a jumble of plateaus. To the east, this assemblage slumps down under the damp plain of Catania, above which rises the majestic, snow-capped cone of Etna, more than 10,000 feet high. The soil of the plain, which is of volcanic origin, is most productive.

The more surprising of the two islands is Sardinia. Because, on the map, it seems to cling to Corsica, we tend to think that Sardinia must be mountainous too; but this is not so. Sardinia is rocky and wild enough, but it is an ancient platform that has been dislocated. Tabular formations predominate and altitudes are not great. There are the high, granite plateaus of the Barbagia (between 5,000 and 6,000 feet), the volcanic caps of the Logoduro, the coal and mineral-bearing masses of the Iglesiente. There is close resemblance to the French Massif Central or, more exactly, the Auvergne. There is even a huge corridor, flat and fertile, the Campidano, not unlike the Limagne in France.

The other islands are all rocky, small and wild. Elba is an ancient weathered mass. Ischia is an extinct but still warm volcano. Capri is white and craggy. Stromboli and Vulcano still throw out their flaming bombs into the sea.

CONTRASTING CLIMATE. Peninsular and insular Italy is set entirely in the Mediterranean zone, which is also termed 'sub-tropical' — this means that in winter Italy receives the warm, damp Atlantic air, while in summer it is swept by an influx of dry, hot, Saharan air. Thus the typically European variable winter weather is succeeded in summer by stable meteorological conditions of an African type. However, it is certain that Italy, because of its shape, feels — more than Spain or the Balkans — the moderating influence of the warm Mediterranean.

Let us take an example: Rome. The winters are cool, the skies often overcast; rain is intermittent, snow unusual. There are a few very fine days when the icy north wind, the *tramontana*, blows. In spring the temperature rises rapidly and rainfall is more abundant. There is often a south wind that is particularly trying at this time because it is both damp and hot; however, this season is short. Then summer bursts forth suddenly; three months of skies that are gloriously and implacably blue. It is hot. There is no rain save an occasional storm. The soil cracks and splits. In October the temperature drops and deluges of rain show that Atlantic air prevails again. It is interesting to note that in any given year Rome has half as much rain again as London. Taking it all in all, it enjoys a climate that is violent, with sudden changes of temperature, torrential rainfall and considerable variation from year to year. The 'mildness' of the Mediterranean climate is a legend.

In such conditions very delicate plants cannot survive, and the climate excludes all those which cannot support cold as well as heat, drought as well as wet. Non-deciduous trees such as the ilex or holm-oak, cork-oak, parasol pine, the *garrigue* or scrub of cistus, myrtle, lentiscus and asphodel, exotic but well acclimatised plants such as cactus, cypress and eucalyptus, all combine to make up landscapes of serene and intense beauty.

If we take into account its geographical position, this climate — with two maximum periods of rainfall — might well be

ITALY

The famous Bridge of Sighs in Venice, which connects the Ducal Palace with the State Prison. There are 177 canals in Venice, spanned by 400 bridges, and the traditional means of transport is the gondola. B. G. SILBERSTEIN, CAMERA PRESS

called 'Tyrrhenian'. On the eastern slopes, behind the screen of the Apennines, we find this climate again, but drier and with colder winters (Ancona, Foggia). This is the 'Adriatic' type of Italian climate. It is excellent for wheat-growing but most unfavourable for citrus fruits.

Inland, distance from the sea and altitude produce mountain climates of astonishing severity. The autumns are warm, the winds violent; in winter there are furious snowstorms rather like those on the high plateau of Auvergne. Naturally the vegetation is stepped: first oak and chestnut, then hornbeam and beech — sometimes fir — which give way to Alpine meadows between 5,500 and 6,000 feet. A few forests, such as those of the National Park in the Abruzzi and of the Sila in Calabria, are justly famous. Wolves are common.

To the south of Naples the climate is warmer. Winter temperatures are over 50° F. The rainfall is like that of Tunisia (not far away); that is, there is only one rainy season, occurring during the cold weather. The torrid summer lasts four months and gives the country the appearance of a steppe. It was in Sicily, scorched by the African sirocco, that the Athenian expeditionary force perished of thirst in 413 B.C. Dwarf palm-trees grow everywhere and bananas ripen in well-watered Calabrian gardens.

The combination of very dry summers and great heat — an essential and distinctive feature of Mediterranean climates —

results in very shallow rivers in summer. But, as their gradient is steep, the streams fill up very rapidly as soon as a storm breaks, causing floods — often disastrous ones. In Calabria especially, devastating torrents heavily charged with pebbles and stones, (the *fiumare*) roll down from the mountains. In peninsular Italy and the islands, then, streams can be used for irrigation and generating electric current, but there can be no thought of making them navigable. In the north there is a 'converging' hydrographic network — it is a factor that has made for economic efficiency and concentration of population. In the south there is a 'diverging' network that has made for the dispersal of population and of human energies and so has favoured the development of individualism.

We cannot in any circumstances ignore the influence such facts have on the destinies of the Italian people.

Who are the Italians?

Wherever he find himself, the traveller to Italy cannot fail to note that beneath turbulent but sincere nationalistic feelings, there are traces of hesitation, even of lack of assurance. It may be argued — and justifiably — that Italian national unity dates only from 1861 and is still young. But how did it come about that peoples that were so early and often so highly civilised

A 'nuraghe' at Silanus, in Sardinia. There are nearly 8,000 of these fortified towers on the island, many of them dating back to the Bronze Age. Traces of Phoenician, Egyptian, Greek and Roman culture have been found on the island. E.N.I.T.

The Basilica at Paestum, an ancient Greek settlement in southern Italy. This temple is the oldest of one of the most interesting and imposing groups in the Hellenic world. J. ALLAN CASH

had to wait so many years before uniting? There is something paradoxical about the situation, but something that has perfectly valid historical explanations. To understand the problem, and a number of other aspects of Italy's human geography besides, we must turn to the past.

FROM CAVE MAN TO PAX ROMANA. We will say little about the earliest inhabitants, for the men who lived on Capri and at Monte Circeo hundreds of thousands of years ago seem to have disappeared long before our era.

The first event of any geographical importance was the great migration of the Neolithic Mediterranean peoples. We do not know where they came from, but about 5000 B.C. these peaceful agriculturists settled on the plains. They made implements of polished stone and fashioned fine pottery, and about 1600 B.C. they began to use imported bronze.

It was about the same time that the first wave of Italic peoples swept over the peninsula. They were a warlike pastoral people from central Europe; they spoke Indo-European languages and built quadrangular villages.

The second Italic wave came about the year 1000 B.C. and was contemporary with the Dorian influx into Greece. The invading tribes, known as 'Villanovans', also spoke Indo-European languages; they pushed their predecessors southwards, for the newcomers had the advantage of wrought-iron arms.

During these troubled times the Mediterranean inhabitants left the plains to the invaders and fled to the Apennines. Sardinia, however, was off the line of advance and the people were left in peace to build their fortified towers, or *nuraghi*, as they had done in the Bronze Age.

By this time, the main populations of the country had taken up their positions, and later invasions affected the fringes rather than other parts of the land. Illyrians settled in Venetia and Apulia; and in the eighth and seventh centuries B.C. the Etruscans colonised Tuscany. An oriental people, probably from Asia Minor, the Etruscans wrote a language which we can read, for they used an alphabetic script, but which we cannot understand; they knew how to construct arches and how to cast iron, and they could produce reasonable portraits. At the same period, emigrant Greeks founded wealthy cities farther south — Naples, Cumae, Agrigentum, Sybaris. In the eyes of the ancient adventurers this *Magna Graecia* had all the glamour of a New World. Some time later, the Carthaginians established a foothold in Sicily and then on the Sardinian coasts. In the fifth century B.C., the north, which had so far been spared, was overrun by the Gauls.

With the emergence of Rome as dominant power the whole historical scene changed. Rome was originally nothing but a settlement of coarse peasants, but as its site commanded the last easy crossing of the Tiber before the sea, the population assimilated the oriental heritage of the Etruscans and the Hellenic traditions of *Magna Graecia*. The spirit of the Romans was practical, and in successive and concentric waves of expansion they succeeded in conquering first Latium, then Italy, then the whole of the Mediterranean. By the first century B.C. the name *Italia* was applied to the whole peninsula. By the third century A.D. the name designated the territory we now call Italy. Methodically, and by the *Pax Romana*, the logic of Roman law was everywhere imposed upon the peoples; they enjoyed the advantages of Roman aqueducts and paved roads — and they were conditioned by the precision of the Latin language. Riches, too, poured into Italy through every frontier, accompanied by soldiers from all nations and by new ideas and influences of every sort. It was in Rome during the fourth century that Christianity was selected from all the religions offered by the East. Italy thus became the first officially Christian country.

AN OBJECT OF INVASION. Then came decadence. Rome, enfeebled partly by the injection of alien influences

A view from the Temple of the Oracle at Delphi

GREECE

Erice, a small town of ancient origin near Trapani in Sicily. It is one of the oldest cities of Europe — older than Rome or Athens — and was inhabited by the Phoenicians. M. A. PRIESTMAN, CAMERA PRESS

The inside arena of the Colosseum, largest of the amphitheatres of Rome, holding 100,000 spectators. It was completed in 80 B.C. and was inaugurated by games in which 5,000 wild beasts fought.

succumbed, and in the fifth century Italy became once more a prey to invaders: Vandals, Visigoths, Huns, Arabs and Hungarians swept through her cities and over the countryside. The nightmare lasted five hundred years. Trade was paralysed and the life of the country withdrew within great self-sufficient domains. The coastal plains were deserted and abandoned to malaria. The people took refuge in the nearby mountains, leaving behind them watchtowers to serve as look-outs for invading pirates. There were, it is true, a few attempts at political organisation, but neither Theodoric's Ostrogoths nor the Byzantines, nor the Lombards, nor the Franks, nor even the Papacy succeeded in reconstituting a coherent State in Italy. Yet there survived a sort of regret for the greatness and unity which had been Rome's gifts to Italy. Parochial rivalries and the political subdivisions to which they gave rise remained constant factors in the Italian story. During the Middle Ages, for instance, it was typical to find that the essential political units were the cities, strongly fortified, overpopulated and teeming with craftsmen. At the beginning of the twelfth century the towns had a communal regime. Then in the thirteenth and fourteenth centuries 'tyrants' and war-lords — the *condottieri* — seized power. This was the period of the 'lordships', when the Este family ruled Ferrara, the Orsinis Rome, the Viscontis Milan. In the fifteenth century, the political framework was greatly enlarged and the cities became the capitals of powerful principalities. Florence of the Medicis — the rival of Siena — dominated much of Tuscany. In the struggle between the great families poignards and poison usually helped to win the day. At Bologna and San Gimignano, the palace towers, vying with each other for height, are lasting witnesses to these ancient rivalries. However, under pressure from foreign Powers in the sixteenth century, the tendency was reversed. Political subdivisions multiplied and were constantly changing right into the nineteenth century.

Among the various patches that made up this harlequin's costume, one calls for especial attention — the Pontifical State. From early times on, the Bishop of Rome was considered the spiritual chief of Christendom, and in the eighth century secured recognition of his temporal sovereignty over part of central Italy, henceforth to be known as the 'Papal States' or the 'States

of the Church'. The establishment of the Papacy as a sovereignty on Italian soil was to have two consequences. The first was that an Italian, 'Roman' conception of religion in the Universal Church was to prevail. The second consequence was that the Church was to become more involved than ever in the administration and the conduct of temporal affairs. Still, even if the Papal States were not always well governed, the Popes were ever the champions of 'Italianism', and without them it is unlikely that the City of Rome would exist today.

Enfeebled by internal quarrels and a crumbling sovereignty, Italy has had the sad privilege of being the European country to suffer most invasions in the course of her history. Time and time again, on the most varied pretexts, foreign armies have invaded the country and established themselves until driven out by rival invading forces. The eighth- and ninth-century invaders were the Carolingian Franks. In the tenth century Italy was annexed to the Holy Roman Empire, and German hegemony began. For four centuries most of the cities were governed by *podestàs*. Meanwhile, in the eleventh century, the Normans succeeded the Moslems as masters of Sicily. After the Normans followed the Hohenstaufen Germans, then the Angevin French, and after them the Aragonese. The fourteenth and fifteenth centuries saw fewer invasions, but in the sixteenth century they started again, more numerous than ever. First there was the French and then the Spanish occupation. The eighteenth century was that of Hapsburg domination, broken for a time by the French but resumed when the Austrians came back in 1815, remaining until the middle of the nineteenth century.

It is true that foreign occupation was not always harmful. The Angevin administration in the south was a model one. But, taking it all in all, the results were disastrous. The usual ravages of war, differences among the Italians themselves (the fierce antoganism between the Guelphs, who supported the Papacy, and the Ghibellines, who were partisans of the German emperors, is well known), oppressive police measures, bad administration (for instance, under Spanish rule), confiscation of works of art (for example, by Napoleon) were some of the results of foreign invasion. The influence on Italian culture and civilisation was profound. It was often the uneven imprint of these influences that made the different regions of Italy so varied in character. For how can we understand Sicily without taking into account the Moslems, or Verona without considering the Austrians, or Ragusa if we ignore Spanish rule?

THE IMPORTANCE OF THE SEA. Italy in the past was a country of seamen. For all sorts of reasons the Italian mariners' calling was an ancient one. As early as the eleventh century, Amalfi was a powerful republic. Venice concluded advantageous agreements with Constantinople. Genoa traded with Morocco, and Pisa with Tunisia. Competition was fierce between these cities. In the twelfth century, Pisa dealt a mortal blow to Amalfi, and in the following century Pisa in its turn fell under the battering of the Genoese. For four centuries the fleets of these sea-powers crossed each other in the Mediterranean, while silks and spices and little Negro slaves enriched the Italian ship-owners. Through her ports came to Italy not only merchandise but ideas, skills, artistic themes. How can we understand Venice unless we take into account the Byzantine East? But the way to the Americas had been opened by Columbus; the Ocean routes drained away European trade, and the Mediterranean ports sank slowly into decay. Venice, the *Serenissima*, in the brilliance of prosperity's last days, seemed to forget she was once the Gateway to the East.

In the past other sectors of Italian activity depended in some measure on sea-borne trade. The craftsmen worked for export, and Florentine cloth, Venetian glass and Faenza ceramics were justly renowned. Because of this commercial activity, the Italians very soon became skilled in the handling of money. Their flexible book-keeping methods and their contacts with their agents abroad ('The Lombards') made them the founders of modern banking, maritime insurance and diplomacy. Some of the old commercial skill and enterprising spirit has survived in present-day Italy. But there was something more. If Italian civilisation from the fourteenth century to the eighteenth was so brilliant, it was certainly due in part to the intense spiritual feeling expressed by Fra Angelico, St Catherine of Siena and Giotto. That cultural brilliance owed much to the liberal patronage of such great and wealthy families as the Medicis, the Borgias and others. Behind Dante and Machiavelli, Raphael and Michelangelo, we find the figures of magnificent, intelligent, and highly prosperous men of business. It was thus by their community of material and spiritual interests that the Italians came gradually to feel that they were Italian — and the ultimate result of this sentiment was national unity.

UNITY AT LAST. National unity indeed — but so late. In 1815 Austria had cut up Italy into small provinces and had imposed in each one a reactionary government. Once more the Italians were plunged into feudalism, but they began a nationalist and liberal agitation. When they were at last freed from foreign control, they united under the leadership of the House of Savoy, whose history it is interesting to recall. The Duchy of Savoy arose on the French slopes of the Alps and spread as far as the line of the Saône. Then, little by little, this 'janitor' State extended over the Piedmontese slopes, and in the fourteenth century the capital was moved from Chambéry to Turin. At the beginning of the eighteenth century, Savoy (to which was attached Sardinia) became a kingdom, and by the middle of the

nineteenth century — thanks to the skill of Cavour — Piedmont was the only more or less independent and sound state in Italy. The rest of the story is well known — alliance with France, victory of the Franco-Piedmontese troops over the Austrians in 1859, Napoleon III's withdrawal from the war after the province of Milan had been obtained for Piedmont. In 1860, Cavour took Tuscany and Emilia, while he handed over Nice and Savoy to France (the plebiscite under Piedmontese auspices resulted in more than 99 per cent of the votes being cast for union with France). Then, thanks to Garibaldi, Piedmont annexed the Kingdom of the Two Sicilies. The Kingdom of Italy was officially proclaimed in 1861. After yet another war Italy absorbed Venetia (1866), while the troublesome problem of Rome, which obviously had to be capital of the new State, was solved by force of arms — despite the Pope's protests — in 1870. Unity was achieved.

Immediately, specifically modern Italian difficulties confronted the new State — backwardness of agriculture, lack of industrial plant, the shocking poverty of the southern peasantry. In attempting to overcome these difficulties the government was handicapped by quarrels between North and South, by the politicians' excessive individualism, the arrogance of the great landowners, the inertia of the illiterate masses and the hostility of the Church. Nevertheless, by the beginning of the twentieth century a good deal of progress had been made. The rail network had been linked up with those in foreign countries. Hydro-electric stations were increasing in number. Universal suffrage had been established ·in 1921. At the same time, however, and despite a mighty stream of emigrants, the number of inhabitants to the square mile had risen to more than 250: Italy's eternal problem of over-population.

After the First World War, matters came to a head; social disturbances became more and more numerous. The government was powerless; there was general stagnation. At this point the alarmed business classes turned to Mussolini who, by drastic measures, re-established order and set up a totalitarian regime in 1921. The only aspect of Fascism that interests us here is the economic one. Mussolini's Italy sought for political reasons to be self-sufficient and, in order to cut down on imports, did manage to produce more wheat and electric current. Substitute materials such as hemp and artificial silk were increasingly used. Under this autarkic system, spectacular improvement schemes were undertaken — the draining of the Pontine Marshes is perhaps the best known of them. But unfortunately, side by side with this quite effective economic policy, Mussolini engaged in an absurd demographic policy: he gave excessive encouragement to an increase in the birth-rate and at the same time forbade emigration. Then, claiming to restore Italy's 'ancient grandeur', he led the country into the most risky adventures. In 1946, ruined by the war, Italy chose to become a democratic and parliamentary republic. Six years afterwards the country had resumed its place in the concert of nations.

This long historical introduction would have been unnecessary were we dealing with any other country in the world, but the sketch is useful in this case so that we can, by starting with its ethnical and linguistic complexity, explain Italy's social complexity.

SI PARLA ITALIANO. Let us say, first of all, that when we speak of 'race' we mean a collection of hereditary physical and psychological characteristics independent of cultural influences such as those of language or religion. There is a Latin culture; there is no Latin 'race'.

Three main ethnical types can be distinguished in Italy. First there is the Mediterranean race: dark, lively, rather short (less than 5 ft. 5 in.), narrow-headed — this is the traditional 'Italian' type and resembles that of the Catalans or Provençals. Then comes the Alpine race: chestnut-coloured hair, broad-headed, medium height, general appearance rather heavy. This type too is found in France — among the people of Auvergne,

A Sardinian girl from Nuoro.
E.N.I.T.

A young Sicilian from Taormina.
ROGER VIOLLET

A girl from Selva, in the Dolomites.
PAUL POPPER, ATLAS PHOTO

Mondine (temporary agricultural workers) in a ricefield of the Po plain.
E.N.I.T.

Shepherds of Ciocciaria (southern Latium), wearing characteristic sandals.
E.N.I.T.

A Venetian gondolier.

A farm labourer. E.N.I.T.

for instance. Lastly there is the Dinaric race, with dark hair, a head both broad and high, tall of stature — a type seen in most Yugoslavs. Generally speaking, the Mediterraneans occupy the peninsula and the islands, the Alpines northern Italy, and the Dinarics Venetia. But on detailed study we find many regional variations. There is the Milanese type that tends to be fair-skinned. There is the brilliant blonde hair of Titian's Venetian women; the rather more subdued fairness of Botticelli's Florentines; the commanding profile of the Romans, and the low stature of the Sardinians. There are the tall, fair inhabitants of the Val d'Aosta and of Trapani; there are the tall, dark people of Liguria and the Abruzzi.

Although we know very little about the origin of these physical types, there is every reason to believe that the Mediterraneans represent the Neolithic natives who were pushed down into the peninsula; the Alpines, the Terramare and Villanovan invaders; and the Dinarics, the immigrants from Illyria.

Logically speaking, we should expect that certain features would have been attenuated, or accentuated, by local infiltrations such as those of the Nordics (Gauls and Germans in Lombardy, Normans in Sicily) and of the Mediterraneans (Etruscans in Tuscany, Albanians in Calabria, Catalans in Sardinia). But nowhere, not even in Sicily, has it been possible to show, in a scientific way, the existence of such influences due to these infiltrations. And, as for the 'general post' of medieval armies, it has left no lasting traces at all.

It is, then, more than probable that the physical appearance of the Italians was established in very ancient times. We can trace their language, too, to ancient sources.

Like Spanish and French, Italian is derived from Latin and is thus Indo-European. Of all the European languages, Italian is probably the most musical in its stress, and by its cadences and its faculty for creating abstract terms the most suited for oratory — and the least fitted for the expression of scientific thought. The grammar, which seems so simple, is really extremely subtle, so that the Italians themselves have in general a poor knowledge of their own language, while they attach the greatest importance to accentuation.

The most striking feature, however, the most geographical characteristic of the Italian linguistic map is the astonishing vigour of local dialects. In order to understand this situation, we must think of Italy as a sort of prehistoric Tower of Babel which, during the course of history, was gradually won over to Latin. Since Latin was spoken by a number of peoples used to a variety of different languages, it did not change everywhere in the same fashion — so we have the existing dialects: northern, Tuscan, and central-southern.

In the northern group, the Piedmontese, Lombard and other dialects have been much influenced by the pronunciation of Gaulish and Germanic speech, while the rather lisping accent of Venetia owes something to the ancient Illyrian tongue. In the Tuscan group, which extends over the smallest area, the aspirated 'c' (for example, *amiho* for *amico*) is characteristic, and probably a legacy from Latin pronounced in the Etruscan fashion. The central-southern group occupies the whole of peninsular Italy with the exception of Tuscany and the islands. This group is very complex since it is based upon a foundation of prehistoric languages. Generally speaking, the dialects of this group tend to slur over — or to drop — final letters and syllables, but the pronunciation is heavily stressed — as in Roman, Neapolitan and Sicilian, for instance. Of all the Mediterranean dialects, Sardinian is that in which the pre-Indo-European foundations are most noticeable.

In addition to the character of the pre-Latin languages, we must take into account the evolutionary phase which Latin itself had reached when it was introduced into any given area. For example, it was Old Latin that was imported into Sardinia, Late Latin into the South, and Classical Latin into Tuscany.

There is an official language everyone learns at school and can speak in addition to his local dialect: the 'divine tongue of Dante', time-honoured by centuries of literature, is of Tuscan origin but has lost its Tuscan accent, and the phrase *lingua toscana in bocca romana* would indicate that 'official Italian' should be spoken in the Roman way.

Again, the national language gives way on its borders to fringes of foreign speech. French is spoken in the high valleys of Piedmont and in the Val d'Aosta. German is the prevalent language in the Upper Tyrol, while the lands bordering on Yugoslavia are permeated with Slovene speech. Elsewhere and in the middle of Italy there are a few scattered patches of language which bear witness to former settlements made for political or social reasons: thus Catalan is still spoken at Alghero in Sardinia, Albanian in about twenty-five villages dotted about from the Abruzzi to Sicily, and Byzantine Greek is still common speech in the extreme south of Apulia and Calabria. But, naturally enough, Italian makes headway everywhere at the expense of these languages.

PSYCHOLOGY OF THE MAN IN THE STREET. It is easy to understand, then, how difficult it is in such conditions of extreme social and physical diversity, to paint a psychological portrait of the average Italian. Perhaps, however, such a portrait may be useful as a starting-point for an understanding of regional variations.

The first thing that must strike any observer is that the Italian is extremely human. He may not be very attentive to formulas of politeness but he is, nevertheless, full of essential kindness. He is obliging, often generous, and susceptible to feelings of pity. He is sentimental and not often severe. His pacifism is quite sincere. These essentially human characteristics make him seek the company of his fellows — he is sociable, inquisitive, talkative, familiar. Solitude, and especially silence, he finds intolerable. He is wise enough to realise that men do not command their own destinies, so what is the good of saving? He lives from day to day and, just as he himself looked after his parents when they were old, so he expects his children to support him at the end of his life. If he is not very punctual in keeping appointments, that is because he knows that nothing is really urgent.

A second point is the vivacity of the Italian intelligence. Italians are full of imagination and at once catch on to a general idea, seize the meaning of an abstract concept — and they excel in jurisprudence and philosophy. On the other hand, they are ill adapted for analysis or for precise observation. They are not realists. They are lively and impatient, they understand intuitively, so that often enough they do not take the time to go deeply into anything, and so fall into the fault of superficiality. The Italian is much too much impressed by showy music, elegant clothes, oratorical effects and superlatives of all sorts, and he pays the price for his fluency and dexterity. However, he is generally much too shrewd to be his own dupe, though he is sometimes deceitful, since it is an exciting and pardonable game to deceive, provided the lie is ingenious and the devious path cleverly trodden.

Italian individualism also presents one major disadvantage: it is recognised that rules are useful, but they are not readily observed. The Italian does what pleases him, and so much the worse for the next man. This lack of public spirit was by no means changed after twenty years of Fascism. On the other hand, it must be admitted that the spirit of individualism scores any number of successes. Whether he is a racing motorist, banker, explorer, industrialist, tradesman or scientist, the Italian makes up for his want of organisation by boldness, initiative and tenacity. In a country such as Italy religious sentiment cannot be ignored. Generally speaking, the Italians are religious. Belief is deep-rooted and wide-spread, but doctrinal knowledge is seldom very great. Italians infuse emotionalism into faith, however, and display an exuberance in religious observances which strikes even the most superficial visitor. The mass of the people live in picturesque familiarity with their Madonnas or saints, and switch over quickly from the most obvious piety to the most offensive expression of anger. Obedience to the commands of the Church, combined with heedlessness, explains the high birth rate among the poorer classes.

Naturally enough, this 'type' is not met with all over Italy, a stock character from one end to the other. The Milanese are cold, precise realists; the Piedmontese are courteous; the people of Venetia fervently religious; the Genoese are astute in business; the inhabitants of the Romagna impetuous; the Apulians glib of tongue. Again, the easy, good-humoured familiarity of the Roman contrasts with the rather distinguished reserve of the Florentine, as does the rough exterior of the men of the Abruzzi with the thin-skinned sensitiveness of the Neapolitans. The Sicilians and the Sardinians, like so many of the other Mediterranean islanders, are rather quick to take offence.

The social factor is of equal importance. In the north, there has been since the eighteenth century a middle-class which has developed in much the same way as the comparable class in France, so that there exists today between the more or less free-thinking wealthy businessmen and the discontented proletariat a sort of intermediate social group made up of people who are by and large faithful to the Church. South Italy, again, is centuries behind-hand: at the top there is a conservative, refined, paternalistic landed aristocracy; at the bottom a wretched, resigned and often illiterate mass. Between the two there is no middle-class. Moreover, in the southern provinces civilisation is what it has always been: a thing of the towns. There is an abyss between the mental outlook of the town-dweller and that of the countryman.

A SWARM OF TOWNS. It is evident that her history predestined Italy to be a land of towns. It is not so much that the number of large cities is disproportionately high. There are 27 towns of more than 100,000 inhabitants, compared with 28 in France. But the number of small towns is immense: more than a hundred have from 30,000 to 100,000 inhabitants,

and it is in the south especially, where insecure conditions lasted long, that the urban centres are the most numerous. In the province of Bari 54 per cent of the inhabitants live in towns of more than 30,000 inhabitants, and almost unknown places such as Andria, Barletta and Molfetta each have more inhabitants than such well-known French towns as Bourges and Poitiers. It is often difficult, moreover, to say what is a town and what is an over-grown village. Nicastro, in Calabria, has 25,000 inhabitants, but farm produce is brought into the town in carts.

The Italian urban centres owe their locations to the same factors as those operating in the rest of Europe. The class of towns that grew up on lines of communication is numerous: places at the foot of a pass, such as Susa; at the entrance to a valley, like Verona; bridge-towns, such as Piacenza; citadels, such as Alessandria. But there are two specifically Italian classes of towns. First, in the north, there are the settlements along the lines of the *fontanili*, for example Turin, Vercelli, Novara, Milan and Treviso. Second, in the south, there is the group of towns whose inhabitants cultivate, at great risk to themselves, the fertile lower slopes of Vesuvius and Etna. Because the subsoil is so poor, there are very few towns near the mines. Carbonia, on the Sardinian coalfield, is quite a recent and artificial creation. Generally speaking, the industrial towns of Italy have an historical origin.

Because of long-lasting insecurity, the Italians have always chosen easily defended sites. There are on the plains, it is true, towns that were Roman colonies, towns that have remained where they are from ancient times, but on the whole, and especially in the peninsula, both pre-Roman and medieval settlements were on heights. In the Apennines the site may be any rocky eminence, but in the regions bordering on the mountains steep-sided hills were the favourite choice: Siena, Perugia, Lucera, Potenza and Agrigentum are typical examples. Sometimes, as at Orvieto, the site is a volcanic table with precipitous sides. In Lucania, whose valleys were infested with malaria, the hill crests were chosen. On the coasts, advantage was taken of easily defensible peninsulas by building across their necks:

Perugia, one of the historic cities of Umbria. The surrounding hills are intensively cultivated with mixed crops. J. ALLAN CASH

A recently built skyscraper in Milan. BOUDOT-LAMOTTE

The Viadotto di Corso Francia, at Rome. Such impressive new motorways have become a feature of the Italian landscape. E.N.I.T.

Aerial view of Bologna, capital of Emilia, showing the radial plan of the old city. At the centre are two medieval towers, both leaning as a result of subsidence. The one on the left, the Torre degli Asinelli, was built in the twelfth century and is about 300 feet high. E.N.I.T.

The Ponte Vecchio over the Arno, at Florence. It is the oldest bridge in the city (fourteenth century), and is lined with the shops of goldsmiths. In the background is the Palazzo Vecchio (thirteenth-fourteenth centuries).   H. HOLMES, CAMERA PRESS

The ancient market-place of Pozzuoli, near Naples, sometimes incorrectly called the 'Temple of Serapis'. It is well known to geographers for, built on the coast, the varying level of the sea over the centuries has been marked on its columns.   J. DEMANGEOT

Gallicano nel Lazio, in Latium. Surrounded by olive groves and perched on a craggy outcrop of volcanic tuff, this village, with its houses clinging to the walls of the castle, is one of many around Rome.

J. DEMANGEOT

The Forum Romanum, which was for centuries the centre of public life in Rome and the heart of the Roman Empire. In the foreground is the Arch of Septimus Severus.

The Bridge and Castle of St Angelo. The bridge was built in A.D. 136 by the Emperor Hadrian; the castle, an immense round tower, was also built by him as a mausoleum for his own body. It has been extensively altered over the centuries.

The Villa Medici, in Rome. Built by the famous Medici family in 1544, it is a fine example of Renaissance architecture, and now houses the French Academy in Rome.

The Castel Vecchio and the Ponte Scaligero at Verona.   E.N.I.T.

A panorama of Rome from the roof of St Peter's.

Syracuse, Orbitello, Gallipoli and Milazzo. In modern times, on the other hand, many of the high-perched towns have moved gradually down into the plain where there are roads and railways, so an upper town, massive and silent, seems to gaze down on a busy lower town. A typical example of this is Bergamo. Often, also, on the shores of Liguria or the Marches, towns long perched on the heights decided in the nineteenth century to build 'marinas' by the shore. Thus Carrara, for instance, now has a twin in Marina di Carrara.

Obviously these different types of towns are not of identical lay-out. Those of the high-perched towns especially are as diverse as they are picturesque. Generally the streets coil round the foot of the castle and unfold down the hillside, as may be seen clearly at Assisi, Urbino and Gubbio. But when the site was a long hill or a spur, as at Aquila or Benevento, the ground-plan was rather like a fern-leaf pattern. On the plains, the plan of the towns was different again. Some are composed of concentric streets round an old piazza — as, for instance, at Bologna. But, in general, the flat ground permitted a strictly geometrical lay-out. The most curious plan is that of a star: star crossroads as at Bitonto in Apulia, star fortresses as at Guastalla and Palmanova on the Po plain. The commonest plan, however, is that of a chessboard, a sign of systematic town-planning, whether a product of Roman colonisation as at Turin, Aosta, Como or Fondi, or of later settlement, as at Vittoria. At Lucca and Piacenza, the chessboard is surrounded by protecting ramparts. Venice, with its winding canals, presents an altogether special case. Certain towns with rectilinear street-plans have been reconstructed in modern times after disastrous earthquakes had destroyed the original town, and are characteristic of southern Italy; Avezzano, Reggio di Calabria and Messina. Very often a chessboard of new roads cuts into the capricious, narrow streets of an old town, as in Milan, Cosenza or Cagliari; but nowhere is the contrast so striking as at Bari.

Rome, the eternal city

Rome has a special place among Italian cities. It has about 1,750,000 inhabitants and is the seventh city in Europe. It has superb monuments, splendid gardens, the finest railway-station in Europe, and an airport of great importance. Rome is the most celebrated city in the West and, at a first glance, this seems very natural. Rome's marvellous past, its position in the heart of Italy at the centre of a network of splendid roads, on a famed site, all combine to make it 'The City' *par excellence*.

The Basilica of St Peter's, Rome, which can hold more than 100,000 people and is one of the masterpieces of Italian Renaissance and baroque art. J. ALLAN CASH

Closer examination, however, reveals that those factors which, as a rule, govern a city's fortunes do not appear, in the case of Rome, to be very favourable. To begin with, Rome has no hinterland. Latium produces nothing for export, nothing to be processed or manufactured, unless we count travertine building stone. Secondly, Rome has no outlet. The Tiber is not navigable, and the Campagna, which only fifty years ago was still malaria-ridden, is only just now beginning to be cultivated. The Roman springs are hot, and water must be brought at great expense from the mountains. There is no labour force, since even now the Roman Campagna has no more than about 50 inhabitants to the square mile. As for the actual site of the city, with its famous hills, it is most unsuited for modern traffic. In short, from the geographical standpoint, Rome is a 'case'.

Fundamentally Rome is a creation of history, and three factors have been of prime importance in its past. First, there was the imperialism of ancient Rome. A simple settlement on the Tiber, Rome would never have become a great metropolis had it not succeeded in conquering the Mediterranean by force of arms. The voracious capital pumped its subject lands for the things it lacked. It was Egyptian wheat, Tunisian oil and Syrian iron that supported a city of a million inhabitants. Thanks to slaves and to booty, Rome was able to live magnificently, to erect splendid buildings, to build fine roads and aqueducts, to construct drains.

The second factor was the permanence of the Papacy. Had not the Popes resided at Rome, the city — deprived of its political power, reduced to its own resources and assailed by brigands — would scarcely have survived the Middle Ages. When the Popes left Rome in the fourteenth century, the population fell to a mere 17,000. In our own days, the attachment of the Roman masses to the Sovereign Pontiff is in part a feeling of instinctive gratitude.

The third factor was the restoration of Rome to its position as the capital of Italy when, in 1870, the House of Savoy was obliged to conform to tradition and come to reside in Rome.

Citrus growing in the Sorrento peninsula. Oranges are grown where possible in the hollows, where the rich earth collects. In cold weather, the trees are protected by wicker roofs, supported by a scaffolding of poles. Here, some of the roofs have been pushed aside to let the sunlight through. J. DEMANGEOT

Flax-growing near Naples. In the foreground is the stagnant pool used for retting. Behind are stacks of flax stems. To the left and in the background, an example of intensive mixed-crop farming: vines climb up the poplars. J. DEMANGEOT

For prestige reasons, Mussolini's government forced the population up to over a million.

As a result of these factors, this huge city has all sorts of functions, but no economic one. Its primary function, as the capital of the Italian Republic, is administrative and political, and, because of various executive and government offices, the city contains a very high percentage of white-collar workers. There is also a double set of diplomatic representatives: those accredited to the President of the Republic, and those accredited to the Holy See. In addition, Rome is the headquarters of some international organisations such as the F.A.O. (Food and Agriculture Organisation). A map showing the radiating spokes of the railway-lines shows diagrammatically the centralisation at the seat of government.

Then Rome is the capital of Catholic Christendom, since over 520 million Catholics are joined by spiritual ties to the Sovereign Pontiff. With its Vatican City, its seminaries and its many churches, the religious importance of Rome is very obvious. The number of pilgrims visiting the city is considerable. In the 1950 Holy Year, for instance, nearly two million

went to Rome. Roman ruins, churches, palaces and museums make up an archaeological assemblage which attracts many other visitors besides pilgrims. Tourists play a most important part in Roman economy, though not such an exclusive one as at Venice. But there is little else besides these various functions. Although Rome has the largest university and the greatest number of newspapers in the country, it is not the intellectual capital; Florence and Naples rank before Rome. From an economic point of view, Rome is a city of many consumers and of few producers. There are some unimportant handicrafts, some factories for processing foodstuffs, and that is all. As a result, there are no suburbs. You pass abruptly from sheep-pastures to the most up-to-date cinemas.

Since the war, the situation has, however, changed a little. As the population increases all the time (a phenomenon that is linked with a policy of ever greater centralisation), and as the town's activities are geared to an increasingly high speed, Rome's outskirts are beginning to be built up and industrialised: factories manufacturing pharmaceutical products, oil refineries, rubber factories, tile-works and film-studios. Market-gardens are pushing out into the Campagna. Another significant point is that Rome has become the second largest banking centre in Italy. It would seem then that the city is destined to lose its artificial character little by little. This is no isolated phenomenon: we shall see that economy of the peninsula as a whole is undergoing a transformation.

Life in the country

Ever since Virgil's time Italy's main resource has been agriculture and to this day some 8,000,000 persons (or about 42 per cent of the labour force) are engaged in agriculture, while industry employs no more than 32 per cent. However — and this fact is fundamental — there are too many workers on the land (10 for every 47 acres of cultivated land) and as a consequence, though 57 per cent of the serviceable soil is farmed, the spread of mechanisation is purposely held up for fear of creating unemployment.

The second point to note is the contrast between the different types of landownership. On close observation we can see on the one hand a mass of tiny holdings quite useless for feeding a family (54 per cent of the holdings are of less than 1¼ acres). These are usually worked by their owners. On the other hand we can see land concentrated in the hands of the few, for 25 per cent of the agricultural land is made up of estates of more than 250 acres. These large estates are generally farmed by share-croppers.

There is, as may well be expected, a great difference between these two Italies.

NORTHERN ITALIAN PEASANTS. In considering northern Italy, we may at once disregard the Alps, for there the physical conditions are such that men have had to adapt themselves to them in more or less the same way in whichever country the conditions exist — from France to Yugoslavia. It is the southern fringe only of the Italian Alps that presents some original features.

Natural conditions in the Po valley are much less favourable than is usually imagined. It is certainly true that the country is open and the climate, on the whole, good. But the soil itself is only fair. The upper terrace has soils that are too acid and too porous, while those of the lower terrace are soaked with water. Therefore what we may call 'elementary' farming can give only indifferent results: flocks and herds scattered about over great expanses of heather moors; the poorer cereals such as rye and millet; some vegetables; some fruits. The vine flourishes, however, on hills with a good exposure.

But the face of rural Italy has been determined much less by natural conditions than by the historical conditions of land ownership. It is, indeed, impossible to separate the agrarian from the social structure. Once again, we must go back to the beginnings.

In Rome's earlier days, when the South was brilliantly civilised and highly developed, the Po plain was almost deserted, still marshy and covered with trees. When Roman colonisation began, there was no pre-existing pattern to interfere with the chessboard design, which was imposed so thoroughly that it can still be recognised in the landscape today. The Romans divided the land into little parcels farmed by free settlers and share-croppers. During the early Middle Ages, the farmers were in some cases reduced to the condition of serfs, but the Lombard Law preserved the smallholdings. About the thirteenth century, the movement for the emancipation of the communes entailed also the freeing of the serfs, who then became share-croppers. From that time onwards the development of the countryside was linked with that of the towns, for townspeople who had made money and had bought land possessed both the means and the will to improve farming methods and conditions. Certainly in the nineteenth century no one factor was more important for Italian agriculture than the industrialisation and consequent wealth of the north Italian towns.

Farming methods were directly influenced by this social development. If he has a long contract or lease, a farmer has a personal interest in increased yield and, also, he feels he has the time to plant trees. Hence the prevalence of multi-course farming, in which the same field is planted with alternate rows of herbaceous plants and shrubs. At present three-quarters of the Po plain have more fields planted with trees than without, and in the province of Como the proportion is ten to one. If the yield is increased, the soil's resources and especially its water supply are naturally exhausted more rapidly. In the north, then, the wet climate has favoured the multi-course system.

We may remember also that this method of farming, together with the division of the land into smallholdings and the abundance of water, has made for the scattering of dwellings. It is true that the North is the region of large towns but, with certain exceptions, more than half the rural population lives in isolated dwellings. In Emilia and Venetia, the proportion is as much as 80 per cent.

Another result of the country's historical evolution has been that the monasteries and the towns exercised much influence upon agricultural methods and skills. In the Middle Ages, Lombardy was, like Flanders, one of the strongholds of European husbandry. It was in Lombardy that the technique of crop rotation was perfected, and it was there, in the thirteenth century, that the monks applied the *marcite* method, which consisted in warming the meadows by flooding them during the winter with the tepid waters from the *fontanili*. It was in Lombardy that, as early as the twelfth century, land was irrigated by tapping the waters of Alpine streams where they reach the plain. Today the Cavour Canal is the largest of these irrigation canals, and about a third of the agricultural land in Lombardy and Piedmont is irrigated.

On the low plains and the delta, the problems were of quite a different kind, since there was no need to irrigate, but rather to drain off surplus water. The Venetians were so occupied with maritime ventures that they long neglected their agricultural land. Drainage operations were undertaken tardily, and the major undertakings date from Mussolini's time. By means of canals and drainage-pumps, nearly 2½ million acres were converted into dry land — especially in the neighbourhood of Ferrara. Some of these polders are over 13 feet below the level of the Adriatic. On the Po flood-plain, upstream of the delta, drainage of the water has been accelerated by the plantation of long rows of poplars. Such very large-scale hydraulic undertakings can be carried on only by powerful concerns: hence large estates have a firm grip of the region, and the men who till the land are mostly labourers.

Therefore, thanks to the full utilisation of water-control methods, the original multi-course farming has been supplemented with wheat, maize and potatoes, temperate zone fruit-trees such as mulberries, as well as tomatoes and forage plants. Industrial crops, or those lately introduced, such as tobacco, sugar-beet, and especially rice and hemp, are grown in special areas.

Much attention must be paid to forage crops since, in the multi-course system, there are no fallow fields to feed live-stock. Still, thanks to the fields of clover and lucerne, many cattle and other beasts are raised in the north. Manure from the cattle stalls is of course most valuable for the soil, and gives the north a great advantage over Mediterranean Italy.

The Po plain agriculture has one further advantage: it has benefited much from capital supplied by industry, and is really modern. North Italy has altogether no more than 32 per cent of the cultivated land in the country, but the north uses 59 per cent of the total amount of chemical fertilizers and employs 75 per cent of the tractors. Certain figures for yields on the Po plain are quite remarkable. Ordinary wheat, for instance, gives from 17 to 23 cwt. to the acre, as it does in the central areas of Europe, whereas in peninsular Italy the yield never reaches 16 cwt. And the north Italian ricefields have a higher yield than those of the Far East.

Although, from the physical point of view, north Italy

Fields under intensive cultivation. They are irrigated with great care, both mechanically and by hand. Such methods have greatly increased Italy's agricultural production. E.N.I.T.

Agrarian reform. Recent reforms have completely remodelled the geography of certain regions. Here, for instance, is part of the Maremma along the Via Aurelia which has been transformed: roads, scattered houses and fields under cultivation in a region which has been totally barren since Roman times. J. DEMANGEOT

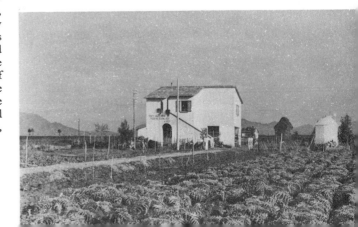

stops at the Apennines, from the point of view of human activity, and especially of rural life, the north spreads over into Mediterranean Italy. It is both logical and curious that sun-drenched Liguria should be a part of northern Italy, but it is still more curious to find northern-type multi-course farming and scattered dwellings in Tuscany and the Marches. This state of things seems to be due to the combined influence of the medieval middle class and impermeable soils.

BACKWARDNESS AND COMPLEX CHARACTER OF SOUTHERN AGRICULTURE.
Mediterranean Italy, both peninsular and insular, offers in its agriculture a violent contrast with northern Italy.

What strikes us first of all is the really appalling number of unfavourable factors. These are due, in part, to physical conditions. The peasant has to till slopes quite unlike those of the north. In the peninsula flat fields are uncommon, since the cultivable surface of this part of Italy is composed of 54 per cent hills, 33 per cent mountains, and 13 per cent plains. The obstacles to husbandry may easily be imagined. It has been estimated that in the whole of Mediterranean Italy (Tuscany and Latium excepted), more than half the arable land is inaccessible to tractors. The soil, moreover, is by no means uniformly good, and for one area of light, fertile, volcanic earth, there may be ten of earth that is stony, or too shallow, or devoid of humus. The climate, whatever may be said, also presents many disadvantages. It is true that more rain falls than in other Mediterranean countries, but the dryness of the summer nevertheless kills many plants, while the sudden, violent showers loosen and wash away the topsoil, cover the fields with mud, and flood the low-lying areas.

Plants that can grow in dry farming, that is to say without any help from irrigation, must be sturdy and push down deep roots. Such plants are almost all shrubs or bushes — gnarled olives, almond and fig-trees, vines and carob trees. Yet wheat (of Mediterranean origin), barley, lentils and maize also thrive.

It may be that in ancient times the native populations managed in the course of time to turn the natural conditions to good account. However, insular and peninsular Italy was not only at a disadvantage from earliest times (probably owing to its division by its physical structure), but it also had the misfortune to be invaded, long ago, by peoples who were stronger and more highly developed than the native population. Now unless special techniques are employed, the soil of the Mediterranean countries can be cultivated only on a large scale, and the poor quality of the pastures necessitates vast untilled areas being left for flocks and herds. Thus new conquerors repeatedly carved out *latifundia* (huge domains), on which they set the enslaved population to work with a view to immediate profits. Slaves of the Carthaginians, of the Greeks, of the Romans, serfs or very short-term share-croppers under Normans, Angevins and Spaniards, the peasants acquired no implements. They did not plant and they did not build. Hence the great estates, open fields, clusters of dwellings — the latter so constructed, in part at least, because of the prevailing insecurity. This state of things lasted right into the nineteenth century, and it must be admitted that to this day feudal ideas have not completely died out.

It would, however, be an error to think of peninsular Italy as made up solely of great estates. We must also take into account the smaller properties which certainly existed near Rome and also to the north of Naples; the voluntary breaking-up of *latifundia*, as at Trapani; reclamation work, as in northern Sardinia; and also the diversity of contracts and leases, which varied from very short ones (as in the Tavoliere) to very long ones granting perpetual rights, as at Bari. We should also remember the great variety of ethnical and technical influences: irrigation works undertaken by the Moslems in Sicily; the Norman fiscal system in Apulia. Nor should we forget the influence of certain towns, such as Naples, Palermo and Bari, the sterilising effect of Rome and far-reaching attraction of the Tuscan cities.

Although we should avoid attaching too much importance to purely physical factors, we must take into account the extreme complexity of the natural conditions. Let us take the case of the water-supply. In the summer, the rivers have no water — at the time of year when it is most needed. Moreover the mountainous, broken nature of the relief is so complicated that no effective canal system can be constructed. The soils formed by decomposition of volcanic lavas and of the granites are deep and remain damp, but the limestone massifs store up the spring rains, while the *karst* underground waters burst out in the most unexpected places. However, although irrigation on a large scale is not practicable, it is often possible locally to divert springs into channels, as is done in the hollows of the Abruzzi. Again, sheets of water lying deep down can be tapped by means of wells, and then we get such very 'oriental' spectacles as the *norias* worked by little blindfold donkeys on the island of Ischia, in the Bari countryside or in the Palermo *huerta*. In such circumstances, water reduces the deadliness of the sun, and the list of local crops is lengthened to include citrus fruits, all sorts of other fruit-trees, various vegetables, and even tropical crops such as cotton, sugar-cane and bananas. Water changes the whole situation, and a variety of crops becomes possible.

Differences of climate due to natural screens and shelters also exist. Thus in some regions, while the windy slope is almost useless for the farmer, the sheltered slope, the so-called *riviera*, is mild and useful. The contrast between the two halves of the Ligurian coast is well enough known and we may add the *rivieras* of Gaeta, of Sorrento, of the southern flanks of Monte Gargano, and those of the Strait of Messina.

Stock-breeding shows a successful adaptation to local conditions. Since there are no high pastures or well-watered meadows, the flocks and herds have to wander about. From the train the traveller can see great cattle with splendid horns moving about in the Tuscan Maremma, black buffaloes wallowing in the mud of the Campagna, and horses galloping wild in Apulia. Everywhere on fallow ground and on the scrubby wastelands and heaths useless for cultivation one may see flocks of sheep and herds of goats with their inseparable companion, a donkey. But the best way to take advantage of the mountains, never far away, is to drive the sheep up on to the high grounds in summer. This custom (*transhumance*) no longer obtains in the northern Apennines, and even in the central section is much less common. All the same, some 400,000 sheep from the Abruzzi still go up in summer to the high plateaus and down in winter to the pastures of Apulia and Latium. A highly evocative sight is that of flocks shut in for the night behind net enclosures, just as they were two thousand years ago, right at the gates of Rome, and watched over by huge white dogs with iron collars. In the Tavoliere it was for long forbidden by law to cultivate the track followed by the migrating sheep, though it was at least a hundred yards wide. Everywhere, and especially in Sardinia, the antagonism between shepherds and agricultural workers is still marked.

It is well known that one of the consequences of extensive (as opposed to intensive) stock-breeding is deforestation. In southern Italy the forests have been shrinking for centuries, and the process is aided by the violent extremes of climate. But if real forests have become rare, brushwood abounds, and the peasants get considerable benefit from it — cork in Sardinia, acorns and mushrooms in Calabria, chestnuts in Tuscany, and, above all, fuel. Mediterranean Italy contains 58 per cent of the wooded areas of the country but produces 96 per cent of the charcoal — and that is too much.

There is in addition the harvest of the sea. Of the 56 provinces of Mediterranean Italy, only twelve have no sea coast. The 44 others have between them about 3,750 miles of shore (not counting small islands). Therefore many of the communes are on the coast, and it is the exception for the high-perched villages on the hills not to have *marine* and a few dozen sailing

Busy Genoa, the major port for imports. It supplies the industrial regions of north Italy with raw materials, and processes some of them itself. E.N.I.T.

Left: Bocadesso, an old fishing port on the Italian Riviera, on the outskirts of Genoa. B. SILBERSTEIN, CAMERA PRESS

Below: A ship passing through the swing bridge at Taranto. Taranto is a naval base and has an important arsenal. E.N.I.T.

boats so that, in addition to the produce of the soil, the inhabitants can count on some crawfish, anchovies, a few swordfish and cuttle-fish.

And now a few words about improvements. On some wet plains, rural living conditions have been revolutionised by drainage and irrigation. Compared with the sporadic attempts made earlier on, the achievement of the Fascist regime must be considered noteworthy, since in the space of eighteen years, 2,222,000 acres of land were made fit for cultivation. Unfortunately, though the strictly economic results were excellent, the social effects were, to all intents and purposes, non-existent. The 160,600 acres reclaimed on the Pontine Plain were let out to share-croppers, while of the 35,600 acres making up the bed of the former Lake Fucino, drained at the instance of Prince Torlonia, 21,250 acres were let on lease to farmers, but each one of them had to live off less than 7½ acres of land.

Agriculture in Mediterranean Italy strikes us as much by its varied character as by its poverty. It is true that the overall picture is not a very bright one, and the average wheat yield is not more than about 10 cwt. to the acre, but whereas, for instance, one can find areas in the Abruzzi where the crops are cut with sickles and the wheat threshed under the hoofs of mules, there are places in Apulia where farming is mechanised and the yield is 20 cwt. to the acre. Again, while in Sardinia the salable amount of agricultural produce is worth 26,000 lire per inhabitant each year, the figure is 133,000 lire for the Campagna. If the land is divided into compartments by natural barriers, it is equally differentiated by the varying resources of its regions.

THROUGH THE COUNTRYSIDE. In the countryside of north Italy there are more different ways of life than the physical conditions would lead one to expect.

As we have seen, the Alps make up that part of Italy which is least typically Italian. In the high valleys (for instance in the upper Maurienne) the country people's subsistence is based on a traditional combination of poor farming and stock-breeding, the latter on Alpine pastures in summer, and in winter in stalls. Less constricted and more specialised is the Pre-Alpine pastoral type of life in the Carnic Pre-Alps and in the Lessini, which depends almost entirely on milch cows. The

Modern farming in the Po plain. Agriculture is mechanised and the fields are long and open, with the emphasis in the Reggio Emilia plain on wheat and maize. But note the line of trees. G. LANDINI & SON

Pre-Alpine forestry type is also limited to a single sort of activity — that of lumbering — as in the Carnic Alps and the Dolomites. But the only really original type of livelihood is that called 'Insubrian', as practised on the foothills of the mountains. There, from one end of the region to the other, chestnut trees, maize and fruit-trees on terraces, together with stock-raising of all sorts, ensure the prosperity of a very dense population. The deepest of the great glacial valleys, the Val d'Aosta and the Valtellina, are great inlets of plain where, thanks to the mild climate, vines and fruit-trees are important.

On the Po plain, different ways of life follow belts running roughly parallel with the river. First, at the foot of the Alps and coinciding with the high stony terrace, runs a long strip of irrigated land bearing a variety of crops: wheat, mulberries, maize. The houses are scattered about and smallholdings predominate. Emilia, on the other side of the Po and bordering the Apennines, has a similar agricultural landscape, but there the main rotation crop is wheat, and stock-breeding is widely practised. This is the country of Parmesan cheese.

Between these two zones of mixed crops is interposed, almost parallel to the river, a long belt of highly specialised farming and of large estates worked by labourers, the *braccianti*. In the western part of this belt (of which Vercelli is the centre) the rice crop is the most important, and at the time of transplanting, the ricefields are covered with crowds of women (taken on temporarily), the so-called *mondine*. In the middle of this belt is Lower Lombardy, a region that is primarily one of forage crops and of cattle-breeding on a large scale; from here comes about a quarter of all the milk produced in Italy, and also Gorgonzola cheese. Lastly, in the eastern part of the belt are the polders of the Po delta, where sugar-beet, hemp and wheat are grown. But here, too, the condition of the agricultural labourers presents a very grave social problem.

The fruit-growing areas are more varied in character. So as to escape fogs and mists, the orchards are generally planted on the edge of the Po plain and border the Insubrian chestnut groves. Except in Emilia, the small landowners cultivate their orchards themselves. Vineyards predominate everywhere, and the wines of Asti, of Barolo, of Berbera, of Valpolicella and Soave are well known. On the cultivated terraces of Liguria, which are watered by force-pumps, there are olives as well as flowers and early vegetables. It is true that this region, although in northern Italy, enjoys a Mediterranean climate.

When we compare the cultivation of peninsular and insular Italy with the regular and well-organised agriculture of the north, it seems to be a jumble of different agrarian systems. First, we have the least evolved type, that of the *latifundia*. The estates are huge; in the Maremma of Tuscany and Latium 53 per cent of the useful land consists of properties of more than 1,200 acres. The fields have no trees, and are covered with wheat or beans which are cultivated extensively, while in the Tavoliere there is still wasteland for seasonal sheep-grazing. The agricultural labourers live in large, often wretched, villages. These *latifundia* must not be confused with the fields (also open) of the Sardinian Campidano or of the small basins in the Abruzzi, where the land is divided into smallholdings and community customs still flourish.

Specialised fruit-growing is a case apart, for careful attention must be given to the trees where the fruit is intended for sale. We may mention too the fig-tree plantations of Cilento (province of Salerno) and the vineyards of Salento (province of Lecce). The parcels of land are small and the houses scattered among the trees in the vineyards of Marsala, the olive-groves of Bari, and the orange-gardens of Sorrento.

But it is in multi-course farming that we find real adaptation to the complex relief of the land. The most intensive and the best developed is in Tuscany, for the historical and geographical reasons we have already mentioned. The landscape resembles that of the Emilian multi-course farming region, but in Tuscany there are also olive-trees. In the well-watered

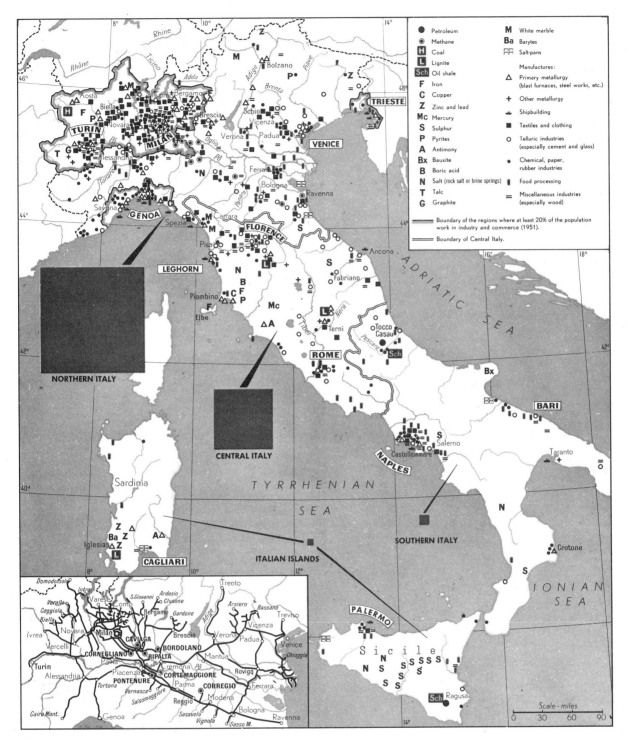

THE PRINCIPAL MINING AND INDUSTRIAL CENTRES OF ITALY. *The greatest industrial concentrations are in northern Italy. The four squares on the left show that they are proportionate to the capital invested in the industries and transport of northern, central, southern, and insular Italy. Inset: the network for methane gas distribution in northern Italy. (After information supplied by J. Demangeot.)*

depressions there are artificial meadows which favour stock-breeding. On the hills around the scattered farms is an astonishing mixture of cereals, vegetables, fruit-trees and vines (Chianti wine). Against the silvery green of the olive-trees the elegant silhouettes of cypresses stand out, as in the paintings of the Sienese Primitives. Everywhere is evidence of care and love of the soil — and of social resentment caused by the large estates and share-cropping. This type of agriculture

is found also in the Marches and as far south as the Adriatic shores of the Abruzzi.

In the centre and south of the country, the mixed-crop farming is even more complicated, though less rich. In Calabria, on the plains of Catania or of Sassari, the peasants grow not only the old combination of crops — wheat, grapes, olives — but also make some profits from small-scale stock-breeding and a primitive sort of exploitation of the coppices. These men

Houses in Apulia. Groups of these trulli *are to be found near Alberobello in the province of Bari; they are round dwelling-houses built of unplastered stones. Note the walled fields.*   J. DEMANGEOT

Mediterranean houses. With their flat roofs to collect rainwater, and even a few cupolas, the houses on the island of Ischia, in the province of Naples, have a North African air.   J. DEMANGEOT

The grape harvest in Maremma.   E.N.I.T.

till the soil and are at the same time shepherds and charcoal-burners. Sometimes one crop predominates: in the Sabini it is the olive, in the Alban Hills the grape (Frascati wine). The houses are generally grouped together, holdings are rather small, and the land is worked either by the owners themselves or by share-croppers.

On the Neapolitan plain, intensive mixed farming is possible because of the damp weather, and gardens, at every altitude, full of wheat, vegetables and fruits, convey an impression of exceptional prosperity. But here also the holdings are too small, and there is misery everywhere. Mixed farming exists also in the famous *huerta* of Palermo and in the large irrigated depressions of the Abruzzi.

The last type of agricultural landscape is that of the 'improved' lands where the estates are held by capitalists and are worked by share-croppers. The fields have neither hedges nor trees; the dwellings are disposed in various ways: scattered on the Pontine Plain or Marshes, or grouped together in large villages on the edges of the Sele Plain. Agriculture is in general of the intensive type, the main crops being wheat, tobacco, market-garden produce and forage plants. In addition, milch cows are kept. These tractor-ploughed fields contrast strikingly with the small-scale, traditional Mediterranean farms.

FIVE TYPES OF PEASANT DWELLING. Though approximately three-quarters of the Italians live in towns and villages, the remaining quarter live in isolated dwellings and since these are peasants, their houses are in most cases remarkably adapted both to the physical setting and to the tasks of the countryside.

The most primitive of the dwellings is the cave. In those regions where the rock is soft, as in the province of Matera (calcareous tufa) or in Viterbo (volcanic tuff), caves with a forward extension, used as homes, are common. Another primitive type of dwelling is the straw hut called *pagliare* found in marshy or wooded areas.

The simplest type of house — that in one block, where everything is under one roof and at ground level — is comparatively rare in modern Italy. The most picturesque examples of such dwellings are to be seen in the *trulli* of Apulia. The *trullo* is simply a cone of dry-course stone, whitewashed outside and of elegant appearance. It is not known whether the *trullo* is a traditional form of building dating from prehistoric times.

Much commoner, especially in the centre and south, is the simple structure of more than one storey where the family lives on the first floor. This type of building demands more advanced construction techniques. The best-known example of such houses is the Alpine chalet. Whether it is in stone and wood, or all in stone, the chalet always has a projecting roof, a hay-loft, a wooden balcony — and the charm of a doll's house. The balcony, which serves for drying as well as for communication within the chalet itself, is a typical feature of the mountain-dwellings and found also in the Apennines. The most commonplace in appearance is the traditional Abruzzi house, with a plain façade and an ordinary roof. But, we may ask, why is it not adapted for the heavy snow of the Abruzzi or for the tending of sheep, which is such a thriving occupation? It is hard to find an answer. In Molise, the rural houses have an outside staircase and a loggia with heavy stone columns. The most complicated type of such dwellings is to be found in Umbria: outside staircase, loggia with pillars, square tower used either as a pigeon-loft or a drying-room. The real Tuscan house is simpler, however, although it often has a pigeon-loft and an arcaded loggia; but its overhanging roof and its square, squat, massive appearance suggest some connection with the architecture of ancient Etruria. On the other hand, the white houses of Capri and Amalfi, half-hidden in green gardens, have low cupolas that recall the dwelling of Arab lands. On Ischia and at Trapani, the houses are plain cubes of completely North African type.

Houses with enclosed courtyards whose life and movement is jealously hidden do not add so gay a note to the countryside, but are marks of greater prosperity. In the case of Lombardy, for instance, the *corte*, with its cattle-sheds and its dairy, conveys an impression of solid economic power. The plan is derived, very probably, from that of the Roman house. In the region of Novara the houses have two courtyards, one of which is reserved for treating the rice and is bordered by the dormitories for the women workers. As such a type of house can easily be transformed into a fortress, it was well suited to central Italy: thus the more elegant Tuscan *fattoria* and the more massive *masseria* of the Roman Campagna often have tall, crenellated walls. In the Tavoliere of Apulia, the *masseria* is both farm-house and sheep-pen combined.

It is probably the house with an open courtyard that is the most uncommon in Italy, although the reason for its comparative rarity is not known. It may be due to a long tradition of insecurity. In Emilia and in the region of Padua the houses are scattered about on a chessboard area typical of Rome.

There are two recent points which should be mentioned in an account of Italian rural dwellings. The first concerns provinces subject to earthquakes (for example Sicily, Calabria, the Abruzzi): here rebuilding of edifices that have suffered damage must, by law, be low and without vaults — a prudent measure, but one that does not make for a very attractive appearance. On the other hand, in those areas where agrarian reform is taking place, the new rural dwellings still conform to purely architectural traditions.

THE ECONOMICS OF ITALIAN AGRICULTURE.
Italian agricultural production, like that of the other Mediterranean lands, shows a striking disproportion between the wealth of plant resources and the poverty of animal resources.

Cereals amount in value to 22 per cent of the total agricultural production. First comes wheat; thanks to unremitting efforts, Italy now has almost as large a wheat harvest as France, though in Italy there is a higher proportion of hard wheats. The amount of wheat grown nevertheless fails to meet the home demand. Next comes maize, covering only one-quarter of the area devoted to wheat. However, thanks to its northern provinces, Italy's crop is larger than that of any other European country except Yugoslavia and Rumania. But the prestige of white flour is such that less and less maize is cultivated each year. In the third place is rice, and more is grown in Italy than anywhere else in Europe. The weight of the rice crop is only one-tenth that of the wheat, but the former suffices to meet the home demand. Other cereals are relatively little grown.

Vegetable crops are developing in various ways. The harvest of vegetables for drying is very heavy, while the potato crop (which suffers from the very dry summers) is only about one-fifth of that in France. Fresh vegetables, on the other hand, are being grown on an increasingly large scale, and of these the most common are undoubtedly tomatoes.

Fruit-growing is still more important than cereal crops, for it makes up 24 per cent of the total agricultural production, and fruit accounts for 12 per cent of all Italy's exports. Specialisation in fruit-growing is increasing, and this branch of agriculture is becoming steadily more commercialised. Grapes and olives are, by tradition, the main standby of Italian farming, and three-quarters of the vines and olive-trees are cultivated in multi-course systems. Italy keeps its place as the world's second greatest exporter of wine (just below France) in the world. Italian wines are, for the most part, either ordinary table wines, rich in tannin and of high alcoholic content, or dessert wines. There are very few fine vintages. The Italian olive oil output is also the second in the world (just below that of Spain), and the amount is (like that of the wine) in excess of home requirements. Citrus fruits are a typical crop of the *riviere*, and the Italian orange production is the second in Europe, below that

of Spain; the lemon crop is the second largest in the whole world. Citrus fruits occupy first place among Italian agricultural exports. Other fruits are also abundant but, with the exception of figs and apricots, are of mediocre quality.

Vegetable resources other than food crops are of little value. The combined profits from industrial crops and lumbering amount, to less than a third of those from fruit-growing. This is not from any lack of woods and forests: thanks to the mountains, the proportion of woodland in Italy (19 per cent) is not much less than in France, but the output of timber is rather small (about 770 cubic feet of wood to the acre). The proportion of wood used for fuel is much too high, and the forests are often worked in an unsystematic fashion. Herbaceous plants for use in industry are rather ill-balanced. There is very little flax, a little cotton and some sugar-beet. However, the tobacco crop, which increases yearly, is the largest in Europe, and the hemp crop (though falling from what it was when raised artificially during the autarkic times of Fascism) is still the largest in the world.

Livestock and its products are, on the other hand, quite definitely insufficient, since they amount in value to no more than 40 per cent of the total agricultural output. The position as regards flocks and herds is, as must be expected, an intermediate one between that of temperate countries such as France (which has almost twice as many cattle and three times as many horses as Italy) and that of the true Mediterranean countries such as Greece, which has more goats, or Spain, which has more than twice as many sheep. Mules, however, are very numerous in Italy. As elsewhere, the proportion of the smaller livestock has diminished during the last fifty years, and that of pigs and cattle has increased. There are at present about 5,000,000 tons of animals on the hoof, which is a relatively low figure. The amount of butcher's meat available is small, and the quantity of milk produced is not great. Most of the milk goes into the making of cheese, and Italy is, in fact, the second largest producer of cheese in the world. The cheeses exported are of high quality.

Not only is the livestock situation unsatisfactory, but the fisheries, too, yield less than might be expected. The Mediterranean is poor in plankton and as a result not rich in fish. Furthermore, except in the Adriatic, the offshore waters are too deep for trawling, while the Italian fishermen's equipment is often still amateurish. The catch is less than a third of that taken by French fishermen.

WHAT DO THE ITALIANS EAT? When it is distributed among 49 million inhabitants, the Italian agricultural output leaves little surplus for export. Nevertheless, foodstuffs amount in value to 23 per cent of the total exports of Italy. First come fruits and vegetables, then — of equal value — citrus fruits and rice. The main customer is West Germany. Then follow tinned tomatoes, sent especially to the United States and Great Britain. Wines and spirits go mostly to Switzerland, while Italian cheeses are bought, above all by Italian emigrants, all over the world.

Of the total imports, foodstuffs amount only to 18 per cent. The most important of these is wheat, mostly from North America. Then, almost as important as the wheat, come livestock from Yugoslavia, meat from Argentina and Denmark, fish from Scandinavia and Portugal, together with milk, butter, eggs and cheese — all needed to make up for the insufficiency of Italian animal products. The third place on the list is occupied by tropical products, among them coffee. It will be seen, then, that the foodstuffs imported are on the whole more expensive than those exported — hence the unfavourable trade balance as far as foodstuffs are concerned.

The main object of agricultural production, however, is to feed a country's inhabitants. What do the Italians eat? Well, let us walk into a small restaurant — say in Rome. The menu is composed, in traditional fashion, of a huge dish of *pasta* — macaroni and the like — generally with a tomato sauce. Then comes a meat dish with a green vegetable and, lastly, a dessert. Bread and wine accompany the meal, which is invariably followed by very strong coffee. The first thing that strikes one is that the Italian, like the Greek, consumes a great quantity of cereals: not only plenty of noodles and rice (and in the north, maize flour), but also, especially in the country, a great deal of bread. The second point about an Italian meal is the small quantity of food of animal origin consumed. The Italians, it is true, eat a reasonable amount of cheese, but only half the number of eggs and only one-third of the quantity of meat eaten by the average Frenchman.

The Italian drinks little milk, nor does he eat much fish or cured pork, and very little butter is consumed. To make up for the lack of animal fats, much olive oil is used for frying and also as an addition to prepared dishes. The final point to note is that very few vegetables are eaten (except tomatoes), or at any rate fewer than in France or Spain. On the other hand, much fruit is consumed, and this provides the necessary amount of sugar, which is otherwise lacking in Italian diet.

Containing as it does three times more vegetable proteins than animal proteins, the diet reflects well enough the nature of Mediterranean agriculture.

Grave industrial problems

Although more workers are engaged in agriculture than in industry, industry is nevertheless more important in the economy of the country, since, together with transport, it supplies 50 per cent of the total national revenue, whereas the share of agriculture is only 30 per cent. The fine quality of Milanese silks and cotton goods, the excellent design and workmanship of Italian motor-cars, the first-class construction of Italian ships are known throughout the world.

But, almost at once, a question arises in our minds. How can this industrial situation exist when, as is obvious, Italy has to all intents and purposes no coal, no oil and none of the raw materials indispensable to modern industry? Let us try to explain this paradox.

LACK OF RAW MATERIALS. If we look at the list of Italian mineral products, our first impression may be a favourable one. Thanks to the old metalliferous rocks of Tuscany, Italy has quite large quantities of antimony, and ranks as second-largest producer of pyrites in Europe. It is, moreover, first in rank of all the countries in the world for the production and export of mercury. In addition, much boric acid is recovered from deposits laid down by natural jets of steam, and in the Alps there are talc and asbestos. Another region rich in minerals is that of Iglesiente in the south-west of Sardinia: barytes and argentiferous lead are found here and, more important still, the finest European deposits of zinc and cadmium. It is well known, too, that Sicily is the second largest producer of sulphur in the world. There is sea-salt on all the coasts, while everywhere is an abundance of building materials: marble in the Alps and at Carrara, alabaster at Volterra, travertine at Tivoli, pozzolana in the volcanic areas.

But in this list the really basic metals such as iron and aluminium (or aluminum), are almost entirely lacking — and this fact constitutes one of the basic problems of the Italian economy. It is true that the island of Elba and a few small deposits elsewhere supply a little iron, but it amounts to barely a fiftieth of the French production. Since Italy lost Istria and, with it, her position as the fourth largest producer of bauxite in the world, bauxite has been worked at Monte Gargano, but the quantities extracted are much smaller than those needed.

Mining industries in Italy contribute no more than 1 per cent to the national revenue. Italy is, then, in the position of having to import twice as much mineral raw material as is extracted from Italian soil. Ferrous metals come from France, Germany, Belgium and Luxembourg; copper is imported from Chile and the United States; tin from Malaya; and bauxite from France and Yugoslavia. And to this list we must add phosphates, graphite and a number of other materials.

The situation is a little less unsatisfactory with regard to raw materials of vegetable or animal origin. It is true that Italy (in common with other European countries) buys from the United States and Egypt almost all the cotton she needs. Indeed, cotton heads the list of Italian imports. It is also a fact that wool comes from Australia and Argentina, hides from South Africa, rubber from Malaya, while the timber shortage necessitates purchase of wood-pulp and cellulose from the Scandinavian countries and the United States. Nevertheless, Italian agriculture is in a position to supply a flourishing foodstuffs industry, while tobacco, hemp and raw silk are sometimes plentiful enough to allow a certain amount of export.

The result of all this is that the purchase of raw materials other than food (iron, copper, coal, cotton, etc.) costs Italy three times as much as the sale of comparable materials (for example mercury, hemp, sulphur, etc.) brings in. Thus, from the very first, industry suffers a heavy handicap. And in all fields, even in those of road construction and the building of hydro-electric dams, this fundamental shortage of raw materials is felt.

HOW ITALY GETS ON WITHOUT COAL. Things would be better if only there were an abundant supply of mineral fuel. But there is not. The geological structure of Italy is, in fact, such that it precludes the existence of extensive coalfields. In central Europe the Hercynian rocks, which are expecially rich in coal, crop out in considerable quantities. In Italy, the Hercynian formations are buried miles deep under layers of limestone and clay. When there is an outcrop, as at Thuile in the Alps and at Carbonia in Sardinia, it is very small, and the total output of Italian coal amounts to hardly one-hundredth that of Germany. Attempts are made locally to fall back on lignite (which is a poor fuel) extracted from the sites of former lakes in Tuscany, Umbria and the Abruzzi.

Luckily enough, those geological formations which are unfavourable for the presence of coal are often favourable for that of the liquid hydrocarbons. The Apennines, like the Carpathians, form an arc of folding bordered on the convex side by deposits that were formerly lagoons and now are oil-bearing. Unfortunately, the Italian oildeposits, unlike those of Rumania, are small and uneconomical to work. The Cortemaggiore deposit, recently discovered in the Po plain, and the small field at Alanno (Abruzzi) do not yield much oil. The best Italian field is doubtless that of Ragusa in Sicily. As good luck would have it, however, methane gas was discovered during the search for petroleum and, at the present time, the borings drilled in the Piacenza-Cremona region yield annually 3,000,000,000 cubic metres of excellent gas that is conveyed as far as Turin and Venice over a network with more than 1,850 miles of pipeline. This abundant supply of natural gas is a factor that will be of great importance in Italy's economic future.

For the time being, the total amount of these fuels is not very large, and for many years past Italian engineers have sought by utilising hydro-electric energy to compensate for the serious lack of power. Naturally enough, the beginning was made in the Alpine regions. In 1914, of 58 hydro-electric stations, 45 were in north Italy. Very quickly the Italian technicians proved that they were equal to the best, and for long the Cardano dam was one of the best known in the whole world. Since the Second World War more work has been done in the central region of the Apennines and in Sardinia,

	Complex economy of the high alpine valleys. Extensive cereal-pastoral economy of the Mediterranean highlands.
	Mountains with chestnut woods.
	Forested regions.
	Rice fields.
	Forage crops (intensive stock-raising).
	Cultivation for land improvement).
	Open fields, latifundia.
	Specialised orchards (vineyards, olive groves, etc.).
	Various crops with maize.
	Various crops with olive trees and Sardinian "bocage".
	Various crops without maize or olives.
	Traditional Mediterranean crops.
	Intensive Mediterranean cultivation, huerta.

TYPES OF FARMING IN PENINSULAR AND INSULAR ITALY. *(After information supplied by J. Demangeot.)*

where huge dams and plant have been erected; among these are the reservoirs of Campotosto and San Chiara Ulas, and the hydro-electric station of San Giacomo (Abruzzi), which, with an installed capacity of 200,000 kW, equals that of Chastang in France. One of the advantages of the hydro-electric stations in peninsular Italy it that their output is at the maximum in winter, the season when that of north Italy declines. At the present time, the amount of hydro-electric current produced in Italy is more than that produced in France; 77 per cent of it comes from northern Italy, 10 per cent from central Italy,

11 per cent from southern Italy and 2 per cent from the Italian islands. To this total must be added the substantial amount of geothermic electricity generated by the *soffioni*, or natural steamjets, at Larderello in Tuscany.

If we reduce all the energy produced annually in Italy to units of coal, we get 23,000,000 tons of coal, which is not much; divided among the population it gives only 1,075 lb per head, whereas the Frenchman has 2,905 lb and the citizen of the United States 19,100 lb. As a result, a great deal of fuel must be imported for the production of power, as well as to furnish raw materials to industry. Through purchase of some 10,000,000 tons of coal from America and Germany, and an equal quantity of oil from Arabia and Iraq, the power resources of Italy are practically doubled and the demands are almost met. But such purchases cost twice as much money as that provided by the export of agricultural produce. Part of this imported solid and liquid fuel is, moreover, transformed into electricity at the generating stations situated in the larger ports, such as Genoa, Naples and Venice, as well as in big inland cities such as Milan — and this produces about a tenth of Italy's current.

DIFFICULT COMMUNICATIONS. There is no need to stress the importance of transport in the industrialisation of a country, but in the matter of communications Italy is, once more, in none too favourable a position. Everywhere, except in the Po plain, land transport is hampered by mountains and ravines. So the necessary engineering work is costly and traffic consequently rather slow. A few examples will make this clear. In the northern Apennines, six out of seven of the railway lines that cross the range run through tunnels, and the tunnel on the *direttissima* line from Florence to Bologna is about 11½ miles long and is thus, after the Simplon, the longest in the world. In Sicily, the Palermo-Trapani line is a good example of unavoidable circuitous track laying — the track is, indeed, 80 per cent longer than the distance as the crow flies. The engineering feats accomplished in the construction of roads cut into the flanks of mountains, such as those on the Ligurian coast, on the coast of Amalfi, or on the northern Sicilian shore, are often quite remarkable. Likewise, the roadbuilding in southern Italy (where there is always a danger of landslides) is noteworthy.

The Italian railways offer some curious contrasts. It is true that the mileage seems sufficient, but far too much of the track (74 per cent to be precise) is still single. There is also a strange contrast between the different sorts of traction used. Some of the runs use old-fashioned steam-engines, yet electric traction is very highly developed in Italy — as is natural enough in a land so poor in coal — and, as in Japan, over one-third of the State railways are electrified. There is a further contrast in the traffic. While the trains carry a very considerable number of passengers, freight is rather limited (less than a quarter of the goods traffic of French railroads). This is astonishing in a country with few waterways (the Venice-Milan canal exists only on paper), but the fact goes to show that Italian industry manages to make do with a minimum of bulky materials. Furthermore, road haulage competes strongly with the railways.

The road network has had to adapt itself to the same natural obstacles as the railways, and is also uneven in quality. There is a great deal of difference between the main highways and the country roads. While lay-out and alignment are excellent, the materials used for surfacing (even on the *autostrade* or motor-ways) are very poor. The number of private cars on the roads is not great; except in the north, there are relatively few vehicles — one for every 93 inhabitants compared with one for every 11 inhabitants in England. But if cars are rather scarce, motor-cycles, scooters and fast 'mopeds' are very numerous indeed. Furthermore, since in some areas there are few railways, buses and motor coaches are very numerous. The freight traffic on the roads is intense, and the splendid heavy lorries with one or two trailers which streak along the roads at night enable half as many goods again to be hauled by road as are sent by rail.

Italy's geography is such that the country is ideal for interior air communications. A Milan businessman gains a great amount of time by flying direct to Palermo, for instance, and avoiding the tiresome rail journey down the peninsula and across the Strait of Messina. But, though Italian aviation is completely modern, the air routes within the country are as yet relatively little used. On the other hand, owing to its position, Italy is a port-of-call of the first importance for inter-national air traffic, especially for that between western Europe and the Near East. The Rome airport (Ciampino), much the busiest in Italy, is the third largest in Europe after those of London and Paris. Transit flights account for three-fifths of the planes using the airport. At the present time, however, Italian air activity calculated in passenger-miles is only one-tenth of Great Britain's.

As we have seen, the Italian maritime tradition is a very old one, and to this advantage must be added another due to the double task which Italian ships have had to assume from the middle of the nineteenth century: first, that of conveying overseas thousands of emigrants, and second, that of keeping Sicily and Sardinia linked with the mainland. At the present time, the Italian merchant navy is the sixth in the world and larger than that of France or the Netherlands. In the traffic of the Italian ports, coastwise shipping occupies an important place, accounting for 37 per cent of the freight and 94 per cent of the passengers. The cargoes carried on ocean-going ships are mostly imports. The main port of entry for freight is Genoa, then comes Venice, and after it Naples. On the other hand, the principal passenger port is Naples — the gateway for emigrants from southern Italy on their way to South America and Australia. Trieste comes next — but a long way behind Naples.

ABUNDANCE OF LABOUR. Scattered about the world are countries which nature seems to have designed for industrialisation: one such is Germany. But, as we have just seen, Italy is not one of these countries. How then does Italy manage to have quite a large industry? The explanation is simple. Italy, like Japan, is literally condemned to industrialisation in order to provide work for a superabundant labour force. This situation has a great many consequences.

There can be no doubt that seven million workers is a very great number for a country that has no raw materials. This figure is, moreover, bound to increase, not only with the natural rise in population, but also with the ever-growing attraction that the industrial towns have for the peasantry. The existence of a mobile mass of unskilled labourers that moves about from field to factory and back again according to the demand for labour is a considerable disadvantage. For there is in Italy much unemployment, and 45 per cent of those out of work were employed in industry. Furthermore, if employers pursued the policy of getting the maximum output there would be even more unemployment — probably half as much again. But both the trades unions and the government in their proper concern for the maintenance of social balance have, in effect, forbidden any laying-off. So the factories are run with staffs that are not only too big but even, in part, useless. If the system can be justified from the social point of view, from the economic one it is disastrous, for it raises the cost-price of all goods considerably, and this is already adversely affected by the very high price of raw materials. Further, this system holds up the modernisation of equipment, plant and techniques, since any such modernisation would risk bringing about an increase in unemployment. All this amounts to a curious brake on progress in the country where Branca invented the steam turbine, Volta the electric battery, Dal Negro the electric motor, and Marconi the radio.

The excess of labour has unavoidable effects on the pattern of industry. Surprisingly, concentration of industry is not encouraged. Whereas throughout western Europe industry has gradually replaced small craftsmen, in Italy the factories have not squeezed out the small workshops. To mention only real craftsmen (since often handicrafts constitute an additional activity for peasant families which have not enough other work to do — and such activities belong more to rural economy): more than a million people are glass-blowers (Venice), straw-plaiters (Tuscany), wool-weavers (Apulia), or coppersmiths (Abruzzi). As they have very small overhead expenses, these craftsmen can turn out products that are extraordinarily cheap. But real industry is not very concentrated. It is true that there are large factories, some indeed splendidly equipped, but there are relatively few of them: factories with more than 500 workers employ only a third of the total labourforce in any given industry. Small and medium-sized enterprises are the most numerous. Thirty-one per cent of the workers are in workshops employing a maximum of ten employees. This is another cause of the low output and high prices of manufactured products.

There is another essential factor: credit. Money to back development is not easily obtained — at least not at a reasonable rate of interest. Low individual incomes (due in part to the poor rates of pay), together with the high cost of living, mean that the average Italian, frugal though he is, can put no money aside. As the total amount of savings is inadequate, rates of interest are high, and this is reflected in the cost price of all products.

Two facts ought, however, to be borne in mind. First, since the war the government has been a very big customer for industrial products, and since a policy of large-scale investment has been followed, a great deal of capital has been injected (rather artificially) into the economic blood-stream. Second, though big industry does not yet dominate the scene, the internal financial structure is very concentrated all the same. Combines such as Fiat (automobiles), Montecatini (chemical products), Pirelli (rubber), Marzotto (textiles) and Edison (electricity) present all the features of modern capitalism.

Although the economic structure of Italian industry is that of a backward country, there are plenty of people in Italy inspired with a will to progress. We may ask, however, whether much progress can be achieved in view of the formidable handicap of over-population.

CONCENTRATION OF INDUSTRY IN THE NORTH.

There is, perhaps, no other country in Europe where industry is so strictly localised as in Italy. The north, which contains 44 per cent of the population, has 65 per cent of the industrial workers and receives 71 per cent of the investments made in industry.

In using the term 'north' we should understand those regions north of the line of the Po. The area that has been industrialised longest is that bordering the Alps. Among the favourable factors were, first, the supply of wool from Alpine sheep, then later on, local silk production, and the existence of electric current from the Alps. All the way from Piedmont to Venetia runs a string of busy factories. Biella turns out three-fifths of the Italian woollens and Como is a great centre of the silk trade. Brescia, Vicenza and Valdagno also produce woollens and cottons. As on the edge of the French Alps, and for the same reasons, there are shoe, cement and paper factories and there are also metallurgical works that supply finished products. Railway rolling-stock comes from Pinerolo, typewriters from Ivrea. Varese produces motors, Brescia arms, and Schio turbines. This industrial strip even has outposts in the Alps themselves — Villar Perosa turns out 80 per cent of Italian ball-bearings. Val d'Aosta has blast-furnaces, and special steels are made at Bolzano.

Not far off is the Milan region. The city owes its origin to commerce, since this Lombard city was the terminus of the medieval routes used for trade with the Germanic countries. In addition, the Milanese wove silk and manufactured arms. Today, Milan is the economic capital of Italy. It is a modern metropolis in central European style, and is a busy hive of industry and commerce. It is no exaggeration to say that all modern industries are represented in its suburban factories. The city is, moreover, the centre of a whole constellation of workshops and industrial plant stretching from the Alps right down to the Po. Saronno, Legnano, Novara, and especially Sesto San Giovanni turn out steel, rolling-stock and machines of all sorts. At Cesano Maderno chemical products are manu-

Drying tobacco on special racks. Tobacco-growing is steadily increasing and Italy's production is the highest in Europe. E.N.I.T.

factured; at Pavia, sewing-machines; at Vigevano, boots and shoes. In Lombardy the mills of Busto Arsizio and Gallarate, produce almost three-quarters of the Italian cotton goods; jute and artificial silk come from Vercelli; and almost everywhere, especially on the low terraces, foodstuff industries have grown up. In fact, the province of Milan. which comprises less than 1 per cent of the area of Italy, possesses 14 per cent of the country's industrial works.

Turin is quite different from Milan. In the first place this former capital began to develop its industry very late (under Cavour), and secondly, unlike Milan, it does not possess a great range of industries. Artificial silk, food-products and clothing are turned out, but the main industry is the manufacture of automobiles: Fiat (with its staff of 71,000) produces 85 per cent of Italian motor vehicles.

The supply of raw materials to the industries of the Po valley naturally enough presents a problem. The most obvious port of entry is Venice, but it is some 220 miles from Turin. Hence a considerable percentage of the materials imported at Venice, especially coal, oil and minerals, go for initial processing to the industrial annexe of Venice, Porto Marghera. Thanks to current from the Alps, aluminium, carbides and special steels are also produced at Porto Marghera. Trieste is still farther off and although with its oil refineries, important shipyards and canning factories the town forms an integral part of the Italian industrial complex, in so far as it is a commercial port, Trieste serves almost exclusively the part of Europe watered by the Danube.

Because of these difficulties, and despite the barrier of the Apennines, Genoa is a much more convenient port of entry. Thus, as soon as they have been unloaded, cargoes are sucked up along a dense network of communicationlines into the industries of the Po valley. Moreover, Genoa rivals Marseilles as a port of entry for goods destined for Switzerland. As in all large ports, a proportion of the raw materials is treated locally, so that, from Sestri Ponente through Cornigliano and Sampierdarena to Genoa itself, there is now a line of factories running along nearly eight miles of the coast. There are coke ovens, steelworks, shipyards, chemical factories, and so forth. Far away, at Savona, Imperia, Albenga and even at Rapallo — all along the coast — factories rise among fields of flowers.

Finally, we must not forget in the north those towns of Emilia that spread from Piacenza to Forli, since they not only have flourishing foodstuff factories and engineering works, but could develop with utilisation of the methane gas supply.

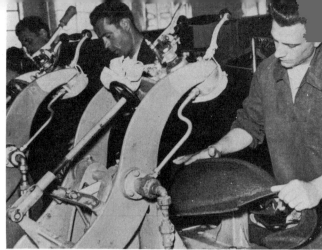

A factory for ready-to-wear clothing at Valdagno, near Vicenza. The prestige of Italian clothes has travelled far and they form an important export. E.N.I.T.

The marble quarries at Carrara, which stretch for about 15 miles. These marbles have been renowned since antiquity and come in a variety of colours for different purposes. Much is exported. E.N.I.T.

The Vajont hydro-electric dam. The production of hydro-electric power makes up in part for the lack of other fuel resources and is, in proportion to population, the highest in Europe. E.N.I.T.

Lacking raw materials and possessing a large labour force, Italy has specialised in precision instruments. Here, in a factory near Naples, a batch of typewriters is being tested before dispatch. E.N.I.T.

Saltworks at Carloforte, in Sardinia. VIOLLON.

The production line in the Fiat works on the outskirts of Turin. The manufacture of automobiles is very important in Italy, and Fiats, Lancias, and Alfa Romeos are sold widely at home and abroad. E.N.I.T.

The 'Rasiom' petrol refinery at Augusta, in Sicily.

'Geothermic' electricity: the works at Larderello, in Tuscany.

INADEQUACY OF PENINSULAR INDUSTRY. Contrasting with this picture of regions thickly covered with industrial towns, peninsular Italy offers one of isolated centres apparently unconnected with each other.

In central Italy some of these industries have been inherited from past times, such as the forges in those parts of Tuscany where there are metals, the woollen industry at Prato, the Fabriano papermills, and even the Leghorn shipyards. Of recent origin are the Pisa, Leghorn and Rosignano chemical industries, the Piombino heavy metallurgy, the Terni electro-metallurgy and engineering works. Still more modern are the electro-chemical works at Bussi (in the heart of the Abruzzi) and the Rome pharmaceutical industries.

Paradoxically, it is in southern Italy, at Naples, that we find the largest single concentration of industry in the peninsula. All the shores of the famous bay are disfigured by blackened industrial plant: the shipyards of Castellammare, the Torre Annunziata canning factories, the Portici chemical works, the oil refineries at Naples itself and, at the two ends of the bay, the Salerno spinning-mills and the Bagnoli blast-furnaces. It is in part due to its industry that the Naples region is, from the economic point of view, fourth in Italy, after those of Milan, Rome and Turin, and ranks before those of Genoa and Bologna. As for the rest of southern Italy, the tale can, unfortunately, be told quickly enough: a few chemical plants at Crotona, some foodstuff factories, some cement works, a few shipyards.

To explain this remarkable lack of balance between northern and southern Italy, we must once more turn to history. In the nineteenth century, before Italy was unified, there existed in the peninsular portion of the country (where, after all, the conditions were not so favourable) numerous long established industrial centres which were still very active. Among these were Tuscany, and especially Naples, which had the first Italian railway, the first system of gas-lighting, and the first arsenal. Then came unification: effected by the Piedmontese, it naturally benefited the north, which was rapidly industrialised, while the sprouts of industrial activity in the south were entirely neglected by the government — and so, they wilted. In industry, then, the 'Southern Question' has existed for a century.

What the Italians call the 'Southern Question' is the whole complex of problems posed by the economic and social backwardness of the islands and of the area south of Rome. Since he can find no work in an agriculture that is anyway very poor, the southern Italian lives in conditions of continual hardship: his average income is less than half that of the northern Italian. In order to mitigate this misery, the population ought to be drawn off into factories. But, as we have seen, the south has almost no industry at all: only 6 per cent of all Italian industrial and commercial investments for 37 per cent of the population. The situation is extremely grave.

THE DEFICIT IN INDUSTRIAL EXPORTS. Given the general conditions of production, it is easy to understand why industrialists hesitate to manufacture objects which demand a great deal of material and little labour. In fact, metallurgy and the extraction of raw materials from the earth represent only 13 per cent of the total industrial revenue. On the other hand, the processing industries (foodstuffs, textiles, clothing, chemical products, and above all, machines) make up 54 per cent of this revenue. Two-thirds of the exports consist of processed goods, which clearly reflects the structure of Italian industry. Textiles and clothing are most important. In addition to silks and woollen goods, Italy turns out excellent cottons and a great quantity of man-made fibres. The main customers for these are the Near East, India, Pakistan and South Africa, and these exports bring in four times as much money as the corresponding imports cost.

The case of the engineering industries is different. Their production exceeds in value that of the textile industry. The most important products are electric motors exported to France, textile machinery sold to the United States and Brazil, and precision machinery, especially typewriters and calculating machines. The automobile industry is about one-third of that of France, but Italian producers are handicapped by excessively high cost-prices. Italian motor vehicles are exported to central Europe and North Africa but, all told, the profits are small, for Italy hardly sells more machines than she imports. The chemical industry, however, is in a better position: sulphuric acid, nitrogenous fertilizers, medicaments and copper sulphate are produced in quantity.

Nevertheless, despite great efforts, the commercial balance of Italian industry is unfavourable — indeed, the deficit is six times greater than that of the food products. Other sources of revenue must be found at all costs.

This additional revenue is looked for in the tourist industry. About 8,000,000 foreigners visit annually famous beauty-spots and museum cities. Everyone the world over has heard of Venice and Capri. The ruins of Pompeii attract 450,000 visitors annually. Tourists leave, either in the government's coffers or with Italian tradesmen, from 150,000 to 200,000 million lire every year, and this sum covers more than a quarter of the Italian foreign trade deficit. Furthermore, the possibilities of tourism are far from being fully exploited, and the whole of the south, with the exception of Naples and Sicily, needs to be developed for tourism.

The serious results of over-population

We have seen, then, that Italy is not such a poor country as it is sometimes stated to be. However, beneath every Italian problem lies that of over-population. As the death-rate continues to fall (so that it is now lower than that of France), and the birth-rate is falling much more slowly, the annual rise in population is about 400,000. So, during the first half of this century, while the population of France increased by 8 per cent, that of Italy rose by 44 per cent. At present there are about 49 million Italians in Italy. The average density of the population is 423 to the square mile — as against 212 in France and 159 in Spain. Again, while the Italian mountains are thinly populated, 28 provinces have a population density of over 500 to the square mile. The first consequence of this is unemployment. One worker out of every ten has no job — and this is the highest figure anywhere in Europe. The second consequence is high prices. To buy a pound of bread the average Italian must do twice as much work as must a Swiss. The standard of living in Italy is affected, and thus the rôle of the Italian as a consumer. Since foodstuffs absorb two-thirds of his income (though the daily ration of 2,500 calories is one of the lowest in Europe), an Italian can rarely afford to buy books, furniture or manufactured goods.

Emigration, mainly to the United States, was for long a safety-valve for the pressure of excessive population. In about half a century, 15 million Italians (principally from the south) left their country. For a time, the Fascists thought that they had found a better solution in colonisation. The present Italian Republic has resumed the emigration policy, but on a moderate scale and directed mainly to Argentina. Far-reaching reforms in the social and economic structure have also been undertaken. Since the first agrarian reforms in 1950, a considerable area has been divided up among 80,000 new smallholders, while the Tuscan Maremma, the Sila and the Tavoliere are almost unrecognisably changed. The 'Fund for the South' has also invested 550,000 million lire in making extensive improvements in agriculture, industry and amenities for tourists. Throughout Italy one is struck by the vigorous efforts put into reconstruction and by an evident determination to make progress.

Western Europe may well identify itself closely with the Italian attempts to adapt its age-old and powerful traditions to the harsh necessities of our present age.

JEAN DEMANGEOT

THE MEDITERRANEAN SEA
AND MEDITERRANEAN COUNTRIES

Moscow

S.   S.   R.

Don

Volga

Dniepr

CASPIAN SEA

SEA OF AZOV

CRIMEA

CAUCASUS

Koura

ARMENIAN MASSIF

CARPATHIANS

RUMANIA

Bucharest

WALLACHIAN PLAIN

Danube

BALKAN

BLACK   SEA

Sofia

RHODOPE

BULGARIA

BOSPORUS

Istanbul

TURKEY

Ankara

PLATEAU OF ANATOLIA

TAURUS

Aleppo

Euphrates

Tigris

SYRIA

ALBANIA

PINDUS MTS.

Salonica

DARDANELLES

GREECE

Afyounkarahissar

Latakia

C. OF OTRANTO

AEGEAN SEA

Izmir

Athens

PELOPONNESE

Rhodes

Tripoli

LEBANON

LEBANON

Beirut

Damascus

Cyprus

C. Matapan

Haifa

Jordan

Messero

IONIAN SEA

Crete

MEDITERRANEAN   SEA

Tel-Aviv

ISRAEL

Jerusalem

Amman

JORDAN

DEAD SEA

Aqaba

Port-Said

Alessandria

SUEZ CANAL

Cairo

Suez

Benghazi

CYRENAICA

GULF OF SIDRA

EGYPT

Nile

LIBYA

LIBYAN   DESERT

TRIPOLI

TUNISIA

THE VATICAN CITY

THE Vatican City, the last remaining relic of the former Papal States, has been a sovereign state since 1929 and occupies a district in the west of the city of Rome. The official language is Italian. The Vatican, with its quiet little streets, its magnificent museums, its old-fashioned customs and its Swiss Guards in their sixteenth-century uniforms, is a unique type of state. It is, moreover, without any economic resources, except those provided by the sale of postage stamps, and with an area of about one-fifth of a square mile and a population of no more than a thousand persons it is the smallest state in the world, both in area and in population.

Nevertheless, it is also one of the most powerful, since it is the personal property of the reigning Pope, Head of the Catholic, Apostolic and Roman Church, and is thus the spiritual capital of about 530,000,000 Christians. The Vatican has all the outward attributes of a modern town — railway station, post offices, garage, etc. Some of its buildings, such as its church (St Peter's), the largest in the world, its administrative offices, its polyglot printing presses, its wireless broadcasting station, its Academy of Science, its newspaper, the *Osservatore Romano*, are on a scale befitting the Vatican City's rôle in world affairs rather than its physical size.

Jean DEMANGEOT.

The Pope giving his 'Urbi et Orbi' benediction in the presence of tens of thousands of people crowded into St Peter's Square, Rome.
LEONARD VON MATT, RAPHO

SAN MARINO

THE republic of San Marino is one of the smallest sovereign states in the world, for its area is 38 square miles and its population only 14,000. Founded, so it is claimed, in the fourth century A.D., it is the oldest republic in Europe.

San Marino is completely surrounded by Italian territory and is situated on the foothills of the Apennines, where the provinces of Romagna and the Marches meet, about six miles from the sea. The capital, San Marino (2,500 inhabitants), rises proudly on the Monte Titano (2,437 feet), a crest of calcareous sandstone whose three peaks dominate a landscape of argillo-schistose hills. The dwellings are scattered, and the diversified agriculture is of the characteristic Romagna type. Not only wheat and livestock but also vines afford a profitable livelihood to the inhabitants. Tourists, too, bring in an appreciable amount of money. Many of the San Marinesi (about 5,000 to 6,000) live abroad.

Jean DEMANGEOT

San Marino and its castle. ROGER VIOLLET

Panorama of Monaco.   GENERAL TOURIST AND INFORMATION OFFICE OF MONACO

THE PRINCIPALITY OF MONACO

THE Principality of Monaco is a tiny notch in French territory. It is an independent state covering an area of 370 acres, bounded to the west and north by the Department of the Alpes-Maritimes and to the south and east by the Mediterranean Sea.

According to the constitution of 1911, the government is conducted by a Minister of State aided by a Council under the supreme authority of the Sovereign. The legislature consists of the Prince and the National Council of eighteen members, elected every four years by the vote of all adult male citizens of the principality. The Communal Council (of fifteen members elected for three years, also by male suffrage) debates the business of the commune. Since 1945 female citizens of Monaco have had the right to vote in municipal elections. Early in 1959, the Prince suspended the constitution, dissolved the National Council, and appointed an eight-member delegation to help him to administer the principality.

The reigning Prince, H.S.H. Rainier III of Monaco, is the thirty-third member of the Grimaldi family to rule over the principality.

The Monegasque national holiday varies in date from reign to reign, and at the present time is held on 19th November.

The Principality of Monaco enjoys a Mediterranean climate, which is particularly mild in winter, and the country has been a great tourist centre since the middle of the nineteenth century, when the city of Monte Carlo, with its casino and big hotels, was created. There are now hotels suited to all types of visitors.

The Prince's palace (begun in 1215) is on the rock of Monaco-Ville, where there are also various public offices and the Oceanographic Museum (opened in 1910), built by Prince Albert I, founder of the science of modern oceanography.

The principality also has a Museum of Prehistoric Anthropology and a National Fine Arts Museum. In the Exotic Gardens (laid out at the beginning of this century) there is a fine collection of flora from semi-arid countries. In the Botanical Gardens is also the Grotto of the Observatory, open to the public since 1950. In 1954 a small zoological garden was constructed.

During the past few years the principality has made much progress both in industry and commerce. At the present time there is a number of textile, mechanical, printing, chemical and pharmaceutical plants, as well as factories turning out foodstuffs, and a number of crafts such as ceramic and glass manufacture flourish.

The financial resources of the principality come mostly from taxes on turnover and on civil registration, which account for 60 per cent of the total revenue. A further 20 per cent is provided by the customs (there is a Franco-Monegasque agreement on customs union) and the profits from the postal, telegraph and telephone services. The duty on tobacco amounts to 12 per cent of the total, and payments from the *Société des Bains de Mer*, which has the monopoly of conducting the gambling in Monte Carlo Casino, total 2 per cent to 5 per cent, according to the year.

The population of the principality increases steadily: it was 15,543 in 1903 and 20,422 in 1956. The density of population thus amounts to the astonishing figure of 52,500 to the square mile.

The number of Monegasque nationals is about 3,000 and they do no military service. There is no land-tax or income-tax, and no estates duty is payable on estates descending in direct line. Foreigners domiciled in Monaco enjoy the same tax exemptions as Monegasque citizens, although French nationals must have resided in the principality for five years before they can claim such exemption.

The number of visitors to Monaco hotels is also constantly increasing, and the port is a busy one for yachts.

Radio Monte Carlo, whose broadcasting station is above the Monte Carlo Golf Club (in French territory) at an altitude of 2,600 feet, transmits its programmes on three different wavelengths. In 1954 the Télé-Monte-Carlo station was opened; its antennae are on Mont Agel, at an altitude of 3,600 feet.

The official currency is the French franc, but the Prince of Monaco, in accordance with his sovereign rights, issues coins of low denomination by agreement with the French government.

Gabriel OLLIVIER

In the Exotic Gardens of Monaco. These were created at the beginning of this century and contain fine examples of tropical and semi-desert plants. GENERAL TOURIST AND INFORMATION OFFICE OF MONACO

Andorra La Vieille, with its Roman church, its houses and slate roofs, is at the junction of Andorra's five valleys. Today, several modern hotels have changed the appearance of these high Pyrenean valleys. SAM WAAGENOOR, RAPHO

ANDORRA

THE interest and, indeed, the importance of Andorra are not to be measured by its area (191 square miles) or by the number of its inhabitants (about 6,000). The outlook and the activities of the Andorrans depend less upon their surroundings and their country's resources than upon the survival of medieval institutions.

Andorra is enclosed within a 70-mile circle of mountains (41 miles of it are over 8,000 feet), and has had a withdrawn existence. Isolation and poverty are its outstanding characteristics, but they have been a guarantee of independence.

Notwithstanding the Andorran national anthem, the country does not owe its existence to Charlemagne and Louis the Pious. However, its history does go back to the agreement concluded in 1278 which put an end to the rival claims of the Counts of Foix and the Bishops of La Seo de Urgel. In this document it was recognised that each of the claimants had equal rights, and condominium was established that was to be exercised jointly 'in undivided soverignty'. Andorra is thus a co-principality of two absolute and hereditary monarchs (Count and Bishop), who enjoy unbounded rights over their subjects; these monarchs govern through *viguiers* or 'vicars'. By usage, though not by right, the co-princes have divided their authority so that one of them exercises secular and the other ecclesiastical dominion, but their authority remains equal and undivided, and they are often rivals, especially as the rights of the Counts of Foix passed by inheritance to King Henri IV of France, and from him to all succeeding heads of the French State. Since the power of the French State far exceeds that of the Bishops of La Seo de Urgel, the latter have tended to rely for support on the Spanish government, although it has no rights at all in Andorra. Rivalry between French and Spanish influence has thus arisen.

During the Spanish Civil War, and then during the Second World War, Andorra was an asylum between France and Spain, a listening-post and an escape route. During the post-war period, free — in theory at least — from all restriction and rationing, Andorra took advantage of the fact that there was a free market in Spain for certain articles but not in France — and vice versa — and imported all sorts of merchandise in great quantities, since objects supposed to be 'Andorran' are free of import duty into both France and Spain. So, from 1947 onwards, there was invasion of tourists arriving in carloads to purchase supplies. From about 1950, however, when the Spaniards opened their frontiers again, and when there was no longer the same scarcity of goods, fewer and fewer tourists have made their way to Andorra, which they find both too small and too dear. There began for Andorra a period of economic and political stability. The far-seeing Andorrans began to invest their very large and indeed surprising profits in sound enterprises, especially in the building of hotels, since the tourist trade, depending as it does upon the geographical conditions of the country, could, if wisely encouraged, provide a source of revenue that would keep Andorra comparatively wealthy.

Andorrans, who are passionately attached to a regime that assures them so many advantages are, nevertheless, at the present time living through a dramatic phase of their history, since our high-geared civilisation no longer permits them to avoid the problems of our time by a policy of isolation as they were able to do up to 1914. The problems are not only of a moral but also of a geographical nature, and they result from the clash between the inventions and achievements of our modern world and ancient ways of life suited to traditional institutions and ways of thought.

Jean SERMET

A typical landscape in La Mancha (Campo de Criptana),
New Castile - the home of Don Quixote's windmills.
RENÉ FERLET

SPAIN

SPAIN occupies a position that is both the most westerly of the European continent and the most southerly (Tarifa, on the Strait of Gibraltar, has the same latitude — 36° N. — as Malta and Antioch). Its westerly position is of great importance: the whole country slopes towards the west so that three-quarters of the rivers empty into the Atlantic. One result has been that the Spaniards have felt what might be called a 'call to the west' which has lured them to the Ocean and led them and other people to discover the American continent, to which they are still linked by strong migratory movements.

The coasts of Spain have been subjected to the full force of the Atlantic, and the sea, in the form of *rias* and estuaries, stretches inland. Thus Spain is the homeland of hardy seamen whose basic activity is fishing and whose main foodstuff is sea food. Spanish maritime enterprises (such as the *Marina de Castilla*, whose seventh centenary was celebrated in 1948) have made Spain a typical land of western Europe. Indeed, Spain has the characteristic features of a Far West.

A LAND OF WEST AND EAST. Since the Ocean was for long centuries unsailed and mysterious, the Spaniards of necessity looked toward the Mediterranean. However, to the Mediterranean peoples — or at least to those who created the civilisations of the Inland Sea — Spain appeared as a far-off peninsula at the limits of the known world. This remoteness might have been a cause of weakness but, on the contrary, it preserved Spain's autonomy. It was Maurice Legendre who pointed out that this peninsula was 'more than an island', with its own civilisation and with such wealth of minerals (the Elder Pliny called it *Hispania preciosa metallis*) that it may have suggested the myth of Atlantis, especially by its realm of Tartessus in Andalusia. In any case, if Spain is not Atlantis, it is the heir of Atlantis and early displayed the most vigorous and marked individuality among western European lands — as is demonstrated by its dolmen civilisation.

All the migrations and all the movements of peoples who have influenced Europe ended in Spain, which is as Celticised as France or Great Britain, as Romanised as Italy, and was for centuries colonised by Germanic invaders.

Spain is, then, European enough, and Africa does not begin at the Pyrenees. Still, Spain is separated from Africa by a narrow strait that is only just over eight miles across. Since prehistoric times Africans have been able to reach the peninsula (as recent experiments with drifting rafts have proved). In caves on the Rock of Gibraltar bones of Neanderthal Man have been found. So Spain was also peopled from the south. Many of the inhabitants of ancient Spain, especially the Iberians, were closely related to the peoples of the Maghreb, particularly the Berbers. North African influences were, of course, accentuated by the Moorish incursions into ancient Baetica and, in the eighth century A.D., by the Moslem invasion. Indeed, during the Almoravide and Almohade dynasties there was a great influx of colonists from across the Strait. No doubt the Spaniards do owe to North African influence some of those characteristics that make them so original a people, but Spain in its turn surged back into North Africa, which became strongly Hispanised.

Again, Spain's mineral wealth made her appear an Eldorado to the ancients, and always attracted travellers and covetous adventurers. The Spanish shores were visited by the men of the East — Cretans, Phoenicians, Greeks, Carthaginians and, later on, Byzantines — who brought a leaven of oriental civilisation together with their commerce. Thus Spain is also an oriental land, as is seen in its *cante hondo*. Spain welcomed the Sephardic Jews, and it was in Spain that Islam reached its most brilliant development by making use of oriental science and thought. The result was an amalgam of African, Western and Eastern influences unique in Europe.

UNITY, DIVERSITY, CONTRASTS. It was some considerable time ago that Jean Brunhes showed that there are two Spains side by side: 'damp Spain' (Oceanic) and 'dry Spain' (Mediterranean). 'Dry Spain' is the larger of the two, since it covers three-quarters of the peninsula, and there irrigation is practised and Mediterranean modes of life flourish. Thus, if from a topographical point of view Spain looks West, she inclines towards the East as far as climate and ways of life are concerned. As soon as you cross the Cantabrian passes, you feel that the Mediterranean is not far away.

Mediterranean influence, moreover, seems to be greater today than it was in the past, since the Mediterranean aspect of Spain is accentuated by the recent development of *regadío*, or irrigation, over huge areas, as a result of which the whole economy of the country is being transformed.

However, Spain will long preserve its individuality, for the country is not only remote from Europe in many ways, but is also separated from the rest of the continent. The Pyrenean chain remains a formidable barrier over which there are roads it is true, but only recent ones. Hence the impression of abrupt change that the traveller receives as soon as he has passed the frontier — especially in Aragon.

The Spanish coasts are not greatly indented and the country resembles, as has been repeated so very often since Strabo's time, a 'bull's hide outstretched'. The coasts look as though they had been hacked out with an axe. Quite close inshore the sea is very deep, and the peninsula rises above it in one mighty mass. It may be concluded from this that Spain's structure is the result of fractures.

The numerous volcanic manifestations to be noted along the Mediterranean shores (the volcanoes of Olot and Bañolas in Catalonia; of Cofrentes and the Columbrete islands, in the eastern part of the provinces of Valencia and Murcia; of Cape de Gata: of the Alborán islet in the south-east; and in the centre and west — Campo de Calatrava and the Portuguese Algarve) are evidence used to support a theory of such fractures. In this connection, also, must be mentioned the numerous earthquakes which are sometimes appallingly destructive (Lisbon, 1755; Andalusia, 1884).

Thus the peninsula is today composed of bits and pieces, though these are certainly clearly and rigidly defined. The Spanish Meseta, which makes up most of central Spain, is surrounded by ramparts of mountains (Sierra Morena, the sub-Baetic folds, the Iberian Mountains), and has gathered around it peripheral depressions which have become sedimentary basins (Ebro, Guadalquivir, Valencia and Portuguese regions), whose horizons are in turn bounded by high mountain ranges (Pyrenees, Baetic chain, Balearics).

Spain, so strongly knit together, is yet the European country within which we find the greatest contrasts. Unity and diversity exist side by side and serve to explain tendencies which are at once centrifugal and centripetal. Sometimes the phrase 'the Spains' (*las Españas*) is used and, indeed, Spain is really a mosaic of lands and peoples, yet all bear the distinctive Hispanic imprint.

So any study of Spain should be undertaken on the regional principle, since there can be clearly distinguished a central Spain (comprising the two Castiles, Estremadura and Aragon), a northern Spain (from Navarre to Galicia), Andalusia, and an eastern Spain.

CENTRAL SPAIN

Central Spain is the heart of the land, and it appears 'internal', that is directed inwards, as compared with the other Spains, which are 'peripheral' and directed toward the outer world.

This central Spain consists, first and foremost, of the lands of the geographical Meseta: the two Castiles, Estremadura and León. The region is in itself a very considerable one: 84,740 square miles with more than 8 million inhabitants — about a third of the population in half the area of Spain. However, to this block must be added Aragon (18,380 square miles), with more than a million inhabitants. It is a region which, despite its original character and long history of ancient laws and institutions, is most decidedly Spanish in ways of thought. Moreover, the Aragonese were, with the Castilians, the architects of Spanish political unity.

THE MESETA AND THE SURROUNDING SIERRAS. The most striking feature is that of the relief. Plateaus and high plains predominate. The landscapes are bounded by flat horizons like those of the sea, with nothing to obstruct the view, nothing to separate land from sky. One must travel for hundreds of miles until the end of these vast plains is reached; then, from afar, appear long narrow mountain ranges stretched out like

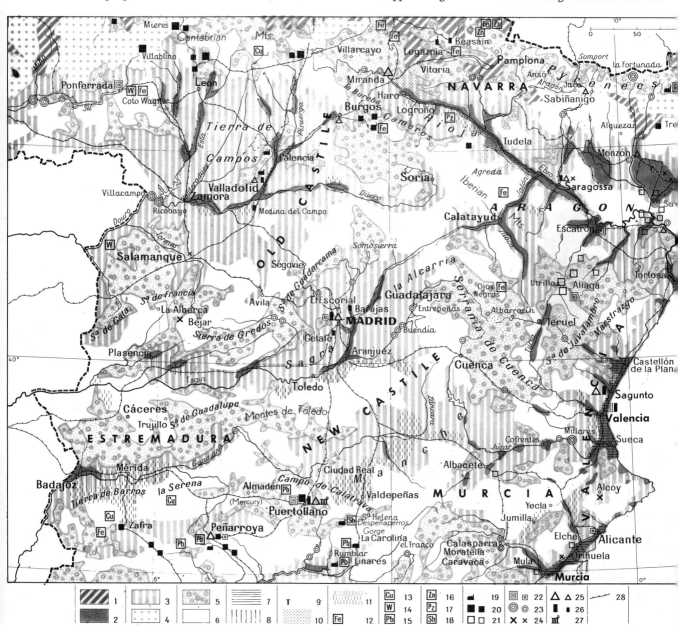

CENTRAL SPAIN: *Old and New Castile, León, Estremadura, Aragon. 1. Pyrenean agriculture under Atlantic influence; maize, potatoes, apples; 2. Irrigated areas (regadío: huertas, vegas); market-gardens and fruit-growing; 3. Mixed-crop farming on unirrigated land (secano); wheat, vines, olives; 4. Pyrenean agriculture under Atlantic influence, passing into natural or artificial prairie; 5. Brushwood or scrub; sheep or goats, pig-rearing under clumps of oak trees; 6. Steppes of the paramos and the sierras; 7. Rice; 8. Cotton; 9. Tobacco; 10. Sugar-beet; 11. Vines (as the only crop); 12. Iron; 13. Copper; 14. Wolfram (tungsten); 15. Lead; 16. Zinc; 17. Lead and zinc; 18. Antimony; 19. Factory for processing non-ferrous metals; 20. Coal; 21. Lignite; 22. Power stations; 23. Hydro-electric power stations; 24. Textiles; 25. Chemical industry; 26. Metallurgy; 27. Oil refinery; 28. Railways.*

a long cord: hence the name *cordillera*. The *cordilleras* surround the central plateau: the central *cordillera* between Old and New Castile; the Toledo Mountains and the Sierra de Guadalupe between New Castile and Estremadura; the complex of the Iberian Mountains between the Castiles and Aragon.

We must seek in the soils and the geological structure the explanation for these formations. The Meseta constitutes a block of Palaeozoic or Pre-Primary rocks which become increasingly ancient as one moves westward. All this so-called 'Hesperic' massif is worn down, and its levelling had been accomplished by the end of the Primary Era. Later movements, it is true, have affected the massif, but only to the extent of fracturing it and making it uneven, especially in the east, without, however, modifying the general landscape. This indicates levelling or even peneplanation.

The present-day relief results, above all, from the deposit of immense horizontal sheets of sedimentary strata on the levelled Hesperic massif: clays, marls, sands and calcareous formations, which gave rise to the *páramos*. Their general appearance is that of tables ending in ledges: hence the term Meseta (applied to the relief and not the geology), which is commonly used to designate the centre of Spain. The horizontal structural surface of the *páramo* remains intact, and the absence of water means that there are few clefts and rifts. This is the case in the Mancha, which is an almost perfect limestone plain, a 'Tertiary landscape' that has been preserved and has fossilised the folds of the substratum. Elsewhere, in the centre of Old Castile, the dissection performed by the River Duero (Douro in Portugal) and by its tributaries has led to the formation of little separate *mesas* called *cerros* or *oteros*, which are dazzling white buttes, evidence of the *páramo's* greater extent in earlier times. On these level surfaces the rivers have smooth profiles, and they meander through quite wide valleys with pebbly terraces. These are the gullies into which the platform of the *páramos* falls abruptly. The steep slopes are sometimes furrowed by stretches of 'badlands' (a term applied particularly to areas impoverished or wasted by erosion). In places the valleys may widen out to become veritable plains of reddish clay called *campiñas*; a typical example is the Tierra de Campos. In León the limestone gives way to the lower strata, in which the peasants dig out their subterranean cellars or *bodegas* and where they find the tawny, earthy substance which serves as *adobe* or *tapia* to make walls for the houses. These structural reliefs are so flat that the waters do not always drain off well. In the heart of the Mancha, the Zancara flows very sluggishly and spreads out into marshes. There are even lagoon areas from which salt is recovered.

In the west of the Castiles, however, and in Estremadura, the superficial deposits are thinner and the ancient siliceous bedrock is sometimes exposed. But, as it is weathered down, the landscape still presents the same form: that of a plateau. It is in Estremadura, though, between the town of Cáceres and the Portuguese frontier, that the flatness of the land is most marked, so that the peneplain seems to stretch infinitely westwards, merging into the base-level of the Atlantic.

But in the western and southern regions of the Hesperic massif there are extensive deposits of water-borne pebbles, which are evidence that there was a large-scale weathering of the relief towards the end of the Tertiary — perhaps in an arid climate. The Meseta appears to have been uplifted from the eastern side. These movements of the earth fractured the ancient bedrock and produced the volcanic relief in the Campo de Calatrava whose outlines are still recognisable. Likewise, a fold seems to have formed near the Portuguese frontier, and is responsible for the sharp bends in the Guadiana and Duero rivers as well as for the high walls enclosing them as they flow towards the steep drop to Portugal. The Duero, for instance, drops 1,378 feet in about 90 miles. The distinct and individual character, then, of Castile on the one hand and Portugal on the other, is not due wholly to historical factors.

The peaks of the Sierra de Guadarrama, near the Puerto (Pass) of Navacerrada (6,129 feet), an important ski resort for the people of Madrid (39 miles away). The upper limit of the forest shows clearly in the distance, with the treeless summer pastures above it.

The high plateaus of Old Castile, between Segovia and Avila. In the background are the great worn blocks of granite separating the *secanos* (non-irrigated fields) with their uncertain wheat crop.
YAN, RAPHO

The 635-feet Bridge of Alcántara over the Tagus in Estremadura which, according to legend, was built by Trajan in A.D. 106.
GILLES DE LA MOTTE ROUGE

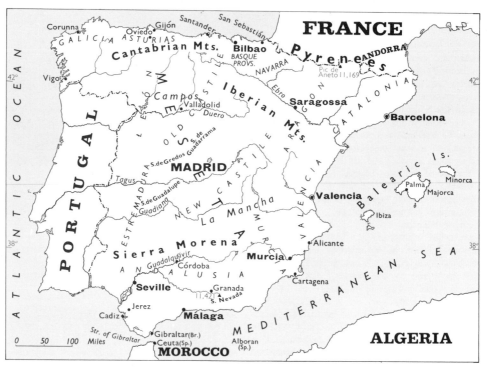

SPAIN

All the watercourses (with the exception of those of Aragon) flow westward, and scoop out ever deeper beds as they go, carving from the Hispanic bedrock vast rocky and deserted gorges such as those of the Tagus near Toledo and those of the Arribes of the Duero, which for some 120 miles mark the frontier. Huge dams will soon transform these canyons into great lakes which will provide irrigation and generation of hydro-electric power. Such transformation has already been effected on the Esla. Similar schemes (known as the 'Cáceres and Badajoz Plans') have been drawn up for the improvement of Estremadura.

Above the level of the peneplain run the ranges of *sierras* composed of hard rocks: the Central Cordillera (Sierras de Guadarrama and de Gredos extended eastward by the Sierra de Gata); the Toledo Mountains; the Estremadura *sierras* — 'Hispanids' rejuvenated by vertical movements. Other movements have pushed against the 'Hesperic' massif a number of folded ranges (generally of limestone), such as the Iberian and Cantabrian mountains.

Thus, surrounded by sierras, the plateaus and plains of central Spain reach a high altitude everywhere — on an average in Old Castile about 2,600 feet, and in New Castile 1,900 feet. The Meseta does not sink appreciably anywhere except in Estremadura (820—1,300 feet). In this respect, the relief anticipates Portugal. Aragon, on the other hand, is lower (Saragossa lies about 650 feet above sea level) but is more enclosed. Throughout the central part of the peninsula, then, altitude combines with continental situation and distance from the sea to exercise a determining influence on the climate, which itself is an essential geographical factor.

VIOLENT CLIMATE: MEDITERRANEAN FLORA.

The Castilian climate is essentially a climate that is continental and harsh. Even though the saying 'nine months winter and three months hell' is not strictly true, it does express a general tendency. The winters are long and cold. Valladolid in Old Castile has 30 days of frost a year, and although the mean temperatures rise in New Castile and in Estremadura, the absolute minimum for Madrid is still 23° F., and the 'subtle air that kills a man but does not put out a candle' seems icy. On the other hand, the summers are very hot indeed. Moreover, the temperature shoots up suddenly. In the southern

half of the Meseta the heat becomes intolerable, with such maxima as 111° F. at Ciudad Real, 117° F. at Badajoz, and 118° F. at Ruidera. The summer in Estremadura is as stifling as in the Guadalquivir valley, and even higher up it is not much cooler. In Aragon, at Saragossa, the thermometer varies between 21° F. and 111° F., and in winter the temperature sinks under the breath of the icy blasts that sweep down from the Moncayo. The annual ranges of temperature, then, are considerable: 94°F. at Salamanca and 101°F. at Segovia. More serious still are the daily variations, which may exceed 36° F., especially in the spring, when the rapid increase in temperature from February to April is often interrupted by sudden bursts of cold weather which are particularly harmful to the crops.

Generally speaking, rainfall is scanty. Furthermore, the intensity and duration of the summer heat accentuates the dryness, since the water lost by evaporation may be twenty-six times greater in volume than actual precipitation. The rainfall is more abnormally low in the centre than in the east of the country, and rain is not only scanty but very irregular, so that the climate is extreme. At Utrillas (in central Aragon) 25 inches fell in 1923, 5.9 inches in 1924, and 60.2 inches in 1925. There is little cloud: the central areas of the country have a boundless, bright, transparent sky, both deep blue and magnificently luminous. In summer, however, a bluish veil (sometimes reddish if it is dusty) known as the *calina* hangs in the air. It is not a fog but a supersaturated atmospheric 'silt' whose density varies with the heat. The *calina* has not yet been studied in great detail, but it is a beneficial phenomenon since it allows vegetation to survive during the dead season of summer.

Continental, extreme and dry, the climate is responsible for many of the features of the natural landscape, among which the most outstanding is the scanty water supply; in the south this amounts to total insufficiency. There is from north to south a gradation of watercourses. León, Old Castile and the Pyrenean part of Aragon have what may be called 'European' rivers, able to feed a whole expanding network of irrigation channels and even to fill a true navigational canal which runs from Alar del Rey to Valladolid in Castile. But in New Castile the rivers are bordered with strips of verdure arranged in a series of oases (such as Aranjuez), and prepare us for the African aspect of parts of the Mancha and Andalusia.

The flora is definitely Mediterranean and remains so right into Portugal. This is surprising when we reflect that the Meseta slopes toward the Atlantic. However, account must be taken of the great influence of the Mediterranean summer on Spain and also of the fact that the uplift of the eastern edge of the Meseta is a recent phenomenon, geologically speaking. Formerly Spain's surface sloped towards the east and thus, in ancient times, the penetration of Mediterranean flora was facilitated. This flora, however, remains in the centre as a sort of relic, preserved from Atlantic influences by the aridity and continental character of the climate and by the mountain-walls which shelter it from humid winds.

The climate of central Spain, even today, is not unsuitable for trees. The forest covering was, in fact, preserved intact for ages. As late as the seventeenth century Velasquez painted his figures against a background of woodlands rich in game, quite near Madrid. Not all these woods have disappeared, but the forests of central Spain exist now only in patches. Change of climate has been put forward as an explanation for the disappearance of the forests, but the real responsibility lies no doubt elsewhere, since to feed their foundries and to extend the arable areas, the Spaniards have in recent times waged fierce war upon trees.

In former days, sheep-farming held a very important place in the economy of Castile, so it was necessary to provide vast grazing grounds for the flocks, and the natural growth of trees was protected. But at the beginning of the nineteenth century the *mesta* (association of stock-breeders) was dissolved after a long and fierce struggle with the peasants and farmers. Then followed a mad scramble to clear the land, which gave a few short seasons of good harvests and then became severly impoverished. It was at this time especially that central Spain took on its barren appearance. Towards the end of the last century it was realised what a sad error had been committed, and the State, in some cases aided by the the local authorities, began systematic reforestation.

ANCIENT AND MODERN ACTIVITIES. The dry, open lands of Castile are pre-eminently areas of grain crops, and have been so since Neolithic times. Before the specialisation in olive-trees and in vines (effected only between the seventeenth and eighteenth centuries), the Mancha was also a land of cereals, and so, to a certain extent, it still remains. An area to the north of Zamora bears the geographical name of *Tierra del Pan*. It is uncommon to find such perfect harmony between landscape and economy, or a spectacle more attractive than the grain threshing floor in summertime.

Estremadura, in contrast, is mainly a land of flocks and herds which in summer are driven up to the cooler mountains of the north or of Soria. Until a few generations ago this transhumance was supervised by the *mesta*. Don Quixote, we may remember, attacked the *mesta's* sheep, taking them for an army of infidels. Nowadays the animals are sent by rail. The very fine wool of these merino sheep built up an industry which was at once the glory and the fortune of Castile and whose products were sold at the celebrated Medina del Campo fairs. Although a number of textile factories still operate, the woollen industry is on the decline, and the numbers of sheep are decreasing, for the reduction in grazing ground area has added considerably to the difficulty of feeding the flocks.

Central Spain is self-supporting. The cereals, the wool, the wood of the sierras, and the cattle that feed there, the pigs in the oak-forests, the olive oil, the vines, beets and market-gardens in the irrigated valleys, as well as the industries that utilise the raw materials, afford an excellent example of man's adaptation to his surroundings.

However, the population of the centre compared with that of the provinces grouped around it is small: on an average, 117 inhabitants to the square mile in Old Castile, 78 in New Castile, 57 in Aragon. Often the visitor is left with the feeling that he is in an empty land. There are, indeed, *despoblados*, regions that became depopulated as a result of the discovery of the 'Indies'. The towns are rather small and provincial. We should not, however, conclude that central Spain is lacking in vitality. On the contrary, the astounding growth of the capital; the setting up near the main towns of large manufacturing enterprises that utilise the surplus of electricity generated by the big barrages and dams; the hundreds of thousands of acres which will be called back into life by irrigation in Estremadura and New Castile; the opening of new railway lines; the very large-scale trade in primary agricultural produce (oil, wine, sugar, flour); the plans for the reorganisation of the countryside, and the hopes based on the transformation of the Aragon salt steppes into rice-fields — all prove that out of the healthy old trunk of Spain's central economy there are sprouting new branches of activity, shoots that are sturdy and productive of wealth.

In fact, we may say that it was the central area that made Spain. Castile created the country, often by the sword; Castile is the land of castles, and here everything reminds us of the Reconquest. Like Rome, Castile was a vigorous and expanding state, and we should not forget that until the early part of the nineteenth century she ruled over the greatest colonial empire that had ever existed. The Castilians, with their eyes ever fixed on the future, made and lived their own history and imposed their faith, their language, their institutions and their policy.

Spain is also a holy land traversed by the *Calzada*, the Way of St James, the route joining Spain to Christendom, to Europe and, above all, to France. This was the way to the most popular

The rich and elaborately decorated cathedral at Burgos, in Old Castile, built in the thirteenth and fourteenth centuries. It contains the tomb of the national hero Roderigo Diaz de Bivar, the 'Cid', who won fame fighting against the Moors. SPANISH NATIONAL TOURIST OFFICE

of all medieval pilgrimage shrines and all along is strung a line of Romanesque and Gothic chapels which are to be found even in the humblest hamlets. On the Aragon frontier lies Soria, with its astonishing collection of Romanesque monuments, much of whose decoration and ornamentation was inspired by motifs of Moslem art. All or nearly all of Spain's history can be traced in the art of central Spain. The centre is the essential Spain, the region that is without doubt the most typically Spanish.

But within the overall uniformity of its historical and economic line of development, we can note some regional differences in the vast spaces of central Spain.

Old Castile

THE 'SHELL' OF OLD CASTILE. The cradle and the heart of central Spain lie in Old Castile and in León. These are two distinct historical entities, but geographically they form only one region, sometimes called the 'Shell of the Duero'; this corresponds to the whole hydrographic network of the river and, for once in a way, the idea of a 'basin' assumes a geographical meaning. This high plateau is, in fact, an immense bowl bordered on all sides by mountains which form its frame and its walls.

In this mountainous wall there are only two large breaches: the Agreda passage, close to the Moncayo, from which Castile looks out upon Aragon and Navarre as from a balcony; and the wide passage of Burgos between the Iberian and Cantabrian mountains, easily traversed and almost flat as far as the Ebro basin. Hence the historical, strategic and economic importance of Burgos: this was the route taken in the Middle Ages by the pilgrims' road to Compostela, while today the main highway and the principal railroad follow the same path. This route has been a thoroughfare for ideas and influences as much as one for merchandise. It is a highway along which Old Castile looks north towards Europe, as well as south.

The soil is fertile but the climate is harsh, especially in the region of Soria, and Castile seems steeped in a simple, age-old rural way of life, but one that expresses well enough the strong and noble personality of the land. The towns are both markets and historic cities: Burgos, a strategic and military stronghold, its streets thronged with traffic, surrounded with barracks, the birthplace of the Cid (who, with Zimena, lies in the transept of the superb cathedral); León, in a strategic position at the foot of the Asturian Pájares pass which may be compared with that of Burgos, unsullied by the modern white suburbs that have risen in the new-found agricultural prosperity; Salamanca, which owes its origin to the north-south Roman road which crossed the Tormes — the most ancient university town in Spain, a nursery of scholars and adorned with colleges, palaces and cathedrals of all architectural styles from Romanesque to Baroque, and one of the most beautiful squares in Europe; Medina del Campo, whose very name shows how closely it is linked with its countryside, a town whose celebrated fairs were held at the foot of the *cerro* crowned with the castle of La Mota, where Isabella the Catholic died; and lastly Valladolid, the most industrialised (foodstuffs and automobiles), the most lively, and the most populous city, a military centre and a university town, but also an astounding art museum where the triumphant yet attractive architectural style of Isabella's reign bears witness to Spain's great riches in the sixteenth century.

All these towns are rather small. They were once, however, little capitals and their names resound in the medieval chronicles. Some of them tend to doze a little in a past that is evoked by lordly mansions with sculptured coats-of-arms, but they are also full of vigour. With the increase in the value of agricultural land and the increasing modernisation of agriculture, the population in some places (Palencia, Soria, León) has risen so rapidly as to increase by 80 per cent during the last few decades. The same thing has happened in the Mancha and in Estremadura.

THE CENTRAL CORDILLERA. The massive range of the central Cordillera, with its snow-capped summits, bounds the horizon of Old Castile to the south. The range is preceded by broad, rocky plateaus weathered down to about 3,000 to 4,000 feet. Stock-breeding and dairy farming flourish here. The clear, sweet waters of the *sierras* are gathered into great artificial lakes which irrigate regions in both Castiles. Although the central Cordillera is cut up into separate *sierras*, each with its own special character, it forms a single great Hispanic region, with picturesque, mountainous landscapes, a variety of ways of life, cool summers, and remote villages in which archaic customs are still preserved.

Eastwards, the Sierra de Guadarrama, a favourite winter sports resort of the people of Madrid, is also suitable for long excursions in summer. The highest point is the Peñalara (7,888 feet). This mountain barrier is broken only by the valley of the Lozoya; the passes are few and lie at considerable altitudes. The rail routes run through the Cordillera in long tunnels at Cercedilla (the Segovia line) and at Somosierra (for the new express line from Madrid to Burgos). To the north and the south the cool rocky plateaus provide land where cattle are bred and city families escape the intense summer heat. To the south-east of the *sierra*, the Escorial plateau (about 3,300 feet), now made prosperous by visitors from Madrid, offers a distant view of the celebrated monastery, which is the quintessence of the Spanish spirit and the very symbol of Spain in her Golden Age. To the west and the north-west, beyond the small resort of San Rafael, the plateau of Avila is crowned with the native city of Saint Teresa, while the Segovia plateau rises to a height of over 3,000 feet, where the town stands with its Gothic palaces, its cathedral and its baroque Alcazar on a spur of rock.

Farther to the west, the Sierra de Gredos rises higher (Almanzor, 8,500 feet), is wilder and more exclusively of granite formation.

Still farther on, beyond the great structural clefts of the passes of Tornavacas and Béjar, come the Sierras de Béjar (Calvitero, 7,875 feet), de Francia (5,651 feet) and de Gata (4,483 feet). These ranges are cold and partially snow-covered; their soil is almost entirely barren, though they hide in the dreary slopes of their southern face valleys of impressive grandeur (Las Batuecas) and the people known as the Jurdes, who for long lived in a state of misery. Northwards there is some industry. The little town of La Alberca, whose houses, dress and customs have remained unchanged for centuries, is one of the most interesting, if not the most remarkable, of Spanish villages.

Estremadura

THE TWO ESTREMADURAS: CÁCERES AND BADAJOZ. To the north, in the Estremadura of Cáceres, the granite bedrock is weathered down to a peneplain and for immense areas appears bare. The soil is very poor and very shallow: some cereals are grown, but for the most part the land affords only scanty pasture. Human life is concentrated on the little *sierras*. Nature, indeed, is so harsh and inhospitable that the *Estremeño* is obliged to eke out his resources by practising various little handicrafts or by seasonal emigration. There was a time, in fact, when emigration brought astonishing benefits to Estremadura. Many of the American *conquistadores* were natives of the province, and these men, when they came back, embellished their home towns. Cáceres, Trujillo and Plasencia are, except in their suburbs, almost dead, but they are filled with splendid palaces, treasure-houses of Renaissance architecture watched over by countless storks.

To the south, in the Estremadura of Badajoz, the granite of the ancient bedrock has been heavily weathered (as in the very fertile Tierra de Barros), or is covered with alluvial deposits laid down by the Guadiana River or by former lakes. Only in the Serena is the ancient rock exposed, and then it forms pastureland. Generally, the soils are rather rich. The climate, although very hot in summer, is milder and more oceanic than in the north, and offers a foretaste of Andalusia and Portugal, whose influences may also be noted in the attractive white houses, towns and villages. This region is, in fact, a rich granary, and was chosen by the Romans as the site of their Lusitanian capital, *Emerita Augusta*, now Mérida, which boasts the finest assemblage of Roman monuments in the Iberian peninsula. The Moslems moved the capital to Badajoz, for long a bone of contention between the Spaniards and the Portuguese, and now, thanks to the frontier trade, a thriving place. Great irrigation works drawing water from the dam on the Guadiana's Cijara loop are beginning to open up for cultivation a huge area of hitherto barren lands. However, the unequal distribution of property and the great area covered by large estates are serious obstacles to economic progress.

To the east, Estremadura is isolated from New Castile by rather low *sierras*. To the south, there are mines, including those of the mercury deposits at Almadén. In the north, the monastery-museum of Guadalupe, perched on a lonely height and heavily perfumed with cistus, is set amid *sierras* that roll away to join the Mountains of Toledo farther east.

New Castile

A GREAT CAPITAL: MADRID. New Castile has a wholly Castilian air because, after the Reconquest, it was peopled with Castilians, and because its level landscapes are just like those of Old Castile. It is in the south, in the Mancha, that these features are most strongly marked. A limestone table, absolutely flat, structurally the most perfect plain in all Spain, it facilitates rapid, easy communications. But the flatness hinders drainage. The waters stagnate, and the cracked and fissured rocks often absorb them. By Cervantes' time, apart from seasonal sheep farming which at other times of the year was practised elsewhere, there was nothing in New Castile but subsistence farming: wheat, a few vines, some olive trees. It was during the eighteenth century that more specialised agriculture developed, and it transformed the land — particularly in the south, where the oil and wine trades thrive. The north and east have remained faithful to cereals, but Don Quixote's windmills have all but disappeared. A special crop is saffron, whose mauve flowers with red pistils brighten the primitive villages of the Mancha in the autumn months. The inhabitants have remained very close to the soil, and often lead a troglodyte life in caves. In the east, much has been done to make the most of the soil by reforestation with pine trees.

Northwards, the Mancha platform stops at the depression of the Tagus river, where the rural population has preserved its old ways of life and costumes (the bright woollen dresses of the Lagartera women and the curious hats of the Talavera men).

Toledo offers a summary of Spanish history. The Visigoths, successors of the Romans, had their capital here. Islam lingered long in the city, and the Toledan translators' schools transmitted to Christendom both classical and oriental science and learning. In Toledo the Gothic arts of the north mingle with the Moorish life of the south, and the most harmonious synthesis of northern and southern Spain, even of West and East, is effected. As a result the town lives more on tourist trade than by handicrafts or official administrative activities.

The modern Spanish capital is a little farther north where, until the end of the Middle Ages, there was only an overgrown village. It was a stroke of genius on Philip II's part to choose

The Avenida José Antonio (Gran Via), one of the busiest thorough-fares of Madrid, the capital of Spain. P. ALMASY

In the Plaza de España, one of the skyscrapers which have sprung up recently in Madrid. J. ALLAN CASH

'Las Casas Colgadas', overhanging houses 300 feet above the gorge, at Cuenca, New Castile. PIERRE DEFFONTAINES

La Alberca, a small city at an altitude of almost 4,000 feet, at the foot of the northern slope of the Sierra de Francia, in the west of the Central Cordillera. Houses, dress and customs have changed little here over the centuries. In the foreground is a two-wheeled cart with railings, drawn by the black oxen of the Sierra. The oxen are yoked by their horns, a very old method of harnessing still found in Spain, Portugal, parts of France and central Europe. RENÉ FERLET

Madrid as his capital city, for thanks to its central, strategic position it not only commands the various provinces of Spain, but also exercises on them a unifying influence. Roads and railways radiating from Madrid like the spokes of a wheel continue to ensure control and contact. The rôle of Madrid is thus above all administrative, political, intellectual and scientific, and comparable with the part played by Paris in France, though its influence is even more marked. Madrid attracts and concentrates all the energies of Spain. During Spain's Golden Age Madrid was the most important city in Europe and, under Philip IV, had more than 100,000 inhabitants. The 1950 census gave a figure of 1,618,000; the estimated population at the end of 1955 was 1,850,000, and exactly two years later was 1,898,000 — the growth of the city proceeds at an astonishing rate. During the last few decades, and particularly since the end of the Second World War, a number of industrial plants such as are usual in other capitals have been erected in Madrid, and current from new dams will permit extension of this industrialisation. Furthermore, despite what some superficial observers may say, the Madrid conurbation maintains a fairly high standard of living, and most of the essential supplies come from nearby. Today a real 'Madrid region' with various activities and resources has grown up and extends from the Tagus to the *sierra*.

On leaving Madrid one reaches to the north-east those areas of New Castile that have best retained their ancient appearance, and form, so to speak, the 'Marches' leading to Aragon. First of all comes the Alcarria, a region of small towns rich in history and in monuments — such as Guadalajara. The rivers have been dammed and the huge *pantanos* of Entrepeñas and Buendia are a sign that great economic transformation is near at hand. The Alcarria touches on the Serranía de Cuenca, an immense, practically uninhabited limestone plateau (4,500 to 6,000 feet high), whose only activity is timber-felling in the pinewoods. The logs must still be floated down the Jucar and the Cabriel, tortuous streams flowing deep down in deserted canyons. The capital, Cuenca, is an unpretentious place but astonishingly picturesque, perched on a spur between two ravines above which the houses hang precipitously.

Aragon

SARAGOSSA. Aragon has its own quite distinctive personality based on its history. The Aragonese Reconquest was undertaken independently of that of Castile, and Aragonese customs, laws and general development have been peculiar to the region. Aragon kept its Moriscos for longer than any

Nuestra Señora de Pilar, a famous Spanish sanctuary on the banks of the Ebro at Saragossa, formerly capital of Aragon. It was partially completed in the eighteenth century and its ten cupolas reflect Moslem architectural influence. Each year the commemoration of the Virgin's appearance on a pillar to St James (hence the name of Pilar) attracts numerous pilgrims. GILLES DE LA MOTTE ROUGE

Panorama of Toledo, in New Castile. The Tagus has dug a gorge through the granite at Toledo and describes a great curve which encloses the rocky hill on which the city stands, providing the perfect site for a fortified town. Toledo is of ancient origin and was for long the capital, notably under Charles V, whence its title of 'Imperial City'. It has preserved traces of every age, and is thus a living museum of Spanish history, in which it has had such an important rôle. To the left is the Cathedral, to the right, the ruins of the Alcazar, destroyed in 1936 during the Civil War. SPANISH NATIONAL TOURIST OFFICE

other part of Spain. The inhabitants, the *Baturros*, have the reputation of being obstinate and hard-headed. They are strongly attached to their native soil, and their character, their accent, their costumes, and their national dance (the *jota*) have the savour of a land that is richly individual. The climate, harsh and severe at all seasons of the year, lends life and manners a touch of austerity and gravity more marked even than in Castile. The endurance and the patriotism of the Aragonese are proverbial, as is shown by the defence of Saragossa against Napoleon and by the veneration of the national sanctuary of Nuestra Señora del Pilar.

Aragon may be compared with Aquitaine. In both regions there are huge, low-lying Tertiary basins whose sediments are deposited in ancient depressions lying between the Pyrenees (common to both Aragon and Aquitaine) and the ancient bedrocks (the Meseta in Spain, and the Massif Central in France). The waters of the two basins join to become one river: in Aragon this river is the Ebro, in Aquitaine the Garonne, and both are relatively powerful. However, Aragon is appreciably more continental as well as being much drier than Aquitaine. On the other hand, despite a few slight differences, the economic structure of the Ebro basin also displays that disposition in concentric, complementary and interdependent areas of rich agricultural land and industrial enterprises typical of Aquitaine.

An Aragonese boy. REFOT, RAPHO

Caspe, Belchite and Cariñena live by the produce of the soil. Farther west the great valley of the Jalón cuts obliquely across the Iberian folds and, passing through Calatayud, with its delicate brick belfries, affords a line of communication between Madrid and Saragossa.

The central part of the Ebro basin is the real heart of Aragon, for not only is the land here lower and warmer but it is also watered by large rivers — the Ebro fed by Cantabrian rains, and its tributaries swollen by melting Pyrenean snows. The valleys of these streams are fertile, well-watered strips with rich alluvial soil which is further invigorated by irrigation canals (e.g. Imperial Canal, Tauste Canal). This region yields valuable crops: olives, sugar-beet, cotton for processing in local mills, early fruits and vegetables for export and for the large urban area of Saragossa.

Saragossa itself (285,000 inhabitants) is in all senses the Aragonese capital. However, the part it has played and still plays is better understood if we note that it is, to the south of the Pyrenees, an almost exact replica of Toulouse to the north of them. Like that city, Saragossa is built of brick, it is a religious and academic metropolis, a regional, administrative, military and economic capital, the centre of a web of communications, a city that dominates the basin in which it is set and one which, as a result of war, has recently become industrialised. In all Europe there are no two cities more aptly called twins than Saragossa and Toulouse. Some small differences may, however, be noted in the traces of Moslem influence, the Mudéjar style of the belfries, and in the more modern and better-planned urban development of Saragossa.

The least complicated and most typical features of the Spanish Pyrenees can be seen in Aragon. Four nearly parallel belts serve to display these features. First there is the zone of the Aragonese *sierras* (Sierra de Guara, 6,800 feet), a region of folds warped in the south and broken by rifts. It is pierced by rivers whose ravines have been dammed to form lakes (Arguis and Barasona) which now irrigate the Somontano and dotted with castles, as at Loarre, and fortified towns such as Alquezar. It is followed by a depressed zone of Tertiary marls, and badlands with an exceptionally dry climate. This is the Aragon syncline, which provides an excellent line of communication: the Berdún canal and the Val Ancha with road and railway. There are industries at Sabiñanigo and, at the entrance to the Somport Pass, the little episcopal, Romanesque and military town of Jaca. The region is less clearly defined to the east though still, recognisable, and it is dotted with small, historical towns such as Boltaña, La Ainsa and Graus.

Next comes the very thick southern layer of Secondary limestones of the axial zone of the range. From Ansó to La Noguera deep, parallel valleys, sometimes with impassable canyons, cut into it. This region contains some magnificent gorges (Ordesa) and the most splendid Pyrenean peaks (the limestone massif of Mont-Perdu-Gavarnie). It isolates and, so to speak, pushes towards France the fourth axial zone, chiefly formed of ancient weathered rocks, although intrusive formations rise as tall massifs surrounded by valleys or passes (Maladetta, 11,165 feet; Posets, 11,056 feet). This is a region of timber, mines, hydro-electric power stations and, above all, of tourist resorts. There is only one railway (built in 1928), but three roads (Somport, Pourtalet, Viella tunnel) cut through the area. However, when finally the decision is taken, it will be quite easy to construct the Franco-Spanish roads whose plans were drawn up long ago. Depending upon this region is the Val d'Aran, the upper valley of the Garonne. It is geographically French, it is green and cool, and the inhabitants speak Gascon, but the area has always been part of Aragon and its contacts have always been with Aragon — through the Viella Pass. Aran may be taken as the symbol of the strong links which, down the ages, have been forged between the populations on the Aragonese and the French slopes of the Pyrenees.

The gentle slopes of the Pyrenean axis have never (despite their altitude) proved an obstacle to communication and exchange of commodities from one side of the range to the other. Not only did pilgrims headed for Compostela pour through the passes and throng the hospices during the Middle Ages, but commercial relations were freely maintained between the French south-west and Aragon (as well as Navarre). Numerous immigrants settled in French territory, while architectural styles from across the Pyrenees were imported into France, so that Toulouse was until the eighteenth century really an Aragonese city.

Still, in spite of these ancient and obvious links with south-west France, Aragon must be considered, first and foremost, in terms of its relations with central Spain. The regions have comparable types of agriculture: sheep and cereals on the steppes, enclosing oases in the valleys. Road and rail communications pass through the Agreda and Jalón corridors. In marked contrast, then, with the almost impassable barrier which has been formed during the centuries between Catalonia and Castile, constant interchange has made for a resemblance between the ideas and sentiments of the Aragonese and Castilians.

Aragon, moreover, encroaches on the Meseta with the high plateaus of Teruel and Albarracín, separated by the long corridor of Daroca Caminreal, which serve rail and road communications. This is a very cold region, sparsely wooded and grazed by sheep. The towns are colourful but small (Teruel, 19,000 inhabitants) and the sturdily built houses seem to huddle together to seek shelter from the cold. It is an unattractive region adjoining the wooded Maestrazgo (where the flocks of sheep belonging to the Military Order, or Maestranza, of the Crown of Aragon were kept) and the snow-capped Sierra de Javalambre (6,625 feet), which cuts off Aragon from the Mediterranean — although there is a way out toward Sagunto and Valencia by the Santander-Mediterranean railway line. Without the Utrillas coal mines this central part of Aragon would have little importance today — the figure of 41 inhabitants to the square mile, which is that for the province of Teruel, is the lowest in all Spain.

From this high plateau the land slopes down towards the north-west to the Tierra Baja of Alcaníz. Near the springs large villages have grown up, and the warmer climate permits the cultivation of extensive olive-groves and vineyards on the marls of the Ebro basin. Isolated little towns such as Alcaníz,

NORTHERN SPAIN

If we look at a map that shows the rainfall and the flora of the Iberian peninsula, we are struck at once by the contrast between 'dry Spain' and 'wet Spain'. On the Pyrenean passes, the sky of Spain is comparable with that of France. Almost abruptly, the blue skies of the Meseta, which disperses the northern clouds, give way to fogs and rain which, all along the Atlantic and the Bay of Biscay, give an unusual appearance to a fairly wide belt of green countryside stretching from Navarre and the Basque country to Galicia. This is the *Norte*, northern Spain.

MOUNTAINS, SEA AND WESTERLY WINDS. For a Spaniard the term *Norte* has just as definite a meaning as has the *Ouest* for a Frenchman or the 'South' for Americans. The term *Norte* and the adjective *norteño* as applied to the inhabitants, the products and the characteristics of the North are in such common use, and moreover are so convenient from a geographical point of view, that we may well be astonished to see them generally ignored in text-books, which use vaguer expressions such as 'Atlantic' or 'Cantabrian' Spain.

The northern landscapes owe their appearance to three factors: the mountains, the sea and the westerly winds. The mountains form an almost uninterrupted *cordillera* that rarely falls below 3,000 feet and very often rises to twice that altitude. The range is often snow-capped, and it rises like a great wall from a shore never very wide, so that there is only occasionally a narrow ribbon of land between beaches and mountains. These ranges look out on to a sea that throbs with life. It is the richest of all those that wash the Spanish shores with its expanse of blues and greens, always in motion and redolent of seaweed and iodine. It is a sea often wild and savage, always magnificent, fresh, full of strength, and has produced such wonderful mariners as the Basques and Cantabrians, who have throughout history formed the backbone of the famed Castilian Navy. It is also a fairly warm sea. Mists and clouds float up from it almost constantly and drift away in wisps along the mountain slopes, there to fall as rain and then be swept up by westerly winds and their ever-shifting cyclonic pressure zones.

Sea, mountains and westerly winds: together these features they explain why there is so much rain: showers, howling tempests, and on days when there is no wind, drizzle.

As a result, there is verdure everywhere: the deciduous oak-trees which, in Vizcaya, are the emblem of the Basque people; the sweet-smelling hay; the lush, grassy meadows and the after-grass; the sturdy maize, so typical of the country and so well adapted to it that one would think it had always been there, though it is known that Indian corn was introduced into the Spanish north at the beginning of the seventeenth century; and, lastly, the cider-apples whose juice, once it has been specially treated, is drunk according to old rites in the local taverns. And there are the forests. Some of them are still extensive and in the Asturias, as farther east in the Pyrenees, still the home of bears. On the slopes the countryside is often of *bocage* character. The heaths are either russet with ferns on the bare, Basque heights or, in Galicia and the Asturias, overgrown with furze and gorse which play their part in the agricultural cycle when, from time to time, they are burned down.

The mountains, high and steep, form an effective screen isolating these northern lands which lie so far from the heart of Spain. The broken nature of the relief accentuates the isolation. Very curious phenomena have survived in the *Norte* — such ethnical groups as the Basques (whose origin and language still present baffling problems to researchers) and, farther west, the Celts, found almost pure in Galicia and in the Asturias.

No other part of Spain is so marked by archaic manners and customs, which are manifested in the almost universal tendency to form into groups. Thus hundreds of Galicians will assemble to sing an *alborada* (serenade), while in other parts of Spain songs are for a single voice. So, also, the group dances to the sound of *gaita* or bagpipes. This, again, follows the Basque ancestral traditions which are based first and foremost on the unity and authority of the family. For instance, there are the shepherds' unions, the *vaqueiros de alzada*, which spend the summer in the high mountains of the western Asturias. These men live in huts or cabins, and make use of tools and equipment of types which have not changed much since Neolithic times.

Other archaic features or peculiarities may, possibly be due less to isolation than to the surroundings and, especially, the climate. Thus, to ensure that the harvest does not rot, it is stacked into the *horreos*, strange granaries on piles, of which there are several types — the Galician, the Asturian and the Basque. Then there is the habit of wearing clogs or *madreñas* with three high strips of wood under them. And there is the *caroza* or straw raincoat worn by Galician shepherds — possibly a Celtic legacy.

MEDITERRANEAN, OCEANIC AND CENTRAL SPANISH INFLUENCES. Everything in the *Norte* recalls much more the Atlantic peninsulas or western Europe than the fiery Spain of legend. However, the *Norte* is undoubtedly Spain. For, when all is said and done, the sky is grey only on occasion, and we must not forget that the *Norte* is a southern land (lat. 42° to 43°30′), and very close to those Mediterranean influences which find their way along the Ebro valley, reach far away to the west and also penetrate the Aragonese Pyrenees, support olive-trees in southern Navarre, even stretch down into eastern Vizcaya and as far as the ocean's edge, and are felt in the Basque country and in the Montaña where the great south-facing limestone slabs are covered with dark ilex. Hence the importance, in the dwelling, of balconies, which are used for drying, so that every ray of the sun may be utilised. Again, the equable winter climate, where frost is unknown, allows orange-trees to be grown out of doors in the Asturias, and also scented eucalyptus groves which are now such a striking feature of the landscape. Moreover, the climate, which is damp and hot in summer, is ideal for hay and maize whose vigorous growth is, in the circumstances, hardly surprising. Again, holiday-makers and tourists are by no means the least of northern Spain's resources.

From demographic, economic and political points of view, central Spain and the North were until the end of the sixteenth century the peninsula's centre of gravity. In recent years this same situation has been re-established and is still more marked than it was before. Since the eighteenth century the lands of the *Norte*, for long neglected and wild, have undergone a development that began with the American trade and continued with the development of heavy industry during the nineteenth century. In the last few decades this movement has been speeded up, so that the *Norte* has become the most important industrial area of the whole peninsula. The Asturias is, in fact, Spain's industrial stronghold and the region that has the brightest future. However, its future cannot be thought of except in conjunction with that of Castile. The centre and the north are together bringing about the transfer of Spain's basic activities to the Bay of Biscay.

Therefore, while we recognise the unique and original character of the Spanish *Norte*, we must not lose sight of its exceptional economic importance. Again, however considerable and fundamental this originality may be, so mountainous a land and one with so broken a relief cannot fail to be divided into compartments. It is, in fact, composed of so many contrasting districts that we must approach it on a regional basis.

Navarre

A MARKED INDIVIDUALITY. If we consider only its physical geography, Navarre may appear but partially a *norteño* land. It is made up of three very distinct regions. In the centre, the broad basin of Pamplona, which extends for a considerable distance from east to west, contains the capital of Navarre, a city whose old walls have given way to gardens and to the very modern town-planning of a huge *ensanche* while, farther off and near the railway station, a real industrial suburb has sprung up. In a physical sense, the Pamplona basin separates northern from southern Navarre; it also serves as a link between the populations of the north and the south.

To the north lies Pyrenean Navarre — damp, cold, well-wooded — which has remained Basque in language, customs, style of dwellings and economy. The inhabitants — woodmen and shepherds — live scattered about in remote hamlets. In the east, Pyrenean Navarre includes several parallel valleys running from north to south. This mountain region is difficult of access and is covered with fine, dense forests whose timber has since the eighteenth century been floated away down the rivers and streams. The inhabitants also practise sheep-farming and stock-raising. Westward, however — and beyond Roncevalles with its historical highway — we find Hercynian massifs, dense and well-wooded, shaped like gigantic almonds extending from east to west: Quint, Cinco Villas and Rhune-Haya. These make up an isolated area abutting on the Basque provinces.

Southern Navarre, on the other hand, is Mediterranean, bright and attractive. It begins at Navarre's central corridor. At the Puerto del Perdón, the old pilgrim's way to Compostela cuts through this region, while farther south lie the sunny plains leading to the banks of the Ebro, an area of rich harvests, a sea of cereals, vines and even olive-trees. And it is furrowed with well-watered valleys — those of the Ega, the Arga and the Aragon which join the Ebro to swell its waters considerably. These wide, well-irrigated strips of alluvial soil which run into the fertile belt of the Ebro itself produce sugar-beet for the refineries at Tudela, and early vegetables and fruits which go to supply a number of flourishing canneries.

Despite these contrasts of soil, climate and modes of life, Navarre, like Switzerland, has too marked an individuality for one to think of cutting it into two parts. It was for long a wholly independent kingdom, and its people are still fiercely attached to their ancient rights. The land as a whole has a common history which serves, together with the abundant natural riches and the homogeneous and splendid people (about 400,000), to secure a remarkable degree of unity. In former days Navarre spread north of the Pyrenees and into the region of the present-day French *Basse Navarre* at Saint-Jean-Pied-de-Port; the country constantly looked towards France rather than Castile and Aragon, and managed to reach as far as the line of the Ebro river and even to cross it in the Tudela area. The Roncevalles road is the historical artery of Navarre along which the country received what was necessary for its economic and political prosperity. After the Pyrenean passes, the highway ran to Puente la Reina, where it was joined by the road from Somport. From there onwards the Way of St James, studded with monasteries and Romanesque churches which show the great extent of French influence, drove right through southern Navarre and crossed the Ebro by the stone bridge of Logroño. A number of bonds linking Navarre to the Pyrenean and Atlantic worlds were thus forged, making it essentially a northern land.

The Rioja
and the lands of the upper Ebro

DIVERSIFIED AND OLD-ESTABLISHED WEALTH. If we leave Logroño and then make our way westward we follow the historic Way of St James, more often locally called the *Calzada* or the *Camino Francés*. Not only chapels and monasteries, but also the style of the dwellings, the habits and even the gestures of the inhabitants make a very 'European'

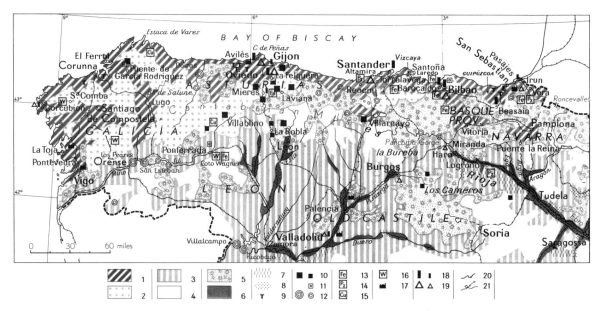

NORTHERN SPAIN. *Navarre, Rioja and the Upper Ebro country, the Basque country, the Montaña de Santander, the Asturias, Galicia. 1. Agriculture under Atlantic influence: maize, potatoes, vegetables, apples; 2. Agriculture under Atlantic influence passing into natural or artificial prairie; 3. Secano farming (without irrigation): wheat, vines, olives; extensive sheep-rearing; 4. Mediterranean steppe; 6. Forest and scrub; 5. Irrigated areas: vegas (mountain huertas); 7. Vines (large estates, no other crops); 8. Sugar-beet; 9. Tobacco; 10. Coal; 11. Power stations; 12. Hydro-electric power stations; 13. Iron; 14. Lead and zinc; 15. Copper; 16. Wolfram (tungsten); 17. Factory for processing non-ferrous metals; 18. Iron-smelting; 19. Chemical industry; 20. Railways; 21. Canals and irrigation dams.*

impression on anyone coming from the heart of Spain. Damp sea-breezes bring clouds and showers from the ocean. Geographically we are no longer in Old Castile. These 'Upper Ebro' lands form, if not a transition zone, at least a region intermediate between central Spain and northern Spain.

The region begins to the east with an area that is both Castilian and *norteño* — the Rioja, whose climate is tempered with western influences and which, practically speaking, has no low winter temperatures. The Rioja is a rich agricultural land with a variety of crops. In the east, the Lower Rioja is irrigated by the big Lodosa Canal which draws its water from the Ebro and from the rivers flowing down from the mountain valleys of the Sierras de Cameros. It is an area of ancient human settlement and of very varied crops, mainly early vegetables and choice fruits for export and for canning. To the west, between Logroño, Nájera and Haro, stretches the Upper Rioja. Here the Ebro flows deep down between pebbly terraces. This is primarily a land of vineyards (about 80,000 acres), which, owing to an excellent selling organisation, produce most of the Spanish table wines. It is, all in all, a diversified, well-established and prosperous agriculture.

However, as we move upstream the appearance of plenty and the atmosphere of charm begin to fade. The Ebro gorges at the Conchas de Haro form the gateway to a rather poor as well as an isolated area. On its meandering course, the river passes from one depression to another, so that we have a world of little units, tiny in size, isolated from each other and remote. Such are the high and snowy Llanos de la Virga, once pastures but now drowned beneath the waters of the reservoir of the Upper Ebro; or the elevated shell of the Valle de Mena and of Espinosa de los Monteros, through which slips the mine-railway from Bilbao to La Robla; or, again, the two large basins of Villarcayo and Miranda de Ebro, the former entirely enclosed, but cut through by the Santander-Mediterranean railway, and the latter traversed from west to east by the Ebro and pierced on the north by the Zadorra and in the south by the Pancorbo gorges through the Obarenes mountains. Miranda is an important railway junction (Irún-Madrid, Irún-Bilbao, Irún-Saragossa) and also a centre where, thanks to the lines of communication, some fairly large factories for foodstuffs (sugar, flour) and chemicals (cellulose) have been developed.

The Basque country

To the north of these Ebro lands lie the Basque Provinces, or Vascongadas, the most unusual, perhaps, of all the northern districts. Some of the curious Basque characteristics are today known everywhere and have become fashionable... Among these are the houses whose great roofs seem to attract all the elements, dwellings that are built around a single ground-floor room, which is open so as to allow carts and farm-implements to be brought in, but sheltered from the weather, so that the harvest can be threshed in it. Then there are the disc-shaped gravestones marked with swastikas; the game of *pelota*; the nimble dancers; the sharp, strongly-marked features of Basque faces; the berets made popular by the Carlists, etc.

There can be no denying that there is a Basque people whose manners and customs and especially language (Euskara) are unique in Europe and probably in the world. The most curious aspect of this survival is the preservation of those archaic features which, one would have thought, would have been swept away long ago, since the Basque country is a corridor. Indeed, its passes (only 2,000 to 2,300 feet high) make it the main highway between Spain and the rest of Europe. Since the sixteenth century the Basque country has played an international rôle. Nevertheless, the Basque cultural area, once more extensive than it is now, has retained a completely original character that helps to ensure the very marked individuality of the Basque lands, which now contain a population of more than a million.

ÁLAVA, GUIPÚZCOA AND VIZCAYA. Geographically speaking, however, we must recognise two Basque lands, the upper and the lower, within the Vascongadas.

The upper country is Álava (118,000 inhabitants), consisting for the most part of a very extensive oval 'shell' or depression stretching from east to west and constituting an excellent corridor through which run the main roads and railways of the peninsula. The edge of this Álava basin is marked by pale, harsh, rigid limestone heights, often snow-covered. These are the curious white Basque *peñas*: the Peñas de Aitzgorri (5064 feet), Peñas de Aloña, de Aitzlluitz, de Amboto (4440 feet), and de Gorbea (4,838 feet). The Álava's soil is very rich and bears a variety of crops. The capital, Vitoria, is a road and rail junction and has become industrialised. Thanks to the old iron mines at Araya, Vitoria manufactures ploughs and agricultural implements that are sold all over Spain. Vitoria's varied activities have been the cause of its rapid growth in recent times.

Down the many twisting roads and the long downward gradients of the electrified railways (for example, at Orduña), we reach the lower country — Guipúzcoa and Vizcaya. This is, generally speaking, a region of lower altitude. However, the relief is no less complex and chequered than in the upper region. Guipúzcoa is more open to the sea than Vizcaya, and also damper and greener, for in Vizcaya a vegetation of almost southern character makes a rather surprising appearance.

For long the agriculture of this lower country languished, but after the discovery of America, perhaps at the end of the sixteenth century, came the introduction of maize which caused a real revolution. Both by the abundance of its yield and by the livestock that could be fed on it, maize made Basque farming flourish.

The sea has, however, always been a source of revenue for the Basques. Every day, in all weathers, the trawlers set out

The Roman bridge which crosses the Sella at Cangas de Onis in the Asturias. The town was the residence of the first Spanish kings after Moorish occupation, and the starting-point for the Christian reconquest in the eighth century. SPANISH NATIONAL TOURIST OFFICE

General view of the round bay of La Concha (the Shell) at San Sebastián, capital of the Basque province of Guipúzcoa. The bay is closed to the west by Mount Igueldo (from which this picture is taken), and to the east by Mount Urgull. Between the two hills is the islet of Santa Clara. The beach seen on the right is one of the most popular in the whole of Europe. LAVERGNE, RAPHO

from the many picturesque little ports sheltered in the *rias*. Only the Galician catch is larger than that of Cantabria, so nearly all the Spanish shipping companies have their head offices in Bilbao, and most of the sailors in the merchant marine are Basques. Bilbao, in the estuary of the Nervión, extends about 7½ miles along the *ria* and is, indeed, the first port of Spain, though it is closely followed by Barcelona and by Gijón. Nor should we forget another benefit that the sea brings to the Basques: bathing-beaches and the visitors they attract. San Sebastián is the principal summer resort of the whole peninsula.

Nevertheless, industry has now become the main resource of the lower country. In the past an abundant supply of wood and power generated by the torrents encouraged the establishment of furniture factories which are today somewhat overshadowed by the big paper mills. The real source of wealth, however, has lain in mines and in metallurgy. The iron ore, from the rich deposits to the west of Bilbao, was originally exported to Great Britain. Then, since coal was brought back as ballast in British ships, the ores were smelted at the local Spanish blast-furnaces, which were set up on the banks of the the Nervión about the middle of the last century. From then

on Bilbao became a city of iron. It is wedged into the winding valley and under its sooty rain is in manners, customs and appearance very like a British city. Bilbao proper has 259,000 inhabitants, but the population totals more than 350,000 if we count the workers' suburbs that surround the city. Vizcaya, which has 689,000 inhabitants, is the most densely populated of all the Spanish provinces (803 inhabitants to the square mile).

Guipúzcoa, in its turn, has also gone over to metallurgy, not so much because of mines, for there is much more zinc than iron in the area, but because of the abundant supply of hydro-electric power. And from electro-metallurgy, Guipúzcoa has gone on to electro-chemistry. On all sides factories producing ceramics, plastics and various synthetic products are being built. Consequently the traffic through its port, Pasajes, is continually increasing. Venezuelan cocoa, which was a main factor in Basque prosperity during the eighteenth century is still used in the chocolate factories. The port of San Sebastián, an attractive little capital and luxury town, has 125,000 inhabitants out of Guipúzcoa's total of 441,000 (572 to the square mile). In summer the population of San Sebastián rises to over 200,000.

The Montaña of Santander

MILK AND MEAT. INDUSTRY AND TOURISM. Though the appearance of the countryside remains *norteño* to the west of Vizcaya (a coast indented with *rias* at the foot of the Cantabrian Cordillera mountain wall), the Santander region has a feature peculiar to itself — the Montaña. It owes its name

to the Castilians of Burgos who, on their way to the sea, found after the Puerto del Escudo a countryside that was greener than their own and cut up and hollowed out into gorges and ravines. Thus, although it lay lower than the high plains of the Meseta, the region seemed more mountainous than those plains. The Montaña, moreover, is Castilian, from both the historical and administrative point of view. Santander is the port through which wheat and flour are exported from Castile.

The Montaña is Castilian, too, in its climate, which is distinctly less wet than that of Vizcaya and that of the Asturias. The decrease in rainfall begins, though, in Vizcaya, and is due to a northerly advance of the Meseta's influence. In the Montaña the landscape is clear and attractive, the little hills and the vales are carefully cultivated and yield a variety of crops, and are also dotted with patches of eucalyptus woods. It is a region which has for long been shaped by man, for the Montaña is one of the most ancient areas of human settlement in all Spain. As in the Asturias, prehistoric caves are numerous. The Palaeolithic pictures of Altamira were the first to be discovered, and are still the finest despite the competition from the recently discovered wall-paintings at El Castillo. In the country districts, where nearly every inch of the soil is cultivated, the dwellings are scattered. Their overhanging roofs and rather exposed balconies are an indication of a fairly dry climate. It rains enough, however, for the lower levels and especially the valleys of the Montaña to produce grass, milk and meat. The rearing of cattle and sheep has brought prosperity to the Montaña.

Thus some compensation has been found for the decline of shipping, for the *rias* are silting up and, unlike the lively little Basque ports, those of the Montaña have a struggle to keep alive. In fact, fishing has become less profitable for them than the income from summer visitors to the beaches. The entire floor of Laredo's fine bay, which was a harbour used by Charles V, has become more or less silted up in the shelter of the formidable mass of the Santoña rock. At Hinojedo, the Besaya *ria* has to be kept dredged so that ships can come up and take on the industrial products of Torrelavega, for the *Compagnie Asturienne des Mines* (a Belgian model enterprise) is working the lead and zinc of Reocin near Torrelavega. Its output in these metals is the largest in Spain. Pyrites are also treated, and have given rise to a chemical industry (sulphur, sulphuric acid, soda, etc.) and production of cellulose and man-made fibres. These products are, however, exported in increasing quantities through the port of Santander.

Santander's fine harbour is silting up too, but only at the back, near the arsenals and the naval shipyards of Astillero, and it is still able to accommodate ships of up to 15,000 tons. In volume of trade Santander remains the tenth port of Spain. The town is busy and attractive. The population is over 100,000; the Montaña has 420,000 inhabitants, 206 to the square mile.

The Asturias

A DEVELOPING INDUSTRIAL AREA. Of all the regions of the *Norte* it is in the Asturias, perhaps, that we can feel most strongly the charm of a number of traditional

Bilbao, capital of the Basque province of Biscay and the most important port of Spain. It is situated 8 miles from the sea, on both banks of the Nervion estuary. GILLES DE LA MOTTE ROUGE

A defile of the Sella. The precipitous rocks are a feature of the Asturias. SPANISH NATIONAL TOURIST OFFICE

characteristics of the region which, most fortunately, have been preserved to this day. Such are the small houses, the granaries, the clogs, the mitre-like head-dresses, the local bag-pipes, the cider drunk in taverns and *xagres*, the Visigothic and Palaeo-Romanesque art, and also the soft and muted manner in which the people speak Castilian. It is in the Asturias, however, that some of the biggest metallurgical works in the peninsula have grown up, and Spaniards feel that their fortunes lie in the development of the region. All these things indicate that the province has its own very pronounced and remarkable individuality.

It is an individuality due, first of all, to an almost complete self-absorption. The Cantabrian Chain, which stretches from east to west for about two hundred miles, raises a formidable rampart between the Meseta and the little world of Cantabria, comparable, though on a smaller scale, with the great wall of the Pyrenees between France and Spain. The Cantabrian Cordillera is a barrier that looks as though it would cut off the Asturias from the rest of Spain and push the province toward the sea.

And this sea in its turn, owing to the very nature of the coast, shuts in the Asturias behind another barrier. The coast is everywhere of recent geological formation and it is precipitous and pierced by grottoes in which the sea is often forced upward through blowholes. The cliffs are very high and inaccessible and nowhere more so than in the great peninsula of Cabo de Peñas (278 feet). The coastal villages are therefore few in number, and those which do exist must be reached by staircases in the rock — as at Cudillero. Had the lower courses of the rivers not been drowned into *rias*, there would be neither beaches nor ports. Some of the *rias* have been adapted for the export trade: one such is at Aviles, which will soon be the port of a great national iron and steel combine that is being set up. No doubt Aviles will then outstrip the Musel of Gijón which, at present, is the largest Asturian port.

The climate is equable and soft. Frosts never occur, so that palm-trees, orange-trees and, of course, early vegetables and fruits grow out-of-doors. The soil is particularly well suited for maize. Stock-breeding has attracted a good deal of speculative capital, and co-operative dairies are numerous. Still, although the cost of living is low, life is hard for the over-abundant rural population. The population pressure is certainly, less marked than in Galicia, but still there has been for long a current of emigration from the Asturias to the Americas — mostly to Mexico.

However, the future holds out other prospects. From 1900 to 1950 the population of the Asturias rose from 627,000 to 895,000, thus increasing by more than a third. This rise is a measure of the ever-growing importance of Asturian industry. In the mining areas there are more than 780 inhabitants to the square mile, for in the area south of Oviedo lie the most extensive and richest coalfields in Spain. Everywhere there are pits with their head-frames, galleries and waste-dumps. This Asturian coal has led to the formation of a great metallurgical industry, the second in Spain after that of Vizcaya. The Duro-Felguera works are the chief centre. But now the discovery of new iron deposits and the opening of new collieries have given rise, at Oviedo, to a project for a coal 'Institute' and at Aviles for an iron and steel combine able to turn out 600,000 tons of steel a year and thus to be the largest in Europe. The plans are perhaps a little ambitious, but they show that the Spaniards think of the Asturias as their land of the future.

The development of the city of Oviedo may be taken as a symbol of the present-day expansion of the Asturias. In order to house its 127,000 or so inhabitants, the city has set up in the green countryside huge housing blocks which have constantly to be enlarged. Also, in order to overcome Oviedo's isolation, an airfield has been laid out so that communications may be speeded up between the Asturias and the rest of Spain.

Galicia

A LAND'S END. Galicia, too, is in its turn is beginning to shake off traditional ways of life and to evolve rapidly. One would, expect that this province would be the last to change, since from the beginning of its history it has been isolated and remote. Galicia lies in the Far West of Spain, a Land's End, a rugged region indented by Atlantic waves. Galicia is far away from everything. France lies 500 miles away to the east along the Cantabrian shore. From Madrid to Corunna the railway is 528 miles long, though a new line linking Galicia more directly with the capital cuts off sixty miles from the distance.

Galicia is indeed remote and isolated, but its remoteness and isolation have enabled it to preserve features which are extremely unusual and rather archaic — languages and dialects that are not Spanish, costume and folklore societies, granite crosses that dot the countryside, carts with solid, creaking wheels, a low cost of living, and a very marked local patriotism. To a certain degree perhaps Galicia is more closely linked with Portugal than with Spain. Galicia received its language from Portugal and shared it again with Portugal after the Reconquest. They have many social and agrarian customs in common. Economic exchanges between the two regions are not, however, important. There was a time when Galicia was relatively less isolated. Its wealth in tin attracted the attention of the ancients, and navigators bound for the 'Cassiterides' touched Galician shores. Galicia was strongly marked by Roman influence, much more strongly in fact than the Asturias. It is not, then, surprising that a legend arose according to which the Apostle St James journeyed to Galicia, where he wished to be buried (at *Iria Flavia*, now Padrón). His tomb, discovered during the eleventh century in a field indicated by a star (*campus stellae*, hence Compostela) became the most famous place of pilgrimage in medieval Christendom and the goal of a migration that was as much economic as social or spiritual. Hundreds of thousands of pilgrims flocked to the superb Romanesque basilica from all over Europe.

From the eighteenth century, when Galicia was allowed to trade with the Indies, the province turned its back, so to speak, on Spain, and yielded to the irresistible attraction of the sea. No seashore, in fact, seems better suited for shipping. The country abounds in *rias*, hence the numerous harbours, and fishing-ports: so many, indeed, that the Galician catch is the largest in all Spain, while Galician canned fish is known all over the world. There are commercial ports and ports of call such as Corunna and Vigo, and naval bases such as El Ferrol. At Marín there is a naval academy. The bathing-beaches are numerous, and both the unpretentious and the luxurious are thronged with summer visitors. All Galicia lives on the sea and by the sea.

The Galician coast, however, like that of Brittany, is harsh and battered by the waves. Bad weather is common and the fishermen, like those almost everywhere, are poor. The peasants are no better off than the fishermen. As in northern Portugal, which is a continuation of granite Galicia although its relief is less broken, the rural population is high, at least in the districts near the shore; the average figures are 313 to the square mile for the province of Corunna, and 401 to the square mile for the province of Pontevedra. Although the Galician peasants are extraordinarily hard-working, the land is too much subdivided into tiny holdings to afford a comfortable livelihood for a family.

The ease of sea communications, then, during the nineteenth century, favoured a great current of emigration across the Atlantic. It was directed partly to Spanish colonies such as Cuba, and partly to the Latin-American republics. There are more Galicians in the Americas than there are in Galicia. They are organised into clubs and are influential both socially and economically, especially in Argentina. However, conditions in Spain and in the Americas have made it much more difficult to emigrate since 1914 than it was before that date. So the population of Galicia has gone on rising; it has, indeed, risen by nearly a million during the last fifty years — between 1900 and 1950 the density per square mile rose from 189 to 293, which is almost double that for Spain as a whole. Galicia is, then, grossly over-populated.

The remedy for this state of things has been recognised: colonisation within Spain itself. As with the Breton *Armor* and *Arcoat* (coast and interior), so we must distinguish between the Galician shore and the inland areas. The latter are, in their natural condition, very poor. Attempts have been made to increase the area of arable land, but despite all efforts, the soil

A Galician shepherd wearing a 'caroza', a straw coat for protection against the rain. H. HOLMES, CAMERA PRESS

remains of very indifferent quality. But there are huge areas which are not utilised in any way, so very large-scale reforestation has been undertaken, and Galicia is now covered with pine-woods. The timber from them is mostly put to use as pit-props in the Asturian mines. But the Galicians, like the inhabitants of western France, have realised that the occupations most suited to their country and climate are those connected with stock-breeding and pasturage. During the last few years, industry in Galicia has been very rapidly developed. The electric power generated (hydro-electric along the Sil and the Miño, thermo-electric elsewhere) has permitted the establishment around Corunna of a fully-fledged industrial area.

A fish-canning factory at Vigo, one of the most important of the many fishing ports in Galicia. Its canned goods are exported all over the world. SPANISH NATIONAL TOURIST OFFICE

ANDALUSIA

From the point of view of its economy and population Andalusia occupies quite an important place among the great units which make up Spain. It is true that the eight Andalusian provinces (about 33,700 square miles) amount in area only to 17.26 per cent of all Spain, but the Andalusian population (5,605,857 at the 1950 census) is 20 per cent of the whole, and the average density of population per square mile is somewhat greater than that for Spain taken as a whole (166 against 159). And Andalusia is rich. The province of Jaén has the highest income in the country after that of Valencia, and it is derived very largely from olive oil and its products. However, to enable us to appreciate Andalusia's wealth, there are other facts still more significant.

UNITY AND INDIVIDUALITY OF ANDALUSIA. First there are the great advantages due to geographical position. Andalusia is washed by two great seas, and is juxtaposed between two continents whose lines of communication it commands. Since prehistoric times, Andalusia has formed a link between civilisations — between Europe and Africa, between the Atlantic and the Mediterranean, between West and East. Later on, through Andalusian monopoly of American trade, the province became a meeting-place, a corridor, a mart shared by the Old World and the New.

Tarifa (36° N.) is the most southerly point of the European mainland, and Andalusia's geographical position secures for the land a mild climate. Frosts are unknown, as is the stifling heat of the tropics. Andalusia lies, in fact, within the zone of maximum vitality. It is true that the summers are very hot, even 'African' in the depression of the Guadalquivir, but, generally speaking, it can be said that the sun invigorates without desiccating, that the luminous, clear sky is cheering and stimulating, and that the Andalusian spring is an enchantment. The climate favours an extraordinary variety of plant life. In addition to the citrus fruits of the Mediterranean shore, subtropical crops flourish: sugar-cane (which 'freezes' at 34° F.), bananas, cherimoyers. Inland, owing to the altitude, it is rather cold in winter (40 days of frost at the Armilla airfield near Granada), but also brilliantly fine. Yet the violence of the winds, of the autumn squalls from the Mediterranean and of the Atlantic rain storms must not be under-estimated.

Provided that it gets water, the soil is remarkably fertile, and the alluvium of the rivers and deltas, or the black earth around Cadiz, is of very high quality. Stock-breeding is an additional source of wealth in the Andalusian plain. Many sheep (nearly 2,500,000 head) graze in the mountains and the pastures of the plains. Acorns in the oak-woods feed a great number of pigs; the Malaga and Granada goats are excellent, and the horses of the Guadalquivir stud-farms are famous. There is a number of celebrated *ganaderías* where fighting bulls are bred, the *toros de lidia*. It was at Ronda that the rules for the *corrida* were drawn up, and the passion of the Andalusian bull-fighting enthusiasts amounts almost to a religious cult. The ancient kingdom of Tartessus with its mineral wealth was the Eldorado of the ancient world, and Andalusian copper, lead, iron and mercury still form an essential part of the province's riches. Thus, the very name Andalusia evokes images of ease and prosperity.

Andalusia is, moreover, the most distinctly defined of all the great regions that make up Spain. From the Sierra Morena to the Strait of Gibraltar, Andalusia can be recognised at a glance. The Sierra Morena is a screen, a frontier, and the division from Castile is most striking. Andalusia is free from the continental influences that prevail in the interior of Spain, for the province spreads out between two seas and enjoys their humid breezes. These seas link Andalusia to the far-off lands of America as well as to the much nearer African shore.

The Cathedral and, to the left, the Giralda at Seville, in Andalusia. The Giralda was built in the twelfth century as a Moslem minaret, but was incorporated into the building of the cathedral in the fifteenth century. A hundred years later the belfry and the statue representing Faith which turns in the wind (hence the name Giralda) were added. This tower, with its mixed architecture and its changing fortunes, is symbolic of the religions and political history of Spain.
SPANISH NATIONAL TOURIST OFFICE

The air you breathe in Andalusia has already something in it that is not European.

AN ANCIENT SEAT OF CIVILISATION. The province of Andalusia is, without doubt, one of the most ancient, and in fact, most venerable seats of civilisation in western Europe. Andalusia has been inhabited from very remote times, and we have already mentioned that remains of Neanderthal Man have been found in caves at Gibraltar. During their voyages toward the West, Greek mariners got to know the rich realm of Tartessus (already highly civilised), for whose trade they had to contend first with Phoenicians and then with Carthaginians. The two centuries during which Andalusia was kept under Byzantine influence served to accentuate certain oriental features. On the other hand, Andalusia was completely absorbed into the Roman Empire. The native language soon faded away and left the field to a southern form of Latin. A number of monuments were so solidly constructed that they are still in use: the bridge at Cordova (Córdoba) and the Almuñecar aqueduct. The ruins of such splendid cities as Italic have been unearthed and certain of them (for example, Malaca) had exemplary municipal laws. The Emperors Trajan and Hadrian came from Baetica, as did Seneca. Christianity was preached in Andalusia from very early times.

Above: *St Mark's Cathedral and the Palace of the Doges, Venice.* EDWARD HOLMES

Opposite: *A Sicilian cart at Taormina; in the background Etna.* EDWARD HOLMES

In spite of this, from the eighth century A.D. onwards, no part of Spain received a deeper Moslem imprint, and it was in Andalusia that Islamic civilisation reached its peak. *Al Andalus* was the most brilliant centre of the medieval Moslem civilisation and together with art and thought went agricultural prosperity (the Guadalquivir mills offer an example) and active seaborne trade. The impetus was checked by the Christian Reconquest of the Guadalquivir basin. In 1248 Ferdinand III captured Seville. But Moslem Spanish civilisation lasted for a further two-and-a-half centuries in the mountainous realm of Granada. All the ancient travellers extolled its market-gardens, its trade and industry, and its wealth, of which a lasting memorial remains in the Alhambra.

In 1492 the Catholic Monarchs conquered the realm of Boabdil. The Moriscos' fierce revolt in 1568 was followed by a terrible repression. All the Moriscos were deported and their places taken by immigrant Castilians. It is to the Reconquest, then, that an economic event of prime importance is due. Andalusia was 'Castilianised'. Estates were granted to the conquerors, and these lands were the forerunners of today's *latifundia* and, to a certain extent, were the cause of Andalusia's agrarian problems. It was from the period of the 'Castilianisation' that the *campiñas* were converted into lands producing grain-crops and olives. This agricultural specialisation was accentuated as time went on, because of the necessity for providing food for the early settlers in the Americas, since the discovery of the New World was primarily an Andalusian enterprise. However, the commerce of the Indies, monopolised by Seville, transformed and enriched Andalusia, which was from the sixteenth century the first of the great Spanish regions to develop without reference to the lands of the Meseta. The riches that poured into Andalusia stimulated a magnificent artistic development which culminated in the 'Plateresque' style. The finest Andalusian buildings date from the sixteenth century, while the seventeenth was the golden age of Andalusian painting.

The eighteenth century was a time of stabilisation. The population increased and, concurrently, more and more land was taken up for cultivation and new industries made their appearance. Increasingly, cereals gave way to olives. The vineyards of Jerez and Málaga developed. Permission was at last granted for Cádiz to engage in overseas trade with the Indies. During the nineteenth century, mining began to occupy an important place in the Andalusian economy — lead, copper, coal and iron. Metallurgical works were built. The nineteenth century was the great period of the Andalusian economy.

But, from 1900, the effects of phylloxera on the vines and the drop in the output of the mines brought about a general decline. It is true that today deep-sea fishing and an increased demand for certain agricultural produce (sugar, oil, cotton) have brought back a degree of prosperity that is tending to increase. In fact, owing to the policy of systematic irrigation pursued by the *Confederaciones hidráulicas*, the development of virgin lands (such as the marshes of the lower Guadalquivir) by the *Instituto de Colonización*, and the establishment of electric power stations (first hydro-electric and now thermal), Andalusia is once more becoming the traditional land of opulence that it was for so long in the past.

The Andalusian regions

In the south, isolated by a continuous barrier of high mountains, lies Mediterranean Andalusia. To the east are high plains, dry and cold, constituting broad 'fossil' corridors between the mountains. This is the Andalusia of the steppes. Contrasting with it, there is, in the west, the Guadalquivir depression lying between the Sierra Morena and the Sub-Baetic range. This region must however be distinguished from that of Cádiz, which looks towards the Atlantic and Gibraltar, and then Intra-Baetic trough which leads to Granada.

ANDALUSIA OF THE GUADALQUIVIR. The 'classical' Andalusia, as it may be called, is made up for the most part of an ancient Tertiary arm of the sea between two ranges of mountains. To the north the Sierra Morena forms the edge of the Meseta. Except for charcoal burning and winter pasturage for Castilian sheep, mining offers most of the employment: lead at Linares and La Carolina, coal at Peñarroya-Bélmez, iron at Constantina, pyrites at Huelva, copper at Rio Tinto and Tharsis. In quite recent times the thalwegs have been sunk under artificial lakes formed behind great hydro-electric dams, while immense cement-lined canals distribute the irrigation waters over the *campiñas*.

To the south the Sub-Baetic ranges (6,905 feet in the Magina) rise blue against the horizon of Mediterranean haze. They consist for the most part of limestone and are much folded. Owing to plentiful springs of the Vaucluse type, cereal crops and olive-trees support a fairly dense population in the marly basins.

The central plain, through which flows the 'Great River', lies very low (at Seville, 75 miles from the sea, the altitude

The harbour and arena of Málaga. GILLES DE LA MOTTE ROUGE

Ronda (Andalusia) at 2,500 feet, on the edge of a sheer rocky plateau whose 650-foot walls look like colossal ramparts. G. VIOLLON

Montoro, on the Guadalquivir above Cordova (Andalusia). The houses in the town are closely packed along the left bank of the 'Great River' which runs right through Andalusia. Like most Spanish rivers, the level of the Guadalquivir varies greatly according to season, and this is shown by marks on the banks. In the background are hills covered with olive-groves, common throughout the region. SPANISH NATIONAL TOURIST OFFICE

is only 29.5 feet), and is thus very hot and hazy. In ancient times the *Betis* (Guadalquivir), like the Rhône, flowed into a lake, the *Lacus Ligustinus*, which has long since been filled in by the delta's alluvial soil and now forms the Marismas which, quite recently, have been brought under cultivation. The soil of the *campiña*, which in natural conditions is dry, is being transformed by new irrigation works. Already there is a visible increase in the area of olive-groves and even of wheatfields. This rich Baetica is, however, inhabited by poor Andalusians. The system of large estates, due at once to the necessity for settling and colonising empty areas and to the mode of farming adopted, is most favourable to the peasants, who are nothing but day labourers.

The two capital cities of the plain are Cordova (Córdoba) and Seville (Sevilla). The former was for long embalmed in its Roman and Moslem past and oppressed by its hot climate. Today the silent squares, the patios and the alleys covered with awnings bear witness to this past. However, Cordova is today spreading out into new industrial districts near the railway-station. Seville, on the other hand, is a metropolis,

lying in a meander of its river, which is yellow with alluvial mud. The city is round, compressed, white and cut through with streets whose twists and turns afford some shelter from the heat. The older districts, especially Santa Cruz, are fascinating. Seville is lively and gay, the city of Don Juan, of processions, of the Feria, of tourists. On the quayside, the Torre del Oro is a reminder of trade with the Indies, while the Triana suburb is becoming more and more industrialised, and the port could well be extended.

Westward, facing the Atlantic, the *campiñas* end in a rather low plain which has, to a large extent, been made more salubrious by the planting of vineyards and of eucalyptus. Here the sea has broadened the river estuaries; hence such fine ports as Huelva on the Odiel and Ayamonte on the Guadiana. But these estuaries are silting up, and the Palos creek, from which Columbus's caravels set sail, is choked. The virgin soils are being brought under cultivation by settlers in new villages, who work on a co-operative plan. The Jerez vineyards, however, still maintain their position as the foundation of one of the most famous and important enterprises in all Spain.

The Rock of Gibraltar, from the sea. Gibraltar is a ridge of Jurassic limestone and its 1,400-foot faulted wall rises vertical at the 8-mile strait between Spain and Morocco. The Rock controls traffic between the Mediterranean and the Atlantic. J. ALLAN CASH

A typical street of Seville, with its narrow passageways, window boxes and barred windows. SPANISH NATIONAL TOURIST OFFICE

The magnificent carving and gardens at the Generalife, one of the palaces of the Sultans at Granada. SPANISH NATIONAL TOURIST OFFICE

CADIZ AND THE STRAIT OF GIBRALTAR. In this region, which has a more Atlantic character, the abundant rains, the mists and the winds favour the growth on a rather poor sandstone soil of a vegetation typical of treeless moors, though the countryside is dotted with dwarf palms (*palmitos*), and so gives one a foretaste of the Moroccan *Gharb*. The mountains, which are more sheltered, alone have trees, mainly fine cork-oaks which are regularly stripped for their bark. The port of Cádiz, founded by Phoenicians and later ruined by English privateers, lived through its golden age in the eighteenth and nineteenth centuries when commerce was active with the American colonies and the Philippines. In quite recent years a free port has been established at Cádiz, and it is hoped that it will become a base for Spanish and American communications both by sea and air. The climate of Cádiz is tempered by the sea air, which makes the town an agreeable place of residence, though it is overcrowded in summer.

The Cádiz area derives also, from its position on the Strait of Gibraltar, a world-wide importance. The strait (at one point no more than eight miles wide) is a no more a barrier than a river. The passage is thus inter-continental: birds cross it during their migrations; men, for thirty centuries past, have crossed it in both directions. In this region, too, full of historical memories, the fate of the Old World has more than once been determined. The geographical importance is not less than the historical. Algeciras, Ceuta and Tangier control the north-south traffic, but it is Gibraltar that keeps watch over the east-west movements. The historic rock, a spur of Jurassic limestone, rises up from the Mediterranean as an impressive, steep and faulted wall (1,396 feet), while a sandy spit of land, with the airfield and hutments, joins the Rock to the mainland.

Mount Calpe was occupied by man in prehistoric times and was one of the ancient Pillars of Hercules. The Spaniards reconquered it from the Moors in the fifteenth century, and lost it to the British in 1704. Since the Treaty of Utrecht (1713) Gibraltar has been a British colony. It has been turned into a formidable fortress and the defensive works have been constantly strengthened. In these days of submarines and aircraft, however, it is no longer the 'key' that shuts the Mediterranean. It is nevertheless improbable that the United Kingdom will yield to Spanish demands for Gibraltar's return to Spain, since the Rock is an important commercial port of call. Gibraltar is a cosmopolitan place, serving as an intermediary for the products both of the West and the East, which are eventually distributed, legally or otherwise, in Spain and Africa. Since the reforms of 1952 this Crown Colony has been on its way to self-government.

MEDITERRANEAN ANDALUSIA. From Gibraltar to Cape de Gata, along the warm shores of the Mediterranean stretches another and distinctive Andalusia. It is isolated by an almost uninterrupted barrier of high mountains: to the north, the Sierra Nevada with the highest peaks in Spain (Mulhacen, 11,420 feet and Veleta, 11,155 feet); to the west, the Serranía of Ronda which is lower (6,271 feet), but very wet and even snowy. There are few passages through this lofty and deserted mountain barrier, and they are difficult. The Málaga highway drops down in hairpin bends from an altitude of over 3,000 feet to the city. The Almería railway was electrified as long ago as 1911, and the Málaga line (built in 1865) is a marvel of engineering skill. But, though Mediterranean Andalusia is isolated on the land side, it benefits from its position on the inland sea. The province has, indeed, always enjoyed easy maritime communications with the rest of the world, so the trade of this part of Andalusia has thrived since Phoenician times. The large towns, Almería and Málaga, are fishing-ports as much as trading ports. Almería was founded in the ninth century, on the shore of the open sea, so as to take the place of the Roman Urci, which had been silted up

by the alluvial matter brought down by its river. Almería was a very busy port in the eleventh and twelfth centuries and there the Moslems set up a splendid fortress. Today Almería's exports are mostly lead and iron from the mines, table grapes and fish. Málaga (283,000 inhabitants) is of Phoenician origin, and later became the principal commercial city of the kingdom of Granada. It has maintained its position as a busy trading town with exports of wines, raisins, other fruits and industrial products and it is also a port of call for several shipping-lines on the east-west route and the home port of quite a large fishing-fleet. Since the war the town has become more and more a tourist resort and has thus added appreciably to its income.

Mediterranean Andalusia enjoys an almost ideal and sheltered climate. Frost is unknown; thus on the well-watered estuaries crops of West Indian character are grown: sugar-cane, bananas and cherimoyers. In the sheltered valleys citrus and early fruits do very well. In the mountains also, especially in the southward-looking high valleys of the Sierra Nevada, the Alpujarras, that for so long remained mysterious and almost unknown, the slopes are cut into terraces which are irrigated and cultivated. At Almería itself, in fact, a closely-planted and dark-coloured strip of cultivated land running between the pink and white mineral slopes of the mountains reminds one rather of Egypt.

Mediterranean Andalusia is self-supporting. The large, ancient villages shine out white against a green background of growing crops. The population is quite large, and the density is as much as 272 to the square mile in the province of Málaga. The economy is varied, well-established and prosperous. Social conditions are less unsatisfactory than by the Guadalquivir, and small landowners are numerous. Nevertheless, since today it is difficult to live in a closed economy, the whole region is a little backward. In order to develop fully the land must participate in an expanding world economy.

THE INTRA-BAETIC TROUGH. An elongated and more or less continuous structural depression, rather like the Alpine trough in the French Alps, drives its way between the northern mountain barrier of Mediterranean Andalusia and the Sub-Baetic ranges.

Granada is the capital of this region and owes its importance to its communications with regions far away over the mountains. Granada was once the seat of a Court, its craftsmen produced articles of luxury, and the town possessed the most magnificent of Moslem palaces. Today the old Moslem town, with its palaces, its gardens and its villas, seems to doze rather on its conical hills of red alluvium, but down below, on the edge of the Vega, is the Christian city, where the bodies of the Catholic monarchs lie behind magnificent wrought-iron gates in the cathedral. This is a city that throbs with modern industrial life.

To the east of Granada stretches the driest region in all Spain, a region where the rainfall is in places less than eight inches a year. The intermittent nature of the rains has led to the formation of the most stupendous landscape of badlands in Europe, or perhaps in any of the Mediterranean countries. Because of its considerable altitude (almost everywhere more than 3,000 feet), it is a region of extremes of temperature. Most of the landscape is of steppe-like appearance, and only the valley of the Almanzora, which lies lower and is irrigated, produces some citrus fruits and has some vineyards. The whole area is sparsely populated, and during the centuries of Spanish Islam it was a sort of eastern March of the kingdom of Granada, giving on to the Christian frontier, so that the region was frequently overrun by raiders from either side.

There are few towns, and those which do exist are small and set on the edge of shrunken *vegas* (upland irrigated areas); such are Baza and Guadix, with its *cuevas* or troglodytic dwellings cut out of the soft rock. There are similar caves

The different phases of a corrida, or bullfight, in Spain: the 'Corral'.
The sport forms part of the country's cultural heritage.
H. HOLMES, CAMERA PRESS

Entry into the arena of the 'cuadrilla'. The arenas are modelled
after the amphitheatres of Rome, and these plazas are found in all
the major cities of Spain. DR MARTY

A pass with the cape. DR MARTY

The picador. GEORGES VIOLLON

Pass with the muleta. GEORGES VIOLLON

Planting the banderillas. T. E. PRATT, CAMERA PRESS

The kill. H. CARTIER-BRESSON, MAGNUM-PHOTO

Removal of the dead bull from the arena. GIGLI, RAPHO

Harvesting oranges.   YAN, RAPHO

A gipsy dancer at Granada.   ROGER VIOLLET

In the Canary Islands: young Guanche girls carrying water.   ROGER VIOLLET

Bodegas at Puerto de Santa Maria, near Cadiz.
SPANISH NATIONAL TOURIST OFFICE

Bottling sherry at Jerez. Sherry is an important export: its chief destinations are Great Britain and the U.S.A.   J. ALLAN CASH

Andalusian carts used for agricultural work. These carts are drawn by a pair of oxen, and are similar to those in other Mediterranean countries where, however, two-wheeled vehicles are much more common than four-wheeled ones.   P. ALMASY

Farmers on their way to dig in cotton fields near Cordova.
BELZEAUX, RAPHO

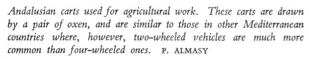

elsewhere, it is true, but nowhere are they so numerous as at Guadix or set in a landscape more wild, more austere and romantic. After the conquest of Granada, the Marqués de Mendoza built a fortress upon the limestone crag of Lacalahorra, near the Alquife iron-mines. Inside was the first Renaissance palace to be built in Spain (1509), and it makes a striking contrast to the immense, icy, desolate steppe of Mendoza's *marquesado del Cenete.*

INDIVIDUAL CHARACTER OF ANDALUSIA. Many

traditional of Andalusia have been preserved and form an integral part of life there today. Such are the dances to the sound of clicking castanets and *taconeo* (stamping with the heels); and local costume: spotted dresses and tall combs for the women and wide-brimmed sombreros, tight-fitting jackets and leather breeches for the men. Religious festivals, in particular processions during Holy Week, are even more elaborate than elsewhere in Spain; the whole population participates, too, in the springtime *ferias*, which were originally cattle-markets. Finally, there are the bullfights, for bulls have been bred in Andalusia since the time of Hercules' labours against Geryon and there is hardly an Andalusian who is not an *aficionado.*

Andalusian art should not be dubbed *flamenco* or *gitano*, since the Flemings came in only with Charles V and there were no gypsies in Spain before the fifteenth century. The special character of Andalusian art can, indeed, be traced much farther back. Although Andalusian houses have Roman patios, and although wrought-iron gates and railings, as well as manners and customs, owe something to Islam, the foundations of Andalusian civilisation are pre-Roman. The inhabitants of the country, moreover, are not Iberians but Tartessians. The original, ancient foundation has absorbed all the influences from abroad. There is no more anciently civilised people in Europe than the Andalusian. Thus we can distinguish a special Andalusian type — lively, gay, intelligent, full of grace and elegance, but lazy, without care for the morrow, poor and proud, mystical but not ascetic, and taken as a whole individualist to the highest degree.

Two metropolitan provinces, extensions of Andalusia: The Canary Islands

Before they conquered America and stamped their imprint upon it, the Andalusians settled in the Canary Islands and in Africa.

The Canaries make up an archipelago of seven islands: Lanzarote, Fuerteventura, Gran Canaria, Tenerife, Gomera, La Palma and Hierro, with a total area of 2,804 square miles.

The islands' most striking feature is that they are very mountainous, of very broken relief and scored with ravines. The mountains are almost exclusively of volcanic origin, and there have been eruptions in historic times (La Palma in 1951). Therefore the outlines are almost intact — they are either of cones (the Teide on Tenerife, 12,332 feet), of *calderas* (La Palma), of shattered craters (Hierro is the quarter of a crater open on the north-west), or of lava-streams called *mal país.* There are mysterious phenomena such as the 'Mountain of Fire' on Lanzarote which has been burning ever since the eighteenth century and which it is now proposed to utilise as a source of energy. These Canaries' volcanoes are sometimes claimed to be remains of Atlantis, but it is more probable that the Canaries' orogenesis is an extension of that of the Atlas Mountains. Thus, the Canaries are African, and a submarine ledge links them with the African shore to the east, from which they are only 57 miles distant. The influence of the Sahara is noticeable in the eastern Canaries, where locusts are a plague

Above: *Terraced fields in the Orotava Valley, Tenerife, one of the Canary Islands. In the distance is the snow-capped peak of Teide (12,192 ft.). The mildness and equability of the oceanic climate in the latitude of the Canaries (south of the Tropic of Cancer, between 15° and 18° N.) favours the cultivation of delicate plants in sheltered valleys: bananas, citrus fruits, tomatoes, tobacco.* Below: *Lemon groves near Valencia.* J. ALLAN CASH and SPANISH NATIONAL TOURIST OFFICE

and where camels are used as beasts of burden; the trade-winds bring very dry weather. The original islanders were also African: the Guanches were Berbers, and their curious manners and customs included mummification of the dead and a 'whistling language' in the mountains.

After the failure of an attempt at colonisation made by the Norman Sire de Béthancourt at the beginning of the fifteenth century, the islands were annexed by Castile and peopled with Andalusians, so that the Canaries became, to all intents and purposes, a part of Andalusia, from whose shores they are no more than about 620 miles distant.

However, the Canaries lie some distance out in the Atlantic, and the meridian of 'Iron Island' (Hierro) was for long the most westerly in the known world. The mildness and the oceanic equability of the temperature (varying between 62° and 70° F.) permit the cultivation not only of wheat and barley on the heights and vines on the volcanic soil, but also of more delicate crops in the sheltered valleys: Canary bananas, citrus fruits, tomatoes, early potatoes, and tobacco. On festival days the streets are covered with closely packed carpets of flowers. The Orotava valley is a little paradise, while higher up are forests of 'Canary pines'. The fish catch in the 'cold current' is by no means negligible.

Atlantic steamship lines call regularly at the islands; Las Palmas and Santa Cruz are international ports and fuel oil is produced by the Santa Cruz refineries. Although the archipelago is fairly prosperous, the islands have a relatively small population — about 890,000 persons. The Canaries make up two provinces of metropolitan Spain.

EASTERN SPAIN

In no part of the country is the difference between central Spain and the surrounding provinces more marked than in the east. Andalusia and Northern Spain, although different from Castile, are closely linked with it, and there is a reciprocal exchange of what may be called 'surplus vitality'. Between these provinces, despite natural barriers, economic ties are strong; there is a continuity in ways of life and in the peoples themselves; and there are, on the human plane, affinities of sentiments and feelings. But on the eastern Marches of the Meseta we meet with quite another Spain.

Yet these lands of the east are not really isolated. Between them and central Spain, there is no equivalent of the Cantabrian range or of the Sierra Morena. Although the coastal plains of the Spanish Levant are bounded on the west by a line of fairly close mountains (which, in the Sierra de Javalambre exceed 6,500 feet in height), the edge of the Castilian high plateau of the Mancha, which hangs like a balcony over Valencia, is really a flight of steps and not a mountain-wall. Neither the highway nor the railroad (the new direct Valencia-Madrid line via Utiel and Cuenca) has much difficulty in ascending to the plateau. In the Murcia region it is true that the breadth of the desolate mountain chains (from 35 to 50 miles) might constitute an effective barrier and act indeed as a sort of isolating 'March', but it is just in the Murcia area that the difference between the Spanish Levant and the rest of the country is the least marked. Therefore this difference cannot be imputed solely to the surface relief.

Can we say, then, that it is climate which gives eastern Spain its highly peculiar character? Admittedly the Mediterranean influence is very marked, yet such influence is not confined to eastern Spain but spreads over the greater part of the Centre; the climatic rhythm, sub-desertic in summer and rainy only in the cool season, is the same in both these parts of the country. Heavy rain is exceptional, and what is most lacking is water. The region between Cartagena and Almería has the lowest annual rainfall in Europe (7½ inches); in 1917 under an inch of rain fell, and generally from June to September the rain can be counted by hours, not by days. For the Moslems Murcia was a serene, azure realm and nowhere, despite the *calina*, is the atmosphere so limpid, the wind more soft, or the sky so blue.

HUERTAS AND IRRIGATION. Eastern Spain is above all the land of early vegetables and fruits. The plains bear the significant name of *huertas*, derived from the Latin *hortus*, a garden. Boat-loads and lorry-loads of vegetables and early fruits leave the Levant for northern Europe. The export of oranges (790,000 tons out of a total of 880,000 tons for all Spain come from the eastern provinces) was for long one of the favourable factors in the Spanish trade balance.

But drought offsets the beneficent effects of the warmth. The vegetation has adapted itself to the climate and takes a summer rest. In these conditions there can be no profitable agriculture without irrigation. The contrast between cultivated land that has to rely on rain alone (*secano*) and land which is irrigated (*regadío*) is marked throughout Spain, but the contrast is greater than ever in the Spanish Levant. Irrigation is regulated by a complicated, delicate and perfected system which goes back not, as is often said, to the Moors but to much more

The port of Alicante, in eastern Spain, on the Mediterranean. Alicante is sheltered by the hill on which the fort of Santa Barbara stands, and has such an even, mild climate that it has become a winter resort. The sheltered port is constantly growing in importance. ROGER VIOLLET

Plaza del Caudillo, at Valencia, the third largest city of Spain and an important industrial and commercial centre. ROGER VIOLLET

ancient times, those of the Romans at least, since use is still made of the engineering works (aqueducts, canals, etc.) constructed in the days of Roman Spain. In their present form, rules the rules relating to the utilisation of the waters date back to the epoch of the medieval Reconquest. The methods employed always depend, of course, on the amount of water available. Where the watercourses are sufficiently fed by rains and still contain water, as in Catalonia and in Valencia (the average rainfall in Barcelona is about 22¾ in.; in Gerona, about 30½ in.; in Valencia 16¼ in.), the riverwaters are usually just tapped by the irrigation canals (*acequias*), and it is not often that any limit is put upon the amount of water that may be utilised. But farther south at Alicante and Murcia where the rain is much scarcer (Alicante, about 14¼ in.; Los Alcazares

just over 11¼ in.), huge *pantanos* or dam-reservoirs have been constructed to retain supplies, and from them water for irrigation can be distributed.

Water, however, remains a rare and precious commodity. The door-to-door water-seller with his *cántaros* is a common sight. At Lorca water left over after irrigation is sold by auction. In the porch of Valencia Cathedral, every Thursday, there is the meeting of the 'Water Tribunal' composed of simple peasants who pass sentence in cases of breach of the water-distribution code. There is no appeal from the court's findings.

However, we should not be misled by the region's present-day hum of activity. The specialisation which has been the main factor in making agriculture more prosperous did not begin until rapid transport made possible the expeditious export of

EASTERN SPAIN: *The Levants, Catalonia. 1. Pyrenean agriculture under Atlantic influence: maize, potatoes, apples; 2. Pyrenean agriculture under Atlantic influence passing into natural or artificial prairie; 3. Mixed-crop farming on unirrigated land (secano): wheat, vines, olives; 4. Irrigated area or regadío (huertas, vegas): Market-gardens and fruit-growing; 5. Steppe of* paramos *(areas of sedimentary soil of horizontal structure) of the sierras; 6. Poor pasture-land and scrub: pig, sheep and goat-rearing; 7. Sugar-beet; 8. Rice; 9. Cotton; 10. Vines; 11. Iron-smelting; 12. Textiles; 13. Chemical industry; 14. Canals and irrigation dams; 15. Railways; 17. Hydro-electric power stations; 17. Power stations; 18. Coal; 19. Lignite; 20. Iron; 21. Lead and zinc; 22. Factories for processing non-ferrous metals; 23. Petrol refinery.*

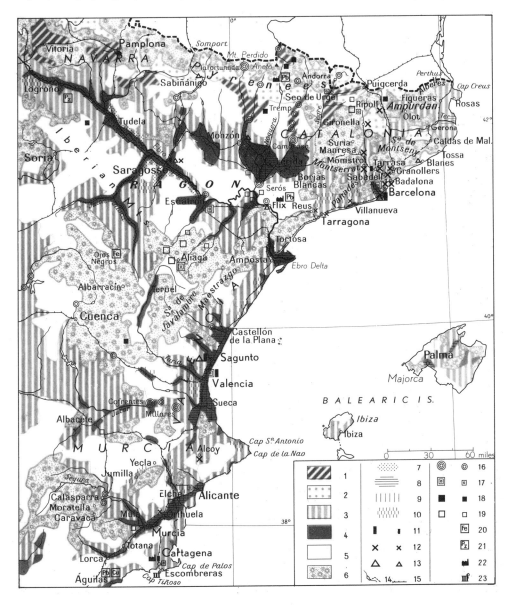

such delicate produce as fruits and early vegetables. Before that time, the Mediterranean areas of Spain differed from those of the interior only by a still more grinding poverty. But during the last half-century the increase in the number of *pantanos* has permitted a rapid extension in the acreage of rice-fields and *huertas*.

THE ATTRACTION OF OTHER LANDS. The Spanish Levant lands lie wide open to the shinning sea which is, from north to south for a distance of 750 miles, a sort of common denominator for them. As we saw at the beginning of this chapter, it was from the Mediterranean that civilisation came to these lands, and oriental influences were felt throughout the Middle Ages. For some time the Byzantines were the lords of the southern part of the Spanish Levant and, then again, Islam has here, more even than in Andalusia, left traces in manners and customs and place-names. No other region of Spain has been subjected more to the attraction of the Mediterranean and the East. For this reason, the narrow coastal plains, peopled by Iberians and lying at the foot of the huge central plateau, have turned their back on the higher lands.

Again, the Reconquest in the Levant followed a peculiar pattern. It began in the eastern Pyrenees and was independently conducted from the Carolingian *Marca Hispanica* which was the forerunner of Catalonia. There it was that eastern Latin changed into Catalan, of which the Valencian and Balearic dialects are variants, for it was men of Catalan speech who reconquered Valencia and Alicante as well as the Balearic islands. Murcia, on the other hand, was reconquered by Castilians, and the Murcian dialect, the *Panocho*, is not Catalan. Nevertheless, Murcia, by its natural features and its economic structure, must be counted as part of the Spanish Levant. With this one exception of Murcia, all the eastern Spanish region has its own peculiar language.

Another special point is that, with the exception of Murcia, these eastern provinces were part of the Kingdom of Aragon, whose focal point was not Saragossa but Valencia. The Crown of Aragon derived its strength not from its possessions on land, but from its overseas trade. From all over the Mediterranean came merchandise and slaves to fill the Aragonese ports to overflowing. The better to protect and further this Mediterranean trade, the administrative headquarters was for a time transferred to the Balearics: so arose the kingdom of Majorca (1260—1343), a real thalassocracy.

At the beginning of the sixteenth century, however, decline set in. The discovery of America switched the focus of world communications to the Atlantic. The Mediterranean, too, had become dangerous, for it was infested by Barbary pirates who were aided by Moriscos who had remained in Spain. Commerce on a large scale deserted the Inland Sea, but such commerce was all that allowed eastern Spain to prosper and grow rich, since the population was never large enough to grow wealthy in any other way (at the end of the fifteenth century there were only a million inhabitants in the realm of Aragon against nine million in Castile). It was not until 1869, when the Suez Canal was opened, that large-scale trade started up again on the Levant shores. Catalonia was the first to benefit, then came Valencia, and lastly Murcia. The population increased rapidly so that by the twentieth century Catalonia and the Spanish Levant had assumed a leading place in Spanish economy and politics.

Dependence upon the fluctuating fortunes of the Mediterranean is one of the essential characteristics of eastern Spain, since it has been this dependence, far more than nature itself, which has been responsible for the moral and social isolation of these regions. All the same, if the destinies of eastern Spain are thus 'orientated', they are not so everywhere to the same degree. From the point of view of landscape, of human reactions and of economy, we should distinguish between the Levants, Catalonia and the Balearics. We shall, then, deal with them separately.

The Levants

The Spanish Levant stretches from the Ebro to the neighbourhood of Almería, a distance of over 300 miles. General conditions are more or less the same, or at least are comparable everywhere: a coastal situation; steep mountains down which rush wild torrents whose deposits and sediments have served, in part, to form the narrow coastal plains which are divided into segments; a dry climate, but one that is offset by irrigation and whose mildness permits an uninterrupted succession of all sorts of crops, mostly intended for export. Hence the sea-borne traffic, the industries, the dense population that covers the plains, in marked contrast to the almost deserted mountains. Valencia, in fact, is the province with the highest per capita income.

Local customs and costume linger: the flower-embroidered dresses and shawls of the Valencian women, the broad white breeches which stop at the knees, the *zaragüelles*, no doubt descendants of the baggy, Moorish trousers (the *jarwal*) of the Valencian and Murcian men. Then there is the *jota*, a dance that is by origin Valencian. In such a burning climate refreshments had to be invented — the Valencian ices. This is also the original home of the *horchata de chufa*, an iced white orgeat obtained by the maceration of the *chufa* or *suchet*, a little tuber. It is a drink the Valencians have made popular throughout Spain. The warmth of the climate accounts for the late hours kept and for the night-watchmen in the streets. And there is a most pronounced taste for festivals, always out of doors: combats between Moors and Christians at Alcoy, St John's fires at Alicante, and, above all, the *fallas*, those satirical manikins that are made and burned at Valencia on St Joseph's day.

THE THREE LEVANTS. The Levantine façade is, however, too long and too diversified to deal with as a single unit. There are, in fact, three Levants: that of Murcia, that of Alicante and that of Valencia.

In the south extends the Murcian Levant which is a province of Castilian speech. It can be further subdivided into a plain and two parallel mountain ranges. The mountains of the coast are completely bare and impoverished, rich only in mines. Those of the interior enclose fairly large basins which are populated and have small local capitals with 10,000 to 25,000 inhabitants. Between these two mountain zones runs a long corridor which the River Segura reaches a little before Murcia. This is an intensively cultivated area. It is, in fact, one continuous *huerta* where all sorts of early fruits and vegetables grow, from oranges to pimentos. Lemon-growing is a speciality, and the *huerta* produces more lemons than any other part of Spain. This corridor is also a route for road and rail communications, and is dotted with towns (Lorca, Orihuela). As for Murcia itself, despite its 220,000 inhabitants it is really an overgrown village. From the top of the cathedral tower you can see the urban area tail off into the *huerta* and become no more than a sprinkling of white dwellings, many of which are still built of dried mud (*adobe*). By contrast, Cartagena, on the coast, with fewer inhabitants than Murcia, is more urban. Petroleum products come by sea and are refined at Escombreras, where one of the most modern thermic power-stations in Spain has recently been set up.

The Alicante Levant is dustier and drier, since it has no large river to water it. A succession of limestone ridges borders a number of narrow, parallel valleys. On the summits are perched castles or picturesque villages, while little industrial towns huddle in the valleys themselves. This whole complex of mountain folding terminates magnificently at the great capes of San Antonio and La Nao and in huge cliffs, often dropping sheer to the sea. The most spectacular cliff is at Calpe, the Peñón of Ifach. The sheltered climate and the sunshine account for the numerous orchards covering thousands of miles

General view of Peñiscola, on a precipitous rock 210 feet high overlooking the Mediterranean near Valencia. Peñiscola is overshadowed by its castle, built by the Templars, and is joined to the mainland by a narrow spit of sand. It was once the residence of an Aragonese antipope. RENÉ FERLET

Gerona, an ancient city in Catalonia, on a hillock protected by the Oñar, a tributary of the Ter. Washing is hanging out to dry on the overhanging balconies of these old houses. ROGER VIOLLET

of terraces supported by dry-course stone walls. In addition to the olives and figs, there are vines, from which the Alicante wines are made and whose grapes provide the raisins of Denia. The almond-trees on the rocky soil yield a fruit which is crushed with honey gathered from the wild flowers to produce the *turrón* sweetmeats that are a speciality of Alicante. At Elche, a factory town which manufactures sandals, the palm-trees form forestgardens, the only places throughout Europe where dates ripen. For the summer visitors there are fine bathing-beaches. Alicante, sheltered by its Santa Bárbara rock and well exposed to the sun, has such a uniformly mild climate (winter mean, 52° F.) that it has become a winter resort, while the port, which is particularly safe, continues to grow.

The Valencian Levant is Valencia's rich plain, bordered to the west by a semicircle of arid and sparsely peopled mountains. Rice cultivation, introduced about the thirteenth century, was for long a means of purifying and improving the soil. Today the output of rice alone is sufficient to make up for the shortage of wheat. The Valencian *paella* has become an almost national dish. Rice cultivation is now carried out on a large scale, so that the province of Valencia alone provides half the total rice crop of Spain.

On either side of the rice-growing area the soil has been longer established and is rich enough to support other crops: around Valencia early fruits and vegetables and, as far as Benicasim and Gandía, oranges. Unfortunately, the slump in exports led to the uprooting of thousands of orange-trees, while the severe frosts in the winter of 1956 also did much damage to the orangegroves. However, the oranges make up a quarter of the total value of Spanish exports.

The province of Valencia has a population of 1,424,000 and takes third place for number of inhabitants among the Spanish provinces. The average is 324 persons to the square mile, but in the low-lying lands the figure in some places exceeds 1,000, which is comparable with that on Asiatic deltas or in the valley of the Nile.

Valencia, with 522,000 inhabitants, is the third largest city of Spain. It has the narrow, zigzagging streets of Moorish quarters, and a few fine buildings, of which the most admirable is the Lonja (fifteenth century), bear witness to the ancient prosperity of the town's trade and of the silk industry. Valencia has grown much of recent years (the population was no more than 154,000 in 1906) and extensive new districts have sprung up. A veritable urban spider's web is being woven for the industries depending upon Aragonese iron brought to the blast-furnaces of Sagunto, the shipyards and new buildings, the chemical industry necessary for agriculture, and the construction of new railways to Madrid, Aragon and Santander. A town-planning scheme has already been drawn up that looks as far ahead as the year 2,000! For the Valencians hope that by then theirs will be the leading city on the Mediterranean — and they have some justification for their hopes.

Catalonia

Catalonia is composed of the four provinces of Lérida, Tarragona, Barcelona and Gerona. It has just under 3,250,000 inhabitants, of whom 1,446,000 live in Barcelona itself. Most of the area has poor soil, and the Catalans have always found the source of their fortunes abroad: for more than a century the rest of Spain was one great market for the industrial products of Catalonia. Today, however, Catalonia has to face both home and foreign competition.

The Sierra and Monastery of Montserrat, high above the Catalonian lowlands, to the north-east of Barcelona. J. ALLAN CASH

Catalonia is less easy to define as a geographical unit than as an ethnic one, for the country is not geographically an entity, since it has spread out beyond its natural framework, from the Pyrenees to the sea, and in the Middle Ages part of the Ebro basin was 'Catalanised'. Today, then, the country extends over two mountainchains forming a V: the Pyrenees, which run from west to east, and the Catalan Coast Range bordering on the Mediterranean coastline and running south-west to north-east. These chains enclose the plains of what we may call 'inland Catalonia', and they meet at the sunken basin of the Ampurdán which is blocked by the Olot volcanoes.

FEATURES OF THE CATALAN COUNTRY. There is a Catalan country, physically as well as linguistically. In eastern Spain, Catalonia is distinguished from the Levant by a cooler climate and by vegetation that is thicker and of a darker green. From the summit of the Tibidabo, above Barcelona, the view is one of wave after wave of hills black with forest. Northward the picturesque Costa Brava offers the surprising vista of trees growing right down to the water's edge in the creeks. The Montseny (5,560 feet) is covered with beech and fir.

Contrary to conclusions which might be drawn from the permanently dry beds of the *ramblas*, Catalonia is a rainy country. Barcelona's average annual rainfall is about 23 inches; sea mists linger long in the mornings. But this humidity does not extend to the Lérida region in New Catalonia which, with an annual rainfall of $14\frac{1}{2}$ inches, shares the dryness of the Ebro valley and was a steppe before its nineteenth century transformation by irrigation.

The plentiful rainfall and the generally low altitude would favour Catalan farming if only the soil were better. But inland stretch huge areas of pudding-stone and conglomerates such as those that make up the picturesque serrations of the crests of the Montserrat, 'the saw-edged mountain', bearing nothing but sparse trees. The good soils of Catalonia are confined to the irrigated areas of the Ebro basin (Lérida, 13,600 acres of *huertas*; the Ampurdán 4,755 acres) and to the little coastal plains (Barcelona, 24,560 acres and Tarragona, 15,125 acres). But the Catalan earth is largely unproductive.

The Catalans have retained a certain number of customs which are peculiar to them. Corduroy clothes and sandals bound on by long laces are still common, but the red cap, the *barretina*, is now seen only at folklore festivals. In the national dance, the grave *sardana*, hundreds of couples meet on the village squares or in the broad avenues of Barcelona. This dance is not an expression of joy but of ritual tension. It is, so to speak, a manifestation of the sacred, almost mystical sentiment the Catalans feel for their country. Catalonia, more than any other Spanish region, keeps aloof from the rest, without which, however, it could not live.

The wealth of Catalonia varies a great deal from one region to another. Four natural regions can be distinguished: The Pyrenees, Inland Catalonia, the Catalan Coast Range, and Ampurdán.

CATALAN PYRENEES AND INLAND CATALONIA. The Catalan Pyrenees, in their western and well defined sector, that of the Nogueras, have been 'Catalanised' only recently. The Nogueras and the Segre, in cutting through the great limestone barriers, have formed extraordinarily deep valleys. In the centre the Conca de Tremp is a well-cultivated synclinal depression where two large artificial lakes furnish water both for irrigation and for hydro-electric current. Farther north lies the axial zone, here very broad and made up of ancient rocks on which are perched miserable villages whose poverty is extreme.

Farther eastward along the Segre, the Cerdaña, which is a sunken area, forms a gap which is still more marked since it is in a belt of low rainfall, and so we have the sunny skies and fruit trees of Puigcerda, now a summer resort, and a centre for winter sports at La Molina. From east to west stretches a small isolated Pyrenean area which has a history all its own, as is shown by the eminent dignity of the Bishop of La Seo de Urgel, who is co-prince of Andorra and spiritual chief of a tiny diocese whose capital is a mountain town with a massive Romanesque church. Still farther on, the real Catalan Pyrenees begin. They are not much more than thin folds of ancient rocks. In the Albères the chain narrows still more and dips as low as 950 feet at the Perthus, the lowest of all the Pyrenean passes, and one that has been used from very ancient times. Then the mountain chain rises again to a height of nearly 4,000 feet before being lost in the Mediterranean at Cape Creus and at Cadaqués.

Inland Catalonia spreads out in a triangle between the Pyrenees, the Ebro and the Catalan Coast Range. The land suffers much from drought, and so formerly bore only meagre crops. But a great irrigation scheme carried out in the nineteenth century transformed these Urgel steppes into a rich area bearing a variety of crops. Not only does the valley of the Segre, now have plentiful vegetation downstream from Balaguer but even the interior of the country, the region of Borjas Blancas, is thickly planted with olive-trees yielding a high quality oil. New channels are being constructed in order to bring the areas on the right bank of the Segre under cultivation, but the soil contains much salt, and to begin with rice-fields are being laid out. Lérida, an ancient Iberian outpost, looks down from the top of its hill crowned by a huge Romanesque-Gothic cathedral on this new landscape of agricultural activity.

CATALAN COAST RANGE AND AMPURDÁN.

The Catalan Coast Range forms, from the Ebro to Ampurdán, a narrow and complex mountainous region. The interior *sierras* reach a height of 5,500 feet at Montseny. The coastal *sierras* are lower, rarely reching more than 2,000 feet, and are wooded with pine and cork-oak. This is the *selva* or *garrotxa* — the 'maquis'. Where this range borders directly on the sea it forms what is known as the *Costa Brava* (Wild Coast), now much frequented by summer visitors and by painters. Tossa attracts the most visitors. A narrow fringe of little coastal plains is devoted to the growing of delicate plants, including carnations, and is part of a zone which from Barcelona to Blanes bears the name of *Costa de Levante* or *Maresma*. It is covered with an uninterrupted string of villages and small towns, some of them industrialised.

A longitudinal depression runs between the coastal and the inland *sierras*. This interior, low-lying strip begins at Gerona, whose monuments of many different epochs indicate its former importance, passes through Caldas de Malavella, and then, to the south-west, broadens out into the Valles, whose capital is Granollers. Beyond the line of the Llobregat river, the depression becomes the Panadés (Villafranca del Panadés).

The most important areas in the Catalan Coast Range are the gaps made by the rivers. The Ebro cuts through to the south. At Tortosa the river turns towards the sea and irrigates fine terraced *vegas*. After Amposta, the Ebro spreads out into an enormous delta whose long spits shelter lagoons. This delta, which is more land than sea, has been transformed into an immense rice-field that makes the province of Tarragona the second rice-producing region of Spain.

Farther to the east, entirely cultivated and covered with almond and hazelnut trees, is the Campo de Tarragona. There once stood *Tarraco*, the capital of Roman *Hispania's* largest province. The medieval cathedral is magnificent. At the present day Tarragona is a commercial city whose volume of trade is still small, but the port has been greatly improved and is a United States naval base. Still farther east and towards the interior are the busy cotton spinning and weaving mills

The steep rocky coast of the Costa Brava, where the trees sweep down almost to the sea. This granite coast extends as far as the French frontier and, since the war, has become a popular resort, particularly with the British. SPANISH NATIONAL TOURIST OFFICE

A small boy watering his mule outside the massive pre-Roman walls of Tarragona. The city was founded in the first century B.C.
SPANISH NATIONAL TOURIST OFFICE

Dramatic rock formations at Ordesa, in the Pyrenees.
SPANISH NATIONAL TOURIST OFFICE

Flower stalls on the Ramblas, a favourite place for an evening stroll for the citizens of Barcelona. SPANISH NATIONAL TOURIST OFFICE

A view of the port of Barcelona, capital of Catalonia. Barcelona is a very important seaport and Spain's major industrial and commercial city. Its population is second only to Madrid. In the foreground is the Columbus monument. J. ALLAN CASH

on the Llobregat, the factories which made the fortune of nineteenth century Catalonia.

In the extreme west is a strange area, folded and fractured, a depressed region through which inland Catalonia reaches the sea. But it is not an easy passage, since the depression is very hilly, even mountainous, and the road rises to as much as 3,383 feet at the Puerto de Santigosa. Furthermore, communications have only just been established and are not, as yet very reliable. Around Olot are Quaternary volcanoes; their wooded cones, their lava-flows (Castellfullit de la Roca), their craters (Bañolas lake) have filled in part of the depression.

That portion which remains of the original depression forms the Ampurdán basin, a subsidence area which has been filled in. The Ter has formed a delta now covered with rice-fields (3,950 acres). But, on the whole, the Ampurdán gives the impression of a region whose agricultural possibilities have not been fully exploited.

In fact, commerce is more important than agriculture. The ancient Greeks had an important outpost on these shores — Ampurias; the port silted up, however, and was in modern times replaced by that of Rosas, now just a fishing-port where oysters are cultivated. The land route over the Perthus Pass is watched over by the citadel and tradesmen of the little town of Figueras.

BARCELONA. Barcino began as a small Roman town built on a square site that covered a small, flattened *cerro*. At the highest point, where a temple of Hercules once stood, are now the medieval cathedral, the town-hall and the palace of the Diputación (fifteenth century). The medieval town remained small and the slow expansion of the city of the Counts of Barcelona reflects the sluggish development of Catalonia as a whole. In more recent centuries, Mediterranean traffic and trade underwent a long-lasting decline. Recovery began only at the end of the eighteenth century, and ships came back once more to Barcelona harbour. Thus the modern town grew up during the second half of the nineteenth century and the beginning of the twentieth. As we have seen, the opening of the Suez Canal as well as the increasing utilisation of electric power explain the great development of the Catalan cotton industry and the sudden prosperity of the whole region. The trade and traffic due to the 1914 war induced a still further expansion of the city, so that its front of new buildings reached right up to the Catalan Coast Range. Barcelona's great boom

years were from 1910 to 1930, when the city doubled in population (from 587,000 to 1,005,000) and had more inhabitants than Madrid (952,000).

But Barcelona's growth has slowed down — wars, blockades and restrictions have had their effect. While most of the other Spanish towns underwent a remarkable expansion and increased their populations by anything from 50 per cent to 80 per cent, Barcelona's increase was hardly 25 per cent. The number of its inhabitants is now about 1,446,000 as against Madrid's 1,898,000. The city is spreading mainly to the south-west and along the highway to Madrid.

The Balearic Islands

The Balearics were reconquered by Aragon and have Catalan-speaking inhabitants, but for centuries the islands have been integrated into the Spanish political system and more especially into that of eastern Spain. Despite natural and historical links, however, the atmosphere of the islands is not very Spanish.

The sea around them lends these islands a certain softness of climate unknown in Spain itself, where it is more harsh and austere. The Balearic climate is equable, too, (mean temperatures at Palma: winter, $51\frac{1}{2}°$ F.; spring, $59°$ F.; summer, $74\frac{1}{2}°$ F.; autumn, $66°$ F.). The light blue skies are intensely clear.

Furthermore, the sea, which during the Middle Ages was the source of importance of the Balearics, still links the islands with shores that are not Spanish. Majorcan sailing-ships discharge their cargoes of oranges at Marseilles. In Algiers the gardeners come from Port-Mahón (Minorca). Those Spanish fruit and vegetable shops which exist in so many French towns, and in those of almost all central European countries, are for the most part run by people from the Balearics.

The islands owe many of their special characteristics to the sea. Though the fishing is not very good, the salt-marshes, especially at Formentera, are by no means unimportant. Seaweed is added to the wine and gives it a taste of violets. Smuggling, also, is fairly profitable. The Balearics have had strategic importance in the politics of the Mediterranean: the Carthaginians had a naval base at Ibiza, where there is an immense Punic cemetery; the Kingdom of Majorca was a thalassocracy. At the head of its long *cala*, or creek, the old fortress of Mahón in Minorca surveys the sea-routes of the western Mediterranean.

Again, the people of the Balearics present a number of characteristics which may well be due to their island isolation. Everywhere in the islands, but especially in Minorca, there are Megalithic buildings, the *talayots* and *navetas*, which seem to show that in prehistoric times the islands were closely linked to others in the Mediterranean. Balearic folklore is in many respects peculiar: the *boléros* executed to the music of songs and of special instruments; the *ensaimadas*, light cakes more oriental (perhaps Turkish) than Spanish; the costumes still worn at Ibiza where the women wear their heirlooms of fringed shawls and heavy necklaces over long, dark pleated dresses.

The economy of the islands, also, is typically Mediterranean. Once more we meet the threefold crops: olives, cereals (mainly wheat and then barley, rice and maize) and vines. As soon as there was a demand in the nineteenth century from Europeans in Algeria for fruit and vegetables (then unobtainable in North Africa), the Balearic islanders planted orchards and cultivated market-gardens. Once started, the export of fruit and vegetables was maintained, and shipping fresh and dried fruits has become a fairly important business: almonds, figs, lemons, oranges and, more recently, grapefruit and apricots are sold almost everywhere and especially at Marseilles.

But the islanders have occupations other than those of farming and shipping. Handicrafts are developing. More and more souvenirs of all sorts are being made for the tourist trade, and these are not without artistic merit. The manual dexterity of the islanders was in olden days displayed in the famed workrooms of the Majorcan cartographers, who prepared the accurate Portolano charts and the so called 'Catalan' atlas of Charles V. In more recent times, the skilful and industrious islanders have been employed in footwear factories where very high class products are turned out.

Since the islands are some distance from each other, each has retained its own personality. Thus Palma is the capital only of Majorca. It is, however, the only town of any size in the whole archipelago. The other urban centres are very small, whether in Majorca, on Ibiza (the township bears the same name as the island), or in Minorca (Ciudadela, Mahón). The tendency towards urban concentrations, is very marked. Palma contains more than a third of the population of Majorca, Ibiza has a third of the island's inhabitants. Ciudadela and Mahón share about one-half of the population of Minorcans. Formentera, an exception, has no town at all.

Palma presents a generally archaic effect that is colourful and racy, but the town is by no means set in old ways, as is obvious from the growth of its population. In 1900 there were

A general view of Palma, capital of Majorca, in the Balearic Islands. The town nestles in a bay surrounded by wooded hills dotted with hotels and houses standing amid beautiful gardens. ROGER VIOLLET

Ibiza, on the island of Ibiza (Balearic Islands). Above the bay rise dazzling white houses on the slope of a hill crowned by the cathedral. Its walls, half-way up the slope and built in the seventeenth and eighteenth centuries as a defence against barbarian invasions, make the cathedral look like a fortress. GILLES DE LA MOTTE ROUGE

63,000 inhabitants. This figure has now almost doubled, while the total population of the archipelago has gone up only 14 per cent — 311,000 in 1900; 437,000 in 1957.

The development of Spain's resources

GREAT INCREASE IN THE POPULATION. Spain's population increased slowly during the nineteenth century. The first official census (in 1857) gave a total of only 15,454,000 Spaniards. By 1900 there were still only 18,854,000. During the twentieth century, however, the rate of increase has speeded up — fairly slowly until about 1930 (23,563,000), but then much more quickly: 25,878,000 inhabitants in 1940; 27,976,000 in 1950; 30,128,000 in 1960. From 1910 to 1950, in the space of forty years and despite the losses in the civil war (certainly more than a million killed), the increase was about 30 per cent, whereas in the preceding half-century it had not reached 18 per cent. From 1950 the Spanish population increased by more than 220,000 a year. In a century, the density of population had doubled. From 78 to the square mile in 1857, it rose to 150 in 1956.

The increase in population has been mostly in the towns. The rural communities have to contend with all sorts of difficulties, so the country people desert the land. But they can go nowhere except into the towns, whose growth therefore has been and still is positively astounding. In fifteen years (from 1940 to 1955) the Madrid population rose from 1,808,000 to about 1,850,000. During the same space of time Barcelona's inhabitants increased from 1,081,000 to 1,280,000, Valencia's from 450,000 to 510,000, Seville's from 312,000 to 376,000, Bilbao's from 195,000 to 230,000, and so forth. But in the large urban areas the newcomers from the country form a pool of unskilled workmen, making up a proletariat that is subjectected to great hardships and presenting the country with still more economic and social problems.

EXTENSION OF IRRIGATED AREAS. As the twentieth century progressed Spain had to deal with two problems which have become more and more insistent. First, the cost of imports had to be met by the sale of exports. Advantage was taken of the climate to develop as far as possible the cultivation of early vegetables and fruits, among which oranges, lemons and grape-fruit took first place. Spain is, in fact, the main producer of citrus fruits in the Mediterranean region. The irrigation of the olive groves in the Guadalquivir basin resulted in a considerable increase in the olive oil output, and Spain has always been the largest producer and the largest exporter of olive oil in the world. But the export crops, or almost all of them, demand a great deal of water; therefore any increase in the amounts available must be preceded by an increase in the irrigated areas.

Secondly, the cultivated areas had to be extended so that too much dependence should not have to be placed on agricultural exports, which might be drastically reduced by bad years or by events abroad. However, since all the areas which could be cultivated without irrigation were fully utilised, it was decided to irrigate some of them in order to increase the yield and also to bring water to some of the waste-lands. The steppe-like, saline lands in the Spanish Levant, in Andalusia, in the Guadalquivir depression, the fallow areas in Estremadura and still more those of Aragon and Catalonia, received irrigation. On such soils, which gradually lose their salt, rice is grown, and it is tending now to become the staple cereal in Spain, for the harvests are remarkable.

The Spaniards, then, are led to practise a systematic policy of *regadío*. Even before 1914 plans had been drawn up for dividing the peninsula into hydrographic units, and this programme, which has been revised several times, is today being carried out. Whereas at the beginning of this century there were only 13 *pantanos* (dam-lakes) with a total capacity of 98,000,000 cubic metres, in 1936 there were 74 *pantanos* capable of holding 4,000,000,000 cubic metres of water, and in 1956 their capacity was no less than 13,664,000,000 cubic metres. More than thirty other dams are either being built or are planned. Little by little, Spain is being transformed into a country where irrigation is the basis of agriculture. From 1918 to 1948 the area of permanently irrigated fields rose from 2,265,000 to 3,885,000 acres; since 1948 new projects have been put into execution — 271,700 acres for the 'Badajoz Plan' alone and 74,100 acres in the Ebro basin. At the present time, 27 per

cent of the arable land is irrigated in the Valencia region. On the Meseta, great irrigation schemes, starting with the damming of the upper Tagus, the Duero and the Esla, will transform the traditional *secano* agriculture into an economy with intensive production. In the south-east, where the dryness of the climate is such that irrigation can hardly be increased, much is expected from plantations of cactus, which will provide fodder and forage as well as help to loosen the hard crust of the soil. Here, moreover, esparto grass is grown and utilized in the manufacture of paper.

Spain is, therefore, carrying out what may be called a real enterprise of home colonisation. The *Instituto nacional de Colonización* has, since 1940, set up 112 new villages. By 1955, 286,500 acres of waste-land had been turned into *secanos*; 350,750 acres had been transformed from *secanos* into *regadíos*; 51,870 acres of salt lagoons had been reclaimed; and 28,400 acres of deltas or marshland had been turned into rice-fields. The greater part of this acreage (about 511,300 out of 717,500 acres) came from the break-up of big estates, most of them in the southern half of the country. The *Instituto* is now busy with the creation of new *regadíos* involving 1,601,680 acres; with the amelioration of the *secanos* (602,800 acres); as well as with the drainage and improvement of sanitary conditions in the marshes (2,336,600 acres). The target is an area of 133,380 acres to be irrigated each year.

Pastureland in Spain is not only becoming more extensive, it is also being modernized. Both the increase in quantity and the improvement in quality of agricultural produce can be judged by the continuous growth of the foodstuffs industries (condensed milk, sugar, flour, noodles, 'processed' pork, etc.); to this must be added sea-food products, for fisheries form the second of Spain's national resources and the catch is the sixth-largest in the world.

THE INDUSTRIALISATION OF SPAIN. The Spaniards now command quite large quantities of energy. The electrical potential has been considerably increased — indeed it has quadrupled during the last forty years. The current is, for the most part, generated by water-power, and in view of the ever-present menace of a very dry year, this dependence on hydroelectric sources is an obvious disadvantage. Therefore a beginning has been made with the erection of thermic plants burning waste products of coal in Galicia (at Puentes de García Rodriquez on lignite deposits), in the Bierzo (Ponferrada) and in Aragon (Escatrón). A thermic power-station has been added to the oil-refinery at Escombreras. During the twenty years from 1935 to 1955 the current produced at these thermoelectric stations increased more than tenfold. But it is in hydroelectric power that there has been the most spectacular development. The principal stations are on the Meseta, and include the new dams on the upper Tagus, on which the industrialisation of the Madrid region depends, and especially the great dams on the Duero and its tributaries, which have made the province of Zamora the best-supplied with electricity. The present plans call for a production of 22,000 million kWh in 1963 (as against 13,750 million kWh in 1956) and this figure would bring Spain, as far as electric energy is concerned, up to the level of other western European countries.

Despite much drilling, no oil has yet been found in Spanish soil, and only a little methane gas at Gastiain in Navarre, so all the petroleum products used must be imported. A beginning has been made, however, in treating crude oil in Spain, and in 1950 a large refinery was set up at Escombreras near Cartagena. Coal-mining is carried on actively in León and the Asturias, but the output is insufficient and coal must be imported. It appears, also, that uranium deposits have been discovered. An atomic pile is being set up near Madrid.

Now that the Spaniards have increased sources of energy, they have been able to turn their minds to the better exploitation of the soil and the subsoil mineral riches for which,

General view of Avila. EDWARD HOLMES

A bullfight: the kill. DR MARTY

Andalusian dancer. ELFER, BRIZEMUR

Holy Week at Seville. MARTIN, DALMAS

SPAIN

Blast furnaces at Sagunto, in Valencia.

in ancient days, the country was renowned. These were exported in their crude state until recently, but now the establishment of a number of processing industries is beginning to turn Spain into a manufacturing country.

The cement output has been stepped up so that now the demand can be met almost entirely by the home production. The metallurgical industries (steel, iron) have been developed, and now employ electric furnaces rather than blastfurnaces. The I.N.I., a State-controlled industrial enterprise, erected and put into production in 1955 the huge iron and steel works at Aviles, near the Asturian coalfield. With 17,000 workmen, the capacity annual output is 750,000 tons of steel. At the same time a new rolling-mill, processing 150 tons every eight hours, was set up at the long-established Duro-Felguera works in the middle of the coalfield.

There are rare metals in Spain: mercury (mostly exported), tin, manganese, wolfram (tungsten ore) and zinc. Thanks to the use of electricity, these metals have enabled Spain to take a high place in the ferro-alloy industry. Electricity is also used in treating copper ores, in which Spain is so rich, while aluminium is produced in plant at Alicante and at Sabiñánigo, near Jaca in the Pyrenees. Only the output of lead, most of which is exported, has not yet risen to its pre-war level.

The metallurgical output is most useful for the engineering industries, which are rapidly developing (machinery, implements, domestic, agricultural and industrial machines, machine-tools). The production of sewing-machines is so great (an average annual output of 100,000) that some are exported to South America. There are Spanish manufactures of small-arms and fire-arms. Bicycles and scooters are manufactured, mainly in Guipúzcoa and in Vizcaya. There are also large workshops in the Basque country turning out railway equipment. Finally, some automobiles are made, either under licence (Renault at Valladolíd, Citroen, D.K.W. at Vitoria, 'Seat' — Spanish 'Fiat' — at Barcelona) or, in the case of the national *Pégaso* cars, by a firm that has put up a large plant just outside Madrid. The Hispano works have, furthermore, produced a prototype Spanish jet plane.

The Spanish textile industry was once the glory of the country, but we have to say *was* since the traditional textile manufactures are in decline. The weaving of natural silk is confined to the province of Murcia. The quality of the fabrics turned out is high, but the quantity is small. The same may be said of woollens. The number of sheep in the country has dropped considerably, and the yield of wool per animal is only about 3¾ ℔, much less than that of Australian sheep, which, incidentally, are of Spanish origin, even if they did reach Australia from South Africa. The quantity of cottons produced has also decreased, for the mills are handicapped by having to import raw cotton; the Spaniards have attempted to grow their own cotton but the quality of the fabrics they produce is only average. Although the industries depending on natural fibres are declining, the man-made textile industry is thriving to a marked degree.

This situation reflects the remarkable progress made in the chemical industrial field — cellulose, soda, boron, sulphuric acid (of which Spain is one of the largest producers in the world), plastics and dyestuffs. The Spaniards have also started a rubber industry, chiefly turning out tyres. The importance that has now been assumed by the chemical and allied industries is something quite new and of importance economically. The chemical works are situated mostly in the province of Santander, around Torrelavega, and the green countryside has been transformed by dozens of works with their slag-dumps, the engineers' chalets, the *viviendas* (or workmen's dwellings), and by the port of Hinojedo and the adaptation to the new industry of a six-mile stretch along the Besaya *ria*.

These various industries, which are almost all expanding, afford proof of the tremendous progress toward industrialisation that is taking place before our eyes in Spain.

Delicate embroidery, particularly of mantillas, is a speciality of Granada.

A textile factory at Burjasot, in Valencia. The textile industry was once the glory of Spain, though it is now tending to decline.

Landing fish at Vigo, in Galicia. Installations are relatively primitive despite the town's pre-eminent position as a fishing port.
SPANISH NATIONAL TOURIST OFFICE

A craftsman at work on the traditional damascening of Toledo. T city was renowned in the Middle Ages for its swords, and these w the first articles so decorated. SPANISH NATIONAL TOURIST OFFI

Aerial view of Aviles. I.N.I., a state-controlled industry opened at Aviles in 1955. This great steelworks, near the coal deposits of the Asturi can produce 750,000 tons of steel and employs 17,000 workers. SPANISH EMBASSY

Aspects of traditional Spain. The Plaza Mayor de Mansilla, near León in Castile, a type of square with wooden porticos, where bullfights are held. DRAWING BY PIERRE DEFFONTAINES

The Talgo, a fast train with light, articulated carriages, which runs between Irún and Madrid. SPANISH RAILWAYS

Above: *At Cantavieja, between Teruel and Morella (Aragon), a square with stone arcades, with the church on the left and the town hall at the back. The plaza mayor is a specifically Spanish creation: it is surrounded on all sides by public buildings and is characterised by its arcades of wood or stone.* Below: *A street of underground wine cellars (bodegas), at Malejon, Aragon. In the foreground are chimneys for ventilation. The grapes are tipped through a small sliding door into the cellars, where there is a small press.*
DRAWING BY PIERRE DEFFONTAINES

The plateau of Old Castile, at Fuente Pelayo. In the foreground is a double-furrowed field of wheat. Grain crops on these vast stretches are kept free of weeds to reduce loss of water. In the distance, the Sierra de Guadarrama. JEAN-PIERRE DEFFONTAINES

A maize granary, Arriondas (Asturias). The horreos, wooden granaries on stilts, protect the crops from rain and rodents. Wagons and agricultural instruments are kept inside the stone walls.
DRAWING BY PIERRE DEFFONTAINES

A field of maize in Gerona. SPANISH NATIONAL TOURIST OFFICE

One of the factors, however, which arouses most anxiety is that of capital. The problem is a complex one, since capital must be sought abroad, and foreign investors demand certain economic and political privileges, which would put Spain once more into a certain position of dependence. By the Hispano-American agreements of 1953 the Spanish government accorded, in return for financial aid, mainly military facilities, comparable with those the U.S.A. enjoys in other countries of Western Europe.

But the increase in industrial output itself has produced a greater deficit in the foreign trade balance, because it has entailed the import of greater quantities of raw materials and equipment.

The invisible imports from tourists (nearly three million visitors in 1956) have largely contributed towards righting the balance and easing the burden that must be borne by the Spaniards. Nevertheless, the threat of economic and social crisis cannot be dismissed as impossible.

INSUFFICIENT MEANS OF COMMUNICATION. Much still remains to be done before Spain is in a position to develop fully all its potentialities and latent energies. The basic weakness of Spain's economy, and one which needs correction as soon as possible, lies in the state of her communications.

Although Spain is one of the few countries, at least in Europe, where railway construction is going on, there are not yet nearly enough lines. Some of those which were planned long ago should be built, especially the grand Mediterranean route Baeza-Albacete-Utiel-Teruel-Caspe-Lérida, connecting with a central Trans-Pyrenean Luchon-Saragossa or Luchon-Lérida track. This would permit the 'economic irrigation' of the Spanish Levant and of Andalusia, and would provide a strong link with France. There is, too, a great number of lines waiting to be electrified. Spain has in all about 8,125 miles of broadgauge line (1.67 metres or 65¾ inches wide, the normal European width being 1.435 metres or 56½ inches). Between 1949 and 1956 the weight of traffic carried rose by 46 per cent. Nevertheless, Spanish railway communications are unsatisfactory, first because Spain is the hilliest country in Europe — and haulage is therefore expensive and slow — and secondly because the radial plan of the network with lines running from the centre to the periphery is ill-suited for linking up the exporting areas of the country.

So it comes about that a considerable proportion of Spain's internal trade is conducted by sea. There are figures which are illuminating in this respect. Spanish coastwise shipping carries a considerable tonnage of freight — double that transported within the country. The figures for 1954 were: 23,400,000 tons in and out of the ports as against 14,600,000 tons hauled on land. The fact is that Spain is a maritime nation. In the eighteenth century the Spaniards had a great mercantile marine, one of the finest of the day. But the Spanish merchant navy was always made up mostly of sailing-ships, since the scarcity of coal greatly hampered the development of steam. Thus the Spanish tonnage, which was still quite large in the nineteenth century (4 per cent of the world's shipping), has continued to drop. Legislation has been effected to encourage the revival of merchant shipping, and this has been remarkably successful — it may not restore the Spanish navy to the first rank, where it was in the eighteenth century, but it will once more take an honourable place on the seven seas. In any case, for a country such as Spain, in whose economy fishing plays such an important part, the re-creation of the merchant fleet is a necessity. But at the present time, owing to slow deliveries and the high cost of shipbuilding, Spain has not yet a merchant navy as large as she really ought to possess.

On the other hand, the Spanish internal airlines are much utilised because of their convenience and because of the great saving of time effected by using them for travel from region to region.

There is a fairly considerable mileage of roads (75,039 miles, 6,875 miles of which carry a heavy traffic), and since 1950 the surfaces have been constantly remade and improved. Since 1953, with the support of the Americans, an enormous amount of work has been done on the Madrid-Cádiz highway, which is now an arterial route as good as can be found anywhere. Similar improvements are to be undertaken on the Madrid-Irún and Madrid-Saragossa highways. It is, indeed, through road communications rather than through the less flexible railroads that the Spaniards are endeavouring to solve the crucial problem of communications. There are reasons, in fact, to think that this problem will be solved fairly soon.

In all — or almost all — departments of social and economic life, Spain today displays changes so great and so fundamental that they have lifted her out of the old ways which for centuries ensured her stable, if modest, strength. But even if there are risks — and these exist at least in relation to the colossal financing necessary for the new equipment plans — there is a trump card in her favour: the vitality and youthfulness of the Spanish people.

Jean SERMET

BIBLIOGRAPHY

EUROPE GENERAL

Egli, E. and **H. R. Müller,** ed. *Europe from the air.*
Funk and Wagnall, New York, 1959.
Gottman, J. *A geography of Europe.* New York, 1950.
Hoffman, G. W., et al. *A geography of Europe, including Asiatic U.S.S.R.* Ronald, New York, 1961.
Houston, J. M. *A social geography of Europe.*
Duckworth, London, 1953.
Hubbard, G. D. *The Geography of Europe.*
Ronald, New York, 1953.
'Ports of Europe'. *Norwegian Shipping News,* April, 1960.
Pounds, N. J. G. *Europe and the Mediterranean.*
McGraw-Hill, New York, 1953.
Shackleton, M. R. *Europe: a regional geography.*
Longmans, London, 1958.
Unstead, J. F. *Europe.* (vol ii. Systematic Regional Geography.) University of London Press, London, 1953.
Van Valkenburg, S. and **C. C. Held.** *Europe.*
Wiley, New York, 1952.

WESTERN EUROPE

Laborde, E. D. *Western Europe.*
University of London Press, London, 1955.
Lowenthal, D. 'Western Europe'. In **S. Haden-Guest** et al., eds. *A world geography of forest resources.*
Ronald, New York, 1956.
Monkhouse, F. J. *A regional geography of Western Europe.*
Longmans, London, 1959.
Van Valkenburg, S. 'Land use within the European common market.' *Econ. Geography,* Jan. 1959, pp. 1—24.
Yates, P. L. *Food, land and manpower in western Europe.*
St Martin's Press, New York, 1961.

CENTRAL AND EASTERN EUROPE

Hoffman, G. W. 'Eastern Europe: a study in political geography.' *Texas Quarterly,* Autumn 1959, pp. 57—88.
Lessner, E. and **A. M. L. Lessner.** *The Danube.*
Doubleday, New York, 1961.
Moodie, A. E. 'The eastern marchlands of Europe'.
In **W. G. East** and **A. E. Moodie,** ed. *The changing world: studies in political geography.* Harrap, London, 1956.
Teclaff, E. M. 'East-Central Europe'.
In **S. Haden-Guest** et al., eds.,
A world geography of forest resources. Ronald, New York, 1956.

MEDITERRANEAN REGION

East, W. G. 'The Mediterranean: some internal problems'.
In **W. G. East** and **A. E. Moodie,** ed. *The changing world: studies in political geography.* Harrap, London, 1956.
Giordano, G. 'The Mediterranean region'.
In **S. Haden-Guest,** et al., eds.,
A world geography of forest resources. Ronald, New York, 1956.
Newbigin, M. I. *Southern Europe.* Methuen, London, 1949.

SCANDINAVIA AND FINLAND

Mead, W. R. *An Economic Geography of the Scandinavian States and Finland.* Univ. of London, Press, 1958.
Ogrizek, D. *Scandinavia.* McGraw-Hill, New York, 1952.
O'Dell, A. C. *The Scandinavian world.*
Longmans, New York, 1957.
Shirer, W. L. *The challenge of Scandinavia.*
Little Brown, Boston, 1955.
Sømme, A., ed. *A geography of Norden.*
J. W. Cappelens Forlag, Oslo, 1960.

Teal, John J. 'Northern Scandinavia'.
In **G. H. T. Kimble** and **Dorothy Good,** eds.
Geography of the Northlands. American Geog. Soc.,
Spec. Pub. No. 32, New York, 1955, pp. 415—432.

DENMARK

Danish Agricultural Organizations. *Danish agriculture.*
Copenhagen, 1954.
Jacobsen, N. K., ed. *Guidebook — Denmark.*
Published for the 19th International Geographical Congress,
Stockholm, 1960. Copenhagen, 1960.
Port of Copenhagen. Port of Copenhagen Authority.
Copenhagen, 1958.
Shankland, G. 'How Denmark lives'. *Geog. Magazine.*
Mar. 1958, pp. 484—498.
Spink, R. *The land and people of Denmark.*
Macmillan, London, 1957.

SWEDEN

Heywood, T. *Background to Sweden.* Constable, London,1905.
Jonasson, O., ed. *Economic geographical excursions to middle Sweden.* Gothenburg School of Econ. pubns., 1960, no. 1.
Göteborg, 1960.
Nordell, P. O. and **H. Rydbgerg.**
From the plains of middle Sweden to the high mountains.
Guidebook to Excursion E. Sw. 3,
19th International Geographical Congress, Stockholm, 1960.
Streyyfert, T. *Forestry in Sweden.*
University of Oregon Press, Corvallis (Ore.), 1958.

NORWAY

Adamson, O. J., ed. *Industries of Norway.* Oslo, 1952.
Lloyd, T. L. *The Norwegian-Soviet boundary: a study in political geography.* Dartmouth Coll.,
Hanover (N.H.), 1954.
Mead, W. R. 'Sogn and Fjordane in the Fiord Economy of Western Norway'. *Econ Geog.,* July 1947, pp. 155—166.
Rodnick, D. *The Norwegians: a study in national culture.*
Public Affairs Press, Washington, D.C., 1955.
Strøm, K. M. 'The geomorphology of Norway'.
Geog. Journal, July 1948, pp. 19—23.

SVALBARD (SPITZBERGEN)

Heintz, A. *Svalbard.* Vanous, New York, 1950.
Rudmose Brown, R. N. 'Svalbard of today'.
Scot. Geog. Magazine, Dec. 1950, pp. 173—177.

FINLAND

Eiro, K. 'The port of Helsinki; its growth and development as the chief port of Finland'. *Dock and Harbour Authority,*
Jan. 1959, pp. 269—272.
Englund, E. *Peat-land farming in Finland.*
Foreign Agriculture, v. 14, 1950, pp. 246—249.
Mead, W. R. *Farming in Finland.* London, 1953.
Platt, R. R., ed. *Finland and its geography.*
Duell, Sloan and Pearce, New York, 1957.

ICELAND

Barth, T. F. W. *Volcanic geology, hot springs and geysers of Iceland.* Carnegie Inst., Washington, D.C., 1950.
Berry, E. *Land and people of Iceland.*
Lippincott, Philadelphia, 1959.

Malmström, V. H. *A regional geography of Iceland.*
National Research Council, Washington, D.C., 1958.
Nawrath, A., et al. *Iceland: impressions of a heroic landscape.*
Rand McNally, Chicago, 1960.
Reich, H., ed. *Iceland.* Hill & Wang, New York, 1960.

BRITISH ISLES

Birch, J. W. 'Economic geography of the Isle of Man'.
Geog. Journal, Dec. 1958, pp. 494—513.
Bird, J. *The geography of the Port of London.*
Rinehart, New York, 1957.
Bowen, E. G., ed. *Wales: a physical, historical and regional
geography.* Methuen, London, 1957.
Brooks, C. E. P. *The English climate.*
English Univ. Press, London, 1954.
Brown, E. H. 'The physique of Wales'.
Geog. Journal, June 1957, pp. 208—220.
Cairncross, A. K., ed. *The Scottish economy.*
Cambridge Univ. Press, London, 1954.
Freeman, T. W. *The conurbations of Great Britain.*
Manchester Univ. Press, Manchester, 1959.
Kinvig, R. H. *A history of the Isle of Man.*
Liverpool Univ. Press, Liverpool, 1950.
Miller, T. G. *Geology and scenery in Britain.*
Batsford, London, 1953.
Ogrizek, D. *British Isles.* McGraw-Hill, New York, 1954.
Rae, G. and Brown, C. E. *A geography of Scotland.*
Bell, London, 1959.
Rees, H. *British ports and shipping.* Harrap, London, 1958.
Roepke, J. G. *Movements of the British iron and steel industry —
1720 to 1951.* University of Ill. Press, Urbana, 1956.
Smith, W. *An economic geography of Great Britain.*
Methuen, London, 1953.
Smith, W., et al., eds. *Scientific survey of Merseyside.*
Liverpool Univ. Press, Liverpool, 1953.
Stamp, L. D. *Britain's structure and scenery.*
Collins, London, 1955.
Stamp, L. D. *The land of Britain: its use and misuse.*
London, 1948.
Stamp, L. D. and S. H. Beaver. *British Isles.*
Longmans, New York, 1954.
Trueman, Sir A., ed. *The coalfields of Great Britain.*
St Martin's Press, New York, 1954.

IRELAND

Abdo, A. N. *Basic data on the Republic of Ireland.*
U.S. Bureau of Foreign Commerce, Washington, D.C., 1959.
Charlesworth, J. K. *The geology of Ireland.* London, 1953.
Evans, E. E. *Mourne country: landscape and life in South Down*
Tempest, Dundalk, 1951.
Freeman, T. W. *Pre-famine Ireland: a study in historical
geography.* Manchester Univ. Press, Manchester, 1957.
Freeman, T. W. 'The prospect for Irish agriculture'
Geog. Journal, Sept. 1954, pp. 329—336.
McCarthy, A. J. P. *The Irish national electrification scheme.*
Geog. Review, Oct. 1957, pp. 539—554.
Meenan, J. and D. A. Webb, ed. *A view of Ireland.*
British Association for the Advancement of Science,
Dublin, 1957.
*Reports of the Commission of Emigration and other Population
Problems, 1948—1954.* Dublin, 1956.

BELGIUM, NETHERLANDS, LUXEMBOURG

Alexander, L. M. 'Economic problems in the Benelux Union'.
Econ. Geog., Jan. 1950, pp. 29—36.
Alexander, L. M. 'Recent changes in the Benelux-German
boundary'. *Geog. Review*, Jan. 1953, pp. 69—76.
Amerongen, C. V. 'The Delta plan: Holland's great
programme of sea defence works'.
Dock and Harbour Authority, Aug. 1958, pp. 109—114.

Burke, G. L. *The making of Dutch towns.*
Simmons Boardman, New York, 1960.
Edelman, C. H. *Soils of the Netherlands.*
North Holland Pub. Co., Amsterdam, 1950.
Eyck, F. G. *The Benelux countries: an historical survey.*
Van Nostrand, Princeton (N.J.), 1959.
Ogrizek, D. *Netherlands.* McGraw-Hill, New York, 1951.
Pannekoek, A. J. ed. *Geological History of the Netherlands.*
The Hague, 1956.
Secrétariat-Général du Benelux. *Benelux 1948—1958.*
(In French and Flemish). Brussels, 1959.

FRANCE

Aron, R. *France, the new republic.* Oceana, New York, 1959.
Bell, J. F. 'Problems of economic reconstruction in France'.
Econ. Geog., Jan. 1946, pp. 54—66.
Dutton, R. and A. H. Holden. *The land of France.*
Hastings House, New York, 1953.
Hyams, E. *Wine country of France.*
Lippincott, Philadelphia, 1960.
Kish, G. 'Hydro-electric power in France: plans and projects'.
Geog. Review, Jan. 1955, pp. 91—98.
Ogrizek, D., ed. *France.* McGraw-Hill, New York, 1954.
Ormsby, H. *France: a regional and economic geography.*
Methuen, London, 1950.
Reed, J. L. *The forests of France.* Faber, London, 1954.
Weigend, G. G. 'Bordeaux: an example of changing port
functions'. *Geog. Review*, Apr. 1955, pp. 217—243.
Weigend, G. G. 'The outlook for the gas and oil industry
of south-west France'. *Econ. Geog.*, Oct. 1953, pp. 307—319.
White, F. *Three rivers of France: Lot, Dordogne and Tarn.*
Transatlantic, London, 1955.

PORTUGAL

Ambrière, F., ed. *Portugal.* Hastings House, New York, 1960
Campbell, R. *Portugal.* Regnery, Chicago, 1958.
Kish, G. and A. Taylor. 'Portugal (the land and the people)'.
Focus (Am. Geog. Soc.), Mar. 1958, pp. 1—6.
Livermore, H. V., ed. *Portugal and Brazil.*
Oxford Univ. Press, New York, 1953.
Ogrizek, D. *Spain and Portugal.*
McGraw-Hill, New York, 1953.
Sitwell, S. *Portugal and Madeira.*
Hastings House, New York, 1955.
Stanislawski, D. *The individuality of Portugal.*
Univ. of Texas Press, Austin (Tex.), 1959.
Trend, J. B. *Portugal.* Praeger, New York, 1958.

SWITZERLAND

Belin, J. *La Suisse et les Nations Unies.*
Manhattan, New York, 1956.
Diem, A. 'The Mont Blanc tunnel: a new route through the
Alps. *Journal of Geography*, Oct. 1959, pp. 344—349.
Meyer, H. F. *Great motor highways of the Alps.*
R. Hale, London, 1958.
Ogrizek, D. *Switzerland.* McGraw-Hill, New York, 1955.
Reist, W., ed. *Switzerland: life and activity.*
Mensch und Arbeit, Zurich, 1953.
Siegfried, A. *Switzerland: a democratic way of life.*
Duell, Sloan & Pearce, New York, 1950.
Soloveytchik, G. *Switzerland in perspective.*
Oxford Univ. Press, New York, 1954.

AUSTRIA

Burghardt, A. F. *The political geography of Burgenland.*
National Research Council (Publ. 587), Washington, D.C.,
1958.

Hoffman, G. W. 'Austria: her raw materials and industrial potentialities'. *Econ. Geog.*, Jan. 1948, pp. 45—52.
Hoffman, G. W. 'The survival of an independent Austria'. *Geog. Review*, Oct. 1951, pp. 606—621.
Marboe, E., comp. *The book Austria.* Heinman, New York, 1958.
Nemschack, F. *Ten years of Austrian economic development, 1945—1955.* Assn. of Austrian Industrialists, Vienna, 1955.
Reynolds, J. *Panorama of Austria.* Putman, New York, 1956.
Rothschild, K. W. *The Austrian economy since 1945.* Royal Institute of International Affairs, London, 1950.
Vansson, C. *Austria.* Viking, New York, 1960.

GERMANY

Dickinson, R. E. *A general and regional geography.* Methuen, London, 1953.
Dickinson, R. E. *The Regions of Germany.* Kegan Paul, London, 1945.
Elkins, T. H. *Germany.* Chatto & Windus, London, 1960.
Elkins, T. H. 'Journey into East Germany'. *Geog. Magazine*, June 1960, pp. 88—100.
Harris, C. D. and Wülker, G. The refugee problem of Germany. *Econ. Geography*, Jan. 1953, pp. 10—25.
Held, C. C. 'The new Saarland'. *Geog. Review*, Oct. 1951, pp. 590—605.
Koehl, R. *RKFDV: German resettlement and population policy, 1939—45.* Harvard Univ. Press, Cambridge, 1958.
Mc Clellan, G. S. *The two Germanies.* Wilson, New York, 1959.
Mellor, R. E. H. 'The German refugee problem; ten years retrospect'. *Scot. Geog. Magazine*, Apr. 1957, pp. 1—18.
Ogrizek, D., ed. *Western Germany.* McGraw-Hill, New York, 1955.
Pounds, N. G. *The Ruhr.* Faber, London, 1952.
Robinson, G. W. S. 'West Berlin: the geography of an exclave'. *Geog. Review*, Oct. 1953, pp. 540—557.
Stembridge, J. H. *Germany: An introductory study in physical and human geography.* London, 1950.
Stolper, W. G. *The structure of the East German economy.* Harvard Univ. Press, Cambridge, 1960.
Stone, A. 'Berlin (background and economic conditions in the western and eastern sectors)'. *Journal of Geography*, Nov. 1958, pp. 390—399.
'The development of agriculture in the Soviet zone of Germany'. *Wirtschaftsdienst* (English ed.), May 1960, pp. 17—23.
'The oil port of Wilhemshaven: post-war industrial development'. *Dock and Harbour Authority*, Dec. 1959, pp. 229—233.
U.S. Dept. of State. *Berlin: city between two worlds.* Publication 7089, Bureau of Public Affairs, Washington, D.C., 1960.
U.S. Joint Publications Research Service. *Developments in the East German coal industry.* (mimeographed) New York, 1958.
Zauberman, A., ed. *Industrial development in Czechoslovakia, East Germany and Poland, 1937—56.* Oxford Univ. Press, New York, 1958.

CZECHOSLOVAKIA

Busek, V. and N. Spulber, eds. *Czechoslovakia.* Praeger publns. in Russian histroy and world communism. New York, 1957.
Douglas, D. W. *Transitional economic systems: the Poilsh-Czech example.* Humanities, New York, 1953.
Marco, M. *Face of a country.* Vanous, New York, 1960.
Shute, J. 'Czechoslovakia's territorial and population changes'. *Econ. Geog.*, Jan. 1948, pp. 35—44.

U.S. Joint Publications Research. *The chemical industry of Czechoslovakia.* (mimeographed) New York, 1958.
Wanklyn, H. G. *Czechoslovakia.* Praeger, New York, 1954.
Wynne, W. *The population of Czechoslovakia.* U.S. Govt. Printing Off., Washington, D.C., 1953.
Zauberman, A. *Industrial development in Czechoslovakia, East Germany and Poland, 1937—1956.* Oxford University Press, New York, 1958.

HUNGARY

Balassa, B. A. *Hungarian experience in economic planning.* Yale Univ. Press, New Haven, 1959.
Dellin, L. A. 'Hungary, Rumania, Bulgaria'. *Focus* (Am. Geog. Soc.), May 1960, pp. 1—6.
Helmreich, E. C., ed. *Hungary.* Praeger pubns. in Russian history and world communism. New York, 1960.
Siegel, J. S. *The population of Hungary.* U.S. Govt. Printing Office, Washington, D.C., 1958.
Sinor, D. *History of Hungary.* Praeger, New York, 1960.
U.S. Foreign Agriculture Service. *The agricultural situation in eastern Europe. 4. Hungary.* Washington, D.C., 1960.

POLAND

Alton, T. P. *The Polish post-war economy.* Columbia Univ. Press, New York, 1955.
Barnett, C. R. *Poland: its people, its society, its culture.* Taplinger, New York, 1958.
Benet, S. *Song, dance and customs of peasant Poland.* Roy, New York, 1951.
Douglas, D. S. W. *Transitional economic systems: the Polish-Czech example.* Humanities, New York, 1953.
Galbraith, J. K. *Journey to Poland and Yugoslavia.* Harvard Univ. Press, Cambridge, 1958.
Mauldin, W. P. and D. S. Akers. *The population of Poland.* Govt. Printing Off., Washington, D.C. 1954.
North, G. 'Poland's population and changing economy'. *Geog. Journal*, Dec. 1958, pp. 517—527.
Pounds, N. J. G. 'The industrial geography of modern Poland.' *Econ. Geog.*, July 1960, pp. 231—253.
Taylor, J. *The economic development of Poland, 1919—1950.* Cornell U.P., Ithaca (N.Y.), 1952.
U.S. Joint Publications Research Service. *Transportation information on Poland.* (mimeographed) New York, 1958.
Zauberman, A. *Industrial development in Czechoslovakia, East Germany and Poland, 1937—1956.* Oxford Univ. Press, New York, 1958.

RUMANIA

Camilar, E. *Bistritsa valley.* Vanous, New York, 1957.
Dalcoviciu, C. *Rumania.* Foreign Languages Publ. House, Bucharest, 1959.
Dellin, L. A. 'Hungary, Romania, Bulgaria'. *Focus* (Am. Geog. Soc.) May 1960, pp. 1—6.
Fischer-Galati, S. A., ed. *Romania.* Praeger, New York, 1957.
Statistical Yearbook of the R.P.R. Vol 2 (English text). Vanous, New York, 1959.

BULGARIA

Dellin, L. A., ed. *Bulgaria.* (Praeger publications in Russian history and world communism) Praeger, New York, 1957.
Dellin, L. A. 'Hungary, Romania, Bulgaria'. *Focus* (Am. Geog. Soc.), May, 1960, pp. 1—6.
Sanders, I. T. *Balkan villages.* Univ. of Kentucky Press, Lexington, 1949.
Wolff, R. L. *The Balkans in our time.* Harvard Univ. Press, Cambridge, 1956.

U.S. Foreign Economic Service. *The agricultural situation in eastern Europe. 2. Bulgaria.* Washington, D.C., 1958.

U.S. Joint Publications Research Service. *Transportation in Bulgaria.* (mimeographed) New York, 1958.

YUGOSLAVIA

Brashich, R. M. *Land reform and ownership in Yugoslavia 1919—1953.* Mid-European Studies Center Publ. No. 17, New York, 1954.

Byrnes, R. F., ed. *Yugoslavia.* Praeger, New York, 1957.

Canada. Dept. of Mines and Technical Surveys. *Yugoslavia: a geographical appraisal.* Ottawa, 1950.

Edwards, K. C. 'The Yugoslav Economy'. *Geog. Review,* July 1954, pp. 425—428.

Fisher, J. C. 'Political decision: a factor in the changing agricultural geography of Yugoslavia'. *Journal of Geography,* Nov. 1959, pp. 399—406.

Galbraith, J. K. *Journey to Poland and Yugoslavia.* Harvard Univ. Press, Cambridge, 1958.

Hoffman, G. W. 'Yugoslavia: changing character of rural life and rural economy'. *Am. Slavic and E. European Rev.,* Dec. 1959, pp. 555—578.

Hoffman, G. W. 'Yugoslavia in transition: industrial expansion and resource bases'. *Econ. Geog.,* Oct. 1956, pp. 294—315.

Johnston, W. B. and **I. Crkvenčić.** 'Changing peasant agriculture in north-western Hrvatsko Primorje, Yugoslavia'. *Geog. Review,* July 1954, pp. 352—372.

Kostanick, H. L. 'Post-war Yugoslavia'. *Geog. Review,* July 1951, pp. 494—497.

Myers, P. F. and **A. A. Campbell.** *The population of Yugoslavia.* U.S. Bureau of the Census (Population Statistics Repts. No. 5), Washington, D.C. 1954.

ALBANIA

Skendi, S., ed. *Albania.* Praeger publications in Russian history and world communism. New York, 1956.

GREECE

Allbaugh, L. G. *Crete: A case study of an underdeveloped area.* Princeton Univ. Press, Princeton (N.J.), 1953.

Ambrière, F., ed. *Greece.* Hastings House, New York, 1960.

Marinatos, S. *Crete and Mycenae.* Abrams, New York, 1960.

McNeill, W. H. *Greece: American aid in action.* Twentieth Century Fund, New York, 1957.

Miller, H. H. *Greek horizons.* Scribner, New York, 1961.

Myres, J. *Geographical history in Greek lands.* Oxford Univ. Press, New York, 1952.

Ogrizek, D., ed. *Greece.* McGraw-Hill, New York, 1955.

Pepelasis, A. A. and **E. Thompson.** 'Agriculture in a restrictive environment: the case for Greece'. *Econ. Geog.,* Apr. 1960, pp. 145—157.

Prentice, A. 'Re-afforestation in Greece'. *Scot. Geog. Mag.,* Apr. 1956, pp. 25—31.

Sweet-Escott, B. *Greece: a political and economic survey 1939—1953.* London, 1954.

CYPRUS

British Information Services. *Cyprus.* New York, 1960.

Cyprus: an economic survey. Barclays Bank D.C.O., London, 1957.

East, W. G. 'The Mediterranean: some internal problems'. In **W. G. East** and **A. E. Moodie,** ed. *The changing world: studies in political geography.* Harrap, London, 1956.

Home, G. *Cyprus, then and now.* Int. Publications Service, New York, 1960.

Jones, D. K. *Carob culture in Cyprus.* United Nations, New York, 1953.

Luke, Sir H. *Cyprus: a portrait and an appreciation.* Roy, New York, 1957.

Meyer, A. J. 'Cyprus: the "copra-boat" economy'. *Middle East Journal,* Summer 1959, pp. 249—261.

Roman, J. R. Transportation on Cyprus. *Middle Eastern Affairs,* Nov. 1959, pp. 204—209.

Royal Institute of International Affairs. *Cyprus, background.* Chatham House Memoranda. Oxford Univ. Press, New York, 1959.

Ward, I. L. *Irrigation in Cyprus.* Colonial Office, London, 1954.

Wideson, R. *Cyprus in pictures.* Heinman, New York, 1953.

MALTA

Cottrell, A. J. *Malta: the future of a naval base.* U.S. Naval Institute Proc., Oct. 1958, pp. 29—37.

East, W. G. 'The Mediterranean: some internal problems'. In **W. G. East** and **A. E. Moodie,** ed. *The changing world: studies in political geography.* Harrap, London, 1956.

Harrison, A. St. B., and **R. P. S. Hubbard.** *Valletta.* Malta, 1945.

Hilary, B., ed. *Malta year book, 1960.* Academy Library Guild, Fresno (Calif.), 1959.

Hyde, H. P. T. *The geology of the Maltese islands.* Malta, 1955.

Luke, H. C. J. *Malta: an account and an appreciation.* Harrap, London, 1949.

Malta. Central Office of Statistics. *The trade of the Maltese islands, 1959.* Valletta, Malta, 1960.

ITALY

Carlyle, M. *Modern Italy.* Hillary House, New York, 1957.

Dickinson, R. E. *The population problem of southern Italy.* Syracuse Univ. Press, Syracuse, N.Y., 1955.

Jenness, D. 'The recovery program in Sicily'. *Geog. Review,* July 1950, pp. 355—363.

Kish, G. 'The "Marine" of Calabria'. *Geog. Review,* Oct. 1953, pp. 495—505.

Medici, G. *Italy: agricultural aspects.* Edizione agricole, Bologna, 1950.

Nelson, L. *Land reform in Italy.* National Planning Assn. (Planning pamphlet no. 97), Aug. 1956.

Ogrizek, D. *Italy.* McGraw-Hill, New York, 1955.

Walker, D. S. *A geography of Italy.* Dutton, New York, 1958.

Weigend, G. G. 'The basis of underdevelopment in Sardinia'. *Geog. Review,* Oct. 1952, pp. 656—658.

SPAIN

Bottineau, Y. *Spain* (Tr. by O. C. Warden) Oxford Univ. Press, New York, 1956.

East, W. G. 'The Mediterranean: some internal problems'. In **W. G. East** and **A. E. Moodie,** ed. *The changing world: studies in political geography.* Harrap, London, 1956.

Houston, J. M. 'Irrigation as a solution to agrarian problems in modern Spain'. *Geog. Journal,* July 1950, pp. 55—63.

Ogrizek, D. *Spain and Portugal.* McGraw-Hill, New York, 1953.

Olague, I. *This is Spain.* Dufour, 1954.

Peers, E. A., ed. *Spain: a companion to Spanish studies.* London, 1956.

STATISTICS

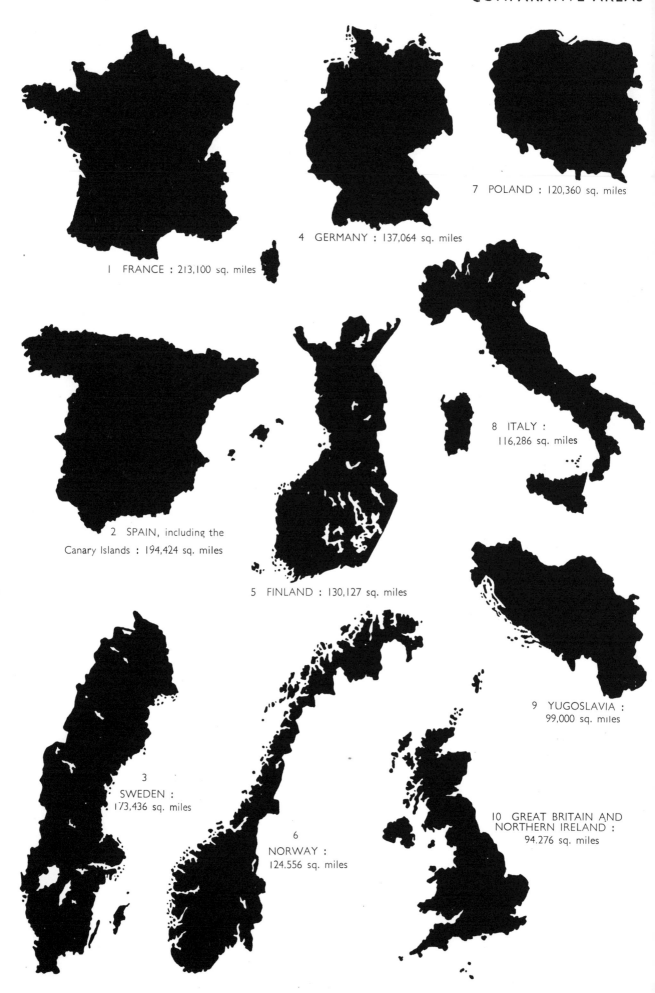

COMPARATIVE AREAS

1 FRANCE : 213,100 sq. miles

4 GERMANY : 137,064 sq. miles

7 POLAND : 120,360 sq. miles

2 SPAIN, including the
Canary Islands : 194,424 sq. miles

5 FINLAND : 130,127 sq. miles

8 ITALY :
116,286 sq. miles

9 YUGOSLAVIA :
99,000 sq. miles

3
SWEDEN :
173,436 sq. miles

6
NORWAY :
124.556 sq. miles

10 GREAT BRITAIN AND
NORTHERN IRELAND :
94.276 sq. miles

OF EUROPEAN STATES

11 RUMANIA : 89,700 sq. miles

15 ICELAND : 39,758 sq. miles

19 REPUBLIC
OF IRELAND :
26,600 sq. miles

24
ALBANIA : 10,629 sq. miles

12 GREECE :
51,168 sq. miles

16 HUNGARY : 35,912 sq. miles

20
DENMARK : 16,580 sq. miles

25
CYPRUS : 3,572 sq. miles

26
LUXEMBOURG : 999 sq. miles

21 SWITZERLAND :
15,944 sq. miles

27 ANDORRA : 175 sq. miles

28 MOUNT ATHOS : 122 sq. mile

29 MALTA, including islands
of Gozo and Comino : 121 sq. mile

30 LIECHTENSTEIN : 62 sq. miles

31 SAN MARINO : 38 sq. miles

CZECHOSLOVAKIA : 49,354 sq. miles

17 PORTUGAL :
35,404 sq. miles

22 NETHERLANDS :
13,514 sq. miles

32 MONACO : 4 sq. miles

33 VATICAN CITY : 109 acres

23 BELGIUM :
11,755 sq. miles

14 BULGARIA : 42,796 sq. miles

18 AUSTRIA : 32,000 sq. miles

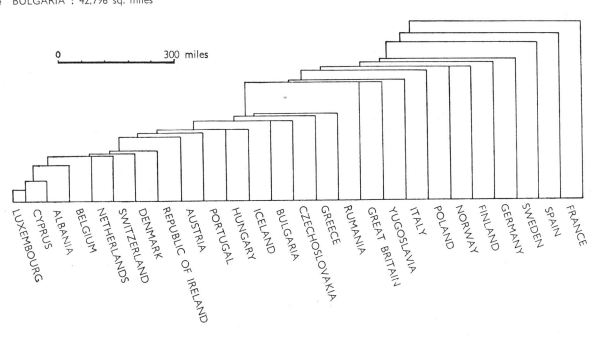

0   300 miles

SCANDINAVIA

All statistics refer to the years 1958 or 1959 unless otherwise indicated

	DENMARK	NORWAY	SWEDEN
Physical features			
Latitude	54°33'–57°45' N.	58°–71° N.	55°20'–69° 4' N.
Longitude	8°10'–12°40' E.	5°–31° E.	10°58'–24°10' E.
Area	16,580 sq. miles	124,556 sq. miles	173,436 sq. miles
Highest point......	561 ft.	8,100 ft.	6,965 ft.
Length of coast line	4,644 miles	12,427 miles	4,737 miles
Length of frontier ..	42 miles	1,619 miles	1,598 miles
Longest river	—	Glomma 373 mls.	Ume 310 miles

	DENMARK	NORWAY S.	NORWAY N.	SWEDEN S.	SWEDEN N.
Average ⎰ annual	46°	44.5°	32°	44.5°	30.25°
Temperatures ⎱ Jan.	32°	33.75°	17.5°	32°	4.5°
(Fahrenheit) July	61°	62.5°	48.25°	62.5°	55.5°

	DENMARK	NORWAY	SWEDEN
Average annual rainfall	24½ in.	126 in. (Bergen)	*Maxima* 39 in. (S.) 12 in. (N.)
		15.5 in. (Lapland)	*Mean* 23.5 in. (S.) 16 in. (N.)
Land utilisation (Percentage of total area)			
Forests	10 %	23.2 %	55 %
Crops and tilled land	63.6 %	} 3.3 %	9 %
Prairies and pasture land	9.2 %	}	1.6 %
Towns, roads, heath, dunes and swamps.	17.2 %	72.7 %	24.3 %
Glaciers and lakes ...		1.2 %	10.1 %
Population			
Total	4,529,000	3,510,199	7,436,066
Density per square mile	274	28	43
Birth rate per 1,000	16.6	18.1	14.2
Expectation of life ..	71	73	72
Rural population (as percentage of whole)	34 %	67 %	49 %
Urban population ...	66 %	33 %	51 %
Working population:			
Industry ⎱ Craftsmen ⎰	36 %	34.3 %	40.8 %
Agricultural ⎱ Forestry ⎰	23 %	21.7 %	20.3 %
Commerce, liberal professions, public service, miscellaneous	22 %	18.8 %	31 %
Transport	7 %	9.2 %	8.1 %
Fishing.............	1 %	5.5 %	
Religion			
Lutheran	98 %	97 %	95 %
Language	Danish	Norwegian	Swedish
Agriculture and forestry			
Production (thousand metric tons)			
Wheat	275	17	598
Barley	2,486	340	659
Oats	648	127	894
Potatoes	1,572	1,202	1,393
Sugar-beet	1,690		1,764
Hay		2,751	4,250
Wood (thousand cubic metres)	1,800	8,300	41,400

	DENMARK	NORWAY	SWEDEN
Livestock and fishing			
Stock (thousand head)			
Cattle	3,273	1,116	2,580
Sheep	36	1,809	146
Horses	237	126	229
Pigs	5,347	423	2,192
Poultry	26,272	3,477	7,913
Production (thousand metric tons)			
Milk..............	5,149	1,655	3,927
Butter	157	16	87
Meat	704	112	354
Eggs	149	—	84
Fish	598	1,415	222
Whale oil		140	
Calories per head of population	3,420	3,080	2,910
Mining. Industry. Power.			
Mining and industrial production (thousand metric tons)			
Coal		288	319
Iron Ore		1,017	11,021
Pig-iron and Ferro-alloys	44	508	1,414
Pyrites		793	335
Steel	255	366	2,431
Cement	1,068	1,031	2,510
Wood pulp........		1,282	4,071
Electric power (million kWh)	3,700	27,500	34,000
Proportion of hydro-electricity		99 %	95 %
Atomic energy:			
Reactors in operation	—	2	4
Reactors planned	—	1	2
Transport and communications			
Roads (in miles)	36,290	31,300	57,850
Motorways		Oslo-Kerkenes	
Numbers of automobiles	297,037	172,275	972,000
Number of passenger vehicles per 1,000 inhabitants	64	49	130
Railways (in miles)..	2,710	2,790 (720 tunnels)	9,700
Electrified lines		964	4,574
Merchant navy (thousand gross tons)............	2,185	9,608	3,493

Airline: *Scandinavian Air Lines System (S.A.S.):* participation of Denmark 2/7, of Norway 2/7, of Sweden 3/7.

Foreign trade. The percentages given for each of the three countries are of the total value of imports or of exports.

DENMARK. Imports: materials for industrial manufacture and commerce, 34.4 %; fuels, electric power, etc., 15.5 %; materials for agricultural production, 11.3 %; capital goods (commerce, agriculture, industry), 13.2 %; consumer goods, 11.2 %. Exports: agricultural products (lard, butter, milk, eggs, bacon and meat, livestock), 60.2 %; industrial products (machines and apparatus), tinned goods, condensed milk, chemical products, etc., 35.3 %.
Principal trading partners: Great Britain, West Germany, U.S.A., Norway, Sweden, Netherlands, Belgium, Brazil.

NORWAY. Imports: cereals, 2.6 %; manufactured goods, 13.7 %; machines, transport, 41.3 %; fuel, oil, 9.1 %; textiles, 7.5 %. Exports: pulp and paper, 19.5 %; edible animal products, 15 %; base metals and manufactures thereof, 26.2 %; oils and fats, 5.9 %.
Principal trading partners: Denmark, West Germany, Netherlands, Sweden, Great Britain, U.S.A.

SWEDEN. Imports: animal and vegetable products, 15.2 %; minerals and metals, 36.7 %; chemical products, 6.3 %; hides and skins, etc., 13.2 %; machinery, transportation equipment, 29 %. Exports: minerals and metals, 25.2 %; wood products, pulp, 38.5 %; machinery and transportation equipment, 28.3 %.

Principal suppliers: West Germany, Great Britain, U.S.A., Netherlands, Belgium, France. Principal customers: Great Britain, West Germany, Norway, Denmark, U.S.A., Benelux, France.

Administrative divisions. Currency. Denmark: 22 counties *(amter)*.

Norway: 20 counties *(fylker)*. Sweden: 24 counties. Currency for all 3 countries: the crown *(krone)*.

Public expenditure. DENMARK: social services, 24.5 %; education, 10.6 %; defence, 14.9 %; health, 5.8 %; roads and drainage, 6.2 %. NORWAY: social services, 9 %; education, 9.1 %; defence, 17.2 %; health, 2.8 %; price subsidies, 11.9 %. SWEDEN: social services, 22.3 %; education, 10.9 %; defence, 18.9 %; public health, 3.4 %; roads, 5.6 %; housing, 6.9 %; subsidies, 3.4 %.

POPULATION OF THE CHIEF TOWNS

	DENMARK	NORWAY	SWEDEN
Capital .... Without surburbs .... With suburbs	Copenhagen: 965,000 (1956) 1,203,000 (i.e. 27 % of the total population)	Oslo: 461,591 (1958)	Stockholm: 804,910 (1959)
Other towns	Frederiksberg .... 123,000 Aarhus .... 119,000 Odense .... 106,000 Aalborg .... 83,200 Esbjerg............... 51,000 Randers .... 42,000 Hörsens 36,500	Bergen .... 115,000 Trondheim .... 59,000 Stavanger .... 53,000 Drammen .... 31,000 Kristiansand 28,000	Göteborg .... 397,000 Malmö................ 222,000 Norrköping .... 90,000 Hälsingborg .... 76,000 Uppsala .... 74,800 Västerås .... 74,700 Örebro .... 74,200 Borås .... 65,600 Linköping 62,200

FINLAND

Physical features. Land utilisation. Latitude: 70°5′-59°30′ N.; longitude: 19°7′-31°35′ E. Area: 130,127 square miles (including 12,200 square miles of freshwater lakes). Highest point: 4,344 feet. Length of coastline: 688 miles.

Mean annual temperature (°F.): 41 in the archipelago; 37.5 in the northwest; 59—62 in the south (summer); 41—44 in the south (winter). Average rainfall (inches:) 27 in south-west; 16 in north-west, mostly in summer; 30—40 % as snow in winter.

Forests: 71 % of the total surface; lakes, 9.4 %; arable land, 13 %.

Population. Language. Religion. Population: 4,433,700. Density per square mile: 34. Birth rate: 18.5 per 1,000 inhabitants. Infant mortality: 24.5 per 1,000 live births. Rural population: 67.7 %. Urban population: 32.3 % (12.5 % in 1900).

Language: both Finnish and Swedish are official languages. Religion: Lutheran (95.4 %).

Chief towns. Capital: *Helsinki (Helsingfors)*, 453,000 inhabitants (197,000 in 1920). Other towns: *Tampere (Tammerfors)*, 123,600; *Turku (Åbo)*, 123,000; *Lahti*, 63,800; *Oulu (Uleåborg)*, 54,700; *Pori (Björneborg)*, 52,400; *Vaasa (Vasa)*, 44,200.

Agriculture and forestry. Livestock and fishing. Agricultural production (thousand metric tons): wheat, 203; barley, 406; oats, 798; rye, 111; potatoes, 1,381; fodder crops, 3,477. Wood, 40 million cubic metres.

Livestock (thousand head): cattle, 1,936; sheep, 407; horses, 261; pigs, 534; reindeer, 151.

Butter, 78,400 tons; cheese, 23,700 tons. Fish: from the sea, 45,000 tons; from lakes, 19,000 tons.

Mines. Industry. Power. Production (metric tons): copper concentrates, 141,142; zinc concentrates, 85,630; iron concentrates, 214,970; titanium concentrates, 106,489; lead concentrates, 3,970; vanadium pentoxide, 697; pig-iron, 100,956; steel, 186,044; wood pulp, 3,063,000. Electric energy: 7,887 million kWh per annum (87 % hydro-electric).

Transport and communications. Commerce. Road network: 41,350 miles; passenger cars, 139,222, i.e. 31.4 per 1,000 inhabitants. Railways: 3,270 miles. Navigable waterways: 4,130 miles; floatable waterways: 25,775 miles. Merchant fleet: 755,000 gross tons. Chief ports: *Helsinki, Kotka, Turku.* Considerable internal and international air traffic.

Foreign trade (millions of Finnmarks). Imports: 233,303 (mineral fuel and oils, 14 %; raw materials and production supplies, 51.2 %; finished goods, 34.8 %). Exports: 247,934 (agricultural products, 4.3 %; forestry products, 7.8 %; wood industry products, 23.3 %; paper industry products, 46.5 %; metal and engineering products, 13.7 %).

Principal trading partners: Great Britain, 15.7 % of imports (by value), 23.3 % of exports; U.S.S.R., 17.9 % of imports, 16.8 % of exports; Germany, 17.9 % of imports, 11 % of exports; U.S.A.; France.

Administrative divisions. Currency. 12 provinces. One of the provinces, the Åland Islands, with a mainly Swedish population, enjoys a high degree of autonomy. The monetary unit is the *markka*, or Finnmark.

ICELAND

Physical features. Land utilisation. Latitude: 63°24′-66°32′ N.; longitude: 13°30′-24°32′ W. Area: 39,758 square miles. Average temperatures (°F.): July, 52 in the south and 51 in the north; January, 30 in the south and 27 in the north; mean annual temperatures, 40 in the south and 37 in the north. Rainfall: 34 inches per annum at Reykjavík.

Crops, arable land: 1 % of the total area.

Population. Language. Religion. Population: 173,855. Density per square mile: 4.4. Birth rate: 28 per 1,000. Infant mortality: 11.8 per 1,000 live births. Expectation of life: men, 66; women, 70. Rural population: 33.3 %; urban population, 66.7 % (growing urbanisation). Distribution of the active population: agriculture, 20 %, industry and crafts, 30 %; fishing, 17 %; commerce and transport, 17 %.

Language: Icelandic, which belongs (together with Norwegian, Swedish and Danish) to the Nordic division of the Germanic group. Religion: Lutheran.

Chief towns. Capital: *Reykjavík*, 69,268 inhabitants (39,000 in 1940: increase of 77 % in 18 years). Other towns: *Akureyri*, 8,200; *Hafnarfjördur*, 6,500; and 9 towns with populations of 1,000 to 5,000, including *Kópavogur*, 5,000; *Vestmannaeyjar*, 4,300; *Keflavík*, 4,500.

Agriculture. Livestock and fishing. Agricultural production (thousand metric tons): hay from cultivated and uncultivated land, 333; potatoes, 7.6. Livestock (thousand head): cattle, 48; sheep, 775; ponies (used for travelling and transport), 31; pigs, 1. Milk, butter, 99,000 metric tons. Fish, principal resource of Iceland, 505.038 metric tons. In order to protect this vital resource, Iceland decided in 1958 to proclaim an extension of her territorial fishing waters from 4 miles to 12. The decision has been disputed by several countries, notably Great Britain.

Industry. Power. Cement: 110,000 metric tons. Electric energy (million kWh): hydro-electric, 431; thermal, 29.

Transport and communications. Commerce. Road network: abous 6,000 miles; number of passenger cars, 13,260, i.e., 76 per 1,000 inhabitantt. No railways. Merchant fleet: 52,769 gross tons; fishing fleet: 57,670 gross tons. Extensive air traffic: aerodromes at Reykjavik and Keflavík, and small aerodromes at almost every town. Foreign trade (thousand *krónur*): imports, 1,397,592; exports, 1,070,197. Fish products account for 90 % of the exports. The chief trading partners are the Soviet Union, the United States, Great Britain, West Germany and Denmark.

Administrative divisions. Currency. 16 provinces *(sýslur)* and 14 urban municipalities. The monetary unit is the *króna*, pl. *krónur*.

GREAT BRITAIN
AND
NORTHERN IRELAND

Physical features. Land utilisation. Latitude: 50°-60° N.; longitude: 2° E.-9° W. Area: 94,276 sq. miles, made up of 89,034 for Great Britain (England, Wales, Scotland, Isle of Man and Channel Isles — Jersey, Guernsey, Herm, Jethou, Alderney, Sark, Brechon and Lihon) and 5,242 sq. miles for Northern Ireland. Highest points: Ben Nevis, in Scotland, 4,406 ft.; Snowdon, in Wales, 3,560 ft. Longest river: Severn, 210 miles.

Average temperatures (°F.): In July, 63 in the south, 53 in the north; in January, 43 in the south and 39 in the north. Annual rainfall (in inches): Ben Nevis, 150—200; London, 23.5.

Forests: 7 % (of total surface of Great Britain only); rough grazing: 29 %; permanent pasture: 20 %; arable land: 28 %.

Population (1959 estimate). Total population: England, 42,764,000 inhabitants; Wales, 2,622,000; Scotland, 5,191,700; Isle of Man, 54,000; Channel Isles, 103,000; Northern Ireland, 1,408,000. Total: 52,144,700. Average density per sq. mile: 552. Birth rate: 16.9 per 1,000; death rate: 11.7 per 1,000. Expectation of life: men, 67 years; women, 73 years.

Rural population (1951): England and Wales, 19.2 %; Scotland, 17.1 %. Urban population (1951): England and Wales, 80.8 %; Scotland, 82.9 %. Working population: 24,272,000 inhabitants. Distribution of working population in Great Britain: agriculture and fisheries, 971,000; industry, 8,834,000; mines, 765,000; building trades, 1,541,000; transport, 1,652,000; public services, 1,611,000; commerce, finance, liberal professions, 4,954,000.

Language. Religion. Language: majority speak English; the original Celtic languages are also spoken in Scotland (Scottish Gaelic), the Isle of Man (Manx), and in Wales (Welsh). In Cornwall the Cornish language has disappeared. French is still spoken in the Channel Isles.

Religion: In England and Wales the majority are Protestants; among these the Anglicans (Church of England) are most numerous. Catholics number about 3,270,000. Scotland: the majority are Presbyterians (Church of Scotland); Catholics about 757,000. Northern Ireland: Catholics, 471,460; Presbyterians, 410,215; Church of Ireland, 353,250.

Principal towns (1959 estimates). 3 cities of more than 1 million inhabitants: *Greater London*, 8,204,800; *Birmingham*, 1,091,500; *Glasgow* (1958), 1,085,100. Four cities of 500,000 to 1 million inhabitants: *Liverpool*, 757,500; *Manchester*, 672,300; *Leeds*, 513,300; *Sheffield*, 499,400. 56 towns of 100,000 to 500,000 inhabitants among which are: *Bristol*, 436,600; *Kingston upon Hull*, 301,800; *Bradfort*, 289,100; *Coventry*, 285,700; *Stoke on Trent*, 270,800; *Cardiff*, 254,200; *Portsmouth*, 220,300; *Plymouth*, 216,300; *Southampton*, 200,000; *Sunderland*, 186,600; *Ealing*, 182,700; *Dundee*, 179,200 (1958); *Ilford*, 178,600; *Swansea*, 164,200; *Salford*, 162,000; *Bolton*, 160,700; *Brighton*, 160,000; *Wolverhampton*, 146,100.

Agriculture. Livestock and fishing. Agricultural production (in 1,000 tons): wheat, 2,786; barley, 4,038; oats, 2,187; potatoes, 6,850; sugarbeet, 5,328.

Livestock (in thousand head): cattle, 11.3 (11 in 1900); sheep, 27.7 (31 in 1900); horses, 189 (2,000 in 1900); pigs, 5,981 (3,000 in 1900). Butter, 38,700 tons. Fish, 850,387 tons (980,380 tons in 1953). Calories per inhabitant: 3,210 per day.

Mining. Industry. Power. Mining and industrial production (in million tons): coal, 201 (292 in 1917; 230 in 1938; 230 in 1951); pig-iron, 15 (14 in 1900; 11 in 1938); steel, 20 (9.7 in 1929). Textiles (in 1,000 tons): cotton, 281; wool yarn, 220.5; rayon and acetate yarn, 103; nylon, terylene, etc., 29.8. Electric power (in million kWh): hydro-electric, 2,707; thermal, 110,553.

Atomic energy: 2 nuclear power stations connected to the National Grid; 7 planned for 1966. Industrial production index (basis 100 in 1948): 96 in 1946; 114 in 1950; 136 in 1956; 140 in 1957.

Communications and transport. Trade. Public highways, 193,072 miles; private cars 5,526,000 (106 per 1,000 inhabitants). Railways, 19,000 miles — 1,118 are electrified. 234 million tons of freight carried each year. Navigable inland waterways, 2,600 miles — there are 1,262 not in use; 9 million tons of goods carried. Merchant fleet (1959): 20,800,000 tons (there are 6.4 million tons of petrol tankers).

Principal ports (in brackets, tonnage handled, in 1,000 tons, in 1959): London (87,020); Southampton (50,010); Liverpool (39,348); Manchester (16,100); Glasgow (15,738); Belfast (14,895); Tyne ports; Bristol; Hull; Swansea; Middlesbrough.

Overseas trade, 1959: exports, £ 3,990,099,000; imports, £ 3,325,699,000.

PRINCIPAL EXPORTS (in millions of £)		PRINCIPAL IMPORTS (in millions of £)	
Machinery other than electric	626	Meat	316
Road vehicles and aircraft	488	Fruit and vegetables	235
Chemicals	293	Cereals	230
Electrical goods	232	Non-ferrous base metals	205
Iron and steel	192	Dairy products	190
Manufactures of metals	146	Coffee, cocoa, tea, spices	176

PRINCIPAL CUSTOMERS (in millions of £)		PRINCIPAL SUPPLIERS (in millions of £)	
Australia	224	Australia	223
Canada	207	Canada	312
India	171	India	143
		New Zealand	183
United States	360	United States	371
South Africa	149	W. Germany	144
W. Germany	142	Netherlands	160
Netherlands	113	Denmark	134
Sweden	112		
Ireland	103		

Administration. Currency. England is divided into 49 counties, Wales into 13 counties, Scotland into 33 counties, Northern Ireland into 6 counties. Currency: the pound sterling (£).

REPUBLIC OF IRELAND
(EIRE)

Physical features. Land utilisation. Latitude: 51°26'-55°25' N.; longitude: 6°-10°40' W. Area: 26,600 sq. miles. Highest point, Carrantuohill, 3,284 ft. Longest river, Shannon, 240 miles. Annual rainfall and number of days of rain: extreme west, 59 in. and 250 days; centre, 39.5 in. and 225; Dublin, 27.5 in. and 218.

Cultivated land: 17,023,700 acres; forests and plantations, 381,000; crops and pasture, 11,796,300 acres; mountain grazing and other land, 4,846,400 acres.

Population. Language. Religion. Cities. Total population (1956 census): 2,898,264. Density: 109 per sq. mile. Birth rate: 20.9 per 1,000. Death rate: 12 per 1,000. Decline in population from 1953—58: 0.7 %.

Language: Serious attempts have been made to revive the ancient national language, Irish, which is one of the Gaelic group of languages. English is recognized as a second official language and is spoken by the majority. Religion: majority are Catholics (2,786,000).

Capital: *Dublin*, 539,476 inhabitants. Other towns: *Cork*, 80,011; *Limerick*, 50,886; *Waterford*, 28,876.

Agriculture. Livestock. Agricultural production (in tons): wheat, 363,600; barley, 452,400; oats, 474,800; potatoes, 2,592,400; turnips, 1,923,900; mangolds, 1,210,600; sugar-beet, 927,600; hay, 3,707,900. Beer: 70,620,000

gallons. Livestock: cattle, 4,683,800; sheep, 4,411,900; horses, 233,600; pigs, 852,200; fowls, 1,407,800.

Mining. Industry. Power. Mining and industrial production (in million tons): coal, 264,750; cement, 476,650. Textiles: wool yarn, 590,300; wool fabric, 74,115 sq. yards. Shoes, 5.2 million pairs. Electric power (in million kWh): hydro-electric, 773; thermal, 1,122.

Communications and transport. Trade. Public highways: 5,927 miles. Railways, 2,221 miles. Inland waterways, 454 miles (they comprise the Grand Canal, the Royal Canal and the Shannon). The principal ports are *Dublin, Cobh, Dun Laoghaire, Cork, Galway, Limerick.*

Trade. Foreign trade (in millions of £): imports, 198 (207 in 1955); exports, 126 (107 in 1955). Principal customers (in millions of £): Great Britain, 79; Northern Ireland, 15; France, 0.994; United States, 7.4; W. Germany, 2.8. Principal suppliers: Great Britain, 103; United States, 13.8; Netherlands, 5.6; Canada, 5.9; Finland, 2.4; Sweden, 2.5; Northern Ireland, 3.3; W. Germany, 7.9.

Administrative divisions. Currency. 27 administrative counties. Currency: Pound sterling (£).

FRANCE

Physical features. Latitude: 41°20'-51°5' N.; longitude: 5°10' W.-8°10' E. Area: 213,100 square miles (including Corsica). Highest point: Mont Blanc, 15,781 ft. Length of coasts: 1,678 miles (Atlantic and Channel coasts, 1,290 miles; Mediterranean coast, 388 miles). Length of frontiers: 1,740 miles. Longest river: Loire, 621 miles.

Mean annual temperatures (°F.): Lille, 49; Fécamp (Paris), 50; Roscoff, 52; Nantes, 51; Biarritz, 55.5; Nancy and Strasbourg, 48; Clermont-Ferrand, 54.5; Nice, 60; Mean temperatures for January and July: Paris, 36.5 and 66; Brest, 41 and 62; Biarritz, 45.5 and 67; Strasbourg, 32 and 65.5; Lyons, 35 and 73; Clermont-Ferrand, 35 and 73.5; Toulouse, 40 and 70; Nice, 44.5 and 73. — Days of frost: Oussant, 4; Brest and Cherbourg, 6; Paris, 70; Nancy, 90—96; Côte d'Azur, 15.

Land utilisation. Forests, 20.8 % (increasing following reforestation); crops and ploughed land, 33.7 %; market-gardens, 2 %; vineyards, 2.7 % rough grazing and pasture, 26 %; towns and roads, 8 %; owner-farmed holdings, 52.9 %.

Population. Language. Religion. Towns. Total population Metropolitan France: (estimate 1960) 45,355,000; (census 1954) 42,777,174. Density: 212 per sq. mile. Birth rate: 18.2 per 1,000. Death rate: 11.2 per 1,000. Expectation of life: men, 65.04; women, 71.15. Rural population, 30 %; urban population, 70 %. Division of working population: industry, 35.2 %; agriculture and forestry, 27.6 %; business, 14 %; transport, 4 %. Foreign population: 1,453,479. Language: French; other languages and dialects spoken locally: Flemish, Alsatian, German dialect of Lorraine, Breton, Basque, Catalan, Occitan, Corsican. Religion: the majority are Roman Catholics; there are about 1 million Protestants.

Capital: *Paris*, 2,850,189 inhabitants (1954 census); Paris and the 80 communes of the Seine département, 5,124,000; *Greater Paris*, 7 million. Other towns with more than 100,000 inhabitants: *Marseilles*, 661,492; *Lyons*, 471,270; *Toulouse*, 268,863; *Bordeaux*, 257,946; *Nice*, 244,360; *Nantes*, 222,790; *Strasbourg*, 200,921; *Lille*, 194,616; *St Etienne*, 181,730; *Toulon*, 141,117; *Le Havre*, 139,810; *Nancy*, 124,797; *Rennes*, 124,122; *Reims*, 121,145; *Rouen*, 116,540; *Grenoble*, 116,440; *Clermont-Ferrand*, 113,391; *Dijon*, 112,844; *Le Mans*, 111,891; *Brest*, 110,713; *Roubaix*, 110,067; *Limoges*, 105,990; *Angers*, 102,142.

Agriculture and forestry. Livestock and fishing. Agricultural production in thousand metric tons: wheat, 9,601; oats, 2,637; maize, 1,673; barley, 3,892; rye, 429; rice, 140; industrial beet, 12,885; potatoes, 12,746; tobacco, 54,500; wine, 47,738 hectolitres (33,374 in 1957, 57,706 in 1956, 65,000 in 1950). Wood, 37 million cubic metres. Fish, 342,000 metric tons; shellfish, 118,600.

Livestock: cattle, 18,465,600; sheep, 8,748,800; horses, 1,903,000; pigs, 8,469,300; milk, 18,813,000 metric tons (1956); butter, 340,000; cheese, 427,000; meat, 2,470,000.

Mining. Industry. Power. Mining and industrial production in 1,000 metric tons: coal, 57,721; lignite, 2,318; iron ore, 59,455; pig-iron, 11,970; crude steel, 14,607; petroleum, 1,386; bauxite, 1,817; aluminium, 169; potash, 1,662; cement, 13,629; cotton yarn, 308 (281 in 1956); wool yarn, 134 (142 in 1956); rayon and acetate filament yarn, 56.3; rayon and acetate staple, 69.7; natural gas, 1,054 million cubic metres (246 in 1950); alcohol, 2,796,249 hectolitres; 1,127,800 motor vehicles, 1,543,000 radio sets, 372,000 television sets; merchant vessels (tonnage launched), 451,000; uranium deposits are being exploited in many parts of the country.

Electrical power (in millions of kWh): hydro-electric, 32,236; thermal, 29,363; industrial production index (100 in 1953): 138 in 1957; 142 in 1958.

Communications. Transport. Trade. Road network: 408,100 miles; 4,512,000 private cars, 99 per 1,000 inhabitants; 1,464,000 commercial vehicles. Railways, 24,550 miles, of which 3,765 electrified; in 1958 they carried 553,000,000 passengers and 212,000,000 metric tons of goods. Waterways in use: rivers, 2,025 miles; canals, 2,855 miles; total traffic, 63,706,500 net tons. Merchant fleet: gross tonnage, 4,280,216 (2.3 m. in 1945). Principal ports: Paris, Marseilles, Le Havre, Rouen, Dunkirk, Nantes, St Nazaire and Bordeaux. Principal airports: Orly, Le Bourget, Marseilles, Le Touquet. The national airline (Air France) carried 2,454,500 passengers in 1958.

Foreign trade (million old francs): imports, 2,355,226; exports, 2,153,127. Principal imports from outside the franc area: Germany, 277,135; Benelux, 126,297; U.S.A., 236,420; U.K., 84,434; Australia and New Zealand, 77,663; exports to Germany, 227,795; Benelux, 136,478; U.S.A., 126,386; U.K., 105,233; Switzerland, 81,567.

Administrative divisions. Currency. France is divided into 90 départements. Currency, the franc. A new currency, the 'heavy franc' or *nouveau franc* (NF) worth 100 of the earlier 'light francs' was introduced on 1 Jan. 1960.

NETHERLANDS, BELGIUM AND LUXEMBOURG

Physical features	BELGIUM		NETHER-LANDS		LUXEMBOURG
Latitude	49°29'-51°30' N.		50°45'-53°52' N.		49°26'-50°10' N.
Longitude	2°32'-6°24' E.		3°21'-7°13' E.		5°44'-6°31' E.
Area (sq. miles) ...	11,775		13,514		1,000
Highest point (ft)..	Botrange, 2,277		South Limburg plateau, 1,053		1,834
Lowest point (ft) ..			— 22.6		
Length of frontiers (miles) .	857		618		
Longest rivers, or part thereof (miles)	Escaut, 123 (out of 267) Meuse, 124 (out of 590)		Maas (Meuse) as far as Gorkum 148; Lower Rhine: Lek, 90, Waal, 53		Sûre, 99 (out of 107) Moselle 25 (out of 319)

Mean temperatures (°F.)	WEST (coast)	EAST	SOUTH	NORTH	LUXEMBOURG CITY
Year	49.3	44.7	50.2	47.5	47.1
January	38.3	32	37.4	35	31.6
July	61.4	59.8	64.2	61.4	63.1
Mean annual rainfall (inches)..	30.8	39.8	26.3	WEST (coast) 27.9	26.3
Number of days of frost	44.4	115.5	WEST (coast) 42.4	EXTREME EAST 78.6	93
Number of days of rain (min. 0.004 in.) .	204		197		176

Language. BELGIUM: Flemish-speaking population, 51.1 %; French-speaking, 43.4 %; German-speaking, 1.2 %; inhabitants pseaking none of the three recognised languages, 4.1 %. NETHERLANDS: only one national language, i.e. Dutch. LUXEMBOURG: one official language, French. Most inhabitants know 'luxembourgeois', which is a German dialect.

Religion. BELGIUM: no figures available; the great majority of practising churchgoers are Roman Catholic; the authorities recognise four faiths — Roman Catholic, Anglican, Non-conformist and Jewish — and subsidise their ministers. NETHERLANDS: Members of Reformed Churches, 3,909,100; Roman Catholic, 3,703,600; other sects, 371,700; no religion, 1,641,300. LUXEMBOURG: Roman Catholic for the majority; 2,500 Protestants.

Chief Towns. BELGIUM. The parishes have kept a large measure of independence and therefore a breakdown of population by parishes does not give a faithful picture of the importance of towns; for this reason the population of the towns is given first and then that of the main parishes of those towns. Capital: *Brussels*, city of 1 million inhabitants made up of the following parishes: *Brussels*, 171,000; *Schaerbeek*, 119,000; *Ixelles*, 93,500; *Anderlecht*, 93,000; *Uccle*, 68,000; *Molenbeek-Saint-Jean*, 63,000; *Saint-Gilles*, 56,000; *Etterbeek*, 51,500; etc. Other towns: *Antwerp*, 620,000 (*Antwerp*, 256,000; *Deurne*, 63,000; *Borgerhout*, 50,000); *Liège*, 450,000 (*Liège*, 157,000; *Seraing*, 42,500); *Charleroi*, 275,000 (*Charleroi*, 26,500); *Ghent* (*Gand*), 230,000 (*Ghent*, 164,000); *Verviers*, 75,000 (*Verviers*, 37,000); *Louvain*, 65,000 (*Louvain*, 34,000); *Malines*, 63,298; *Ostend*, 54,297; *Namur*, 53,000; *Bruges*, 52,278.

NETHERLANDS (1959). 34 towns with 25,000 to 50,000 inhabitants; 13 with 50,000 to 75,000; 5 with 75,000 to 100,000, and 14 with more than 100,000. Towns with more than 75,000 are: the capital, *Amsterdam*, 872,000, and the political capital, *The Hague*, 607,000; *Rotterdam*, 723,000; *Utrecht*, 248,000; *Haarlem*, 167,000; *Eindhoven*, 158,000; *Groningen*, 143,000; *Tilburg*, 131,000; *Nijmegen*, 123,000; *Arnhem*, 120,000; *Enschede*, 118,500; *Breda*, 102,000; *Apeldoorn*, 98,000; *Hilversum*, 97,000; *Leyden*, 95,000; *Maastricht*, 86,500; *Leeuwarden*, 81,500; *Dordrecht*, 78,000; *Schiedam*, 77,000.

LUXEMBOURG. Capital, *Luxembourg City*, 70,158. Other towns: *Esch-sur-Alzette*, 29,000; *Differdange*, 18,000; *Dudelange*, 15,000; *Pétange*, 11,500.

	BELGIUM	NETHER-LANDS	LUXEMBOURG
Land use (As a percentage of the total area)			
Arable land	32.7	31.9	30.2
Permanent meadow and pasture	23.7	39.1	23.9
Forests	19.4	8.1	33.1
Built on land, waste and other	24.2	20.9	12.8
Average size of holdings of more than 2½ acres (in acres)	17	22	26
Holdings worked by their owners (% of the total worked area)....	32	47	73

	BELGIUM	NETHER-LANDS	LUXEMBOURG
Population			
Number (1959) ...	9,104,000	11,480,000 (1960)	324,000
Density (to the square mile)	773	922	324
Maximum density (to the square mile)	1,527 (Brabant)	2,455 (South Holland)	
Birth rate	17.1 per 1,000	21.1 per 1,000	15.5 per 1,000
Death rate.......	11.7 per 1,000	7.5 per 1,000	11.0 per 1,000
Infant mortality rate (number dying in first year, per 100 live births)	30.3	17.2	34.7
Expectation of life			
men	62.0	71.0	61.7
women	67.3	73.9	65.7
Distribution of the population (%):			
Parishes of less than 5,000	25	12.7	46.5
Parishes of 5,000 to 20,000........	43	28.7	53.5
Parishes of more than 20,000	32	58.6	
Distribution of the active population (latest published percentages):			
Manufacturing and crafts	37.7	23.9	
Mining and quarrying	5.5	1.3	39.5
Building trades ...	5.7	7.0	
Agriculture and forestry	12.2	19.3	26.0
Commerce and banking ...	13.4	14.1	18.8
Transport and communications	7.0	6.2	
Services	14.9	21.4	15.1
Foreign population (1954)	379,528	127,868	33,834

	BELGIUM		NETHER-LANDS		LUXEMBOURG	
	PRODUCTION (thousand metric tons)	YIELD (cwts. per acre)	PRODUCTION (thousand metric tons)	YIELD (cwts. per acre)	PRODUCTION (thousand metric tons)	YIELD (cwts. per acre)
Agriculture and Forestry						
Wheat............	797	28.2	402	28.9	44	18.4
Rye	200	23.3	427	23.5	10	17.6
Barley	318	26.8	315	30.8	16	20.8
Oats............	443	24.9	446	25.9	40	20
Flax	28.1	9.4	19.5	9.7		
Potatoes	1,956	193	3,606	221	94	129
Sugar-beet	3,200	34.3	3,878	38.3		
Onions..........			212	226		
Fruit	345		424			
Grapes	13		10		18	
Timber (round-wood in 1,000 cub. metres).....	1,000		400			
Livestock (thousand head)						
Cattle	2,596		3,204		138	
Pigs	1,423		2,472		112	
Sheep...........	174		543		2	
Horses	178		210		7	

OTHER PRODUCTS (thousand metric tons). *Belgium*: pork, 214; beef and veal, 193; butter, 90; margarine, 101; milk, 3,747; fish, 50. *Netherlands*: pork, 273; beef and veal, 209; butter, 92; cheese, 188; margarine, 226; milk, 6,240; condensed milk, 290; dried milk, 98; fish, 164. *Luxembourg*: pork, 10; beef and veal, 8; butter, 4.6.

	BELGIUM	NETHER-LANDS	LUXEMBOURG
Mining, Industry and Power			
	(mineral and industrial production in thousand metric tons)		
Coal	27,062 (23,400 in 1900)	11,880	
Iron ore (metal content)..	43		1,750
Crude petroleum..		1,621 (714 in 1951)	
Salt		795	
Pig-iron and ferro-alloys	5,519	913	3.3
Crude steel	6,011	1,438	3.4
Cement..........	4,057	1,366	196
Wood pulp	121	116	
Paper incl. newsprint	315	529	
Textiles:			
Cotton yarn ...	86.3	68.8	
Wool yarn	38.1	24.6	
Rayon yarn	10.3	31.6	
Electric energy (million kWh) ..	13,435	13,854	1,229
Index of Industrial Production in 1959 (100 in 1953)	119	139	127

Communications and transport. BELGIUM, Road network: 6,987 miles; motorways: 75 miles; passenger cars: 641,200, i.e. 71 per 1,000 inhabitants. Railways (excluding narrow gauge lines): 3,016 miles, of which nearly 540 miles are electrified; goods carried: 58.4 million tons. Navigable inland waterways: 984 miles; goods carried: 51.2 million tons. Merchant fleet (gross registered tons): 601,000. Tonnage of vessels entering port of Antwerp: 42,554,600; tonnage cleared: 42,574,300. Principal airports: Melsbroek (Brussels) and Deurne (Antwerp).

NETHERLANDS. Road network: 8,646 miles; passenger cars: 420,000, i.e. 38 per 1,000 inhabitants. Railways: 2,005 miles, of which 1,009 are electrified; goods carried: 23.6 million tons. Navigable waterways: 4,205 miles; goods carried: 126.1 million tons (75 million international traffic). Merchant fleet (gross registered tons): 4,600,000. Total seaborne freight traffic at Rotterdam, 72.1 million tons; at Amsterdam, 11.1 million tons. Principal airport: Schiphol (Amsterdam).

LUXEMBOURG. Road network: 2,972 miles; passenger cars: 31,000, i.e. 97 per 1,000 inhabitants. Railways: 244 miles, of which 22 miles are electrified; goods carried: 16.9 million tons. Principal airport: Luxembourg City.

Trade. BELGIUM—LUXEMBOURG CUSTOMS UNION. The Union was concluded in 1921 and lifted all customs barriers between Belgium and Luxembourg; the statistics for external trade apply always to both countries together. External trade (million Belgian francs, 1959): imports, 172,090; exports, 164,757.

NETHERLANDS. Foreign trade (million guilders, 1959): imports, 14,967; exports, 13,704.

BELGIUM-LUXEMBOURG CUSTOMS UNION

MAIN ITEMS	IMPORTS		EXPORTS	
	million francs	*percentage of total*	*million francs*	*percentage of total*
Food and tobacco	24,923	14.5	7,673	4.7
Crude materials, inedible except fuels	31,821	18.5	10,338	6.3
Mineral fuels and lubricants	19,783	11.5	8,590	5.2
Animal and vegetable oils and fats	1,475	0.9	650	0.4
Chemicals	11,395	6.5	12,893	7.8
Manufactured goods	50,180	29.2	102,148	62.1
Machinery and transport equipment	32,151	18.7	21,332	12.8

PRINCIPAL SUPPLIERS

	value million francs	*% total imports*
Western Germany	28,133	16.4
Netherlands	27,171	15.8
France	21,645	12.6
United States	16,263	9.5
United Kingdom	14,342	8.3
Congo	9,790	5.7
Sweden	4,714	2.7
Italy	4,035	2.3

BELGIUM-LUXEMBOURG CUSTOM UNION

PRINCIPAL CUSTOMERS

	value million francs	% total imports
Netherlands	35,008	21.2
United States	22,172	13.5
Western Germany	21,864	13.3
France	14,959	9.1
United Kingdom	9,743	5.9
Switzerland	4,559	2.9
Sweden	4,545	2.8
Congo.........................	4,535	2.8

NETHERLANDS

MAIN ITEMS	IMPORTS		EXPORTS	
	million guilders	percentage of total	million guilders	percentage of total
Food and tobacco	2,322	15.5	3,885	28.3
Crude materials, inedible, except fuels	2,084	13.9	898	6.6
Mineral fuels and lubricants	2,037	13.6	1,473	10.7
Animal and vegetable oils and fats	251	1.7	172	1.2
Chemicals	926	6.2	1,211	8.8
Manufactured goods	4,285	28.5	3,524	25.7
Machinery and transport equipment	2,905	19.5	2,437	17.8

PRINCIPAL SUPPLIERS

	value million guilders	% total imports
Western Germany	3,093.2	20.7
Belgium and Luxembourg..........	2,747.0	18.3
United States	1,651.1	11.0
United Kingdom	1,132.4	7.6
France	536.8	3.6
Kuwait	512.0	3.4
Sweden	430.8	2.9
Argentine	277.1	1.8

NETHERLANDS

PRINCIPAL CUSTOMERS

	value million guilders	% total imports
Western Germany	2,955.4	21.6
Belgium and Luxembourg..........	2,008.9	14.6
United Kingdom	1,470.4	10.7
United States	789.1	5.8
France	735.1	5.4
Sweden	574.0	4.2
Italy	370.0	2.7
Denmark	345.0	2.5

TRADE WITH OTHER EUROPEAN COMMON MARKET COUNTRIES
(in million guilders)

IMPORTS	1938	1948	1955	1957
Western Germany	301	267	2,145	2,888
Belgium and Luxembourg ...	162	730	2,205	2,816
France	65	239	483	512
Italy	13	56	127	200

EXPORTS	1938	1948	1955	1957
Western Germany	154	160	1,742	2,173
Belgium and Luxembourg ...	106	422	1,411	1,826
France	60	216	505	576
Italy	12	55	250	319

Administrative divisions. Currency. Budget. BELGIUM. 9 provincines: Antwerp, Brabant, West Flanders, East Flanders, Hainaut, Liège, Limburg, Luxembourg, Namur. Currency: the Belgian *franc*, dividend into 100 *centimes*. National Expediture (1959 estimates in million francs): 125,816, of which 15 % on defence. Receipts: 101,879, of which 33 % from income tax and 19 % from customs and excise duties.

NETHERLANDS. 11 provinces: Groningen, Friesland, Drente, Overijssel, Gelderland, Utrecht, Noordholland, Zuidholland, Zeeland, Noordbrabant, Limburg. Currency: the guilder or florin (Neth. *gulden*) of 100 cents. National Expenditure (1960 estimates in million guilder): 8,799, of which 18 % on defence, 16 % on education and 0.9 % on public health. Receipts: 8,265, of which 42 % from income tax and 21 % from customs and excise duties.

LUXEMBOURG. One electoral district only. Currency: the Luxembourg *franc*, divided into 100 *centimes*. National Expenditure (1958 estimates in million francs): 5,080, of which 8 % of defence.

PORTUGAL

Physical features. Land Use. Latitude: 36°57'-42°9' N.; longitude: 6°11'-9°30' W. Area: 34,168 square miles (excluding the Azores, 922 and Madeira, 314 square miles). Highest point: Serra da Estrela, 6,562 feet. Lenght of coastline: 517 miles; length of frontiers: 755 miles. Longest river, or part thereof: Douro, 200 miles (out of 528); Tagus (Portug. *Tego*), 171 miles (out of 625). Mean annual temperature (°F.): Oporto, 57.2; Lagos, 63; mean January temperature: Oporto, 47.9; Lagos, 53.6; July: Oporto, 67.3; Lagos, 72.9. Annual rainfall (inches): Oporto, 45.8; Lisbon, 23.7; Lagos, 19.6. Agricultural land, 46.5 %; forests, 28.1 %; unused, but potentially productive, 16.2 %; built on area, waste and other, 9.2 %. Area under vineyards: 795,000 acres; cereals, 5,145,000 acres. Average size of holdings (acres): 1 in the north-western third of the country; 10 in the south.

Population. Language. Religion. Total population (1960): 9,124,000; Madeira, 266,990 and Azores, 317,409 (1950). Density per square mile: 257 mainland, 867 Madeira, 356 Azores. Birth rate: 23.7 per 1,000; infant mortality rate: 84 per 1,000 live births; rate of increase: 0.8 % per annum; expectation of life: men, 59.8 and women, 65. Distribution of active population: industry and crafts, 26 %; agriculture and forestry, 53 %; commerce, 7.5 %; transport, 3.7 %; fishing, 1.4 %.
Language: Portuguese. Religion: predominantly Roman Catholic.

Chief Towns (1950 census). Capital: *Lisbon*, 800,000; *Oporto*, 285,000; *Setúbal*, 44,030; *Coimbra*, 42,640; *Funchal*, capital and port of Madeira, 37,200; *Braga*, 32,600; *Evora*, 25,500; *Ponta Delgada*, principal port of the Azores, 22,700.

Agriculture and forestry. Livestock and fishing. Agricultural production (thousand metric tons): wheat, 815; maize, 425; rice, 158; pota-

toes, 1,087; cork, 125 (Portugal is the largest producer in the world); olive oil, 61 (101 in 1957); wine (thousand hectolitres), 8,585 (12,183 in 1954). Livestock (thousand head): sheep, 3,592; cattle, 895; mules and donkeys, 358; horses, 68; goats, 707; pigs, 1,419. Fish (thousand metric tons): 455, one-third sardines.

Mining. Industry. Power. Mineral and industrial production (thousand metric tons): coal, 576; lignite, 156; copper pyrites, 598; iron ore (metal content), 116; tungsten, 1.1; cement, 1,024. Electric energy (million kWh), 2,667 (94 % hydro-electricity).

Communications and transport. Trade. Road network: 17,881 miles; pasenger cars per 1,000 inhabitants: 13.2 Railways: 2,235 miles. Merchant fleet: 552,000 gross registered tons. Principal airport: Lisbon. Tourists (1959): 296,000.
Foreign trade (million *escudos*): imports, 13,809; exports, 8,299.
Principal exports: cork, 1,310; wine, 951; sardines, 733; resin, 229; pyrites, 131. Principal imports: iron and steel, 1,088; raw cotton, 870; motor vehicles, 844.
Principal customers (million *escudos* and percentage of whole): Angola, 1,330 and 16 %; United Kingdom, 940 and 11.3 %; United States, 686 and 8.3 %; Western Germany, 641 and 7.7 %. Principal suppliers: Western Germany, 2,431 and 17.6 %; United Kingdom, 1,780 and 12.9 %; France, 1,062 and 7.7 %; Mozambique, 1,059 and 7.7 %.

Administrative divisions. Currency. Budget. Continental Portugal is divided into 18 districts. Currency: the *escudo*, divided into 100 *centavos*. National expenditure: army and navy, 14 %; administration and pensions, 10 %; education, 8 %; public works, 6 %,

SWITZERLAND

Physical features. Latitude: 45°49'-47°48' N.; longitude: 5°57'-10°29' E. Area: 15,944 square miles (15,418 without lakes). Highest point: Monte Rosa, 15,226 feet. Length of frontiers: 1,170 miles. Longest river, or part thereof: Rhine, 233 miles (out of 839); Rhône, 106 miles from its source in Lake Geneva (out of 505 miles).

Mean annual temperature (°F.): Basel, 48; Lausanne, 48.4; Sion, 49.5;

Lugano, 53.6; Annual rainfall (inches): Basel, 32.2; Lausanne, 40.9; Sion, 23.2; Lugano, 67.9.

Land Use. Arable land, 10.8 %; permanent meadow and pasture, 41.8 %; forests, 23.8 %; built on land, waste and other, 23.6 % (glaciers 3 %). Area under cereals, 405,000 acres; vineyards, 30,000 acres. Average size of holdings, without forest and mountain pasture, 15 acres.

Population. Language. Religion. Total population (1960): 5,298,000 (2,831,787 in 1880). Density per square mile: 333. Birth rate: 17.6 per 1,000; infant mortality rate, 22.2 per 1,000 live births. Expectation of life: men, 66.4, women, 70.8 years. Rural population (parishes of less than 2,000), 31 %; urban population (parishes of more than 10,000), 36 %. Distribution of active population: industry and crafts, 42 %; agriculture and forestry, 15 %; commerce and hotels, 14.7 %; transport, 4.3 %. Foreign population, 6 %. Language: 72.1 % speak German; 20.3 % French; 5.9 % Italian; 1 % Romansch. Religion: Protestant, 56.3 %; Roman Catholic, 42.2 %.

Chief Towns. Federal capital: *Bern*, 163,000. Seven other towns have more than 60,000 inhabitants: *Zürich*, 433,400; *Basel*, 203,300; *Geneva*, 172,000; *Lausanne*, 118,900; *Winterthur*, 77,400; *St Gallen*, 74,100; *Lucerne*, 67,100.

Agriculture and forestry. Livestock. Agricultural production (in thousand metric tons; in brackets, yield per acre in cwts): wheat, 349 (25.8); barley, 71 (23.2); potatoes, 1,590 (229); sugar-beet, 292 (39.6); apples, 760; pears, 360; cherries, 65. Timber: 3.4 million cubic metres. Wine and beer (thousand hectolitres), 654 and 3,150.
Livestock (thousand head): cattle, 1,664 (of which 891 are dairy cattle); sheep, 202; goats, 110; horses, 107; pigs, 1,190; poultry, 6,490. In thousand tons: butter, 33; cheese, 64; milk, 2,921; sugar, 36; meat, 224.

Mining. Industry. Power. Mineral and industrial production (thousand metric tons): salt, 124; iron ore (metal content), 39; cement, 2,185; wood pulp, 196; paper and newsprint, 287; textiles: rayon staple, 7.6; rayon yarn, 11.6; cotton (thousands of spindles and thousands of looms), 1,202 and 15.9. Electric power (million kWh): 16,878, of which 16,703 hydro-electricity.

Communications and Transport. Commerce. Road network: 4,602 miles; passenger cars: 386,417, i.e. 74 per 1,000 inhabitants. Railways (1957): 3,198 miles, of which 3,108 are electrified. Merchant fleet: 23 vessels of 109,405 gross registered tons and approximately 400 Rhine barges; chief port Basel with an annual traffic of 5 million tons of which 90 % comes from downstream. Principal airports: Basel, Geneva and Zürich.
Foreign trade (million Swiss francs, 1959): imports, 8,262.6; exports, 7,233.3. Principal imports: foodstuffs, 1,187; machinery and apparatus, 713.6; motor vehicles and aeroplanes, 623; chemicals and pharmaceuticals, 619; iron and steel, 482; textile yarns and fabrics, 467; petroleum products, 408. Principal exports: machinery, 1,425; clocks and watches, 1,125; chemicals and pharmaceuticals, 862; textiles and clothing, 779; scientific instruments, 554.
Principal suppliers (million francs and percentage of whole): Western Germany, 2,308 and 27.9 %; Italy, 951 and 11.5 %; France, 931 and 11.3 %; United States, 875 and 10.6 %. Principal customers: Western Germany, 1,242 and 17.1 %; United States, 816 and 11.3 %; Italy, 593 and 8.2 %; France, 500.9 and 6.9 %.

Administrative divisions. Currency. Budget. Confederation of 22 cantons of which 3 are divided into two parts: Zürich, Bern, Lucerne, Uri, Schwyz, Upper and Lower Unterwalden, Glarus, Zug, Fribourg, Solothurn, Basel (town and country) Schaffhausen, Appenzell (Outer and Inner Rhoden) 2,393 (657 in 1937); cement, 2,154; wood pulp, 644; paper and newsprint, Neuchâtel, Geneva.
Currency: the Swiss *franc*, divided into 100 *centimes* (*Rappen*). Federal expenditure (1960 estimates) by government departments as percentage of total: Military, 38 %; Finance and Customs, 23 %; Interior, 19 %; Commerce, Industry and Agriculture, 11 %. Education is the responsibility of the cantons.

LIECHTENSTEIN

Physical features. Latitude: 47°3'-47°14' N.; longitude: 9°28'-9°32' E. Area: 62 square miles. Highest point: 8,526 feet. Length of frontiers: 45 miles. Longest river, or part therof: Rhine, 17 miles (out of 839).

Population. Language. Religion. Towns. Total population: 15,000 (1955 census). Density per square mile: 224. Population growth: 372 births against 142 deaths. Urban population (in parishes of more than 2,000 inhabitants): 36 %. Distribution of the active population: industry, handicrafts and commerce, 50 %; agriculture and forestry, 19 %. Foreigners: 2,751 (of whom 733 born in Liechtenstein) — 1,191 Swiss, 876 Austrians, 402 Germans, 125 Italians. Language: German, 97 %; other languages, 3 %. Religion: Roman Catholic, 92 %; Protestant, 6 %.
Capital: *Vaduz*, (3,170).

Agriculture and livestock. Agricultural production: potatoes, vegetables for preserving, dairy produce. Livestock (thousand head, 1954): cattle, 6; sheep and goats, 2; pigs, 4; poultry, 35.

Industry and Power. Industrial production: textiles (spinning and weaving), leather goods, pottery, artificial teeth, etc. Hydro-electricity (million kWh), 50.1.

Communications and transport. The Arlberg Express (Paris-Vienna) passes through the principality (station at Schaan-Vaduz).
Exports: preserves, textiles and clothing, precision instruments. Principal customers: Western Germany, Switzerland (for re-export), Austria, United States, France. Currency: the Swiss *franc*.

AUSTRIA

Physical features. Land Use. Latitude: 46°50'-49° N.; longitude: 9°45'-17°10' E. Area: 32,000 square miles. Highest point: Grossglockner, 12,457 feet. Length of frontiers: 1,639 miles. Longest river, or part thereof: Danube, 221 miles (out of 1,839). Mean annual temperature (°F.): Vienna, 48.5; Linz, 47.1; Salzburg, 46.2; mean January: Vienna, 29; Linz, 27.7; Salzburg, 27.7; mean July: Vienna, 67.3; Linz, 65.7; Salzburg, 64.
Mean annual rainfall (inches): Vienna, 25.3; Innsbruck, 33.7; Linz, 33.2; Graz, 34.4; Salzburg, 52.6.
Arable land, 21.1 %; permanent pasture and meadow, 27.6 %; forest, 37.3 %; built on area, waste land and other, 14 %. Area under cereals, 2,175,000 acres; vineyards, 90,000 acres. Average size of holdings: 30 acres.

Population. Language. Religion. Towns. Population (1959): 7,049,000. Density per square mile: 217.5. Birth rate: 17.1 per 1,000; infant mortality rate: 40.7 per 1,000. Expectation of life: men, 61.9; women, 67.0 years. Urban population (in parishes of more than 5,000 inhabitants): 50.2 %. Distribution of the active population: industry and handicrafts, 38 %; agriculture and forestry, 32 %; commerce, 9 %; transport, 5 %. Language: the majority speak German. Religion: Roman Catholic, 89 %; Protestant, 6.2 %.
Capital: *Vienna (Wien)*, 1,616,125. Other towns with more than 60,000 inhabitants: *Graz*, 226,453; *Linz*, 184,685; *Salzburg*, 102,927; *Innsbruck*, 95,055; *Klagenfurt*, 62,782.

Agriculture and Forestry. Livestock. Agricultural production (in thousand metric tons; in brackets, yield per acre in cwts.): wheat, 549 (16.7); rye, 397 (23.2); barley, 335 (14.9); oats, 333 (15.9); potatoes, 3,542. Timber: 10,240,149 cubic metres. Livestock (thousand head): cattle, 2,297; sheep, 207; goats, 209; horses, 200; pigs, 2,917; poultry, 9,767. Milk (thousand tons), 2,836.

Mining. Industry. Power. Mineral and industrial production (thousand metric tons): lignite, 6,494; iron ore, 3,410 (1,880 in 1937); magnesite (largest world producer), 1,221 (398 in 1937); brine, 325; petroleum, 2,400 (1960 estimate — 33 in 1937); aluminium, 74.3; pig-iron, 1,820 (384 in 1937); steel, 2,393 (657 in 1937); cement, 2,154; wood pulp, 644; paper and newsprint, 428. Textiles: cotton yarn, 26.5 (612,000 spindles and 11,978 looms). Electric power (million kWh), 13,605, of which 10,734 hydro-electricity. Index of industrial production (100 in 1953): 86 in 1950; 156 in 1959.

Communications and transport. Trade. Road network: 19,291 miles; passenger cars: 282,580, i.e. 40 per 1,000 inhabitants. Railways: 3,691 miles of which 1,044 are electrified. Navigable waterways: 1,077 miles. Principal airports: Schwechat (Vienna), Linz, Salzburg, Graz, Klagenfurt and Innsbruck.
Foreign trade (in million *Schillings*, 1959): imports, 29,759.5; exports, 25,160.9. Principal imports: foodstuffs, 4,645; raw materials, 3,435; mineral fuels, 3,191; manufactured goods, including textiles and base metals, 5,625; machinery, other than electrical, 4,180; electrical machinery, 1,104; motor vehicles, 2,262. Principal exports: timber, 3,411; electric power, 512; textiles, 1,993; iron and steel, 4,245; machinery, other than electrical, 2,122; electrical machinery, 944. Principal suppliers (million *Schillings* and percentage of whole): Western Germany, 11,979 and 40 %; Italy, 2,339 and 7.8 %; United States, 2,032 and 6.8 %; United Kingdom, 1,375 and 4.6 %. Principal customers: Western Germany, 6,671 and 26.5 %; Italy, 4,140 and 16.4 %; United States, 1,484 and 5.9 %.

Administrative divisions. Currency. The Austrian republic comprises 9 provinces (*Bundesländer*): Vienna, Lower Austria, Upper Austria, Salzburg, Styria, Carinthia, Tirol, Vorarlberg, Burgenland. Currency: the *Schilling*, divided into 100 *Groschen*.

GERMANY

Chief Towns. *Berlin*: East and West (1959), 3,296,000.

WESTERN GERMANY. Capital: *Bonn*, 142,540. Other towns: *Hamburg*, 1,807,640; *Munich (München)*, 1,033,964; *Cologne (Köln)*, 760,236; *Essen*, 725,580; *Düsseldorf*, 685,033; *Frankfurt-am-Main*, 647,623; *Dortmund*, 632,848; *Stuttgart*, 566,000; *Hanover (Hannover)*, 563,152; *Bremen*, 541,891; *Duisburg*, 498,932; *Nuremberg (Nürnberg)*, 441,367; *Wuppertal*, 416,050; *Gelsenkirchen*, 390,363; *Bochum*, 359,616; *Mannheim*, 300,490; *Kiel*, 265,864;

Oberhausen, 255,487; *Wiesbaden*, 252,156; *Brunswick (Braunschweig)*, 245,644; *Karlsruhe*, 231,472; *Lübeck*, 230,562; *Krefeld*, 205,004; *Augsburg*, 204,398; twenty-seven towns with populations between 100,000 and 200,000.

EASTERN GERMANY. Capital: *Berlin* (Eastern sector). Other towns: *Leipzig*, 593,902; *Dresden*, 491,646; *Karl-Marx-Stadt (Chemnitz)*, 285,928; *Halle*, 278,828; *Magdeburg*, 258,712; *Erfurt*, 184,588; *Rostock*, 151,811; *Zwickau*, 129,069; *Potsdam*, 114,132.

	WESTERN GERMANY	EASTERN GERMANY
Physical features		
Latitude	47°16′–55°3′ N.	50°10′–54°41′ N.
Longitude	5°52′–13°51′ E.	9°54′–15°2′ E.
Area (square miles)	95,683	41,380
Highest point (feet)	Zugspitze, 9,721	Fichtelberg, 3,983
Length of frontiers (miles)	2,659	1,553
Length of longest river (miles)	Rhine, 537 (out of 839)	Elbe, 352 (out of 724)

Mean temperatures (°F.)	Hamburg	Munich	Dresden	Erfurt
Year	47.3	45.3	48.7	46.4
January	32.6	27.9	32.6	30
July	62.8	63.7	65.5	64
Mean annual rainfall (inches)	29.1	36.8	26.3	20.1
Number of days of rain	198	189	173	172
Number of days of snow	33	50	28	36

	WESTERN GERMANY	EASTERN GERMANY
Land Use		
Arable land	35.2 %	48.1 %
Permanent meadow and pasture	23.1 %	12.1 %
Forests	28.8 %	27.4 %
Built on land, waste and other	12.9 %	12.4 %
Acreage under cereals ...	11,262,500	5,752,500
Acreage under vineyards	185,000	
Average size of holdings (acres)	17	25
Holdings worked by their owner	87 %	26 %
'Socialised' sector of farmland		52 %

	WESTERN GERMANY	EASTERN GERMANY
Population		
Number (thousands)	55,373 (1960)	16,213 (1959)
Berlin	2,226	1,090
Density (to sq. mile)	578	392
Birth rate	17 per 1,000	15.6 per 1,000
Infant mortality rate	36 per 1,000	44 per 1,000
Rate of increase and decrease	1.3 %	—0.9 %
Expectation of life (years)		
men	64.6 (1951)	66.3
women	68.5 (1951)	71.0
Rural population	28 %	28.6 %
Urban population	72 %	71.4 %
Active population:		
Industry and handicrafts	42 %	51 %
Agriculture and forestry	20 %	19.5 %
Commerce	10 %	10 %
Transport	6 %	4.5 %
Public and private service	17 %	14.6 %
Movement of population 1950—58	From East to West 2,050,662	From West to East 379,613

	WESTERN GERMANY	EASTERN GERMANY
Religion		
Protestants	51.1 %	80.5 %
Roman Catholics	45.2 %	11.0 %

Mining. Industry. Power. WESTERN GERMANY. Mineral and industrial production (thousand metric tons): coal, 133,582 and 16,423 in Saarland (i.e. 14 % of world production); coke, 47,753; lignite, 93,487; petroleum (1960 estimate), 5,500; iron ore (metal content), 4,132; pig-iron, 16,659; steel ingots and castings, 22,785; rolled finished products, 15,220; aluminium, 134; lead ore (metal content), 60.9; zinc ore (metal content), 85.4; potassium fertilizers, 1,711; salt, 3,573; cement, 19,390; paper and newsprint, 2,175; synthetic rubber, 23; merchant vessels: tonnage launched, 1,429,000 GRT (15 % of world production); textiles: cotton yarn, 393; woollen yarn, 106; rayon staple fibre, 139; rayon filament, 65; (thousands) clocks and watches, 29,014; radio and television sets, 4,476; shoes, 131,981 pairs.

Passenger cars, 1,180,738 (14 % of world production); commercial vehicles and buses, 187,764. Electric power (million kWh), 95,270, of which 13,162 hydro-electricity. Index of industrial production (100 in 1953) 162 in 1959.

EASTERN GERMANY. Mineral and industrial production (thousand metric tons): coal, 2,903; lignite, 268,978 (35 % of world production); iron ore (metal content), 395; pig-iron, 1,889; steel, 3,207; copper (metal content), 23; tin (metal content), 700; cement, 3,558; sulphuric acid, 530; synthetic rubber, 85; textiles: cotton yarn, 64.2; woollen yarn, 25·7; motor vehicles, 54,100; electric power (1959: million kWh), 37,200 (lignite provides nearly 90 % of electricity production; 2 % hydro-electricity). Index of industrial production (100 in 1953) 170 in 1959.

	WESTERN GERMANY	EASTERN GERMANY
Agriculture and forestry. Livestock and fishing.		
Agricultural production (thousand metric tons; in brackets, yield per acre in cwts.)		
Wheat	3,720 (22.6)	1,363 (24.8)
Rye	3,749 (22)	2,368 (17.3)
Barley	2,423 (22)	931 (22.1)
Oats.................	2,172 (20.8)	1,143 (21.4)
Potatoes	22,855 (171)	11,498 (120)
Sugar-beet	12,049 (33.2, 1957)	6,830 (25, 1957)
Wine (thousand hectolitres)..	4,413	
Timber (million cubic metres)	23.5	3.1 (sawn timber)
Livestock (thousand head)		
Cattle	11,948	3,744
Pigs	15,418	8,255
Sheep	1,127	2,019
Horses	967	624
Poultry..............	60,161	31,136
Milk (thousand metric tons)	18,308	6,003
Butter (thousand metric tons)	391	128 (1957)
Fish (thousand metric tons)	651	97.6

Communications and transport. WESTERN GERMANY. Road network (1959): 82,580 miles, including 1,496 miles of *Autobahnen*; passenger cars, 3,260,400, i.e. 63 per 1,000 inhabitants. Railways: 22,366 miles, of which 2,386 miles are electrified; goods carried: 295 million metric tons. Navigable waterways: 2,703 miles; goods carried: 137.1 million metric tons. Merchant fleet (1959): 4.58 million gross registered tons. Principal ports: Hamburg, Bremen, Emden, Lübeck. Sea-going ships: loaded, 14,321,700 metric tons entering and unloaded, 40,592,300 metric tons clearing. Principal airports: Frankfurt, Hanover, Hamburg, Berlin, Düsseldorf.

EASTERN GERMANY. Road network: 29,759 miles; road freight traffic amounted to 11 % of traffic. Passenger cars (1957): 170,000, i.e. 10 per 1,000 inhabitants. Railways: 10,000 miles (82 % of traffic). Navigable waterways: 1,642 miles (7 % of traffic). Chief ports: Wismar, Rostock, Stralsunde. Principal airports: Berlin, Leipzig, Dresden.

Trade. WESTERN GERMANY. Foreign trade (million dollars, 1959): imports, 8,477.3; exports, 9,804.3. Principal imports: foodstuffs and tobacco, 2,239; inedible raw materials, except fuels, 1,861; mineral fuels, 681.2; manufactured goods (textiles, paper, metals), 1,826; machinery and transport equipment, 752.3. Principal exports: coal, 489; chemicals, 1,105; manufactured goods (base metals, textile yarns and fabrics), 2,455; machinery and transport equipment, 4,283. Principal suppliers (million dollars and percentage of whole: United States 1,094 and 12.9 %; Netherlands, 744 and 8.8 %; France, 657 and 7.7 %; Italy, 520 and 6.1 %; Belgium-Luxembourg, 423 and 5 %; United Kingdom, 388 and 4.6 %; Sweden, 365 and 4.3 %. Principal customers: United States, 913 and 9.3 %; Netherlands, 825 and 8.4 %; France, 707 and 7.2 %; Belgium-Luxembourg, 593 and 6.1 %; Switzerland, 574 and 5.9 %; Sweden, 544 and 5.6 %; Italy, 525 and 5.4 %; Austria, 467 and 4.8 %. Trade with Eastern Germany (million dollars): exports, 256.8; imports, 212.3.

EASTERN GERMANY. Foreign trade (million roubles 1959): imports, 7,969.5; exports, 8,485.6. Principal imports (thousand metric tons): iron ore (metal content), 1,018; cereals, 1,889; coal, coke and petroleum, 18,094; motor cycles (number), 45,411; motor cars (number), 9,858. Principal exports (thousands): watches and clocks, 1,735; rubber tyres and tubes, 1,864; bricks, 25,977; passenger cars, 10.5; electric motors, 22.6; wireless sets, 100.7; photographic film (thousand square metres), 13,194. Principal suppliers (million roubles and percentage of whole): U.S.S.R., 3,878 and 48.6 %; Western Germany, 914 and 11.4 %; Czechoslovakia, 619 and 7.7 %; China, 447 and 5.6 %; Poland, 419 and 5.2 %; Hungary, 327 and 4.1 %. Principal customers: U.S.S.R., 3,766 and 44.4 %; Western Germany, 919 and 10.8 %; Poland, 706 and 8.3 %; Czechoslavakia, 686 and 8.1 %; China, 426 and 5 %; Hungary, 346 and 4.1 %.

Administrative divisions. Currency. Budget. Plans. WESTERN GERMANY. 10 *Länder* and the Western sector of Berlin. Currency: *Deutsche Mark (D.M.)*. National expenditure (1960 estimates): occupation and defence, 32.3 %; social security, 32.2 %; housing, 5.0 %; aid to Berlin, 3.1 %.

EASTERN GERMANY. 15 districts. Currency: *Deutsche Mark* (East). National expenditure: health and social services, 25 %; vocational training and sport, 6 %; science and culture, 5 %. Two-year plan (1949—50): repair of war damage and Russian dismantling; 1st five-year plan (1951—55): industrial production doubled; 2nd five-year plan (1956—60); 3rd five-year plan (1961—65).

CZECHOSLOVAKIA

Physical features. Latitude: 47°44′-51°03′ N.; longitude: 12°05′-22°34′ E. Area: 49,354 square miles. Highest point: Stalin Peak (Gerlachovka), 8,737 feet. Length of frontiers: 2,208 miles. Longest river, or part thereof, Labe (Elbe), 225 miles (out of 716).
Mean temperatures (°F.): January, 30.2 in the west and 24.8 in the east; July, 68 in the west and 69.8 in the east. Annual rainfall (average 1876—1900): 27.5 inches; lowest around Prague, less than 19.7 inches; in Bohemia, the west is wetter than the east. Number of days with rain: Prague, 130—140; mountain areas, 170—180; south and south-east: less than 100.

Land Use. Arable land, 42.2 %; permanent meadow and pasture, 15.2 %; forests, 34 %; built on land, waste and other 8.6 %. Vineyards, 55,000 acres; hopfields, 19,750 acres. End of 1959, 82 % of farmland in 'socialist sector' (i.e. co-operative and state farms).

Population. Language. Religion. Total population (1959): 13,559,000. Density per square mile: 274. Rate of increase: 1 % per annum. Rural population: 1,756,000 (about 13 % of the population) against 2,127,000 in 1949. Distribution of the active population: industry and handicrafts, 29.1 %; agriculture and forestry, 24.9 %; commerce, 7.1 %; building, 5.7 %; transport, 7.4 %; public service, 8.5 %. Population largely Slavonic: nationalities in 1957: Czechs, 8.8 million; Slovaks, 3.7 million; Magyars, 404,000; Germans, 164,000; Poles, 78,000; Ukrainians and Russians, 75,000; others, 41,000. Language: Czech in Bohemia, Moravia and Silesia; Slovak in Slovakia. Religion: predominantly Roman Catholic; over 1 million Protestants.

Chief Towns. Capital: *Prague (Praha)*, 988,949 (1959). 12 other towns (1957) have more than 50,000 inhabitants: *Brno*, 306,371; *Bratislava*, 246,695; *Ostrava*, 199,206; *Plzeň, (Pilsen)* 134,273; *Košice*, 79,460; *Olomouc*, 73,899; *Liberec*, 66,796; *Ústí nad Labem*, 64,798; *České Budějovice*, 57,974; *Gottwaldov*, 57,974; *Hradec Králové*, 55,250; *Pardubice*, 54,077.

Agriculture and forestry. Livestock. Agricultural production (thousand metric tons): wheat, 1,346; rye, 937; barley, 1,199; oats, 871; sugarbeet, 6,946; maize, 479; potatoes, 6,589; hops, 6.5. Timber (thousand cubic metres): 13,464.

Livestock (thousand head): cattle, 4,091, of which 2,317 are cows; pigs, 5,435; sheep, 889; horses, 517; poultry, 24,251. In thousand tons: meat, (commercial production only), 415 (beef and veal, 177; pork, 235); sugar, 932; milk, 4,029. Honey, 3,430 tons (1957) from 804,000 beehives.

Mining. Industry. Power. Mineral and industrial production (thousand metric tons): coal, 25,800; lignite, 54,300; coke, 7,400; iron ore (metal content), 841,000; pig-iron, 3,800; steel, 5,500; petroleum (1960 estimate), 110; aluminium, 16.2; cement, 4,110; paper, 404. Textiles (million metres): cotton, 420; wool, 43; linen, 62. Footwear (leather and rubber): 68 million pairs. Electric power: 19,620 million kWh. Index of industrial production (100 in 1953): 52 in 1948, 172 in 1959.

Communications and transport. Trade. Road network: 43,967 miles of which 5,667 miles first-class (1946); Railways: 8,182 miles of which 1,678 double track and 173 electrified). About 90 % of freight traffic is carried by rail. Inland waterways, 298 miles. Principal airports: Ruzyne (Prague), Cernovice (Brno), Vajnory (Bratislava), Holice (Olomouc), Barca (Košice).
Increase in volume of foreign trade: 100 in 1953, 202 in 1959. Imports (million korunas, 1959): 11,537; exports: 12,435. Principal imports: wheat, coffee, tea, coal, petroleum products, iron ore and motor cars. Principal exports: coal, metallurgical machinery, motor cars, motor cycles and bicycles, cotton and silk fabrics, footwear. Over two-thirds of the foreign trade of Czechoslovakia is with the U.S.S.R., Eastern Europe and China. Imports from the U.S.S.R. (million korunas): 4,305 and 37.3 %; exports to the U.S.S.R.: 4,229 and 34.0 %.

Administrative divisions. Currency. Plans. 10 regions and the city of Prague, which forms a separate administrative unit. Currency: the *koruna* (Kčs), or crown, of 100 *haler*.
A two-year plan of reconstruction 1947—48; 1st five-year plan (1949—53); yearly plans of readjustment, 1954 and 1955; 2nd five-year plan (1956—60) gave priority to the production of capital goods, to increasing agricultural production and co-operative farming and improvement of transport; 3rd five-year plan (1961—65) continues to lay stress on production of capital goods, especially in the chemical industry, engineering and metallurgy.

HUNGARY

Physical features. Land Use. Latitude 45°45′-49° N.; longitude: 16°15′-22°45′ E. Area: 35,912 square miles. Highest point: Mátra, 3,314 feet. Longest river, or part thereof, Danube (Duna), 559 miles (out of 1,839); Tisza, 828 miles. Area of Lake Balaton, 251 square miles; greatest depth 39.37 feet.
Mean temperatures at Budapest (°F): January, 28.4; July, 71.6. Mean annual rainfall (inches): 27.6 in the west; 23.6 in the east; less than 19.7 in the Tisza basin.
Area under cereals: 40 %.

Population. Language. Religion. Total population: 10,002,000 (1960). Density per square mile: 279. Birth rate, 16.1 per 1,000; rate of increase, 0.6 %. Rural population, 62.5 %. Distribution of the active population: industry and handicrafts, 35 %; agriculture and forestry, 48 %; commerce and transport, 16 %.
The majority of the people are Magyars, 92.8 %; other ethnic groups according to their mother tongue: Germans, 5.1 %; Slovaks, 0.8 %; Croats, 0.2 %; Gypsies, 0.2 %; Rumanians, 0.2 %; Serbs, 0.1 %. Religion: Roman Catholics, 65 %; Protestants, 27 %.

Chief Towns. Capital: *Budapest*, with its suburbs, 1,850,000 (1957). Other towns: *Miskolc*, 150,000; *Debrecen*, 130,000; *Pécs*, 110,000; *Szeged*, 100,000; *Győr*, 68,000; *Kecskemét*, 67,000; *Nyíregyháza*, 56,000.

Agriculture. Livestock. Agricultural production (thousand metric tons): wheat, 1,487; rye, 371; barley, 735; oats, 192; maize, 2,833; potatoes, 2,600; sugar-beet, 2,070; sugar, 272. Wine, 5,295,000 hectolitres. Yield per acre of wheat: 10 cwts.
Livestock (thousand head): cattle, 1,937; pigs, 5,338; sheep, 2,050; horses, 724; poultry (1957), 23,880. Milk (thousand tons), 1,951; wool, 7.3.

Mining. Industry. Power. Mineral and industrial production (thousand metric tons): coal, 2,626; lignite, 21,615; iron ore (metal content), 100; pig-iron, 902; steel, 1,355; bauxite, 877; petroleum (1960 estimate), 1,200; cement, 1,302; cotton yarn, 46.4; woollen yarn, 13.1. Leather footwear: 16 million pairs. Electric power: 5,504 million kWh.

Communications and transport. Trade. Road network: 17,918 miles. Railways: 8,878 miles. Navigable waterways: 804 miles; the Hungarian Danube-Sea Navigation Company had in 1959 8 sea-going vessels of 8,000 gross tons altogether. Principal airport: Ferihegy, 12½ miles from the capital. Foreign trade (million *forints*): imports, 9,269.4; exports, 8,994.4. Principal imports: coal, coke and petroleum; iron ore; fertilizers; timber. Principal exports: motor cycles and lorries, lathe machines; textiles. Principal trading partners: U.S.S.R. (provides 2,975.7 imports and takes 2,399.2 exports), Czechoslovakia, Eastern Germany and China.

Administrative divisions. Currency. There are 19 counties (*megyek*) and 5 county boroughs. Currency: the *forint*, divided into 100 *fillér*.

POLAND

Physical features. Land Use. Latitude: 49°-54°50′ N.; longitude: 14°5′-24°19′ E. Area: 120,360 square miles. Highest point: Mount Rysy (Carpathians), 8,199 feet. Lenght of coastline: 361 miles; lenght of frontiers: 2,080 miles. Length of longest rivers: Wisła (Vistula), 653 miles; Odra (Oder), 527 miles.
Temperatures (mean annual 1891—1930 and January and July means for 1956, °F.): 46, 29.3 and 64 in the centre (Warsaw); 43.8, 27.1 and 61.4 in the north (Lidzbark); 47.8, 30.9 and 63.7 in the south (Tarnów). Rainfall (mean annual 1891—1930 and January and July means for 1956, in inches): 22.2, 0.86 and 3.78 in Warsaw; 24.96, 1.93 and 4.57 at Lidzbark; 29.09, 0.39 and 1.53 at Tarnów.
Arable land, 52 %; permanent meadow and pasture, 13.4 %; forests, 24.1 %; built on land, waste and other, 10.5 %.

Population. Language. Religion. Towns. Total population (1959): 29,257,000. Density per square mile: 242 (highest in Silesia). Birth rate, 26.3 per 1,000; death rate, 8.4 per 1,000. Rural population (1957), 54.5 %; urban, 45.5 %. Distribution of the active population: industry and handicrafts, 17.7 %; agriculture and forestry, 53.3 %; commerce, 5 %; transport, 3.6 %. National minorites include (1957) Ukrainians, 200,000; Byelorussians, 65,000; Germans, 50,000.
Language: Polish. Religion: Roman Catholic.

Capital: *Warsaw (Warszawa)*, 1,095,000 (1959). Other towns: *Łódź*, 698,000; *Kraków*, 463,000; *Wrocław (Breslau)*, 415,000; *Poznań*, 395,000; *Gdańsk (Danzig)*, 266,100; *Szczecin (Stettin)*, 249,400; *Bydgoszcz*, 219,700; *Katowice*, 266,500; *Zabrze*, 181,200; *Bytom*, 175,100; *Częstochowa*, 159,600; *Lublin*, 148,200; *Chorzów*, 143,600; *Gdynia*, 140,200; *Sosnowiec*, 125,600; *Gliwice*, 124,700; *Radom*, 121,200; *Białystok*, 111,400; *Wałbrzych*, 110,900.

Agriculture and forestry. Livestock and fishing. Agricultural production (thousand metric tons): wheat, 2,322; rye, 7,329; barley, 1,210; oats, 2,669; potatoes, 34,800; sugar-beet, 8,220; tobacco, 37. Timber: 16.5 million cubic metres.
Livestock (thousand head): cattle, 8,210; pigs, 11,959; sheep, 3,882; horses, 2,732. Meat, milk and butter (thousand metric tons): 1,765; 11,871; 162. Fish: 137.7.

Mining. Industry. Power. Mineral and industrial production (thousand metric tons): coal, 94,981 (5.4 % of world production); coke, 11,143; lignite, 7,541; iron ore (metal content), 581; pig-iron, 3,864; steel, 5,631; petroleum (1960 estimate), 200; salt, 1,610; sulphuric acid, 573; super-phosphates, 581; cement, 5,041; wood pulp, 389; paper and newsprint, 432; nitrogenous fertilizers, 227; textiles: cotton fabrics, 607.9 million metres; woollen fabrics, 78.1 million metres; silk fabrics, 97.1 million metres; linen and hemp fabrics,

440

73.7 million metres. Shipbuilding, 162,300 GRT; motor vehicles, 23,000. Electric power, 23,946 million kWh. Index of industrial production (100 in 1953) 39 in 1948, 178 in 1959.

Communications and transport. Trade. Road network: 63,310 miles; passenger cars, 59,200, i.e. 2.1 per 1,000 inhabitants. Railways: 16,970 miles, of which 416 miles are electrified. Navigable waterways: 4,292 miles. Merchant fleet: 458,000 gross registered tons. Shipping entering Polish ports: 8.4 million net registered tons. Principal airports: Warsaw, Poznań, Gdańsk.

Foreign trade (million *zlotys*): imports: 5,678.4; exports: 4,580.5. Principal imports: petroleum products, 285.6; iron ore, 278; cereals, 496; cotton, 307.4; rolled steel products, including pipes, 245; wool, 155.4. Principal

exports: coal, lignite and coke, 1,142.3; rolled steel products, including pipes, 409.8; ships and boats, 223.9; meat and meat products, 313.8; sugar, 108.1. Principal suppliers (million *zlotys* and percentage of whole): U.S.S.R., 1,809.2. and 31.8 %; Eastern Germany, 749 and 13.2 %; Czechoslovakia, 451.6 and 7.9 %; United Kingdom, 346.1 and 6.1 %; Western Germany, 267.4 and 4.7 %; China, 224.2 and 3.9 %.

Principal customers: U.S.S.R., 1,251.9 and 27.4 %; Eastern Germany 547.5 and 12.2 %; United Kingdom, 346.8 and 7.6 %; Czechoslovakia, 322.5 and 7 %; Western Germany, 311.9 and 6.8 %; China, 171.5 and 3.7 %.

Administrative divisions. Currency. 17 voivodships and 5 cities of voivodship status. Currency: the *zloty*, divided into 100 *groszy*.

RUMANIA

Physical features. Latitude: 43°38'–48°20'N.; longitude: 20°20'–29°40'E. Area: 89,700 square miles. Highest points: Negoiul, 8,920feet and Mindru, 8,297 feet (Southern Carpathians); Rodnei mountains, 7,559 (Moldavian Carpathians). Length of coastline, 152 miles; length of land frontiers, 665 miles; river frontiers, 1,142 miles. Longest river, or part thereof, Danube (Dunărea), 668 miles (out of 1,839); Mureș, 478 miles (out of 547); Prut, 439 miles (out of 534); Olt (Oltu), 438 miles.

Temperatures (mean annual, January and July means, °F.): 53.1, 43.5 and 59.9 in the south (Bucharest); 56.6, 42.8 and 61.2 in the north (Jaşi). Annual rainfall (inches) is very irregular: 16.46 at Jaşi (22.8 in 1955); 22 at Bucharest (30.7 in 1954); 18.5 at Cluj (26.4 in 1954).' Frost and snow: 95 days of frost a year at Bucharest; 37 days of snow at Brăila, 44 days in Transylvania.

Land Use. Arable land, 42.6 %; permanent meadow and pasture, 17.5 %; forests, 27.1 %; built on land, waste and other, 12.8 %. Vineyards: 600,000 acres. At the beginning of 1960, 76 % of the agricultural land was said to be in the socialist sector (collective farms, state farms and agricultural co-operatives).

Population. Language. Religion. Total population (1959): 18,256,000. Density per square mile: 203. Birth rate: 21.6 per 1,000; death rate: 8.7 per 1,000; infant mortality rate: 69 per 1,000 live births (206.9 average 1920—24; 187 in 1945). Rural population: 68.8 % (79.8 % in 1930); urban population, 31.2 %. Distribution of the active population: agriculture, 69 %; industry, 13.1 %; construction, 4.4 %; commerce and food, 2.6 %; transport and telecommunications, 1.8 %; public service, 2.3 %; teaching, medecine, 3 %. Language: Rumanian is spoken by nearly 88 % of the people; Hungarian, 9 %; German, 2.2 %; Slav, 0.8 %. Religion (before the present regime, according to the 1930 census): Rumanian Orthodox, 72.6 % (13.67 million members in 1950); Uniate (Greek-Catholic), 7.6 %; Roman Catholic, 6.8 %; Protestant, 6.8 %; Jews, 4.2 %; Moslems, 1 %.

Chief Towns. Capital: *Bucharest (Bucureşti)*, 1,279,000 (639,000 in 1930; 902,000 in 1941). 16 other towns have more than 50,000 inhabitants: *Cluj*, 161,000; *Timişoara*, 147,000; *Stalin*, 127,000; *Suceava*, 124,000; *Ploeşti*, 122,000; *Iaşi*, 121,000; *Arad*, 110,000; *Constanţa*, 109,000; *Brăila*, 107,000; *Oradea*, 104,000; *Craiova*, 103,000; *Galaţi*, 100,000; *Sibiu*, 95,000; *Tîrgu-Mureş*, 69,000; *Bacău*, 59,000; *Satu Mare*, 55,000.

Agriculture. Livestock. Agricultural production (thousand metric tons; in brackets yield per acre in cwts.): wheat, 2,914 (7.8); maize, 3,657 (8); potatoes, 2,777; sugar-beet, 1,732; sunflower seed, 286. Livestock (thousand head): cattle, 4,470; sheep, 10,374; pigs, 3,249; horses, 1,309. In thousand tons: milk, 2,373; meat, 903; tobacco, 31.

Mining. Industry. Power. Mineral and industrial production (thousand metric tons): petroleum (1960 estimate), 11,550 (6,240 in 1939); coal, 7,388 (6,240 in 1939); iron ore (metal content), 230; pig-iron, 737; steel, 934; lead ore, 200; cement, 2,570; salt, 1,000. Natural gas, 8,313 million cubic metres (1,860 in 1938). Electric power (million kWh): 6,184, of which 280 was hydro-electricity. Index of industrial production: 100 in 1955, 147 in 1959.

Communications and transport. Trade. Road network: 47,000 miles; passenger cars (1950): 14,560, i.e. 1 for every 1,106 inhabitants. Railways (1955): 7,610 miles. Principal airport: Baneasa (4½ miles from the centre of Bucharest).

Foreign trade (by value): with western and central Europe, 15 % (81.5 % in 1937, before the Anschluss; 14.9 % in 1954); with eastern Europe and China, 78.9 %. Imports (million *lei*), 3,011.6; exports, 3,130.3. Principal customers (million *lei* and percentage of total exports): U.S.S.R., 1,500.6 and 47.9 %; Eastern Germany, 213 and 6.8 %; Czechoslovakia, 210.4 and 6.7 %; China, 176.5 and 5.6 %; Western Germany, 143.9 and 4.6 %; Hungary, 136.8 and 4.4 %; Poland, 131.7 and 4.2 %; France, 84.2 and 2.7 %. Principal exports: petroleum and petroleum products; timber and wood products; foodstuffs; cement; glass; industrial machinery. Principal imports: machine tools; passenger cars and motor cycles; industrial machinery.

Practically all domestic trade is under state control. In 1956 only 2.7 % was in private hands; the rest in state and co-operative stores.

Administrative divisions. Currency. Budget. Plans. 16 regions and the administrative district of Bucharest City. Currency: the *leu* (plural *lei*) divided into 100 *bani*. Main items of expenditure in 1960: national economy, 60 %; social and cultural development, 24 %; defence, 6 %; administration, 3 %.

The first five-year plan (1951—55) aimed at establishing the economic basis of socialism, increasing industrial output fivefold and doubling the 1948 agricultural production figure, and rationalising industry in relation to local resources; the second five-year plan (1956—60) aimed at developing national resources (electricity, uranium) and the chemical industry, increasing productivity.

BULGARIA

Physical features. Latitude: 41°14'–44°12' N.; longitude: 22°21'–28°37' E. Area: 42,796 square miles. Highest point: Mount Varna Stalin (Musala), 9,596 feet. Length of coastline: 193 miles. Length of land frontiers: 1,358 miles. Longest river: Iskăr, tributary of the Danube, 249 miles.

Temperatures (°F): mean annual, 53.6; July, 71.6 in the north and 75.2 in the south; January, 28.4 in the north and 53.6 in the south. Mean annual rainfall: Danube region, around 20 inches; maximum in the Stara Planina (Mount Varna Stalin), 39.4 inches. Number of days of rain per year: 60 to 70 in the north; 20 to 30 in the south.

Land Use. Arable land, 40.6 %; permanent meadow and pasture, 9.1 %; forests, 33.2 %; built on land, waste, and other, 17.1 %. Area worked by co-operatives: 11 million acres, i.e., 80 % of the farmland.

Population. Language. Religion. Towns. Total population (1959): 7,798,000 (7,029,000 in 1946). Density per square mile: 182. Birth rate: 20 per 1,000 (average 1948—52: 23.3 per 1,000); death rate: 9 per 1,000. Rural population: 66.5 % (77.3 % in 1926); urban population: 33.5 % (22.7 % in 1926).

Distribution of the active population: industry and handicrafts, 11 %; agriculture and forestry, 72.6 %; commerce, 2.7 %; transport, 3 %; construction, 3.1 %. Nationalities: Bulgars, 92 %; Russians 0.8 %; Gypsies, 1.2 %; Armenians, 0.8 %; Turks, 0.4 %.

Language: 88 % speak Bulgarian, 9.8 % Turkish. Religion: Eastern Orthodox.

Capital: *Sofia*, 725,756. Other towns with more than 50,000 inhabitants: *Plovdiv*, 162,518; *Varna*, 119,769; *Ruse*, 83,472; *Burgas*, 72,795; *Dimitrovo*, 59,721; *Pleven*, 57,758; *Stara Zagora*, 55,322.

Agriculture and forestry. Livestock. Agricultural production (thousand metric tons): wheat, 2,328; maize, 872; barley, 58; oats, 134; rye, 102; sunflower seeds, 222; unginned cotton, 45; tobacco, 76; potatoes, 246; grapes, 837. Timber: 4.4 million cubic metres. Livestock (thousand head): cattle, 1,442; sheep, 7,742; pigs, 1,993; horses, 431; poultry, 13,384. Milk (thousand tons): 1,006.

Mining. Industry. Power. Mineral and industrial production (thousand metric tons): coal and lignite, 12,700; petroleum (1960 estimate), 190; iron ore (metal content), 137; steel, 211; copper ore, 78; lead-zinc ore, 139; cement, 934 (1,433 in 1959); textiles (1959): cotton fabrics, 209 million metres; woollen fabrics, 19 million metres. Footwear: 6.4 million pairs. Electric power: 3,024 million kWh, of which 962 hydro-electricity. Index of industrial production: 100 in 1953, 222 in 1959.

Communications and transport. Trade. Road network: 15,870 miles. Railways: 2,670 miles (9 % narrow gauge); the bulk of freight traffic is carried by rail. Merchant fleet (1959): 35,783 gross registered tons; traffic of all ports (1955): about 2.7 million tons (60 %, Danube ports; 40 %, Black Sea). Danube ports: Ruse, Svishchtov, Lom, Somovit; Black Sea ports: Varna, Burgas. Principal airport: Vrajdebna (near Sofia).

Foreign trade (million *leva*, 1957): imports, 2,494; exports, 2,548. Principal imports: petroleum products, 102.4; raw cotton, 122.9; chemicals, 101.1; iron and steel sheets, 75.1; construction steel, 29.4; fertilizers, 61.3; synthetic rubber, 40.8; cotton textiles, 131.4; tractors, 38.5; wheat, 102.2. Principal exports: raw tobacco, 348; metal ores and concentrates, 256.8; fresh fruit, 59.7; meat, 44.8; eggs, 54.9; cigarettes, 73.9; timber and manufactures, 56.6; cotton and woollen fabrics, 120.6; railway locomotives, 61.4; mint and rose oil, 27.7. Principal trading partners: U.S.S.R., 53.3 %: Czechoslovakia, 10.4 %; Eastern Germany, 9.3 %; China, 2.4 %; Hungary, 2.4 %.

Administrative divisions. Currency. Plans. 30 administrative units comprising 27 provinces and three large towns (Sofia, Plovdiv and Varna). Currency: the *lev* (plural *leva*). The third five-year plan (1958—62) gives priority to heavy industry; industrial production is expected to rise by 60 %; investments to be made in light industry are lower; a rise of 35 % in agricultural production is expected. The merchant fleet is expected to increase by 98 %; the standard of living to rise by 50 %.

YUGOSLAVIA

Physical features. Land Use. Latitude: 40°51'-46°53' N.; longitude: 13°23'-23°01' E. Area: 99,000 square miles. Highest point: Triglav, 9,393 feet. Length of frontiers: 2,969 miles. Longest river: Sava, 584 miles.

Mean January and July temperatures (°F.): Zagreb, 30.9 and 70.9; Dubrovnik, 35.8 and 78; Belgrade, 30.7 and 72.3; Skopje, 29.5 and 76.7. Mean annual rainfall (inches): Zagreb, 35.4; Dubrovnik, 51.2; Belgrade, 24.4; Skopje, 17.3.

Arable land, 32.5 %; permanent meadow and pasture, 25.9 %; forests, 34.5 %; built on land, waste, and other, 7.1 %. Vineyards: 675,000 acres.

Population. Language. Religion. Towns. Total population (1960): 18,655,000. Density per square mile: 187. Birth rate: 23.8 per 1,000; infant mortality rate: 86.2 per 1,000 live births; rate of increase: 1.3 % per annum. Rural population: approximately 65 %. Distribution of the active population: agriculture, 65 %; forestry, 6 %; industry, 8 %; handicrafts, 4 %; buildings 2.5 %; commerce, 3 %; transport, 2 %; administrative services, 5 %.

Language: Serbo-Croat spoken by 76.4 %; Slovene by 9 %; Macedonian, 5.7 %; Albanian, 4.8 %; Hungarian, 3 %; Turkish, 1 %. Religion: 41.4 % Orthodox; 12.3 % Moslem; 0.9 % Protestant; 12.3 % without religion.

Capital: *Belgrade (Beograd)*, 522,000 inhabitants. Other towns of more than 70,000: *Zagreb*, 400,000; *Ljubljana*, 140,000; *Sarajevo*, 136,000; *Skopje*, 121,500; *Subotica*, 115,500; *Novi Sad*, 90,000; *Maribor*, 80,000; *Split*, 75,300; *Rijeka*, 75,000; *Niš*, 70,000.

Agriculture and Forestry. Livestock and Fishing. Agricultural production (thousand metric tons): wheat, 2,453; maize, 3,950 (5,660 in 1957); sugar-beet, 1,480; potatoes, 2,620. Wine, 5.78 million hectolitres. Timber: 15.5 million cubic metres. Livestock (thousand head): cattle, 4,863; sheep, 10,633; pigs, 4,243; horses, 1,296; mules and donkeys, 195; poultry, 28,503. Fish: 31,400 tons.

Mining. Industry. Power. Mineral and industrial production (thousand metric tons): coal, 1,208; lignite, 17,778; copper, 35.3; bauxite, 733; iron ore (metal content), 959; pig-iron, 780; steel, 1,119. Electric power (million kWh): 7,356, of which 4,301 hydro-electricity. Index of industrial production (100 in 1953): 82 in 1948, 214 in 1959.

Communications and transport. Trade. Roads: 32,938 miles, of which 3,116 have asphalt surface; passenger cars, 28,389, i.e., 1.5 per 1,000 inhabitants. Railways: 7,324 miles; freight carried: 57.2 million tons. Navigable waterways: rivers, 1,170 miles; canals, 118 miles; lakes, 56 miles; freight carried, 3.8 million tons. Merchant fleet, 451,000 gross tons. Principal airports: Belgrade, Zagreb. Tourists (1959): 834,000.

Foreign trade (million *dinars*): imports, 206,156; exports, 142,995. Main imports: machinery and transport equipment, 57,606; foodstuffs, 39,796; manufactured goods, 32,314; raw materials, 28,774; chemicals, 22,590; mineral fuels, 13,589. Main exports: foodstuffs (meat, fish cereals, fruit), 36,505; manufactured goods (base metals, wood and cork), 35,556; machinery and transport equipment, 24,816; raw materials (timber, metal ores), 22,766; tobacco, 7,075. Principal suppliers (million *dinars* and percentage of whole): United States, 42,004 and 20.4 %; Western Germany, 28,932 and 14 %; Italy, 19,189 and 9.3 %; U.S.S.R., 17,288 and 8.4 %; United Kingdom, 10,638 and 5.15 %;. Principal customers: Italy, 17,316 and 12.1 % U.S.S.R., 14,154 and 9.9 %; Western Germany, 13,437 and 9.4 %; United Kingdom, 10,216 and 7.15 %; Poland, 10,151 and 7.1 %; United States, 9,344 and 6.5 %.

Administrative divisions. Currency. 6 republics (capitals in brackets): Serbia (Belgrade) with the autonomous province of Vojvodina (Novi Sad) and the autonomous region of Kosovo-Metohija (Pristina); Croatia (Zagreb); Slovenia (Ljubljana); Bosnia-Herzegovina (Sarajevo); Macedonia (Skopje); Montenegro (Titograd). Currency: the *dinar*, divided into 100 *paras*.

ALBANIA

Physical features. Land Use. Latitude: 40°45'-42°30' N.; longitude: 19°20'-8' E. Area: 10,629 square miles. Two-thirds of the country is above 3,250 feet in altitude. Length of coasts: 155—160 miles. Mean January and July temperatures (°F.): Vlonë, 48.2 and 77; Tirana, 45.9 and 77; Durrës, 50.5 and 77.7. Mean annual rainfall: Tirana and Durrës, 47.2 inches.

Arable land, 12.3 %; permanent meadow and pasture, 29.6 %; forests, 39.3 %; unused but potentially productive, 9 %; built on land, waste, and other, 9.8 %.

Population. Language. Religion. Towns. Total population (1959): 1,556,000. Density per square mile: 146. Rate of increase: 3 % per annum. Rural population: 81 %; 60 % live by stock-rearing. Nationalities: Albanians, 95.85 %; Greeks, 2.36 %. Language: Albanian (Ghegs in north, Tosks in south). Religion: Moslem, 68.9 %; Orthodox church of Albania, 20.7 %; Roman Catholic, 10 %.

Capital: *Tirana*, 80,000. Other towns: *Vlonë (Valona)*, 34,000; *Shkodër (Scutari)*, 34,000; *Korçë (Koritza)*, 24,000.

Agriculture and forestry. Livestock. Agricultural production (thousand metric tons): tobacco (1957), 1.1; olive oil, 2.8; sugar, 10.3; wool, 2.2. Timber: 146,913 cubic metres.

Livestock (thousand head): cattle, 405; sheep, 1,612; goats, 1,029; horses, mules and donkeys, 119; pigs, 96.

Mining. Industry. Communications. Mineral and industrial production (thousand metric tons): lignite, 147; petroleum (1960 estimate), 600 (pipeline from Kuçovë to port of Vlonë); bitumen, 32.2; copper ore, 87.5; iron ore, 88.2; chrome ore, 201.3; cement, 77.6. Under the 3rd five-year plan (1961—65) the mining of chrome, copper and nickel-iron ores will continue to expand and a chemical-metallurgical combine will be erected to produce sulphuric acid and chemical fertilizer.

Road network: 1,370 miles. Railways: 80 miles; extension of the rail system is planned. Merchant fleet: 3 ocean-going and 12 coastal vessels. Airport: Tirana.

Administrative divisions. Currency. 10 prefectures: Berat, Dibër, Durrës, Elbasan, Gjinokastër, Korçë, Kukës, Shkodër, Vlonë, Tirana. Currency: the *lek*, divided into 100 *quintars*.

GREECE

Physical features. Land Use. Latitude: 34°41'-41°44' N.; longitude: 19°22'-29°38' E. Area: 51,168 square miles. Highest point: Mount Olympus, 9,573 feet. Length of coastline: 8,311 miles; length of land frontiers, 733 miles. Longest rivers: Aliakmon, 195 miles; Achelous, 132 miles.

Mean annual temperatures (°F.; average for the period 1921—31 in which great extremes occurred): Salonica, 66.2 (January mean, 41.9; July, 78.6); Jannina, 59 (January, 43; July, 76.3); Zante, 66.7 (January, 53.6; July, 81); Athens, 65.1 (January, 50; July, 81.1); Santorin, 63.7 (January, 52.2; July, 76.3). Rainfall (inches) and number of days with rain in 1937: Salonica, 21.8 and 153; Jannina, 52.8 and 170; Athens, 21 and 114; Canea (Crete), 18.9 and 103. Days with snow: 1 to 3 days a year, but only every two or three years.

Arable land, 26.6 %; permanent meadow and pasture, 39.1 %; forests, 14.8 %; built on land, waste, and other, 19.5 %.

Population. Language. Religion. Towns. Total population (1959): 8,258,000. Density per square mile: 161, but 864 in the Ionian Islands. Age structure: a quarter of the population is under 15 years; another quarter, 15—30; another quarter, 30—50; 15 %, 50—70, and 4.23 %, over 70. Rural population, 52 %; urban, 48 %. Distribution of the active population: industry and handicrafts, 19.4 %; agriculture, forestry and fishing, 48.5 %; commerce, 19.4 %; transport, 7.7 %; public service, 5 %.

Language: Greek. Religion: Greek Orthodox.

Capital: *Athens*, 565,000; *Greater Athens (Athens* and *Piraeus)*, 1,368,000. Other towns of more than 40,000: *Salonica*, 226,147; *Patras*, 79,338; *Volos*, 54,919; *Iraklion (Crete)*, 51,144; *Kavalla*, 42,102; *L-risa*, 41,016.

Agriculture and forestry. Livestock and fishing. Agricultural production (thousand metric tons): wheat, 1,787; barley, 267; oats, 175; maize, 224; potatoes, 460; tomatoes, 456; cotton, 192; tobacco, 83.8; olive oil, 111 (183 in 1957); grapes, 111; citrus fruit, 260; sultanas, 42; currants, 82. Wine, 3,159,000 hectolitres. Timber (1957): 4.1 million cubic metres.

Livestock (thousand head): cattle, 1,010; sheep, 9,195; goats, 4,939; pigs, 650; horses, 333; mules and donkeys, 731. Fish: 75,000 metric tons.

Mining. Industry. Power. Mineral and industrial production (thousand metric tons): lignite, 1,196; bauxite, 856; iron ore (metal content), 140; cement, 1,361; salt, 96; textiles: cotton yarn, 23.7; wool yarn, 4.79; rayon yarn, 1.5. Electric power (million kWh): 1,802, of which 449 hydro-electricity. 125,000 metric tons steel ingots and castings: shipyards, an oil refinery and a lignite plant indicate the beginnings of heavy industry in Greece. Index of industrial production (manufacturing only; 100 in 1953): 52 in 1948, 156 in 1959.

Communications and transport. Road network: 29,306 miles, of which 20,675 are all-weather roads. Railways: 1,611 miles. Merchant fleet (1960): 839 vessels of 3,460,085 gross registered tons. To this should be added the large tonnage belonging to Greek shipping companies but sailing under flags of convenience. Piraeus is the principal port: a ferry for motor vehicles crosses the Gulf of Corinth from Patras to Navpactos. Principal airport: Elliniko (near Athens).

Trade. Foreign trade (million *drachmai* 1959): impor s, 16,942; exports, 6,128 (1953, 7,156 and 3,397). Principal imports: machinery and transport equipment (lorries, railway stock, electrical appliances, ships), 6,344; manufactured goods (paper, textiles, base metals), 3,267; foodstuffs, 2,300; chemicals, 1,519; raw materials (timber, woodpulp, textile fibres), 1,517; mineral fuels, 1,484. Principal exports: tobacco, 2,052.8; foodstuffs (currants, sultanas, fresh fruit), 1,850; raw cotton, 781; metal ores, 325.9.

Principal suppliers (million *drachmai* and percentage of whole): Western Germany, 3.273 and 19.3 %; United Kingdom, 2,022 and 11.9 %; United States, 1,757 and 10.4 %; Italy, 1,193 and 7.05 %; Netherlands, 755 and 4.5 %. Principal customers: Western Germany, 1,254 and 20.4 %; United States, 789.6 and 12.9 %; United Kingdom, 571 and 9.3 %; Italy, 452 and 7.4 %; France, 448 and 7.3 %. Tourists (1957): 221,900.

Administrative divisions. Currency. Budget. The mainland of Greece and the islands are divided into 51 prefectures *(nomoi)*. Currency: the *drachma;* the *drachma* was devalued by 50 % in 1954. Government expenditure: in 1958, 40 % of expenditure on defence: revenue included 471 million *drachmai* of United States aid and 367 million from NATO. Development plans include the extension of cultivated area by irrigation or reclamation; an increase in production of industrial crops (cotton) and high-yielding food crops (rice, fruit, sugar-beet); afforestation; equipment of power plants (coal and hydro-electric); construction of industrial plants (textiles, fertilizers, cement, metallurgy, oil refineries); equipment of fishing fleet; improvements in communications (railways, roads, airways, ports and merchant fleet).

CYPRUS

Physical features. Land Use. Latitude: 34°33'-35°41' N.; longitude: 32°20'-34°36' E. Area: 3,572 square miles. Highest point: Mount Olympus (Troödos Massif) 6,403 feet. Mean annual rainfall: 21.25 inches.

Arable land, 46.9 %; permanent meadow and pasture, 10 %; forests, 18.4 %; unused, but potentially productive, 3.3 %; built on land, waste, and other, 21.4 %.

Population. Language. Religion. Towns. Total population (1959): 558,000 (186,172 in 1881). Density per square mile: 156. Infant mortality rate per 1,000: 30 (63 in 1950). Rate of increase: 1.7 % per annum. Religion: Greek Orthodox, 79 %; Turkish Moslem, 17.5 %. Language: Greek, Turkish and English are the official languages.

Capital: *Nicosia*, 50,900 inhabitants. Other towns: *Limassol*, 38,000; *Famagusta*, 27,900; *Larnata*, 18,500.

Agriculture. Livestock. Mining. Industry. Agricultural production (thousand metric tons): wheat, 81; barley, 73; potatoes (two crops annually), 52; grapes, 70; citrus fruit, 10; olives, 1; tobacco, 0.4. Livestock (thousand head): cattle, 33; pigs, 39; sheep, 381; goats, 159; mules and donkeys, 51.

Minerals (copper and iron pyrites, chrome ore), gypsum, asbestos, etc., are exported, almost all in the raw state.

Communications. Trade. Administration. Road network: 974 miles of main roads; 2,900 miles of feeder roads. No railway or navigable waterway.

Foreign trade (£ thousand): imports, 41,039; exports, 19,000, of which nearly half are mineral products. Principal suppliers (thousand £ and percentage of whole): United Kingdom, 14,694 and 35.8 %; Western Germany, 3,955 and 9.65 %; Italy, 3,053 and 7.45 %; principal customers: United Kingdom, 5,328 and 28 %; Western Germany, 4,781 and 25.2 %; Netherlands, 1,796 and 9.45 %; United States, 898 and 4.7 %. Other Commonwealth countries provide 5.5 % of imports and take 1.9 % of exports.

Cyprus is divided into 6 administrative districts.

MALTA

Physical features. Land Use. Latitude: 35°48'-36° N.; longitude: 14°19'-14°35' E. Area: Malta, 95 square miles; Malta, Gozo and Comino 122 square miles. Highest point: 932 feet. Length of coastline: Malta, 85 miles; Malta and Gozo, 111.4 miles. No permanent river courses.

Temperatutes (°F.): mean annual, 62.6; January, 53.6; July, 73.4. Annual rainfall: 21.6 inches. Number of days of rain: 90—95 annually.

Arable land, 62.5 %; unused, but potentially productive, 3.1 %; built on land, waste, and other, 34.4 %. Average size of holdings: 80 acres.

Population. Language. Religion. Towns. Total population: Malta and Gozo, 325,000 (1959; 123,496 in 1851); several small islands, including Comino, are uninhabited. Density per square mile: 2,663. Birth rate: 26.5 per 1,000; infant mortality rate: 40 per 1,000. Malta is the most densely peopled territory in Europe and the population is increasing rapidly. Emigration 1946—58: 69,697.

Rural population, 34.6 %; urban population, 65.4 %; the majority live in small towns and villages. Distribution of active population: industry and handicrafts, 16 %; agriculture, 9 %; commerce, 3.6 %; transport, 1 %; fishing, 1 %; public services, 65 %.

Language: Maltese and English are official languages.

Religion: Roman Catholic.

Capital: *Valletta*, 18,247. Other towns: *Sliema*, 23,521; *Paola* and *Tarxien*, 19,286; *Birkirkara*, 17,234; *Hamrun*, 16,925.

Agriculture. Livestock. Industry. Communications. Agricultural production (thousand metric tons): wheat, 3; potatoes, 23 (two crops annually); tomatoes, 10; grapes, 6. Livestock: cattle, 9,798; horses, 1,980; mules, 1,819; donkeys, 2,776; sheep, 15,011; goats, 36,914; pigs, 16,362. Fish: 1,059 metric tons. Salt: 1,500 metric tons. There is a variety of light industries, including the manufacture of tomato paste and other foodstuffs, wine, footwear, hosiery, clothing, buttons, lace and filigree work. Electricity (million kWh): 49.1.

Road network: 503 miles surfaced roads; passenger cars: 12,452. Valletta harbour is one of the most magnificent in the Mediterranean. It was the site of a Royal Naval Dockyard until 1959 when it was handed over to a private firm. Airport: Luqa.

Trade. Currency. Budget. Foreign trade (£ thousand): imports, 27,779; exports, 4,035. Chief imports: foodstuffs, 9,785; manufactured goods, 5,063; machinery and transport equipment, 3,392; mineral fuels, 2,328. Principal exports: foodstuffs, including potatoes, 1,185; raw materials, 532. Principal suppliers (£ thousand and percentage of whole): United Kingdom, 11,212 and 40.3 %; Italy, 3,296 and 11.9 %; Netherlands, 1,482 and 5.3 %; France, 1,296 and 4.7 %; Western Germany, 1,195 and 4.3 %. Principal customers: United Kingdom, 920 and 22.8 %; Libya, 710 and 17.6 %; Italy, 402 and 9.95 %. Other Commonwealth countries take approximately 8 % of exports and provide 8 % of imports.

Currency: the pound sterling. Approximately 15 % of Government expenditure is on education and 23 % on health and other social services. Defence and external relations are the responsibility of the United Kingdom.

ITALY

Physical features. Latitude: 36°35'-47°6' N.; longitude: 6°40'-13°54' E. Area: 116,286 square miles. Highest point: Mont Blanc, 15,782 feet. Length of coastline: peninsula, 2,294 miles; islands, 2,340 miles. Longest river: the Po, 405 miles.

	MILAN	FLORENCE	ROME	PALERMO
Mean temperatures (°F.):				
Coldest month......	35.4	42.1	45.3	50.5
Hottest month	76.6	77.0	78.3	77.5
Number of days of frost annually	61	37	10	1
Rainfall (inches):				
Total for year.......	33.4	30.3	32.6	37.9
Average for the wettest month	3.54 (Nov.)	4.21 (Nov.)	4.84 (Oct.)	7.05 (Dec.)
Average for the least wet month ..	1.85 (July)	0.90 (July)	0.24 (July)	0.24 (July)
Number of days of rain a year	94	80	83	82

Land Use. Arable land, 52.6 %; permanent meadow and pasture, 17 %; forests, 19.2 %; unused, but potentially productive land, 3.4 %; built on land, waste, and other, 7.8 %. Area under cereals, 17,240,000 acres; vineyards, 4,442,500 acres.

Under the land reform laws of 1950, about 2 million acres were acquired for redistribution to peasants. By May 1959 more than 1.5 million acres had been allocated to over 108,000 families.

Population. Language. Religion. Towns. Total population (1959): 49,052,000 (42,919,000 in 1936). Density per square mile: 423; 83 in the Val d'Aosta; 5,001 in the province of Naples. Birth rate, 17.9 per 1,000; infant mortality rate, 48.2 per 1,000; rate of increase 0.5 % per annum; expectation of life: men, 65.7 years; women, 70 years. Distribution of the active population: industry and handicrafts, 32.1 %; agriculture, forestry and fishing, 42.2 %; commerce, 8.5 %; transport, 4 %; public service, 8.5 %. Emigrants overseas: 70,000 in 1946; 135,000 in 1956; 96,700 in 1958.

Lauguage: Italian; the Val d'Aosta is French-speaking and mainly German is spoken in the Alto Adige. Religion: Roman Catholicism is the State religion; Roman Catholics, 99.6 %.

Capital: *Rome (Roma)*, 1,853,000 inhabitants. Other towns: *Milan (Milano)*, 1,370,000; *Naples (Napoli)*, 1,105,000; *Turin (Torino)*, 869,000; *Genoa (Genova)*, 731,000; *Palermo* (in Sicily), 564,000; *Florence (Firenze)*, 408,000; *Bologna*, 394,000; *Catania* (in Sicily), 340,000; *Venice (Venezia)*, 334,000; *Trieste*, 284,000; *Messina* (in Sicily), 239,000; *Taranto*, 186,000; *Padua (Padova)*, 185,000; *Cagliari* (in Sardinia), 157,000; *Leghorn (Livorno)*, 153,000; *Brescia*, 152,000.

Agriculture and Forestry. Livestock and Fishing. Agricultural production (thousand metric tons; in brackets, the yield per acre in cwts.): wheat, 9,815 (16.2); maize, 2,674 (24.2); rice, 705 (42); potatoes, 3,664 (76); sugar-beet, 7,451; tomatoes, 2,540; olive oil, 260; oranges, 842; lemons,

433; tobacco, 79.8. Wine: 67.4 million hectolitres. Timber: 20.7 million cubic metres.

Livestock (thousand head): cattle, 8,649; sheep, 8,626; pigs, 5,980; horses, 563; mules and donkeys, 1,673. Milk and cheese (thousand tons): 7,500 and 319. Fish: 209,300 metric tons.

Mining. Industry. Power. Mineral and industrial production (thousand metric tons): coal, 724; lignite, 816; petroleum (1960 estimate), 2,000; bauxite (1959), 292; iron ore (metal content), 650; manganese (1959), 52; zinc (1959), 272; sulphur, 1,498; iron pyrites (1959), 1,522; mercury, 1.58; steel, 6,271; cement, 12,597; sulphuric acid, 3,250; silk, 828 metric tons (1.08 million spindles); cotton yarn, 162; synthetic fibres, 160; natural methane gas (million cubic metres), 5,182. Motor cars (number), 369,374; typewriters, 396,900. Electric power (million kWh): 45,492, of which 35,953 is hydroelectricity. Indices of industrial production (100 in 1953): mining, 46 in 1948, 171 in 1959; manufacturing, 61 in 1948, 159 in 1959; electricity and gas, 72 in 1948, 141 in 1959.

Communications and transport. Trade. Road network: 112,500 miles, of which 15,658 miles are state roads; passenger cars: 1,421,297. Railways: 13,512 miles, of which 10,343 are state railways and 4,231 electrified. Navigable waterways: 1,330 miles of rivers and canals. Merchant fleet (1959): 4,009 vessels of 5,123,852 gross tons. Chief ports: Genoa, Naples, Venice, Trieste; in 1959, 59.82 million tons of cargo were unloaded and 24.67 million tons loaded at Italian ports. Passengers carried by air: 1,846,600. 9 international airports: Rome's new Leonardo da Vinci airport became fully operational early in 1961. Tourists (1959): 16,780,000, of which 4,568,000 from Germany; 1,983,000 from France; 1,458,000 from United Kingdom; 826,000 from United States.

Foreign Trade (million *lire*): imports: 2,077,805; exports: 1,809,329. Principal imports and exports: raw materials, inedible, except fuels, 572,099 and 81,378; mineral fuels, 363,279 and 132,760; foodstuffs, 338,888 and 298,764; manufactured goods, 299,591 and 460,766; machinery and transport equipment, 235,124 and 470,578. Principal suppliers (million *lire*): Western Germany, 289,545; United States, 232,724; France, 159,542; United Kingdom, 115,902; Austria, 91,881; Kuwait, 80,644. Principal customers: Western Germany, 293,868; United States, 214,715; United Kingdom, 135,614; Switzerland, 131,210; France, 107,873.

Administrative divisions. Currency. 92 provinces for administrative purposes: the 19 regions are only geographical entities. Currency: the *lira* of 100 *centesimi*.

Standard of living: a comparison between the North and the South. Since the Second World War great efforts have been made to develop the South (the regions of Abruzzi and Molise; Campania; Apulia; Basilicata; Calabria; Sicily and Sardinia) which, in terms of economic development, lags far behind the industrialised North.

	SOUTH	NORTH
Population (millions; 1951 census) ...	17.6	29.5
Agricultural workers	53 %	37 %
Industrial workers................	27 %	39 %
Annual consumption per head of electricity (kWh)	138	605
Passenger cars per 1,000 inhabitants	29	103
Annual consumption per head:		
Meat (kg)	8.6	19.7
Sugar (kg)	7.3	16.6
Milk (litres)	15.6	68.3
Tractors per 2,500 acres of arable land	1.4	6.9

VATICAN CITY

Physical features. Land Use. Latitude: 41°54′ N.; longitude: 12°30′ E. Area: 109 acres. Climate: that of Rome. About half of the Vatican City comprises buildings, the rest gardens.

Population. Language. Currency. 1,000 inhabitants, engaged chiefly in administrative duties. Language: Italian. Currency: the Italian *lira*.

Vatican nationality is given to cardinals living in Rome and to persons with a fixed address — even though temporary — in the Vatican City. Certain outside communities belong to the Vatican: Castel Gandolfo, Saint Calixte Palace, and the basilicas of St Paul, St Mary-Major and St John Lateran.

SAN MARINO

Physical features. Agricultural production. Latitude: 43°54′ N.; longitude: 12°25′ E.; an enclave on the boundary between the Italian provinces of the Marches and Emilia Romagna. Area: 38 square miles. Highest point: 2,457 feet. Mean temperatures (°F.) in the capital (1,709 feet in altitude): January, 35.6; July, 71.9. Annual rainfall: 35.4 inches; least in July, most in autumn. Production: principally wheat and wine.

Population. Language. Currency. Total population (unofficial estimate): 14,000. Density per square mile: 368. Birth rate: 18.1 per 1,000 (1954). Nearly 3,000 people live in the capital. About 6,000 citizens of San Marino live abroad. Language: Italian. Currency: the Italian *lira*.

MONACO

Physical features. Latitude: 43°43′49″ N.; longitude: 7°25′36″ E. Area: 0.4 square mile. Mean annual temperature (°F.): 61.4; average minimum for January—February, 46.8; average maximum for July—August; 77.9. Sunshine: an average of more than 10 hours a day during the summer months; more than five hours a day for the rest of the year, except February (4½ hours). Number of rainy days: on average, never more than 7 a month, even during winter; whole months go by without any rain (once every 3 years in summer, once every 10 years in winter); maximum: 17 rainy days in one month (once in 40 years, in October 1944).

Population. Language. Religion. Tourism. Total population: 20,422 (1956). Density per square mile, 52,500. More than 60 % of the people are engaged in industry and commerce. Language: French. Religion: Roman Catholic. Number of tourists staying in hotels in Monaco: 74,781 in 1952; 92,560 in 1957; 95,000 in 1959.

Monaco is divided into three parts: Monaco-Ville, La Condamine, Monte Carlo. It is in a customs union with France and derives most of its revenue from the Casino.

ANDORRA

Physical features. Latitude: 42°25′-42°39′ N.; longitude: 5°6′-5°29′ E. Area: 175 square miles. Highest point: Mount Corna Pedrosa, 9,665 feet. Length of frontiers: 70 miles. Three rivers: the Northern Valira and the Eastern Valira join to form the Gran Valira; longest course in Andorran territory, 22 miles.

Mean temperatures (°F.): Ransol, 21.3 (average minimum) and —2.2 (actual minimum); 70.9 (average maximum) and 84.2 (actual maximum); Les Escaldes, 25.5 and 5; 75.8 and 96.8. Average rainfall (inches) and number of days of rain and snow: Ransol, 39.1, 80 and 42; Les Escaldes, 33.7, 91 and 11; Ordino, 37.2, 86 and 19; San Julián de Loria, 27.8, 76 and 8.

Population. Language. Religion. Towns. Population (unofficial estimate): 6,000. The volume of Andorran emigration and of Catalan immigration is constantly changing; estimates suggest 2,000 Andorrans and 3,000 Catalans. Density per square mile: 31.6. Language: Catalan is the official language, but Spanish and French are also spoken. Religion: Roman Catholic. Principal settlements: *Andorra, San Julián de Loria, La Massana, Ordino, Encamp, Canillo*. Les Escaldes is the most important settlement.

Land Use. Production. Arable land, 4 %; meadows and pastures, 43 %; forests greatly down-graded. Agricultural production: no statistics available but estimated at: wheat and rye, 600 tons; potatoes, 200; tobacco, 50—60; a little maize and a few olive groves and vineyards. Timber is used freely. Livestock (thousand head): cattle, 1.3; sheep, 20; horses and mules, 1.1.

Mineral and industrial production: tobacco is the main cash crop and is manufactured; there is a small woollen industry; Les Escaldes has a hydroelectricity plant and is noted for its hot sulphur springs.

Communications. Trade. Tourism. Road network: 43 miles; about 1,000 passenger cars, nearly 170 per 1,000 inhabitants. Exports into Spain: livestock, timber, electricity; imports: foodstuffs (olive oil from Spain, wheat and flour from France) and motor cars; smuggling is considerable but it is not possible to give its value. Tourists are numerous from France and Spain.

Administration. Currency. Budget. Absolute sovereignty of the co-principality is shared by the President of the French Republic and the Bishop of Urgel, each represented by a *viguier*. Currency: the *peseta* and the *franc*. Very small budget: public expenditure financed by the co-princes or industrial enterprises. The *quistia* due is paid in alternate years to France (960 francs) and to the bishop (450 pesetas); defence is the responsibility of France, education that of France and of the bishop.

SPAIN

Physical features. Latitude: 35°59'-43°47' N.; longitude: 3°19' E.-9°18' W. Area: 194,424 square miles, of which the Balearic Islands, 1,935 square miles and the Canaries, 2,807 square miles. Highest point: Mulhacén (Sierra Nevada), 11,420 feet. Length of coastline: 1,953 miles (Mediterranean coast 1,033; Atlantic coast, 920 miles). Length of frontiers: 1,177 miles (France and Andorra, 421; Portugal, 755; Gibraltar, 0.9). Longest river: Ebro 577 miles.

Temperatures (mean annual, mean winter and summer, °F.): north-west, 55.4, 48.2 and 66.2; south-west, 62.6, 53.6 and 75.2; south-east, 62.6, 55.4 and 73.4; northern Meseta, 51.8, 41 and 64.4; southern Meseta, 57.2, 46.4 and 71.6. Rainfall (mean annual in inches and number of dry summer months): north-west, from 27.5 to 69, no dry month; south-west, 29.5 (maximum) and 3 dry months in summer; south-east, 19.7 (maximum) and 4 months; northern Meseta, 15.7 and 2 months; southern Meseta, 17.8 and 3 months. Number of days of rain: throughout the north, more than 150; Pyrenees, Upper Ebro and interior Galicia, from 100 to 150; Old Castile and Catalonia, from 75 to 100; New Castile, Guadalquivir and Levant, from 50 to 75; south-east, less than 50.

Land Use. Arable land, 41 %; permanent meadow and pasture, 2.6 %; forests, 47.1 % (three-quarters of this is used for grazing); built on land, waste, and other, 9.3 %. Area under cereals, 18,715,000 acres; under vineyards, 4,175,000 acres.

Population. Language. Religion. Total population: 30,128,000 (1960). Density per square mile: 159; maximum, 681 (in Viscaya). Birth rate, 21.9 per 1,000; death rate, 8.7 per 1,000; expectation of life: men, 58.8 and women, 63.5 years. Rural population, 39.5 %; urban population, 36.9 %. Distribution of active population: industry and handicrafts, 25 %; agriculture, forestry, hunting and fishing, 48.8 %; commerce, 6.4 %; transport, 3.9 %. Official language is Castilian, spoken by 76 % of Spaniards; other languages: Catalan and Balearic, spoken by 9.2 %; Valencian, by 6.5 %; Galician, by 5.5 %; Basque, by 2.8 %. Religion: Roman Catholic.

Principal Towns. Capital: *Madrid*, 1,897,827. 24 other towns have more than 100,000 inhabitants: *Barcelona*, 1,446,184; *Valencia*, 521,721; *Seville*, 419,307; *Saragossa*, 284,685; *M-laga*, 283,002; *Bilbao*, 259,731; *Murcia*, 240,931; *Cordova*, 187,417; *Las Palmas*, 174,125; *Vigo*, 162,114; *Corunna*, 158,553; *Granada*, 156,550; *Palma de Mallorca*, 147,925; *Valladolid*, 137,106; *Oviedo*, 126,669; *San Sebastián*, 124,952; *Jerez*, 124,567; *Cartagena*, 121,122; *Gijón*, 119,008; *Santa Cruz de Tenerife*, 115,979; *Alicante*, 112,196; *Cádiz*, 109,154; *Santander*, 108,267; *Hospitalet*, 103,813.

Agriculture and Forestry. Livestock and Fishing. Agricultural production (thousand metric tons): wheat, 4,550; barley, 1,778; oats, 519; rye, 515; maize, 916; rice, 375; sugar-beet, 3,182; potatoes, 4,300; onions, 718; tomatoes, 962; grapes, 3,207; citrus fruit (largely oranges), 1,246; olives, 1,644; olive oil, 345; cotton, 40. Wine: 19,834,000 hectolitres. Timber: 9,900,000 cubic metres.

Livestock (thousand head 1955): cattle, 4,234; sheep, 26,000; goats, 7,189; horses, 705; mules and donkeys, 2,008; pigs, 5,709. Meat, 535,900 metric tons; milk, 2,420,000 tons. Silk: 480 tons of cocoons and 40 tons raw silk (chiefly in the province of Murcia).

Mining. Industry. Power. Mineral and industrial production (thousand metric tons): coal, 14,428 (7,300 in 1935), of which four-fifths comes from Asturias and León; lignite, 2,656; anthracite, 3,119; iron ore (metal content), 2,263; pig-iron, 1,342; steel, 1,574; copper (metal content), 4.1; zinc ore, 148; mercury, 68; lead, 96.6; potash, 1,515; salt, 1,832; cement, 4,817; sulphur, 27.8; woollen manufactures, 13.8; cotton manufactures, 95.8; rayon, 1.6. A uranium plant to supply material for nuclear energy was inaugurated in 1960. Electric power (million kWh): 16,350, of which 11,285 hydro-electricity. Indices of industrial production (100 in 1953): mining, 80 in 1948, 123 in 1959; electricity and gas, 63 in 1948, 170 in 1959.

Communications and transport. Trade. Road network: 75,039 miles; passenger cars, 657,006, i.e. 21.9 per 1,000 inhabitants. Railways: 13,314 miles broad gauge, of which 1,566 miles electrified; narrow gauge, 3,068 miles. Navigable waterways: only one navigable river, the Guadalquivir, for 75 miles, from the sea as far as Seville; one canal only, that of Castile (from Alar del Rei to Valladolid). Merchant fleet (1959): 1,693 vessels of 1,592,579 gross registered tons. In 1957, 26,251,000 tons cargo discharged at Spanish ports; 23,763,000 tons loaded. Principal airports: Barajas (Madrid), Muntanos (Barcelona), San Bonet (Palma de Mallorca), San Pablo (Seville). Tourists: 4,195,000 in 1959.

Foreign trade (million *pesetas*): imports, 2,670.5; exports, 1,487. Principal imports: mineral fuels, 593.8; raw materials, 574.7; machinery and transport equipment, 469; foodstuffs, 225. Principal exports: foodstuffs (citrus fruit, vegetables, nuts), 731.5; wines, 129.8; metallic ores and concentrates, 100.5; petroleum products, 128.5; manufactured goods, 152.9. Principal suppliers: United States, 576.6; Germany, 230.8; Saudi Arabia, 219.8; United Kingdom, 207; France, 180.9. Principal customers: United Kingdom, 241.4; Germany, 196.1; United States. 180; France, 79.9; Italy, 50.9.

Administrative divisions. Budget. 50 provinces, of which 47 are on the mainland and three are islands (1 in the Balearics and 2 in the Canaries), and 5 'places of sovereignty' — Spanish territories in North Africa. Currency: the *peseta*. National expenditure: defence, 22.7 %; public works, 16.25 %; administration and justice, 14.2 %; education, 9 %; expenditure in Africa, 3 %.

Principal sources of statistics: Statistical Yearbook of the United Nations, Demographic Yearbook of the United Nations, Monthly Statistical Bulletin of the United Nations, Food and Agricultural Organisation annual statistical reports, Statistical Data of the Council of Europe, Statesman's Yearbook, International Trade Statistics: United Nations, International Travel Statistics: British Travel and Holiday Association.

INDEX

AARHUS, 36
Aberdeen, 98
Albania, 319—21
  ancient trade routes, 319
  climate, 320
  economy, 320—21
    agrarian reform, 321
    communications, 321
    crops, 320, 321
    dependence on Greece
      and Yugoslavia, 321
    drainage schemes, 321
    industrialisation, 321
    mineral resources, 321
    state-owned herds, 321
  history, 320—21
  language, 320
  natural vegetation, 320
  political structure, 320
  population, 319, 320
  Shkodër (Scutari), 320
  statistics, 442
  structure and physical
    features, 319
Alderney, 104
Alkmaar, 130, 135
Almería, 406
Alps, 189—94
  climate, 189—90
  Dolomites, 190
  economy, 193—4
    agriculture, 194
    power sources, 194
    tourism, 194
  geographical location, 189
  Grand Alps, 190
  height, 196
  map, 190
  mountain ranges, 189
  passes, 193
  valleys, 189
Amsterdam, 117, 129, 141
Andorra, 381, 444
Angra do Heroismo, 186
Antwerp, 128, 137—9
Apennines, 340—42
Apuan Alps, 342
Aragon, 390—92
Aromani, 301
Asturias, 397—8
Athens, 328
Austria, 207—15
  area, 207
  Bohemian massif, 212
  Danube, 213, 214
  Drava, river, 212
  economy
    agriculture, 208, 213, 214
    communications, 208
    effect of war, 215
    financial stability, 215
    industry, 208, 211, 212, 215
    mineral resources, 212
    power sources, 208, 211,
      212, 215
    tourism, 208, 211, 215
  eastern Alps, 211—12
  Eisriesenwelt, 208
  government, 207
  Gross Glockner Pass, 211
  Ill, river, 208
  Klostertal, 208
  Lowlands, 213
  maps, 207
  Montafon, 208
  population, uneven
    distribution, 214
  Salzach, river, 208—11
  Salzburg, 208—11
  Tyrol, 208
  Vienna, 213—14
  Vorarlberg, 206—8
Azores, 186

BALEARIC ISLANDS,
  416—17
Banat, 292
'Battle Act', 282
Bear Island, 46
Belfast, 113—14
Belgium, see 'Netherlands,
  Belgium and Luxembourg'
Belgrade, 315—18
Benelux, see 'Netherlands,
  Belgium and Luxembourg'
Bergen, 46
Bergslagen, 48, 51

Bernese Oberland, 201
Beskid Mountains, 272
Bilbao, 396
Birmingham, 88
Bohemia, 253
Bordeaux, 162, 175
Boulogne-sur-Mer, 157, 162
Brabant, 126
Bradford, 83
Bristol, 75—6
British Isles, see also 'Great
  Britain', 69—72
  climate, 70
  economic history, 72
  geological structure, 69—70
  influence of sea, 70—72
  language, 70—71
  monarchy, 71
  physical features, 69
  racial origins, 70—71
  political history, 70—71
  urban development, 72
  variety of landscape, 72
Bruges, 128
Brussels, 128
Budapest, 269
Bulgaria, 295—8
  climate, 295
  Danube, advantages, 298
  economy, 296—8
    agriculture,
      agrarian reform, 296
      crops, 296
      livestock, 296
      rose cultivation, 296
    communications, 298
    industry,
      chemicals, 298
      Dimitrovo, expansion
      298
      industrialisation, 296
      mineral resources, 296,
      298
      silk, 296
      textiles, 298
      trade, 298
    U.S.S.R., influence, 298
  geographical location, 295
  history, 295
  land of plains, 295—6
  language, 295
  maps, 296, 298
  Plovdiv, 295
  population, 295
  Rhodope massif, 295
  rivers, 295
  Sofia, 295
  Sredna Gora, 295
  Stara Planina, 295
  statistics, 441
  strategic position, 295
  structure and physical
    features, 295
  towns, 295

CALABRIAN APENNINES,
  342
Calais, 157, 175
Caledonian Canal, 98
Campine, 127, 134, 136
Canary Islands, 409—10
Cape Verde Islands, 186
Capri, 343
Cardiff, 92
Carpathian Mountains, 254,
  286—7
Charleroi, 136
Chartres, 150
chernozem, 272, 288
Chester, 85
Clyde, river, 95
Compostella, 399
Concarneau, 162
Condroz, 126
Copenhagen, 25, 32—6
Côte de Moselle, 136
Courtrai, 136
Coventry, 88
cuevas, 406
Curzon Line, 271
Cyprus, 335, 443
Czechoslovakia, 252—62
  Bohemia, 253
  Carpathian Mountains, 254
  climate, 254
  economy, 255—6
    agriculture, 259

Czechoslovakia cont'd
    cereal crops, 259
    co-operatives, 259
    distribution of land,
      259
    livestock, 259
    communications, 260—61
    Five Year Plan, 257
    industry, 257—9
      foodstuffs, 258—9
      footwear, 258
      textiles, 258
    mineral resources, 257
    power sources, 256—7
      coal and lignite, 256
      hydro-electricity, 256,
      257
      pitchblende, 256
      thermo-electricity, 256
    trade, 262
  maps, 255, 256, 260
  Moravia-Silesia, 253
  Plzeň, industrial develop-
    ment, 257
  political history, 253
  population, 254—5
  Prague, 253, 260
  statistics, 440

DANUBE, advantage to
  Bulgaria, 298
  importance in Czecho-
    slovakia, 261
Danubian climate, 288
Denmark, 31—6
  agriculture, 31—2
    agrarian policy, 31
    co-operatives, 32
    production, 32
    soil fertility, 32
  Copenhagen, 32, 36
  Faeroe Islands, 36
  fishing, 32
  government, 31
  map, 32
  mineral deposits, 32
  population, 31
  religion, 31
  social policy, 36
  statistics, 432—3
  trade, 32
Derby, 88
Dimitrovo, 298
Dniester, river, 287
Dolomites, 190
Dordogne, river, 164
Drente, 127
drumlins, in Hungary, 271
Dublin, 115
Dundee, 98
Dunkirk, 139, 157, 175
Durance, river, 166

EAST ANGLIA, 75
Edinburgh, 96—8
Eindhoven, 137
Eire, see under Great Britain
Elba, 343
Elsinore, 36

FAEROE ISLANDS, 36
ferreto, 340
Finland, 55—62
  climate, 55—6
  economy, 59—62
    agriculture, 58—9
      collectivisation, 59
      fur-farming, 59
      principal crops, 59
      stock-farming
        increases, 59
    industry, 57—8, 59
      metallurgy, 59
      paper, 58
      textiles, 59
      timber, 57
      wood pulp, 58
    merchant navy, 62
    mineral deposits, 59
    trade, 59—62
      exports, 59
  flora, 57
  forests, 57
  government, 62

Finland cont'd
  Helsinki, 62
  history, 56
  language, 62
  map, 56
  new developments, 59
  population, 59, 62
  religion, 62
  statistics, 433
  structure and physical
    features, 55, 56, 57
    effect of glaciation, 57
    lakes, 56—7
    peat-bogs, 57
  territorial changes, 56, 59
  tunturi, 56
  urban development, 62
firn, 41
Flanders, 127, 134
Florence, 349
Forth, river, 96
France, 143—78
  Alps, 164
  Alsace, potash, 168
  Aquitaine, 159, 164
  Brittany, 158
  Burgundy, 164
  Camargue, 158
  climate, 144
    influence of sea, 143
  coastline, triple, 143—4
  Durance, river, 166
  economy, 178
    agriculture, 158—62
      forests, 162
      fruit crops, 159
      irrigation, 161
      market-gardening, 159
      mechanisation, 161
      natural vegetation, 144
      pays, 145
      principal crops, 158
      stock-rearing, 161
      viticulture 160-61
    communications, 150,
      175, 176—8
      air, 176
      navigable waterways,
      177
      railways, 176—7
      roads, 178
    fishing, 162
    food industry, 149, 162
    industry, 166—75
      aluminium, 167—8
      chemicals, 168—9
      cutlery, 170
      electrical, 170
      electro-chemistry, 169
      engineering, 170
      iron and steel, 166—7
      leather, 170
      non-ferrous metals,
      167—8
      rubber, 175
      shipbuilding, 175
      textiles, 169—70
      wood pulp, 169
    power sources, 163—6
      coal, 164
      hydro-electricity,
      164—6
      petroleum, 166, 175
      natural gas, 166
      nuclear power, 166
    sea resources, 162
    tourism, 178
    trade, 175
      principal imports and
      exports, 175
  history, 143, 146
  Isère valley, 166
  Lacq, sulphur, 168
  Lille, 157
  Loire, 164
  Loire valley, 159
  Lorraine, 164
  Lyons, 157
  maps, 160, 177
  Marseilles, 157
  Massif Central, 164
  natural and agricultural
    regions, 144—5
  Paris, 150—51
  population, 145—9, 156
  ports, 157, 175
  Provence, 159

France cont'd

Pyrenees, 144, 164
Rhine, 164
Rhône valley, 159
Rouen, 157
sea influence, 143
Seine, river, 150—51
statistics, 435
structure and physical
  features, 143
urban development, 156—7
frane, 342
Fuerteventura, 409

GARONNE, river, 166, 169
Gdańsk, 282
Gdynia, 282
Genoa, 369
Germany, 216—51
ancient massifs, 218—20
Bavaria, 218
Bavarian Alps, 218
Bergstrasse, 221
Black Forest, 218—20
Brandenburg, 223
climate, 218
dwellings, typical, 224—5
Erzgebirge, 222
forests, 222
geographical location, 217
Gaue, 222
Geest, 223
  statistics 438—9
German Democratic Republic
  (East Germany) 244—50
Berlin, 250
economy,
  agriculture, 245
  communications, 250
  industry, 245—6
    engineering, 246
    chemicals, 246
    precision instruments,
      246
    textiles, 246
  mineral resources, 245—6
  power sources, 246
Leipzig, 250
population, 244
German Federal Republic
  (West Germany), 226—44
Aachen, coalfield, 239
Baden-Württemberg, 231
Bavaria (Bayern), 232
Bonn, 226
Bremen, 231
Cologne, 241
economy,
  agriculture, 236—8
    fisheries, 238
    fruit growing, 238
    forests, 238
    mechanisation, 237
    principal grain crops,
      237
    stock-breeding, 237
    viticulture, 238
  communications, 241—2
  industry,
    concentration, 240
    development, 238, 239,
      Konzerne, 233, 238
  mineral resources, 238—9 244
  power sources, 239
  trade, 244
heathlands, 222
map, 219
Main, river, 222
Marschen, 223
Mecklenburg, 223
natural regions, 218
Neckar, river, 222
Northern Plain, 222-3
population, 223—4
religion, 225—6
Rhine, river, 218, 220, 242
  gorge, 221
  Middle, 220—21
Schleswig-Hollstein, 218,
  223, 226—31
Swabia, 218, 222
Swabian-Franconian basin,
  222
territorial limits, 217
urban settlement, 225
Weinstrasse, 221
Ghent, 128, 136, 139
Glasgow, 95—6
Glomma, river, 41
Gomera, 409
Götaland, 51
Gothenburg, 51
Gotland, 51

Gran Canaria, 409
Great Britain, 73—108
Channel Islands, 104
England and Wales, 73—94
  Black Country, 87—8
  Cheshire, 85
  climate, 80, 89—90, 92
  coastline, 75, 84
  Cornwall, 89
  demographic axis, 85
  economy,
    agriculture, 73, 75, 80
      stock-farming, 87
    fishing, 76, 84, 89
    industrialisation, 75
    industry,
      cement, 94
      chemicals and
        pharmaceuticals,
        85, 88
      clothing, 76, 83
      coal, 80—83, 85, 87,
        93—4
      electrical equipment,
        76
      engineering, 76, 88,
        92, 93
      iron and steel, 81—2,
        83—4, 87—8, 91,
        92
      leather, 88
      metallurgy, 83—4,
        91, 92
      motor vehicles, 75,
        88
      new industries, 75
      oil refineries, 76, 92
      shipbuilding, 93—4
      steel, 83
      textiles, 79, 80—83,
       85, 88
    mineral resources,
      80—83, 84, 87, 89
    power sources, 106
    tourism, 76, 89
    trade, 76, 106, 108
  English Plain, 79
  Lancashire, 85
  Lincolnshire, 80
  London, 76—9
    maps, 77, 83, 87
  Midlands, 85—8
  mountain areas, 89—94
  Isle of Man, 104
  Ireland, 109—115
    geological structure,
      109—110
    history, 110
    language, 113
    Northern Ireland
      113—14
      agriculture, 113
      engineering, 113
      flax cultivation, 113
      government, 113
      industry, 113
      linen industry, 113
      map, 110
      population, 114
      shipbuilding, 113
      statistics, 434
    Republic of Ireland,
      114—15
      Cork, 115
      distilling, 114—15
      Dublin, 115
      hydro-electricity, 114
      industry, 114—15
      peat-bogs, 110, 114
      population, 110, 115
      statistics, 429
      stock-farming, 114
  Scotland, 94-103
    Aberdeen, 98
    Clyde, 95—6
    climate, 94, 98
    communications, 94, 96
    Dundee, 98
    economy, 103
      agriculture, 95, 98
        sheep-farming, 94,
          103
        stock farming, 95
      fishing, 98, 103
      industry, 95—6, 98
        chemicals and
          pharmaceuticals,
          95, 96
        coal, 95, 96, 98
        engineering, 95
        iron and steel, 96,
          106
        jute, 98
        metallurgy, 98
        oil refineries, 96

Great Britain cont'd

      power, 103, 106
      shipbuilding, 95, 96
      textiles, 95, 103, 106
      trade, 95
    islands, 103
    map, 94
    Perth, 98
    population, 94—5, 103
    ports, 96, 98
    Southern Uplands, 94—5
    statistics, 434
    structure and physical
      features, 94
Greece, 323—34
Athens, 328
climate, 323, 324
economy, 328
  agriculture, 328—30
  fisheries, 330
  forests, 330
  industrialisation, 330—32
  mineral resources, 330
  monetary instability, 328
  power sources, 330
  shipping, 332
  stock-breeding, 330
  tobacco, 330, 332
  trade, 332—4
  transformation of plains,
    328
  transport and
    communications, 332
history, 325
  political background, 328
  Trianon Treaty, 325
influence of Balkans, 323
Ionian islands, 323
islands off mainland, 324—5
Kavalla, 323
landscape, northern Greece,
  323
map, general, 324
Mount Olympus, 323
Peloponnese, 323
population, 325—8
  emigration, 328
religion, 325
statistics, 442—3
structure and physical
  features, 323
Thessaly, 323
town development, 328
Grimsby, 84
Guernsey, 104
Gypsies, in Bulgaria, 295

HAGUE, The, 129
Hainaut, 126, 134
Halifax, 83
Hamburg, 244
Hammerfest, 46
Hebrides, 103
Helsinki, 62
Hierro, 409
Hinnöy, 41
Huddersfield, 83
huertas, 410
Hull, 84
Hungary, 263—9
Alföld, 264—5
area, 263
Budapest, 269
climate, 264
Danube, effect on economy,
  263—4
economy, 266—9
  agriculture, 264, 267—8
    agrarian reform, 266—7
    collectivisation, 267
    development, 267
    maize, 265, 267
    principal crops, 267
    problems, 267—8
    sub-tropical crops, 267
  industrial development,
    268—9
    bauxite, 268
    Five Year Plan
      ('50—'54), 268—9
    heavy industry, 269
    manufacturing
      industries, 269
    nationalisation, 268—9
  mineral resources, 268
  trade, 269
Kisaföld, 264
language, 263
maps, 264, 266, 267
Nagyalföld, ('Great Plain'),
  265
political history, 263
population, 263

Hungary cont'd

Pannonia, development, 264
Pannonian Sea, deposits,
  264
puszta, 264—5
Rába valley 264
salt deposits, 265
statistics, 440
structure and physical
  features, 264
varos (vasar), 265

IBIZA, 417
Iceland, 63—6
boer, 63, 66
climate, 63
economy,
  bird catching, 66
  communications, 66
  fishing, 66
  stock-farming, 66
geographical location, 63
history, 63
language, 63
map, 66
population, 63
racial origin, 63
statistics, 433
urban development, 66
varda, 66
inlandsis, 22
Intra-Baetic trough, 406
Ireland, *see under*
  'Great Britain'
Ischia, 343
Isère, river, 166
Istria, 306
Italy, 338—72
Alps, classical division, 339
  effects of glaciation, 339
  geological zones, 339
  karst topography, 339
  longitudinal furrows, 339
Apuan Alps, 342
Apennines, 340—42
  Calabrian Apennines, 342
Capri, 343
climate, 340
  'Adriatic', 345
  Tyrrhenian type 343—5
  inland, 343
complexity of natural
  conditions, 360
dwellings, typical, 364—5
earthquakes, 340—42
economy,
  agriculture, 358—65
    distribution of land,
      359, 360
    economics, 365
    effect of social develop-
      ment, 359
    forage crops,
      importance, 359
    fruit crops, 365
    Insubrian type, 362
    irrigation methods,
      359, 362
    land ownership, 359
    latifundia, 360, 362
    livestock and products,
      365
    marcite method, 359
    mixed-crop farming
      in south, 363—4
    multi-course methods,
      362—3
    olive oil, 365
    plains, drainage, 359
    principal crops, 365
    regional agrarian
      system, 362
    rice yield, 359
    sheep, 360
    soil, 360
    stock-breeding, 360
    traditional regional
      types, 362—4
    viticulture, 362
    wheat yield, 359
  communications, 350, 368
  economic structure, 369
  forests, 360
  industry,
    coal shortage, 366
    combines, 369
    early industrialisation,
      359
    government purchases,
      369
    labour excess, 368
    national problems, 366
    mineral resources, 366

Italy cont'd

power sources, 350, 366—7
trade, 350
  exports, 365, 366, 377
  imports, 366
Elba, 343
Fascism, demographic policy, 350
  economic aspects, 350
Ischia, 343
language, 352
Lombardy, agriculture, 362
Milan, 369
maps, 344 (general), 363, 367
marshland, disadvantages, 342
Naples, 372
Po plain, 340
  effect on physiognomy, 340
  flood plain, 340
  geological history, 340
  lagoon formation, 340
  springs, 340
Pontine marshes, draining, 350
population, 345—6, 350
  ethnical types, 350—52
  history, 346—50
  individualism, 352
  national unity, 350
  origin, 346
  religion, 346, 352—3
Pre-Apennine Chain, 342
Rome, 357—8
  climate and vegetation, 343
  economy, 358
  effect of Papacy, 357
  functions, 358
  history, 357
  lack of hinterland, 357
  religious importance, 358
  restoration as capital, 357
Ragusa, oil area, 366
Sardinia, 343
Sicily, 343
sea, influence on trade, 350
statistics, 443—4
structure and physical features, 339
Trieste, 369
Turin, 369
Tuscany, landscape and fertility, 342
towns, development, 353, 357
'Tyrrhenis', 340
volcanoes, 342, 343

JAN MAYEN ISLAND, 46
Jersey, 140
Julian Alps, 305
Jura mountains, 196

KARAWANKEN ALPS, 305
karst topography, in Italy, 339
  in Yugoslavia, 302
Kavalla, 323
Kiruna, 46, 48
Kotka, 59
Kristiansand, 43

LA PALMA, 409
Lake Geneva, 197—8
Lake Lucerne, 201
Lancaster, 85
Lanzarote, 409
Lapps, 25, 41, 47, 54
Lausanne, 198
Lapland, 54
Le Havre, 156, 157, 175
Leeds, 83
Leicester, 88
Leipzig, 250
Liechtenstein, 205
Liège, 128, 136
Lille, 156, 157
Lisbon, 185
Liverpool, 85
Ljubljana, 306
Lofoten Islands, 41, 42, 46
Lorient, 156, 162
Lorraine, 167, 169
Lombard Alps, 339
London, 76—9
Londonderry, 113
Lowestoft, 76
lug, 305
Luxembourg, *see under* 'Netherlands, Belgium and Luxembourg'
Lyons, 157, 169

MACEDONIA, 303
Madeira, 186
Madrid, 389—90
Main, river, 222
Majorca, 417
Malaga, 406
Malmö, 51
Malta, 336—7
  history, 336—7
  industries, 336
  Order of St John of Jerusalem, 337
  political autonomy, 337
  religion, 337
  statistics, 443
  strategic position as naval base, 337
  structure and physical features, 336
Manchester, 85
Marseilles, 157, 175
Massif Central, 156, 164
Mecklenburg, 223
Meuse, river, 117, 123, 139
Milan, 369
Minorca, 417
Miranda, 395
Monaco, 379—80—444
Monte Carlo, 379
Moravia-Silesia, 253
Mount Athos, 323

NAMSOS, 42
Namur, 128, 129
Nantes, 159, 175
Naples, 372
Narvik, 46, 48
Neckar, river, 241
Newcastle, 93
Netherlands, Belgium and Luxemburg, 117—41
  Amsterdam, 117, 129, 144
  Brussels, 128
  economy, 141
    agriculture, 134
    dairy cattle, 135
    horticulture, 134—5
    inland waterways, 139
    principal crops, 134
  communications, 137—41
  fishing, 135
  industry, 135—7
    Belgium, 135—6
    Luxembourg, 136—7
    Netherlands, 136
    coal, 129, 135—6
    electrical goods, 137
    food, 137
    iron and steel, 136
    textiles, 18, 136, 137
    shipbuilding, 136, 137
    merchant navy, 141
    mineral resources, 135, 136
    trade, 117, 139, 141
  landscape, 126, 127
  language, 130
  maps, 126, 132
  natural regions, 126—8
  polders, 122—3, 134
    Wieringermeer, 123
  population, 132
  ports, 137—41
  religion, 130—32
  Rotterdam, 129, 139—41
  standard of living, 141
  sea danger, 122
  shifting coastline, 122
  statistics, 435—7
  The Hague, 129
  urban development, 128—30
  waarden, 126
Norrland, 54
Northampton, 88
Norway, 41—6
  Bergen, 46
  Bear Island, 46
  climate, 46
  economy,
    agriculture, 42
    communications, 43
    fishing, 42
    forests, 2—3
    fur farming, 42—3
    industry, 43
    mineral resources, 43, **46**
    power sources, 43
    trade, 42
  glaciation, 41
  Hammerfest, 46
  Jan Mayen Island, 46
  Kristiansand, 43
  map, 43
  Oslo, 43
  Östland, 43, 46

Norway cont'd

religion, 42
skjaergard, (skerrygard), 41
Spitsbergen, 46
statistics, 432—3
Stavanger, 43
structure and physical features, 41, 46
Trondheim, 46

OIL, Albania, 321
France, 166
Hungary, 268
Italy, 366
Poland, 274
Rumania, 291—2
Oland, 51
Olympus, 323, 326
Oporto, 180, 184
Orkneys, 103
Orléans, 159
Oslo, 43
Östland, 43, 46
Oviedo, 398
Oxford, 75

PALMA, 417
Pamplona, 394
Pannonia, 264, 304
Paris, 150—51
Pennine Chain, 92
Pico, 186
Piedmont Alps, 339
Plovdiv, 295
Plzeň, 257
Po, river, 340
Podgoria, 286—7
Poland, 271—82
  area, 271
  'Battle Act', 282
  climate, 272
  economy, 276—82
    agriculture,
      agrarian reforms, 276
      development, 276—7
      collectivisation, 276
      crops, 276—7
    communications, 281
    food production, 279
    foreign trade, 281—2
    industry, 279—81
      nationalisation, 277, 278
      Six Year Plan, 278
      new, 279—81
      agricultural machinery, 280
      chemicals, 280
      electro-technical materials, 280
      machine tools, 280
      metallurgy, 280
      motor vehicles, 280
      non-ferrous metals, 280
      shipbuilding, 280
      textiles, 279
      wood and wood products, 281
    mineral resources, 274—6
      coal, 274
      lignite, 274
      oil, 274
      salt, 274
      sulphur, 276
      zinc, 274
    power sources, 278
  Gdańsk, 282
  Gdynia, artificial port, 281—2
  glaciation, effects of, 271
  maps, 273, 279,
  mountain ranges, 272
  Polish Plain, 271
  political background, 271
  population, 272—3, 278
  ports, 274, 281—2
  post-war frontiers, 271
  Silesia, acquisition, 274
  soil, 272
  structure and physical features, 271—2
  Vistula, course, 271
polje, 302
ponor, 302
Pori, 59
Porkkala, 56
Portsmouth, 76
Portugal, 179—86
  Atlantic islands, 186
  climate, 179—80
  economy, 179, 185

Portugal cont'd

agriculture, 180—82
fishing, 184
industrialisation, 185
industry, 180
irrigation, 180, 182
over-population, 180, 185
power sources, 185
sea influence, 184
trade, 184—5
emigration, 180
historical background, 179
language, 179
Lisbon, 185
map, 180
Oporto, 184
physical features, 179—82
population, 180
Porto, 184
regions, 180
statistics, 440—41
Prague, 253, 260
Pre-Alps, 200—201
puszta, 264, 265
Pyrenees, 392
  French, 156, 164

RAGUSA, 366
Reykjavik, 63
Rhine, Lower, 117, 123, 218
  Middle, 218, 220—21
  navigation, 139, 177
  Upper, 164, 220
Rhine-Rhône valley, 150
Rhodope massif, 295
Rhondda, 92
Rhône, river, 166, 169
Rochdale, 80
Rochefort, 156
Rome, 357—8
  climate, 343
Rotterdam, 129, 139—41
Rouen, 157, 175
Ruhr, 239—40
Rumania, 283—93
  area, 284
  Banat, industrial area, 292
  Carpathian Mountains, 286—7
  climate, 288—90
  Danube, 287
  Dniester, an old frontier, 287
  Dobrogea, 287
  economy, 288—93
    agricultural development, 288—90
    agrarian reform, 290—91
    collectivisation, 285
    forests, 291
    land ownership, 284—5
    post-war famine, 291
    principal crops, 290
    communications, 292—3
    industry, 292
    mineral resources, 286, 291
      coal, 292
      natural gas, 291, 292
      oil production, 291
    power sources, 292
    trade, Russo-Rumanian companies, 293
      foreign capital, 293
  geographical location, 283
  highest peaks, 286
  history, 283—4
    early political units, 286
  irrigation, 290
  language, 284
  maps, 285, 290
  national customs, 284
  Oltenia, 287
  Podgoria, 286—7
  population, 284, 288
  provinces, differences, 285
  soil, 288
  statistics, 441
  structure and physical features, 286—7
  Transylvania, 286, 292
  Turkish influence, 288
  volcanic massifs, 286

SAAR COALFIELD, 238
St Etienne, 164, 167, 169
San Marino, 378—444
San Sebastian, 396
San Miguel, 186
Saragossa, 390—91, 392
Sardinia, 343

Sark, 104
Sava, river, 306
Scandinavia, *see also* Norway, Sweden, Denmark, Iceland and Finland.
  education, 30
  fauna, 23—4
  fish, 22
  forests, 23
  geographical location, 21
  geological formation, 22
  glaciation, 22
  history, 25
  livestock, 26
  maps, 28—9
  merchant navy, 25
  racial types and characteristics, 24—5
  rivers, influence, 22—3
  sea influence, 22, 25
  social policy, 29
  standard of living, 29
  statistics, 432—3
Scapa Flow, 103
Schaffhausen, 203
Scheldt, river, 117, 138—9
Schleswig-Holstein, 32, 218
Scotland, *see under* 'Great Britain'
Scutari (Shkodër), 320
Seine, river, 150, 157, 169
Sète, 175
Severn, river, 75
Seville, 404
Shannon, river, 110, 114
Sheffield, 83
Shetland Islands, 103
Shkodër (Scutari), 320
Sicily, 343
Sierra Morena, 400
Sierra Nevada, 406
Skopje, 303
Slavonia, 305
Slovakia, 254
Sofia, 295
Southampton, 76
Spain, 383—424
  African influences, 383
  Alava, 395
  Alicante, 412—13
  Almeria, 406
  Altamira, palaeolithic discoveries, 397
  Ampurdán, 415
  Andalusia, 400—409
    climate, 400
    history, 400—3
    sea influence, 400
  Aragon, 390—92
  Asturias, 397—8
  Aviles, 398
  Badajoz, 388—9
  badlands, 406
  Balearic Islands, 416—17
  Barcelona, 414, 416
  Basques provinces, 395—6
  bullfighting, 400
  Cáceres, 388
  Cadiz, 406
  Canary Islands, 409—10
  Cantabrian Chain, 398
  Castile, New, 389—90
    Old, 388
  Catalonia, 414—16
  Central Cordillera, 388
  Central Spain, 384—7
  climate,
    Andalusia, 400, 406
    Aragon, 391, 392
    Asturias, 393
    Cadiz, 406
    Catalonia, 414
    central Spain, 386
    eastern Spain, 410
    Estremadura, 389
    Galicia, 399
    Gibraltar, 406
    Granada, 406
    Montaña of Santander, 397
    Navarre, 394
    northern Spain, 393
    Upper Ebro, 395
  Compostela, 399
  Cordova, 404
  Costa Brava, 415
  cuevas, 406
  Eastern Spain, 410—17
  Ebro, 392, 394—5, 415
  economy,
    agriculture,
      Alaval 395

Spain cont'd

  Alicante, 412—13
  Andalusia, 400, 403, 404
  Asturias, 398
  Balearic Islands, 417
  Canary Islands, 410
  co-operatives, 404
  cork-oaks, 406, 415
  cotton, 423
  date palms, 412
  Ebro valley, 392
  effect of Suez Canal, 416
  Galicia, 399
  irrigation, 403, 410—11, 415, 418
  land development, 389 390, 393
  Montaña, 397
  Murcia, 412
  Navarre, 394
  olive oil, 400, 418
  oranges, 410, 413
  rice, 413, 415
  Rioja, 395
  saffron, 389
  Upper Ebro, 394
  Valencia, 413
  viticulture, 395, 403
  communications, 424
  fishing, 396, 399
  industry, 418—24
    chemicals, 423
    coal, 392, 398, 414
    engineering, 423
    foreign capital, 424
    iron and steel, 396, 414, 425
    rare metals, 423
    rubber, 423
    textiles, 423
  mineral resources, 395, 396, 397, 398, 418
  power sources, 396, 399, 418
  trade, 424
  Escorial plateau, 388
  Estremadura, 388—9
  Galicia, 398—9
  geographical location, 383
  Gibraltar, 406
  Granada, 406
  Guipuzcoa, 396
  Huelva, 404
  huertas, 410
  Intra-Baetic trough, 406
  language,
    Basque provinces, 395
    Catalan, 412
    Galicia, 399
  Levant, 412
  Madrid, 389
  Majorca, 412
  Malaga, 406
  maps, 384, 386, 394, 411
  Meseta, 383, 384—6
  mesta, function, 387
  Montaña of Santander, 396—7
  Mount Calpe, 406
  Murcia, 412
  Musel of Gijon, 398
  New Castile, 389—90
  Oceanic and Mediterranean Spain, 383
  Old Castile, 388
  Oviedo, development, 398
  population, 417—18
  ports, 396
  San Sebastian, 396
  Santander, 396—7
  sea influence, 383
  Seville, 404
  Sierra Morena, 400
  Sierra Nevada, 406
  sierras, 386
  statistics, 445
  structure and physical features, 383—6
  Tarragona, 415
  Valencia, 413—14
  volcanic features, 383
  volcanoes, 409
Spanish Levant, 412—14
Spitsbergen (Svalbard), 46
Split, 308
Sredna Gora, 295
Stara Planina, 295
Stari Vlah, 302
Stavanger, 43

Stirling, 96
Sunderland, 93
Svalbard (Spitsbergen), 46
Svealand, 51
Swabia, 218, 226
Swansea, 92
Sweden, 47—54
  agriculture, 49
  climate, 54
  economy, 49
    agriculture, 49
      co-operatives, 49
      forests, 47—8
    communications, 49, 51
    industry, 48—9
      metallurgy, 48—9
      steel, 48
      timber and wood pulp, 47—8
    merchant navy, 49, 51
    mineral resources, 48
    power sources, 49
    trade, 49, 51
  Götaland, 51
  Gothenburg, 51
  Gotland, 51
  history, 47
  Lapland, 54
  Malmö, 51
  Norrland, 54
  maps, 49, 51
  Öland, 51
  physical features, 51
  population, 47
  religion, 47
  social policy, 54
  statistics, 432—3
  Stockholm, 51
  Svealand, 51
Switzerland, 195—204
  Alps, 196, 200—201
  Biel, 198
  Bernese Oberland, 201
  Central Switzerland, 201
  climate, 195
  Eastern Switzerland, 203—4
  economy, 204
    agriculture, 197—8, 200
    communications, 196, 204
    industry, 198, 199, 201—2
      chemicals, 202
      engineering, 202
      textiles, 202, 203
      watchmaking, 198, 199—200
  geographical location, 195
  Jura, 196, 199—200
  Lake Geneva, 197—8
  Lake Lucerne, 201
  landscape, 195
  language, 195
  Lausanne, 198
  maps, 196, 197, 202
  Middle Lands, average height, 196, 198—9
  Pre-Alps, 200—201
  religion, 195—6
  Rhine valley, 204
  Schaffhausen, 203
  statistics, 437—8
  Tessin (Ticino), 202
  Thurgau, 203
  Western Switzerland, 196—7

TAGUS, river, 180
Tampere, 59
Tatry Mountains, 000
Tenerife, 409
Terceira, 186
Tessin (Ticino), 202—3
Thames, river, 73, 76
Thessaly, 323
Thorshavn, 36
Toledo, 389
Tournai, 128, 129
tramontana, 343
Transylvania, 292
Trieste, 369
Trondheim, 46
Turin, 369
Turku, 59
Tyne, river, 93

VALLETTA, 337
Valladolid, 388
Vatican City, 377
Venetian Alps, 339
Venice, 340, 350, 368

Versailles, 156
Vistula, river, 271
viticulture, France, 160—61
  Italy, 362, 365
  Portugal, 180
  Spain, 395, 403, 413
Vitoria, 395
Vltava, source, 253
volcanoes, Canary islands, 409
  Italy, 342—3, 353
Vosges Mountains, 156, 169
WALES, *see* 'Great Britain'
Wallachs, distribution, 301
Westphalia, 240
whaling, 42

YARMOUTH, 76
York, 84
Yugoslavia, 301—18
  Adriatic Sea, influence, 306
  Belgrade, 315—18
  Bosnia, 302
  climate, Adriatic coast, 306, 308
  Croatia, landscape and crops, 305
  droughts, 308
  economy, 308—12, 318
    agriculture, 308
      agrarian reform, 309
      centralisation, 311
      co-opeartives, 310
      forests, 305, 310
      new crops, 310
      rice, 310
      special crops, 305
      State management, 310, 311
    communications, 306, 311, 318
    industry, 311—12
      handicaps, 311
      nationalisation, 312
    mineral resources, 302, 306, 312
    power sources, 312
    trade, 311, 318
  geographical location, 301
  influence of the East, 302
  Istria, 306
  language, 301
  Ljubljana, former capital, 306
  lug, 305
  Macedonia, climate and landscape, 303
    economy, 303
  maps, 303, 308, 311
  Morava-Vardar trough, 303
  Pannonia, 304
  political history, 301
    six republics, 301
  population, 301, 311—12
    emigration patterns, 318
    migration to industrial centres, 312
  ports, 306, 318
  Raška, 302
  religion, 301
  Sarajevo Basin, importance, 302
  Sava trough, 306
  Skopje, 303
  Slavonia, landscape and crops, 305
  Slovenian Alps, 305—6
  Split, 306
  Stari Vlah, 302
  structure and physical features, 301—2
    Dinaric karst, 302
    Dinaric redoubt, 301
      decline of pastoral farming, 302
      vegetation, 302
      mountain areas, development, 301
      poljes, 302
      ponors, 302
    towns, development, 312—18
  Vojvodina, wheat and other crops, 304—5
  Zagorje, 305
  Zagreb, 315—18

ZAGREB, 315—18
Zuider Zee, 123, 134

ATLAS SECTION

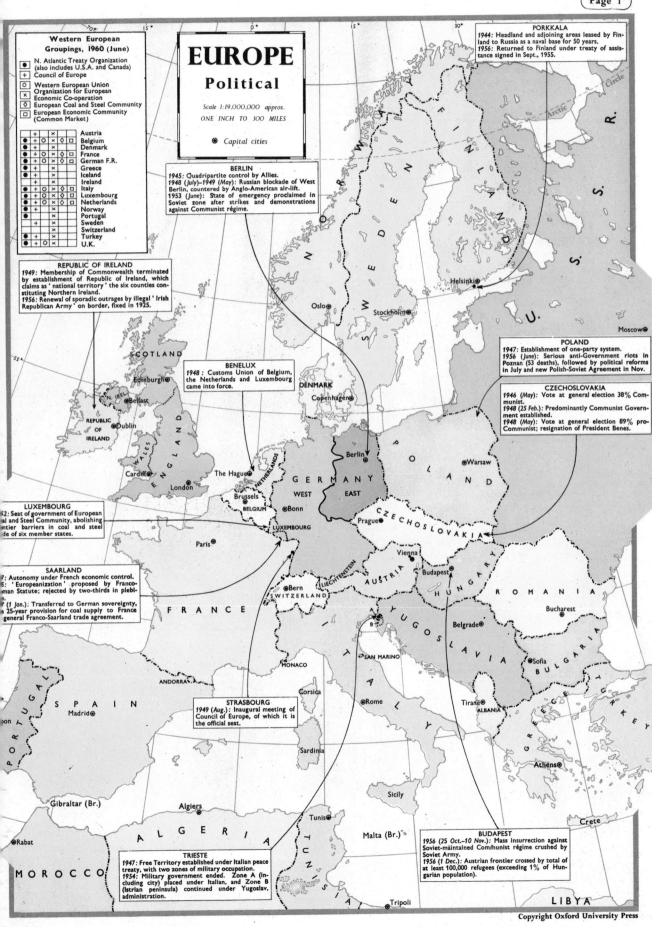

EUROPE
Political

Scale 1:19,000,000 approx.
ONE INCH TO 300 MILES

● *Capital cities*

Western European Groupings, 1960 (June)

- ● N. Atlantic Treaty Organization (also includes U.S.A. and Canada)
- + Council of Europe
- ○ Western European Union
- × Organization for European Economic Co-operation
- ◇ European Coal and Steel Community
- □ European Economic Community (Common Market)

	+		×				
●	+		×			Austria
●	+	○	×	◇	□	Belgium
●	+		×			Denmark
●	+	○	×	◇	□	France
●	+	○	×	◇	□	German F.R.
●	+		×			Greece
●	+		×			Iceland
●	+					Ireland
●	+	○	×	◇	□	Italy
●	+	○	×	◇	□	Luxembourg
●	+	○	×	◇	□	Netherlands
●	+		×			Norway
	+		×			Portugal
			×			Sweden
	+		×			Switzerland
●	+		×			Turkey
●	+	○	×			U.K.

PORKKALA
1944: Headland and adjoining areas leased by Finland to Russia as a naval base for 50 years.
1956: Returned to Finland under treaty of assistance signed in Sept., 1955.

BERLIN
1945: Quadripartite control by Allies.
1948 (July)–1949 (May): Russian blockade of West Berlin, countered by Anglo-American air-lift.
1953 (June): State of emergency proclaimed in Soviet zone after strikes and demonstrations against Communist régime.

REPUBLIC OF IRELAND
1949: Membership of Commonwealth terminated by establishment of Republic of Ireland, which claims as 'national territory' the six counties constituting Northern Ireland.
1956: Renewal of sporadic outrages by illegal 'Irish Republican Army' on border, fixed in 1925.

BENELUX
1948: Customs Union of Belgium, the Netherlands and Luxembourg came into force.

POLAND
1947: Establishment of one-party system.
1956 (June): Serious anti-Government riots in Poznan (53 deaths), followed by political reforms in July and new Polish-Soviet Agreement in Nov.

CZECHOSLOVAKIA
1946 (May): Vote at general election 38% Communist.
1948 (25 Feb.): Predominantly Communist Government established.
1948 (May): Vote at general election 89% pro-Communist; resignation of President Benes.

LUXEMBOURG
52: Seat of government of European al and Steel Community, abolishing ntier barriers in coal and steel de of six member states.

SAARLAND
7: Autonomy under French economic control.
5: 'Europeanization' proposed by Franco-man Statute; rejected by two-thirds in pleb-
7 (1 Jan.): Transferred to German sovereignty, a 25-year provision for coal supply to France general Franco-Saarland trade agreement.

STRASBOURG
1949 (Aug.): Inaugural meeting of Council of Europe, of which it is the official seat.

TRIESTE
1947: Free Territory established under Italian peace treaty, with two zones of military occupation.
1954: Military government ended. Zone A (including city) placed under Italian, and Zone B (Istrian peninsula) continued under Yugoslav, administration.

BUDAPEST
1956 (25 Oct.–10 Nov.): Mass insurrection against Soviet-maintained Communist régime crushed by Soviet Army.
1956 (1 Dec.): Austrian frontier crossed by total of at least 100,000 refugees (exceeding 1% of Hungarian population).

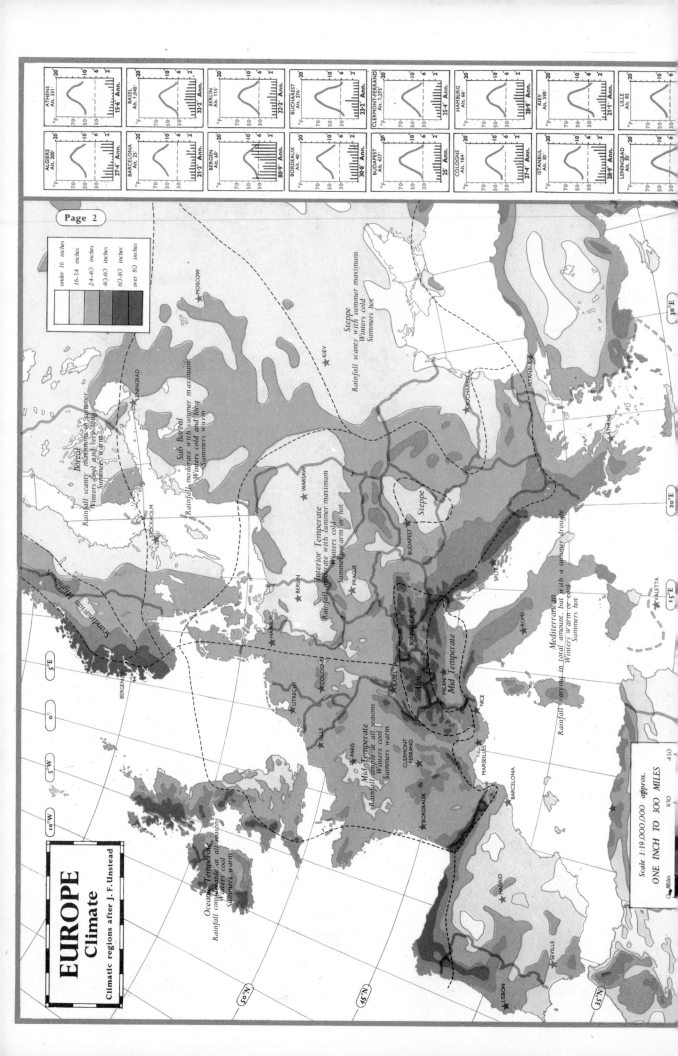

EUROPE
Climate

Climatic regions after J. F. Unstead

Legend (rainfall):
- under 16 inches
- 16-24 inches
- 24-40 inches
- 40-60 inches
- 60-80 inches
- over 80 inches

Oceanic Temperate
Rainfall considerable at all seasons
Winters cool
Summers warm

Mid Temperate
Rainfall ample at all seasons
Winters cool
Summers warm

Interior Temperate
Rainfall moderate with summer maximum
Winters cold
Summers warm or hot

Sub Boreal
Rainfall moderate with summer maximum and long
Winters cold
Summers warm

Boreal
Rainfall scanty maximum in summer
Winters cool and very long
Summers warm

Steppe
Rainfall scanty with summer maximum
Winters cold
Summers hot

Mediterranean
Rainfall varying in total amount, but with a summer drought
Winters warm or cool
Summers hot

Mid Temperate (Alps)

Scale 1:19,000,000 approx.

ONE INCH TO 300 MILES

Miles 0   150   300   450

Climate station graphs (temperature °F and rainfall):

Station	Alt.	Ann.
ATHENS	351'	15·6"
BASEL	1,040'	32·2"
BERLIN	115'	22·2"
BUCHAREST	276'	23·2"
CLERMONT-FERRAND	1,275'	25·4"
HAMBURG	66'	28·9"
KIEV	590'	21"
LILLE	85'	
ALGIERS	200'	27·4"
BARCELONA	25'	21·2"
BERGEN	60'	80·9"
BORDEAUX	40'	30·8"
BUDAPEST	427'	25"
COLOGNE	184'	27·4"
ISTANBUL	30'	28·9"
LENINGRAD	30'	

Labelled locations on map: MOSCOW, LENINGRAD, KIEV, STOCKHOLM, BERGEN, WARSAW, HAMBURG, UTRECHT, COLOGNE, BERLIN, PRAGUE, BUDAPEST, BUCHAREST, ISTANBUL, ATHENS, LILLE, PARIS, CLERMONT-FERRAND, BORDEAUX, BASEL, INNSBRUCK, MILAN, NICE, MARSEILLES, BARCELONA, MADRID, LISBON, SEVILLE, ROME, SPLIT, VALETTA

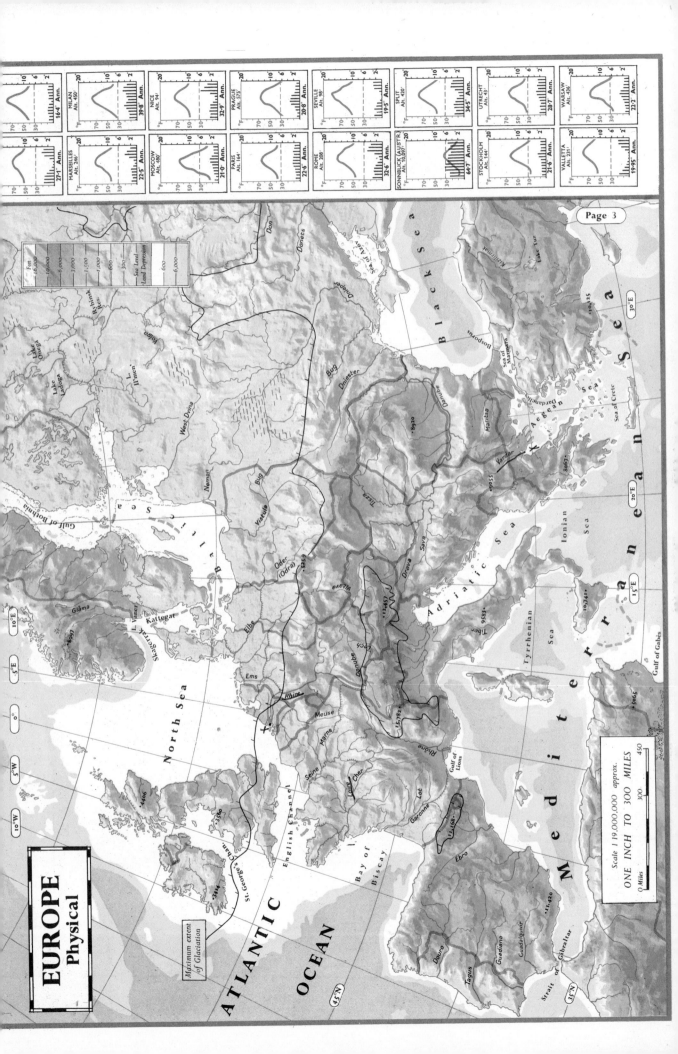

EUROPE
Physical

Maximum extent of Glaciation

Feet
16,000
10,000
6,000
3,000
1,000
600
300
Sea Level
Land Depression
600
6,000

Scale 1 : 19,000,000 approx.

ONE INCH TO 300 MILES

0 Miles   300   450

ATLANTIC OCEAN

North Sea

English Channel

Bay of Biscay

St. George's Channel

Mediterranean Sea

Black Sea

Aegean Sea

Adriatic Sea

Ionian Sea

Tyrrhenian Sea

Gulf of Bothnia

Baltic Sea

Kattegat

Skagerrak

Gulf of Lions

Gulf of Gabès

Strait of Gibraltar

Sea of Azov

Sea of Marmara

Bosporus

Dardanelles

Lake Onega

Lake Ladoga

L. Ilmeni

L. Vaner

Sea of Crete

10°W   5°W   0°   5°E   10°E   15°E   20°E   30°E

45°N   35°N

Rivers and features
Don, Donets, Dnieper, Dniester, Bug, Danube, Volga, West Dvina, Vistula, Niemen, Oder (Odra), Elbe, Ems, Rhine, Meuse, Marne, Seine, Loire, Cher, Lot, Garonne, Ebro, Douro, Tagus, Guadiana, Guadalquivir, Rhône, Tiber, Sava, Drava, Tisza, Vltava, Glâma, Maritsa, Vardar

Climate graphs

MILAN Alt. 450'	16·4' Ann.
NICE Alt. 94'	39·8' Ann.
PRAGUE Alt. 575'	32·9' Ann.
SEVILLE Alt. 98'	20·8' Ann.
SPLIT Alt. 420'	19·5' Ann.
UTRECHT Alt. 43'	34·5' Ann.
WARSAW Alt. 436'	22·7' Ann.
MARSEILLES Alt. 246'	27·1' Ann.
MOSCOW Alt. 480'	22·5' Ann.
PARIS Alt. 164'	21·0' Ann.
ROME Alt. 208'	22·6' Ann.
SONNBLICK (AUSTR.) Alt. 10,097'	32·6' Ann.
STOCKHOLM Alt. 144'	21·6' Ann.
VALLETTA Alt. 231'	19·95' Ann.

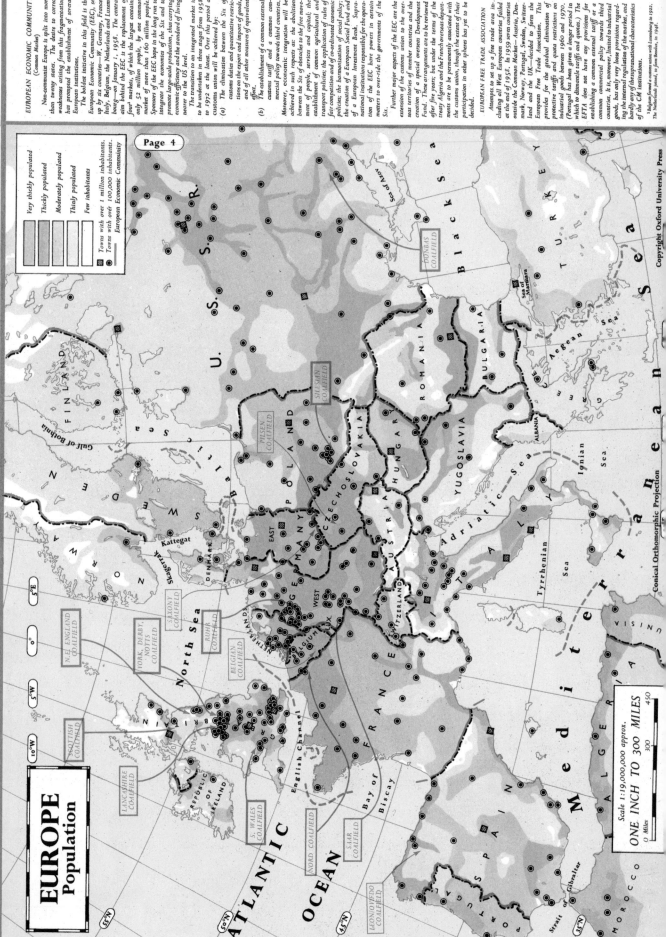

EUROPE
Population

EUROPEAN ECONOMIC COMMUNITY
(Common Market)

Non-communist Europe is split into more than twenty states. The desire to correct weaknesses arising from this fragmentation has prompted the establishment of several European institutions.

The boldest initiative in this field is the European Economic Community (EEC), set up by six countries—W. Germany, France, Italy, Belgium, the Netherlands and Luxembourg—on January 1, 1958. The central aim behind the EEC is the replacement of four[4] markets, of which the largest contains only 52 million people, by one common market of more than 160 million people. Sponsors of the EEC hope in the long run to integrate the economics of the Six and to promote large-scale production, thus carrying economic efficiency and the standard of living nearer to the US level.

The transition to an integrated market is to be undertaken in three stages from 1958 to 1972 at the latest. Over this period a customs union will be achieved by:

(a) The elimination between the Six of customs duties and quantitative restrictions on the export and import of goods, and of all other measures of equivalent effect.

(b) The establishment of a common external customs tariff and a common commercial policy towards third countries.

Moreover, economic integration will be achieved in such respects as: the abolition between the Six of obstacles to the free movement of people, services and capital; the establishment of common agricultural and transport policies; the application of rules of fair competition and of co-ordinated economic policies; the harmonization of social policy; the creation of a European Social Fund and of a European Investment Bank. Supranational institutions responsible for the operation of the EEC have powers in certain matters to over-ride the governments of the Six.

EUROPEAN FREE TRADE ASSOCIATION

Attempts to set up a free trade area including all West European countries failed at the end of 1958. In 1959 seven countries outside the Common Market—Austria, Denmark, Norway, Portugal, Sweden, Switzerland and the UK—decided to form the European Free Trade Association. This provides for the gradual elimination of protective tariffs and quota restrictions on industrial goods between 1960 and 1970. (Portugal has been given a longer period in which to dismantle tariffs and quotas.) The EFTA does not have any provisions for establishing a common external tariff or a common commercial policy towards third countries. It is, moreover, limited to industrial goods, has only very loose provisions regarding the internal regulation of the market, and hardly any of the supranational characteristics of the CM institutions.

Further major aspects of the EEC are the extension of the customs union to the overseas territories of member countries and the creation of a special overseas Development Fund. These arrangements are to be reviewed after five years; but under the terms of the treaty Algeria and the French overseas departments are to be permanently associated with the customs union, though the extent of their participation in other spheres has yet to be decided.

[1] Belgium formed a customs union with Luxemburg in 1922.
The Netherlands joined, to form Benelux, in 1948.

Page 4

Copyright Oxford University Press

Conical Orthomorphic Projection

Scale 1:19,000,000 approx.
ONE INCH TO 300 MILES
0 Miles   300   450

Very thickly populated
Thickly populated
Moderately populated
Thinly populated
Few inhabitants
Towns with over 1 million inhabitants.
Towns with over 100,000 inhabitants.
European Economic Community

SCOTTISH COALFIELD
N.E. ENGLAND COALFIELD
YORK, DERBY, NOTTS COALFIELD
LANCASHIRE COALFIELD
S. WALES COALFIELD
NORD COALFIELD
SAAR COALFIELD
LÉON/OVIEDO COALFIELD
BELGIAN COALFIELD
RUHR COALFIELD
SAXONY COALFIELD
PILSEN COALFIELD
SILESIAN COALFIELD
DONBAS COALFIELD

U. S. S. R.
FINLAND
SWEDEN
NORWAY
DENMARK
NETHERLANDS
EAST GERMANY
WEST GERMANY
BELGIUM
Lux.
FRANCE
SWITZERLAND
AUSTRIA
POLAND
CZECHOSLOVAKIA
HUNGARY
ITALY
YUGOSLAVIA
ROMANIA
BULGARIA
ALBANIA
GREECE
TURKEY
SPAIN
PORTUGAL
ALGERIA
MOROCCO
TUNISIA
REPUBLIC OF IRELAND
BRITAIN

ATLANTIC OCEAN
North Sea
Baltic Sea
Gulf of Bothnia
Kattegat
Skagerrak
English Channel
Bay of Biscay
Mediterranean Sea
Tyrrhenian Sea
Adriatic Sea
Ionian Sea
Aegean Sea
Sea of Marmara
Black Sea
Sea of Azov
Strait of Gibraltar

10°W 5°W 0° 5°E
55°N 50°N 45°N 35°N

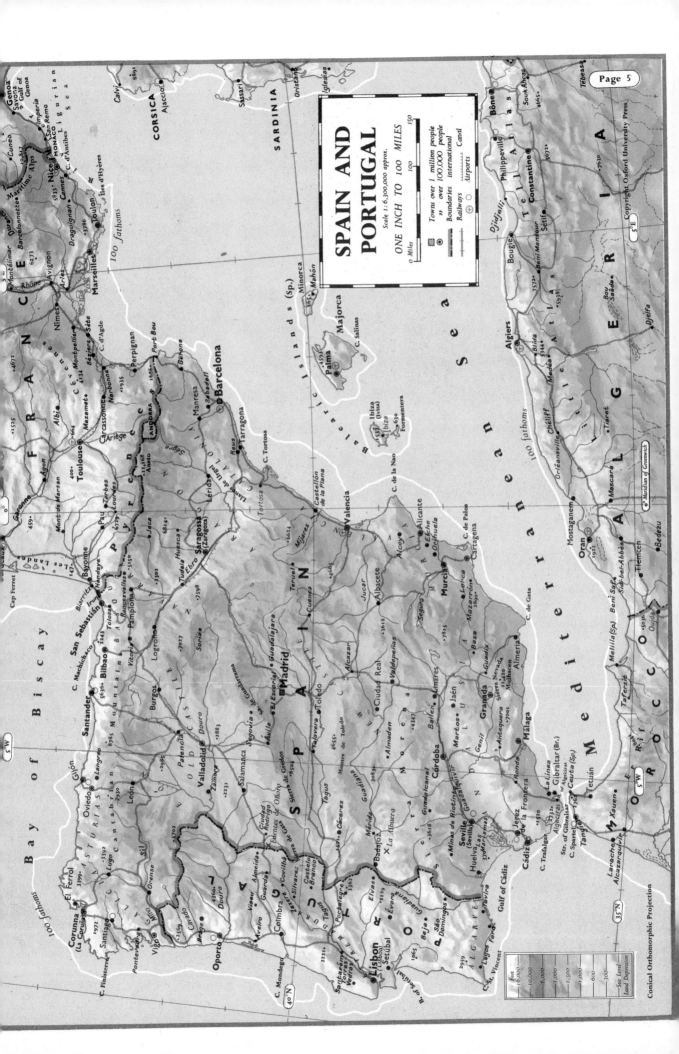

SPAIN AND PORTUGAL

Scale 1 : 6,300,000 approx.

ONE INCH TO 100 MILES

0 Miles   50   100   150

Towns over 1 million people
,,   ,,   over 100,000 people
Boundaries international
Railways   Canal
Airports

Conical Orthomorphic Projection

feet
16,000
10,000
6,000
3,000
1,500
1,000
600
300
Sea Level
Land Depression

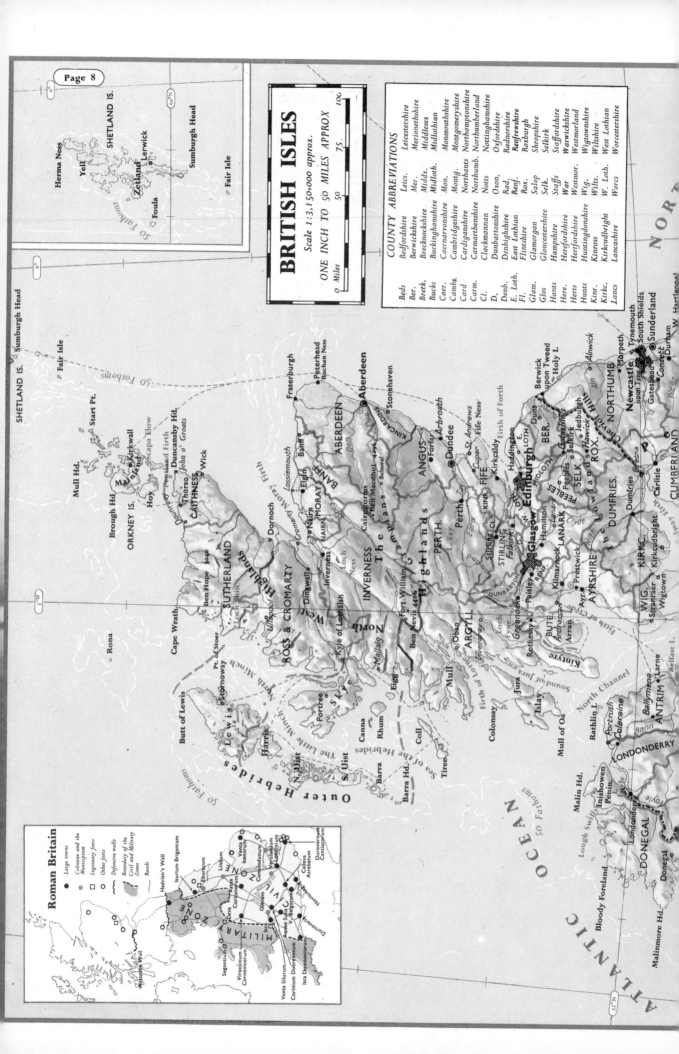

BRITISH ISLES

Scale 1:3,150,000 approx.

ONE INCH TO 50 MILES APPROX

Miles

0 50 75 100

COUNTY ABBREVIATIONS

Beds	Bedfordshire
Ber.	Berwickshire
Breck.	Brecknockshire
Bucks	Buckinghamshire
Caer.	Caernarvonshire
Cambs.	Cambridgeshire
Card	Cardiganshire
Carm.	Carmarthenshire
Cl.	Clackmannan
D.	Dunbartonshire
Denb.	Denbighshire
E. Loth.	East Lothian
Fl.	Flintshire
Glam.	Glamorgan
Glos	Gloucestershire
Hants	Hampshire
Here.	Herefordshire
Herts	Hertfordshire
Hunts	Huntingdonshire
Kinr.	Kinross
Kirk.	Kirkcudbright
Lancs	Lancashire
Leics.	Leicestershire
Mer.	Merionethshire
Middx.	Middlesex
Midloth.	Midlothian
Mon.	Monmouthshire
Montg.	Montgomeryshire
Northants	Northamptonshire
Northumb.	Northumberland
Notts	Nottinghamshire
Oxon.	Oxfordshire
Rad.	Radnorshire
Renf.	Renfrewshire
Rox.	Roxburgh
Salop	Shropshire
Selk.	Selkirk
Staffs	Staffordshire
War	Warwickshire
Westmor.	Westmorland
Wig.	Wigtownshire
Wilts.	Wiltshire
W. Loth.	West Lothian
Worcs	Worcestershire

Roman Britain

- ● Large towns
- ● Coloniae and the Municipium
- □ Legionary forts
- ○ Other forts
- ▨ Defensive walls
- — Roads

Hadrian's Wall
Antonine Wall

Isurium Brigantum
Eburacum
Lindum
Venta Icenorum
Deva
Viroconium
Cornoviorum
Glevum
Verulamium
Camulodunum
Londinium
Calleva
Atrebatum
Durovernum
Cantiacorum
Novioma gus
Noviomagus
Venta Belgarum
Aquae Sulis
Durnovaria
Venta Silurum
Corinium Dobunnorum
Isca Dumnoniorum
Segontium
Isca
Silurum

CIVIL ZONE
MILITARY ZONE

SHETLAND IS.
Herma Ness
Yell
Zetland
Lerwick
Foula
Sumburgh Head
Fair Isle

50 Fathoms

OTHER PACKET-BOAT & FERRY DESTINATIONS

1. St. Malo
2. Dunkirk
3. Ostend
4. Göteborg
5. Hook of Holland
6. Esbjerg
7. Hamburg
8. Bergen & Oslo
9. Lerwick

Meridian of Greenwich

Conical Orthomorphic Projection

Copyright Oxford University Press

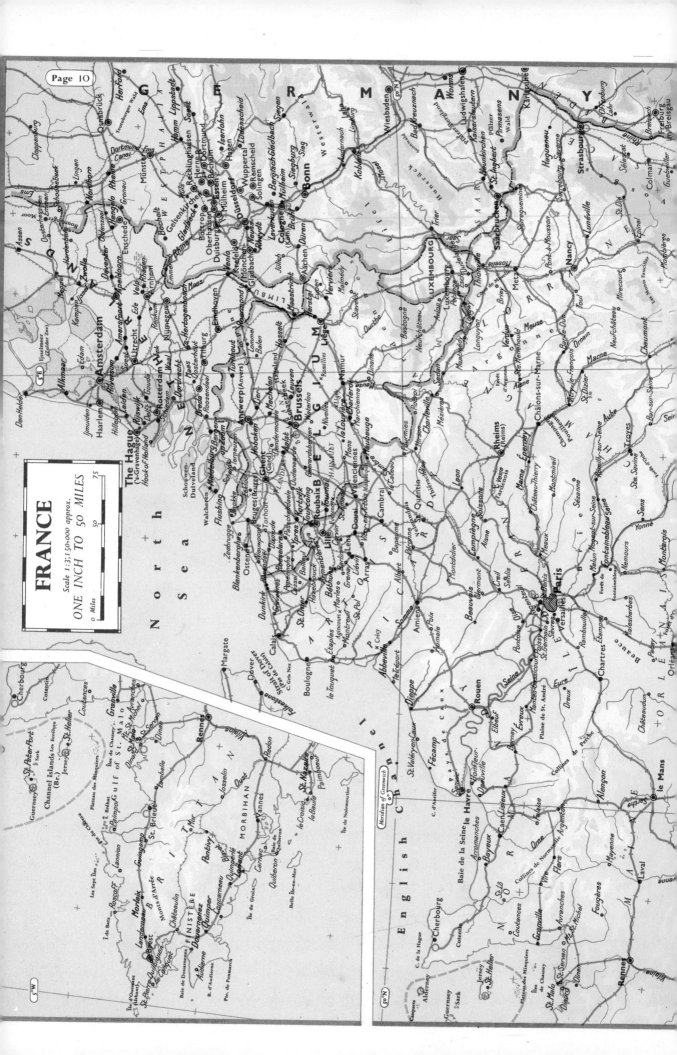

FRANCE

Scale 1:3,150,000 approx.

ONE INCH TO 50 MILES

0 Miles   50   75

Page 11

Copyright Oxford University Press

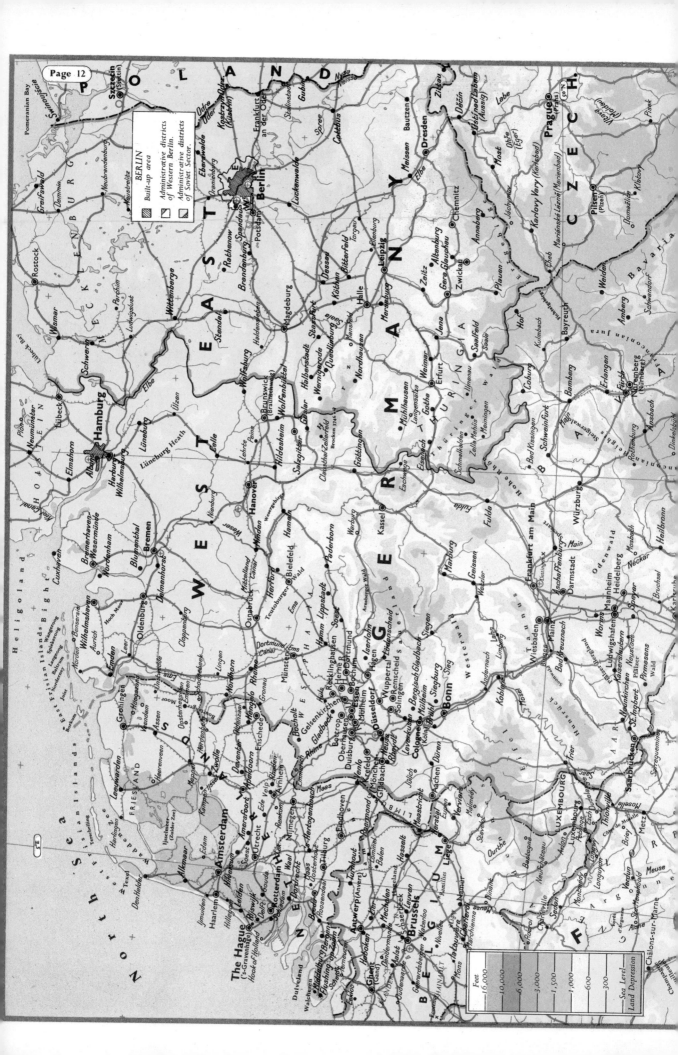

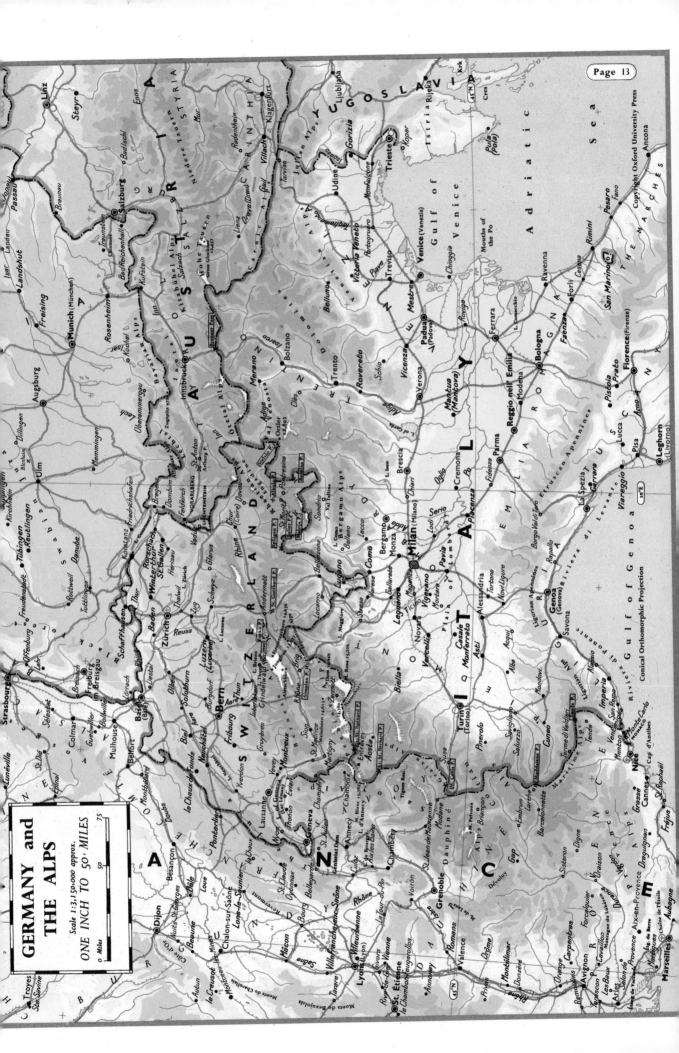

GERMANY and
THE ALPS

Scale 1:3,150,000 approx.
ONE INCH TO 50 MILES

0   Miles   50   75

Copyright Oxford University Press

Conical Orthomorphic Projection

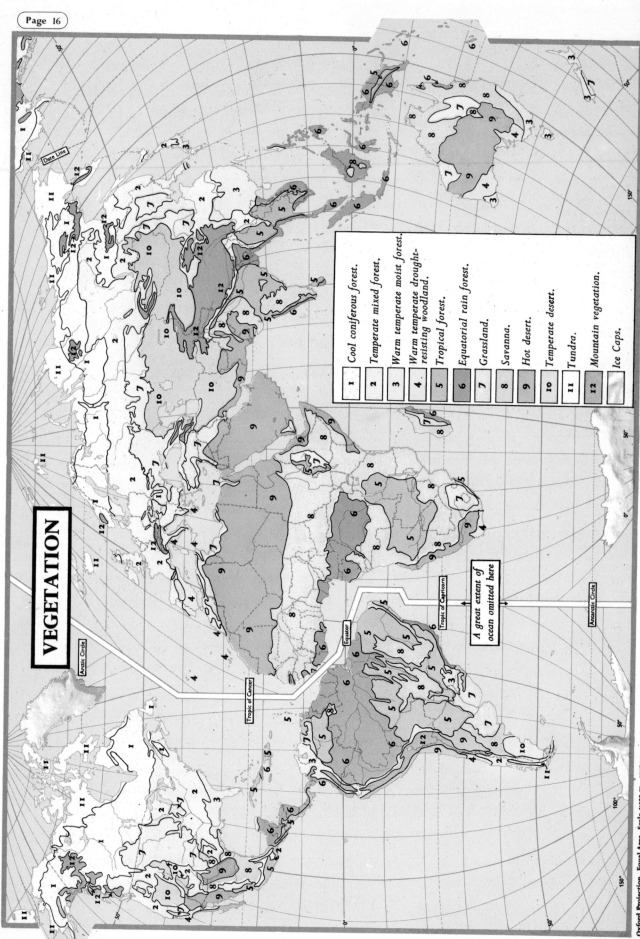

VEGETATION

Cool coniferous forest.
Temperate mixed forest.
Warm temperate moist forest.
Warm temperate drought-resisting woodland.
Tropical forest.
Equatorial rain forest.
Grassland.
Savanna.
Hot desert.
Temperate desert.
Tundra.
Mountain vegetation.
Ice Caps.

A great extent of ocean omitted here

Arctic Circle
Tropic of Cancer
Equator
Tropic of Capricorn
Antarctic Circle
Date Line

Oxford Projection. Equal Area. Scale 1:100 m. approx.